THE WORKS

OF

VICTOR HUGO

One Volume Edition

BLACK'S READERS SERVICE COMPANY

ROSLYN, NEW YORK

TABLE OF CONTENTS

POEMS

THE HUNCH-BACK OF NOTRE-DAME
(*Continued*)

BOOK IV—GRATITUDE—*Continued*

BOOK V—THE NEW POWER

BOOK VI—THE PILLORY

BOOK VII—THE INSCRIPTION

BOOK VIII—HEARTS

THE HUNCH-BACK OF NOTRE-DAME
(*Continued*)

BOOK IX—ACCUMULATED AFFLICTIONS

BOOK X—THE KING

BOOK XI—MARRIAGE

STORIES OF CRIME

ESSAYS ON HUMANITY

The Fallen Veil

THE SISTER

WHAT has happened, my brothers?
  Your spirit to-day
Some secret sorrow damps:
There's a cloud on your brow. What
  has happened? Oh, say,
For your eyeballs glare out with a sin-
  ister ray
Like the light of funeral lamps.
And the blades of your poinards are
  half unsheathed
In your belt—and ye frown on me!
There's a woe untold, there's a pang
  unbreathed
In your bosom, my brothers three!

ELDEST BROTHER

Gulnara, make answer! Hast thou,
  since the dawn,
To the eye of a stranger thy veil withdrawn?

THE SISTER

As I came, oh, my brother! at noon—
  from the bath—
As I came—it was noon, my lords—
And your sister had then, as she con-
  stantly hath,
Drawn her veil close around her, aware
  that the path
Is beset by these foreign hordes.
But the weight of the noonday's sultry
  hour
  Near the mosque was so oppressive
That—forgetting a moment the eye of
  the Giaour—
  I yielded to th' heat excessive.

SECOND BROTHER

Gulnara, make answer! Whom, then,
  hast thou seen,
In a turban of white and a caftan of
  green?

THE SISTER

Nay, he might have been there; but I
  muffled me so,
  He could scarcely have seen my
    figure.—
But why to your sister thus dark do
  you grow?
What words to yourselves do you mut-
  ter thus low,
  Of "blood" and "an intriguer"?
Oh! ye cannot of murder bring down
  the red guilt
  On your souls, my brothers, surely!
Though I fear—from the hands that
  are chafing the hilt,
  And the hints you give obscurely.

THIRD BROTHER

Gulnara, this evening when sank the red
  sun,
Didst thou mark how like blood in descending it shone?

THE SISTER

Mercy! Allah! have pity! oh, spare!
  See! I cling to your knees repenting!
Kind brothers, forgive me! for mercy,
  forbear!
Be appeased at the cry of a sister's de-
  spair,

1

For our mother's sake relenting.
O God! must I die? They are deaf
    to my cries!
Their sister's life-blood shedding;
They have stabbed me each one — I
    faint—o'er my eyes
A *veil of Death* is spreading!

THE BROTHERS

Gulnara farewell! take *that* veil; 'tis
    the gift
Of thy brothers—a veil thou wilt never
    lift!

ZARA, THE BATHER

IN a swinging hammock lying,
        Lightly flying,
Zara, lovely indolent,
    O'er a fountain's crystal wave
        There to lave
Her young beauty—see her bent.

As she leans, so sweet and soft,
        Flitting oft,
O'er the mirror to and fro,
    Seems that airy floating bat
        Like a feather
From some sea-gull's wing of snow.

Every time the frail boat laden
        With the maiden
Skims the water in its flight,
    Starting from its trembling sheen,
        Swift are seen
A white foot and neck so white.

As that lithe foot's timid tips
        Quick she dips,
Passing, in the rippling pool,

(Blush, oh! snowiest ivory!)
        Frolic, she
Laughs to feel the pleasant cool.

Here displayed, but half concealed—
        Half revealed,
Each bright charm shall you behold,
    In her innocence emerging,
        As a-verging
On the wave her hands grow cold.

For no star howe'er divine
        Has the shine
Of a maid's pure loveliness,
    Frightened if a leaf but quivers
        As she shivers,
Veiled with nought but dripping trees.

By the happy breezes fanned
        See her stand,—
Blushing like a living rose,
    On her bosom swelling high
        If a fly
Dare to seek a sweet repose.

In those eyes which maiden pride
        Fain would hide,
Mark how passion's lightnings sleep!
    And their glance is brighter far
        Than the star
Brightest in heaven's bluest deep.

O'er her limbs the glittering current
        In soft torrent
Rains adown the gentle girl,
    As if, drop by drop, should fall,
        One and all
From her necklace every pearl.

Lengthening still the reckless pleasure
        At her leisure,
Care-free Zara ever slow
    As the hammock floats and swings

Smiles and sings,
To herself, so sweet and low.

"Oh, were I a capitana,
     Or sultana,
Amber should be always mixt
In my bath of jewelled stone,
     Near my throne,
Griffins twain of gold betwixt.

"Then my hammock should be silk,
     White as milk;
And, more soft than down of dove,
Velvet cushions where I sit
     Should emit
Perfumes that inspire love.

"Then should I, no danger near,
     Free from fear,
Revel in my garden's stream;
Nor amid the shadows deep
     Dread the peep
Of two dark eyes' kindling gleam.

"He who thus would play the spy,
     On the die
For such sight his head must throw;
In his blood the sabre naked
     Would be slakéd,
Of my slaves of ebon brow.

"Then my rich robes trailing show
     As I go,
None to chide should be so bold;
And upon my sandals fine
     How should shine
Rubies worked in cloth-of-gold!"

Fancying herself a queen,
     All unseen,
Thus vibrating in delight;
In her indolent coquetting

Quite forgetting
How the hours wing their flight.

As she lists the showery tinkling
     Of the sprinkling
By her wanton curvets made,
Never pauses she to think
     Of the brink
Where her wrapper white is laid.

To the harvest-fields the while,
     In long file,
Speed her sisters' lively band,
Like a flock of birds in flight
     Streaming light,
Dancing onward hand in hand.

And they're singing, every one,
     As they run;
This the burden of their lay:
     "Fie upon such idleness!
     Not to dress
Earlier on harvest-day!"

─────────

GASTIBELZA

GASTIBELZA, the man with the carabine,
     Sung in this wise:
"Hath one of you here known Doña
     Sabine
With the gentle eyes?
Ay, dance and sing! For the night
     draws nigh
O'er hill and lea.
─*The wind that wails o'er yon moun-
     tain high*
     Will madden me.

"Hath one of you here known Doña
     Sabine,
     To me so dear?

Her mother, the old, old, Maugrabine,
  Erst made one fear,
For each night from the haunted cavern
    she'd cry
  With an owlet's glee.
—*The wind that wails o'er yon moun-*
    tain high
  Will madden me!

"Ay, dance ye and sing! The hour's
    delight
  One needs must use.
How young she was, and those eyes
    how bright,
  Which made one muse.—
To this old man whom a child leads by,
  A coin cast ye!
—*The wind that wails o'er yon moun-*
    tain high
  Will madden me!

"In sooth the queen for envy had wept,
  Had she seen her, alack!
As o'er Toledo's bridge she light-tript
  In a corset black.
A chaplet of beads that charmed one's
    eye,
  From her neck hung free.
—*The wind that wails o'er yon moun-*
    tain high
  Will madden me!

"The King, bedazed with her loveliness,
  Bespake one there:
'For one only smile, for one only kiss,
  One tress of her hair,
I would give my Spain and gold realms
    that lie
  O'er yonder sea!'
—*The wind that wails o'er yon moun-*
    tain high
  Will madden me!

"I know not well if I loved this sweet,
  But well I know,
If but one glance of her soul might
    greet
  My soul, I would go
On the galleys to toil, on the galleys
    to die,
  Right cheerfully.
—*The wind that wails o'er yon moun-*
    tain high
  Will madden me!

"One summer morn when all heaven
    was bright,
  All earth was gay,
To the stream with her sister for dear
    delight,
  This sweet must stray.
The foot of her comrade I there did
    spy,
  And saw *her* knee.
—*The wind that wails o'er yon moun-*
    tain high
  Will madden me!

"When thus of me, a poor shepherd, was
    seen
  This glorious May,
Methought, 'tis Cleopatra the queen
  Who once, they say,
Won Cæsar, great Emperor of Ger-
    many,
  Her slave to be.
—*The wind that wails o'er yon moun-*
    tain high
  Will madden me!

"Dance ye and sing—lo, the night doth
    fall!
  Sabine, one while
Her dovelike beauty, her soul, her all,
  Her angel-smile,

For a ring of gold to the Count hath
sold—
Saldane is he.
—*The wind that wails o'er yon moun-
tain high
Will madden me!*

"On this bench for a moment suffer me
rest,—
Full-weary each limb.
With this Count then fled this love-
liest—
Alas! with him!
By the road that leads . . . but I
know not, I,
Where then fled she.
—*The wind that wails o'er yon moun-
tain high
Will madden me!*

"I saw her pass at the death of day,
And all was night.
And now I wander and weary alway,
In pain's despite.
My soul's on quest; my dagger's put by,
Ne'er-used to be.
—*The wind that wails o'er yon moun-
tain high
Has maddened me!*"

THE FEAST OF FREEDOM

TO YE KINGS

WHEN the Christians were doomed to
the lions of old
By the priest and prætor, combined to
uphold
An idolatrous cause,
Forth they came while the vast Colos-
seum throughout

Gathered thousands looked on, and they
fell 'mid the shout
Of "the People's" applause.

On the eve of that day of their eve-
nings the last!
At the gates of their dungeon a gor-
geous repast,
Rich, unstinted, unpriced,
That the doomed might (forsooth)
gather strength ere they bled,
With an ignorant pity the gaolers would
spread
For the martyrs of Christ.

Oh, 'twas strange for a pupil of Paul to
recline
On voluptuous couch, while Falernian
wine
Fill'd his cup to the brim!
Dulcet music of Greece, Asiatic repose,
Spicy fragrance of Araby, Italian rose,
All united for him!

Every luxury known through the earth's
wide expanse,
In profusion procured was put forth to
enhance
The repast that they gave;
And no Sybarite, nursed in the lap of
delight,
Such a banquet ere tasted as welcomed
that night
The elect of the grave.

And the lion, meantime, shook his ponderous chain,
Loud and fierce howled the tiger, impatient to stain
The bloodthirsty arena;
Whilst the women of Rome, who applauded those deeds

And who hailed the forthcoming enjoyment, must needs
   Shame the restless hyæna.

They who figured as guests on that ul-
timate eve,
In their turn on the morrow were des-
tined to give
   To the lions their food;
For, behold, in the guise of a slave at
that board,
Where his victims enjoyed all that life
can afford,
   Death administering stood.

Such, O monarchs of earth! was your
banquet of power,
But the tocsin has burst on your fes-
tival hour—
   'Tis your knell that it rings!
To the popular tiger a prey is decreed,
And the maw of Republican hunger will
feed
   On *a banquet of Kings!*

THE GRANDMOTHER

STILL asleep! We have been since the
noon thus alone.
   Oh, the hours we have ceased to
number!
Wake, grandmother! — speechless say
why thou art grown.
Then, thy lips are so cold!—the Ma-
donna of stone
   Is like thee in thy holy slumber.
We have watched thee in sleep, we have
watched thee at prayer,
   But what can now betide thee?
Like thy hours of repose all thy orisons
were.

And thy lips would still murmur a
blessing whene'er
   Thy children stood beside thee.

Now thine eye is unclosed, and thy
forehead is bent
   O'er the hearth, where ashes smoul-
der;
And behold, the watch-lamp will be
speedily spent.
Art thou vexed? have we done aught
amiss?   Oh, relent!
   But—parent, thy hands grow colder!
Say, with ours wilt thou let us rekindle
in thine
   The glow that has departed?
Wilt thou sing us some songs of the
days of lang syne?
Wilt thou tell us some tale, from those
volumes divine,
   Of the brave and noble-hearted?

Of the dragon who, crouching in forest
green glen,
   Lies in wait for the unwary—
Of the maid who was freed by her
knight from the den
Of the ogre, whose club was uplifted,
but then
   Turned aside by the wand of a fairy?
Wilt thou teach us spell-words that pro-
tect from all harm,
   And thoughts of evil banish?
What goblins the sign of the cross may
disarm?
What saint it is good to invoke? and
what charm
   Can make the demon vanish?

Or unfold to our gaze thy most wonderful book,
   So feared by hell and Satan;

At its hermits and martyrs in gold
   let us look,
At the virgins, and bishops with pas-
   toral crook,
   And the hymns and the prayers in
     Latin.
Oft with legends of angels, who watch
   o'er the young,
   Thy voice was wont to gladden;
Have thy lips yet no language—no wis-
   dom thy tongue?
Oh, see! the light wavers, and sinking,
   hath flung
   On the wall forms that sadden.

Wake! awake! evil spirits perhaps may
   presume
   To haunt thy holy dwelling;
Pale ghosts are, perhaps, stealing into
   the room—
Oh, would that the lamp were relit!
   with the gloom
   These fearful thoughts dispelling.
Thou hast told us our parents lie sleep-
   ing beneath
   The grass, in a churchyard lonely:
Now, thine eyes have no motion, thy
   mouth has no breath,
And thy limbs are all rigid! Oh, say,
   Is this death,
   Or thy prayer or thy slumber only?

ENVOY

Sad vigil they kept by that grand-
   mother's chair,
   Kind angels hovered o'er them—
And the dead-bell was tolled in the
   hamlet—and there,
On the following eve, knelt that inno-
   cent pair,
   With the missal-book before them.

THE GIANT IN GLEE

Ho, warriors! I was reared in the land
   of the Gauls;
O'er the Rhine my ancestors came
   bounding like balls
Of the snow at the Pole, where, a babe,
   I was bathed
Ere in bear and in walrus-skin I was
   enswathed.

Then my father was strong, whom the
   years lowly bow,—
A bison could wallow in the grooves of
   his brow.
He is weak, very old—he can scarcely
   uptear
A young pine-tree for staff since his legs
   cease to bear;

But here's to replace him!—I can toy
   with his axe;
As I sit on the hill my feet swing in
   the flax,
And my knee caps the boulders and
   troubles the trees.
How they shiver, yea, quake if I hap·
   pen to sneeze!

I was still but a springald when, cleaving the Alps,
I brushed snowy periwigs off granitic
   scalps,
And my head, o'er the pinnacles,
   stopped the fleet clouds,
Where I captured the eagles and caged
   them by crowds.

There were tempests! I blew them back
   unto their source!
And put out their lightnings! More
   than once in a course,

Through the ocean I went wading after
    the whale,
And stirred up the bottom as did never
    a gale.

Fond of rambling, I hunted the shark
    'long the beach,
And no osprey in ether soared out of
    my reach;
And the bear that I pinched 'twixt my
    finger and thumb,
Like the lynx and the wolf, perished
    harmless and dumb.

But these pleasures of childhood have
    lost all their zest;
It is warfare and carnage that now I
    love best:
The sounds that I wish to awaken and
    hear
Are the cheers raised by courage, the
    shrieks due to fear;

When the riot of flames, ruin, smoke,
    steel and blood,
Announces an army rolls along as a
    flood,
Which I follow, to harry the clamorous
    ranks,
Sharp-goading the laggards and press-
    ing the flanks,
Till, a thresher 'mid ripest of corn, up
    I stand
With an oak for a flail in my unflagging
    hand.

Rise the groans! rise the screams! on
    my feet fall vain tears
As the roar of my laughter redoubles
    their fears.
I am naked. At armour of steel I
    should joke—

True, I'm helmed—a brass pot you
    could draw with ten yoke.

I look for no ladder to invade the king's
    hall—
I stride o'er the ramparts, and down
    the walls fall,
Till choked are the ditches with the
    stones, dead and quick,
Whilst the flagstaff I use 'midst my
    teeth as a pick.

Oh, when cometh my turn to succumb
    like my prey,
May brave men my body snatch away
    from th' array
Of the crows—may they heap on the
    rocks till they loom
Like a mountain, befitting a colossus'
    tomb!

THE CYMBALEER'S BRIDE

My lord the Duke of Brittany
    Has summoned his barons bold—
Their names make a fearful litany!
Among them you will not meet any
    But men of giant mould.

Proud earls, who dwell in donjon keep,
    And steel-clad knight and peer,
Whose forts are girt with a moat cut
    deep—
But none excel in soldiership
    My own loved cymbaleer.

Clashing his cymbals, forth he went,
    With a bold and gallant bearing;
Sure for a captain he was meant,
To judge his pride with courage blent,
    And the cloth of gold he's wearing.

But in my soul since then I feel
  A fear in secret creeping;
And to my patron saint I kneel,
That she may recommend his weal
  To his guardian-angel's keeping.

I've begged our abbot Bernardine
  His prayers not to relax;
And to procure him aid divine
I've burnt upon Saint Gilda's shrine
  Three pounds of virgin wax.

Our Lady of Loretto knows
  The pilgrimage I've vowed:
"To wear the scallop I propose,
If health and safety from the foes
  My lover be allowed."

No letter (fond affection's gage!)
  From him could I require,
The pain of absence to assuage—
A vassal-maid can have no page,
  A liegeman has no squire.

This day will witness, with the duke's,
  My cymbaleer's return:
Gladness and pride beam in my looks,
Delay my heart impatient brooks,
  All meaner thoughts I spurn.

Back from the battlefield elate
  His banner brings each peer;
Come, let us see, at the ancient gate,
The martial triumph pass in state—
  With the princes my cymbaleer.

We'll have from the rampart walls a
    glance
  Of the air his steed assumes;
His proud neck swells, his glad hoofs
    prance,
And on his head unceasing dance,
  In a gorgeous tuft, red plumes!

Be quick, my sisters! dress in haste!
  Come, see him bear the bell,
With laurels decked, with true love
    graced,
While in his bold hands, fitly placed,
  The bounding cymbals swell!

Mark well the mantle that he'll wear,
  Embroidered by his bride!
Admire his burnished helmet's glare,
O'ershadowed by the dark horsehair
  That waves in jet folds wide!

The gypsy (spiteful wench!) foretold,
  With a voice like a viper hissing
(Though I had crossed her palm with
    gold),
That from the ranks a spirit bold
  Would be to-day found missing.

But I have prayed so much, I trust
  Her words may prove untrue;
Though in a tomb the hag accurst
Muttered: "Prepare thee for the
    worst!"
  Whilst the lamp burnt ghastly blue.

My joy her spells shall not prevent.
  Hark! I can hear the drums!
And ladies fair from silken tent
Peep forth, and every eye is bent
  On the cavalcade that comes!

Pikemen, dividing on both flanks,
  Open the pageantry;
Loud, as they tread, their armour
    clanks,
And silk-robed barons lead the ranks—
  The pink of gallantry!

In scarves of gold the priests admire:
  The heralds on white steeds;
Armorial pride decks their attire,

Worn in remembrance of some sire
Famed for heroic deeds.

Feared by the Paynim's dark divan,
  The Templars next advance;
Then the tall halberds of Lausanne,
Foremost to stand in battle van
  Against the foes of France.

Now hail the duke, with radiant brow,
  Girt with his cavaliers;
Round his triumphant banner bow
Those of his foe. Look, sisters, now!
  Here come the cymbaleers!

She spoke—with searching eye surveyed
  Their ranks—then, pale, aghast,
Sunk in the crowd! Death came in
  aid—
'Twas mercy to that loving maid—
  The cymbaleers had passed!

CHILDREN OF CAIN

THEN, with his children, clothed in
  skins of brutes,
Dishevelled, livid, rushing through the
  storm,
Cain fled before Jehovah. As night fell
The dark man reached a mount in a
  great plain,
And his tired wife and his sons, out of
  breath,
Said: "Let us lie down on the earth
  and sleep."
Cain, sleeping not, dreamed at the
  mountain foot.
Raising his head, in that funereal
  heaven
He saw an eye, a great eye, in the night
Open, and staring at him in the gloom.

"I am too near," he said, and trem-
  blingly woke up
His sleeping sons again, and his tired
  wife,
And fled through space and darkness.
  Thirty days
He went, and thirty nights, nor looked
  behind;
Pale, silent, watchful, shaking at each
  sound;
No rest, no sleep, till he attained the
  strand
Where the sea washes that which since
  was Asshur.
"Here pause," he said, "for this place
  is secure;
Here may we rest, for this is the
  world's end."
And he sat down; when, lo! in the sad
  sky,
The self-same Eye on the horizon's
  verge,
And the wretch shook as in an ague
  fit.
"Hide me!" he cried; and all his watch-
  ful sons,
Their finger on their lip, stared at their
  sire.
Cain said to Jabal (father of them that
  dwell
In tents): "Spread here the curtain of
  thy tent."
And they spread wide the floating canvas roof,
And made it fast and fixed it down with
  lead.
"You see nought now," said Zillah then,
  fair child,
The daughter of his eldest, sweet as
  day.
But Cain replied, "That Eye—I see it
  still."
And Jubal cried (the father of those

That handle harp and organ): "I will
build
A sanctuary;" and he made a wall of
bronze,
And set his sire behind it. But Cain
moaned,
"That Eye is glaring at me ever." He-
noch cried:
"Then must we make a circle vast of
towers,
So terrible that nothing dare draw near;
Build we a city with a citadel;
Build we a city high and close it fast."
Then Tubal Cain (instructor of all them
That work in brass and iron) built a
tower—
Enormous, superhuman. While he
wrought,
His fiery brothers from the plain
around
Hunted the sons of Enoch and of Seth;
They plucked the eyes out of whoever
passed,
And hurled at even arrows to the stars.
They set strong granite for the canvas
wall,
And every block was clamped with iron
chains.
It seemed a city made for hell. Its
towers,
With their huge masses, made night in
the land.
The walls were thick as mountains. On
the door
They graved: "Let not God enter here."
This done,
And having finished to cement and
build
In a stone tower, they set him in the
midst.
To him, still dark and haggard, "Oh,
my sire,

Is the Eye gone?" quoth Zillah trem-
blingly.
But Cain replied: "Nay, it is even
there."
Then added: "I will live beneath the
earth,
As a lone man within his sepulchre.
I will see nothing; will be seen of none."
They digged a trench, and Cain said:
" 'Tis enow,"
As he went down alone into the vault;
But when he sat, so ghost-like, in his
chair,
And they had closed the dungeon o'er
his head,
The Eye was in the tomb and fixed on
Cain.

EVIRADNUS

THE ADVENTURER

WHAT was it Sigismond and Ladislāus
said?

I know not if the rock, or tree o'erhead,
Had heard their speech;—but when the
two spake low,
Among the trees, a shudder seemed to
go
Through all their branches, just as if
that way
A beast had passed to trouble and dis-
may.
Darker the shadow of the rock was seen,
And then a morsel of the shade, between
The sombre trees, took shape as it
would seem
Some spectre walking in the sunset's
gleam.

'Tis not a monster rising from its lair,
Nor phantom of the foliage and the air,
'Tis not a morsel of the granite's shade
That walks in deepest hollows of the glade.
'Tis not a vampire nor a spectre pale,
But living man in rugged coat of mail.
It is Alsatia's noble Chevalier,
Eviradnus the brave, that now is here.

The men who spoke he recognized the while
He rested in the thicket; words of guile
Most horrible were theirs as they passed on,
And to the ears of Eviradnus one—
One word had come which roused him. Well he knew
The land which lately he had journeyed through.

He down the valley went unto the inn
Where he had left his horse and page, Gasclin.
The horse had wanted drink, and lost a shoe;
And now, "Be quick!" he said, "with what you do,
For business calls me, I must not delay."
He strides the saddle and he rides away.

In Holy Rage

Eviradnus was growing old apace,
The weight of years had left its hoary trace,
But still of knights the most renowned was he,
Model of bravery and purity.
His blood he spared not; ready day or night
To punish crime, his dauntless sword shone bright

In his unblemished hand; holy and white
And loyal all his noble life had been,
A Christian Samson coming on the scene.
With fist alone the gate he battered down
Of Sickingen in flames, and saved the town.
'Twas he, indignant at the honour paid
To crime, who with his heel an onslaught made
Upon Duke Lupus' shameful monument,
Tore down the statue he to fragments rent;
Then column of the Strasburg monster bore
To bridge of Wasselonne, and threw it o'er
Into the waters deep. The people round
Blazon the noble deeds that so abound
From Altorf unto Chaux-de-fonds, and say,
When he rests musing in a dreamy way,
"Behold, 'tis Charlemagne!" Tawny to see
And hairy, and seven feet high was he,
Like John of Bourbon. Roaming hill or wood
He looked like a wolf endeavouring to do good.
Bound up in duty, he of nought complained,
The cry for help his aid at once obtained.
Only he mourned the baseness of mankind,
And—that the beds too short he e'er must find.
When people suffer under cruel kings,
With pity moved, he to them succour brings.
'Twas he defended Alix from her foes

As sword of Urraca—he ever shows
His strength is for the feeble and op-
    pressed;
Father of orphans he, and all distressed!
Kings of the Rhine in strongholds were
    by him
Boldly attacked, and tyrant barons grim.
He freed the towns—defying in his lair
Hugo The Eagle; boldly did he dare
To break the collar of Saverne, the ring
Of Colmar, and the iron torture-thing
Of Schlestadt, and the chain that Ha-
    guenau bore.
Confront with evil he an aspect wore
Good but most terrible. In the dread
    scale
Which princes weighted with their hor-
    rid tale
Of craft and violence, and blood and ill,
And fire and shocking deeds, his sword
    was still
God's counterpoise displayed. Ever alert
More evil from the wretched to avert,
Those hapless ones who 'neath Heaven's
    vault at night
Raise suppliant hands. His lance loved
    not the plight
Of mouldering in the rack, of no avail,
His battle-axe slipped from supporting
    nail
Quite easily; 'twas ill for action base
To come so near that he the thing could
    trace.
The steel-clad champion death drops all
    around
As glaciers water. Hero ever found
Eviradnus is kinsman of the race
Of Amadys of Gaul, and knights of
    Thrace.
He smiles at age. For he who never
    asked
For quarter from mankind—shall he be
    tasked

To beg of Time for mercy? Rather he
Would girdle up his loins, like Baldwin
    be.
Aged he is, but of a lineage rare;
The least intrepid of the birds that dare
Is not the eagle barbed. What matters
    age,
The years but fire him with a holy rage.
Though late from Palestine, he is not
    spent,—
With age he wrestles, firm in his intent.

IN THE FOREST

If in the wood a traveller there had been
That eve, had lost himself, strange sight
    he'd seen.
Quite in the forest's heart a lighted
    space
Arose to view; in that deserted place
A lone, abandoned hall with light aglow
The long neglect of centuries did show.
The castle-towers of Corbus in decay
Were girt by weeds and growths that
    had their way;
Couch-grass and ivy, and wild eglantine
In subtle scaling warfare all combine.
Subject to such attacks three hundred
    years,
The donjon yields, and ruin now ap-
    pears.
E'en as by leprosy the wild boars die,
In moat the crumbled battlements now
    lie;
Around the snake-like bramble twists
    its rings;
Freebooter sparrows come on daring
    wings
To perch upon the swivel-gun, nor heed
Its murmuring growl when pecking in
    their greed
The mulberries ripe. With insolence the
    thorn

Thrives on the desolation so forlorn.
But winter brings revenges; then the
    Keep
Wakes all vindictive from its seeming
    sleep,
Hurls down the heavy rain, night after
    night,
Thanking the season's all-resistless
    might;
And, when the gutters choke, its gar-
    goyles four
From granite mouths in anger spit and
    pour
Upon the hated ivy hour by hour.

As to the sword rust is, so lichens are
To towering citadel with which they war.
Alas! for Corbus—dreary, desolate,
And yet its woes the winters mitigate.
It rears itself among convulsive throes
That shake its ruins when the tempest
    blows.
Winter, the savage warrior, pleases well,
With its storm clouds, the mighty cita-
    del,—
Restoring it to life. The lightning flash
Strikes like a thief and flies; the winds
    that crash
Sound like a clarion, for the Tempest
    bluff
Is Battle's sister. And when wild and
    rough,
The north wind blows, the tower ex-
    ultant cries
"Behold me!" When hail-hurling gales
    arise
Of blustering Equinox, to fan the strife,
It stands erect, with martial ardour rife,
A joyous soldier! When like yelping
    hound
Pursued by wolves, November comes to
    bound

In joy from rock to rock, like answer-
    ing cheer
To howling January now so near—
"Come on!" the Donjon cries to blasts
    o'erhead—
It has seen Attila, and knows not dread.
Oh, dismal nights of contest in the rain
And mist, that furious would the battle
    gain,
The tower braves all, though angry
    skies pour fast
The flowing torrents, river-like and vast.
From their eight pinnacles the gorgons
    bay
And scattered monsters, in their stony
    way,
Are growling heard; the rampart lions
    gnaw
The misty air and slush with granite
    maw,
The sleet upon the griffins spits, and all
The Saurian monsters, answering to the
    squall,
Flap wings; while through the broken
    ceiling fall
Torrents of rain upon the forms be-
    neath,
Dragons and snak'd Medusas gnashing
    teeth
In the dismantled rooms. Like armoured
    knight
The granite Castle fights with all its
    might,
Resisting through the winter. All in
    vain,
The heaven's bluster, January's rain,
And those dread elemental powers we
    call
The Infinite — the whirlwinds that
    appal—
Thunder and waterspouts; and winds
    that shake
As 'twere a tree its ripened fruit to take.

The winds grow wearied, warring with
    the tower,
The noisy North is out of breath, nor
    power
Has any blast old Corbus to defeat,
It still has strength their onslaughts
    worst to meet.
Thus, spite of briars and thistles, the
    old tower
Remains triumphant through the dark-
    est hour;
Superb as pontiff, in the forest shown,
Its rows of battlements make triple
    crown;
At eve, its silhouette is finely traced
Immense and black—showing the Keep
    is placed
On rocky throne, sublime and high;
    east, west,
And north and south, at corners four,
    there rest
Four mounts; Aptar, where flourishes
    the pine,
And Toxis, where the elms grow green
    and fine;
Crobius and Bleyda, giants in their
    might,
Against the stormy winds to stand and
    fight,
And these above its diadem uphold
Night's living canopy of clouds unrolled.

The herdsman fears, and thinks its
    shadow creeps
To follow him; and superstition keeps
Such hold that Corbus as a terror reigns;
Folks say the Fort a target still re-
    mains
For the Black Archer—and that it con-
    tains
The cave where the Great Sleeper still
    sleeps sound.
The country people all the castle round

Are frightened easily, for legends grow
And mix with phantoms of the mind;
    we know
The hearth is cradle of such fantasies,
And in the smoke the cotter sees arise
From low-thatched hut he traces cause
    of dread.
Thus rendering thanks that he is lowly
    bred,
Because from such none look for valor-
    ous deeds,
The peasant flies the Tower, although it
    leads
A noble knight to seek adventure there,
And, from his point of honour, dangers
    dare.

Thus very rarely passer-by is seen;
But—it might be with twenty years be-
    tween,
Or haply less—at unfixed interval
There would a semblance be of festival.
A Seneschal and usher would appear,
And troops of servants many baskets
    bear.
Then were, in mystery, preparations
    made,
And they departed—for till night none
    stayed.
But 'twixt the branches gazers could
    descry
The blackened hall lit up most bril-
    liantly.
None dared approach—and this the rea-
    son why.

A WEIRD MEAL

When died a noble Marquis of Lusace
'Twas the custom for the heir who filled
    his place
Before assuming princely pomp and
    power

To sup one night in Corbus' olden tower.
From this weird meal he passed to the degree
Of Prince and Margrave; nor could ever he
Be thought brave knight, or she — if woman claim
The rank—be reckoned of unblemished fame
Till they had breathed the air of ages gone,
The funeral odours, in the nest alone
Of its dead masters. Ancient was the race;
To climb the upward stem of proud Lusace
Gives one a vertigo; descended they
From ancestor of Attila, men say;
Their race to him—through Pagans— they trace back;
Becoming Christians, they their line could track
Through Lechus, Plato, Otho to combine
With Ursus, Stephen, in a lordly line.
Of all those masters of the country round
That were on Northern Europe's boundary found—
At first were waves, and then the dykes were reared—
Corbus in double majesty appeared,
Castle on hill and town upon the plain;
And one who mounted on the tower could gain
A view beyond the pines and rocks, of spires
That pierce the shade the distant scene acquires;
A walled town is it, but 'tis not ally
Of the old citadel's proud majesty;
Unto itself belonging this remained.
Often a castle was thus self-sustained

And equalled towns; witness in Lombardy
Crama, and Prato in fair Tuscany,
And in Apulia Barletta too;—and each one
Was powerful as a town, and dreaded none.
Corbus ranked thus; its precincts seemed to hold
The reflex of its mighty kings of old;
Their great events had witness in these walls,
Their marriages were here and funerals,
And mostly here it was that they were born;
And here crowned Barons ruled with pride and scorn;
Cradle of Scythian majesty this place.
Now each new master of this ancient race
A duty owed to ancestors which he
Was bound to carry on. The law's decree
It was that he should pass alone the night
Which made him king, as in their solemn sight.
Just at the forest's edge a clerk was met
With wine in sacred cup and purpose set,
A wine mysterious, which the heir must drink
To cause deep slumber till the day's soft brink.
Then to the castle tower he wends his way,
And finds a supper laid with rich display.
He sups and sleeps: when to his slumbering eyes
The shades of kings from Bela all arise.

None dare the tower to enter on this night,
But when the morning dawns, crowds are in sight
The dreamer to deliver,—whom half dazed,
And with the visions of the night amazed,
They to the old church take, where rests the dust
Of Borivorus; then the bishop must,
With fervent blessings on his eyes and mouth,
Put in his hands the stony hatchets both,
With which — even like death impartially—
Struck Attila, with one arm dexterously
The south, and with the other arm the north.

This day the town the threatening flag set forth
Of Marquis Swantibore, the monster he
Who in the wood tied up his wife, to be
Devoured by wolves, together with the bull
Of which with jealousy his heart was full.

Even when woman took the place of heir
The tower of Corbus claimed the supper there;
'Twas law—the woman trembled, but must dare.

UNMARRIED

Niece of the Marquis—John the Striker named—

Mahaud to-day the marquisate has claimed.
A noble dame—the crown is hers by right:
As woman she has graces that delight.
A queen devoid of beauty is not queen,
She needs the royalty of beauty's mien;
God in His harmony has equal ends
For cedar that resists, and reed that bends,
And good it is a woman sometimes rules,
Holds in her hand the power, and manners schools,
And laws and mind;—succeeding master proud,
With gentle voice and smile she leads the crowd,
The sombre human troop. But sweet Mahaud
On evil days had fallen; gentle, good,
Alas! she held the sceptre like a flower;
Timid yet gay, imprudent for the hour,
And careless too. With Europe all in throes,
Though twenty years she now already knows,
She has refused to marry, although oft
Entreated. It is time an arm less soft
Than hers — a manly arm — supported her;
Like to the rainbow she, one might aver,
Shining on high between the cloud and rain,
Or like the ewe that gambols on the plain
Between the bear and tiger; innocent,
She has two neighbours of most foul intent:
For foes the Beauty has, in life's pure spring,
The German Emperor and the Polish King.

THE EVIL PAIR

The difference this betwixt the evil pair,
Faithless to God—for laws without a
    care—
One was the claw, the other one the will
Controlling. Yet to mass they both went
    still,
And on the rosary told their beads
    each day.
But none the less the world believed
    that they
Unto the powers of hell their souls had
    sold.
Even in whispers men each other told
The details of the pact which they had
    signed
With that dark power, the foe of
    human kind;
In whispers, for the crowd had mortal
    dread
Of them so high, and woes that they
    had spread.
One might be vengeance and the other
    hate,
Yet lived they side by side, in powerful
    state
And close alliance. All the people near
From red horizon dwelt in abject fear,
Mastered by them; their figures darkly
    grand
Had ruddy reflex from the wasted land,
And fires, and towns they sacked. Be-
    sides the one,
Like David, poet was, the other shone
As fine musician—rumour spread their
    fame,
Declaring them divine, until each name
In Italy's fine sonnets met with praise.
The ancient hierarch in those old days
Had custom strange, a now forgotten
    thing,
It was a European plan that King

Of France was marquis, and th' imperial
    head
Of Germany was duke; there was no
    need
To class the other kings, but barons
    they,
Obedient vassals unto Rome, their stay.
The King of Poland was but simple
    knight,
Yet now, for once, had strange un-
    wonted right,
And, as exception to the common state,
This one Sarmatian King was held as
    great
As German Emperor; and each knew
    how
His evil part to play, nor mercy show.
The German had one aim, it was to take
All the land he could, and it his own to
    make.
The Pole, already having Baltic shore,
Seized Celtic ports, still needing more
    and more.
On all the Northern Sea his crafts
    roused fear;
Iceland beheld his demon navy near.
Antwerp the German burnt; and Prus-
    sias twain
Bowed to his yoke. The Polish King
    was fain
To help the Russian Spotocus—his aid
Was like the help that in their common
    trade
A sturdy butcher gives a weaker one.
The King it is who seizes, and this done,
The Emperor pillages, usurping right
In war Teutonic, settled but by might.
The King in Jutland cynic footing gains,
The weak coerced, the while with cun-
    ning pains
The strong are duped. But 'tis a law
    they make

That their accord themselves should never break.

From Arctic seas to cities Transalpine,
Their hideous talons, curved for sure rapine,
Scrape o'er and o'er the mournful continent,
Their plans succeed, and each is well content.
Thus under Satan's all paternal care
They brothers are, this royal bandit pair.
Oh, noxious conquerors! with transient rule
Chimera heads—ambition can but fool.
Their misty minds but harbour rottenness
Loathsome and fetid, and all barrenness—
Their deeds to ashes turn, and, hydrabred,
The mystic skeleton is theirs to dread.
The daring German and the cunning Pole
Noted to-day a woman had control
Of lands, and watched Mahaud like evil spies;
And from the Emp'ror's cruel mouth—with dyes
Of wrath empurpled—came these words of late:
"The empire wearies of the wallet weight
Hung at its back—this High and Low Lusace,
Whose hateful load grows heavier apace,
That now a woman holds its ruler's place."
Threatening, and blood suggesting, every word;
The watchful Pole was silent—but he heard.

Two monstrous dangers; but the heedless one
Babbles and smiles, and bids all care begone—
Likes lively speech—while all the poor she makes
To love her, and the taxes off she takes.
A life of dance and pleasure she has known—
A woman always; in her jewelled crown
It is the pearl she loves—not cutting gems,
For these can wound, and mark men's diadems.
She pays the hire of Homer's copyists,
And in the Courts of Love presiding, lists.

Quite recently unto her Court have come
Two men—unknown their names or native home,
Their rank or race; but one plays well the lute,
The other is a troubadour; both suit
The taste of Mahaud, when on summer eve,
'Neath opened windows, they obtain her leave
To sing upon the terrace, and relate
The charming tales that do with music mate.
In August the Moravians have their fête,
But it is radiant June in which Lusace
Must consecrate her noble Margrave race.
Thus in the weird and old ancestral tower
For Mahaud now has come the fateful hour,
The lonely supper which her state decrees.

What matters this to flowers, and birds,
    and trees,
And clouds and fountains? That the
    people may
Still bear their yoke—have kings to rule
    alway?
The water flows, the wind in passing by
In murmuring tones takes up the ques-
    tioning cry.

LOVE AND FEAST

The old stupendous hall has but one
    door,
And in the dusk it seems that more and
    more
The walls recede in space unlimited.
At the far end there is a table spread
That in the dreary void with splendour
    shines;
For ceiling we behold but rafter lines.
The table is arranged for one sole guest,
A solitary chair doth near it rest,
Throne-like, 'neath canopy that droop-
    eth down
From the black beams; upon the walls
    are shown
The painted histories of the olden
    might,
The Wendish King Thassilo's sturdy
    fight
On land with Nimrod, and on ocean
    wide
With Neptune. Rivers too personified
Appear—the Rhine as by the Meuse be-
    trayed,
And fading groups of Odin in the shade,
And the wolf Fenrir and the Asgard
    snake.
One might the place for dragon's stable
    take.
The only lights that in the shed appear
Spring from the table's giant chandelier

With seven iron branches — brought
    from hell
By Attila Archangel, people tell,
When he had conquered Mammon—and
    they say
That seven souls were the first flames
    that day.
This banquet hall looks an abyss out-
    lined
With shadowy vagueness, though indeed
    we find
In the far depth upon the table spread
A sudden, strong, and glaring light is
    shed,
Striking upon the goldsmith's burnished
    works,
And on the pheasants killed by traitor
    hawks.
Loaded the table is with viands cold,
Ewers and flagons, all enough of old
To make a love feast. All the napery
Was Friesland's famous make; and fair
    to see
The dishes, silver-gilt and bordered
    round
With flowers; for fruit, here strawber-
    ries were found
And citrons, apples too, and nectarines.
The wooden bowls were carved in cun-
    ning lines
By peasants of the Murg, whose skilful
    hands
With patient toil reclaim the barren
    lands
And make their gardens flourish on a
    rock,
Or mountain where we see the hunters
    flock.
A golden cup, with handles Florentine,
Shows horned Acteons, armed and
    booted fine,
Who fight with sword in hand against
    the hounds.

Roses and gladioles make up bright
  mounds
Of flowers, with juniper and aniseed;
While sage, all newly cut for this great
  need,
Covers the Persian carpet that is spread
Beneath the table, and so helps to shed
Around a perfume of the balmy spring.
Beyond is desolation withering.
One hears within the hollow dreary
  space
Across the grove, made fresh by sum-
  mer's grace,
The wind that ever is with mystic might
A spirit ripple of the Infinite.
The glass restored to frames to creak is
  made
By blustering wind that comes from
  neighbouring glade.
Strange, in this dream-like place, so
  drear and lone,
The guest expected was a living one!
The seven lights from seven arms make
  glow
Almost with life the staring eyes that
  show
On the dim frescoes—and along the
  walls
Is here and there a stool, or the light
  falls
O'er some long chest, with likeness to a
  tomb;
Yet were displayed amid the mournful
  gloom
Some copper vessels, and some crockery ware.
The door—as if it must, yet scarcely
  dare—
Had opened widely to the night's fresh
  air.

No voice is heard, for man has fled the
  place:

But Terror crouches in the corners'
  space.
And waits the coming guest. This
  banquet hall
Of Titans is so high, that he who shall
With wandering eye look up from beam
  to beam
Of the confused wild roof will haply
  seem
To wonder that the stars he sees not
  there.
Giants the spiders are, that weave with
  care
Their hideous webs, which float the
  joists amid,
Joists whose dark ends in griffins' jaws
  are hid.
The light is lurid, and the air like death,
And dark and foul. Even Night holds
  its breath
Awhile. One might suppose the door
  had fear
To move its double leaves—their noise
  to hear.

LEGION OF DEATH

But the great hall of generations dead
Has something more sepulchral and
  more dread
Than lurid glare from seven-branched
  chandelier
Or table lone with stately daïs near—
Two rows of arches o'er a colonnade
With knights on horseback all in mail
  arrayed,
Each one disposed with pillar at his
  back
And to another vis-à-vis. Nor lack
The fittings all complete; in each right
  hand
A lance is seen; the armoured horses
  stand

With chamfrons laced, and harness
    buckled sure;
The cuissarts' studs are by their clamps
    secure;
The dirks stand out upon the saddle-
    bow;
Even unto the horses' feet do flow
Caparisons,—the leather all well clasped,
The gorget and the spurs with bronze
    tongues hasped,
The shining long sword from the saddle
    hung,
The battle-axe across the back was
    flung.
Under the arm a trusty dagger rests,
Each spiked knee-piece its murderous
    power attests.
Feet press the stirrups—hands on bridle
    shown
Proclaim all ready, with the visors
    down,
And yet they stir not, nor is audible
A sound to make the sight less terrible.

Each monstrous horse a frontal horn
    doth bear,
If e'er the Prince of Darkness herdsman
    were
These cattle black were his by surest
    right,
Like things but seen in horrid dreams
    of night.
The steeds are swathed in trappings
    manifold,
The arméd knights are grave, and stern,
    and cold,
Terrific too; the clench'd fists seem to
    hold
Some frightful missive, which the phan-
    tom hands
Would show, if opened out at Hell's
    commands.
The dusk exaggerates their giant size.

The shade is awed—the pillars coldly
    rise.
Oh, Night! why are these awful war-
    riors here?

Horses and horsemen that make gazers
    fear
Are only empty armour. But erect
And haughty mien they all affect
And threatening air—though shades of
    iron still.
Are they strange larvæ—these their
    statues ill?
No. They are dreams of horror clothed
    in brass,
Which from profoundest depths of evil
    pass
With futile aim to dare the Infinite!
Souls tremble at the silent spectre sight,
As if in this mysterious cavalcade
They saw the weird and mystic halt was
    made
Of them who at the coming dawn of
    day
Would fade, and from their vision pass
    away.
A stranger looking in, these masks to
    see,
Might deem from Death some mandate
    there might be
At times to burst the tombs—the dead
    to wear
A human shape, and mustering ranks
    appear
Of phantoms, each confronting other
    shade.

Grave-clothes are not more grim and
    sombre made
Than are these helms, the deaf and
    sealed-up graves
Are not more icy than these arms; the
    staves

Of banner—mistress so august and
dear—
But not an arm can stir its hinges here;
Behold how mute are they whose threats
were heard
Like savage roar—whose gnashing teeth
and word
Deadened the clarion's tones; the hel-
mets dread
Have not a sound, and all the armour
spread,
The hauberks, that strong breathing
seemed to sway,
Are stranded now in helplessness alway
To see the shadows, still prolonged, that
seem
To take at night the image of a dream.

These two great files reach from the
door afar
To where the table and the daïs are,
Leaving between their fronts a narrow
lane.
On the left side the Marquises main-
tain
Their place, but the right side the Dukes
retain,
And till the roof, embattled by Spignus,
But worn by time that even that sub-
dues,
Should fall upon their heads, these
forms will stand
The grades confronting—one on either
hand.
While in advance beyond, with haughty
head—
As if commander of this squadron
dread—
All waiting signal of the Judgment Day,
In stone was seen in olden sculptors'
way
Charlemagne the King, who on the earth
had found

Only twelve knights to grace his Table
Round.

The crests were an assembly of strange
things,
Of horrors such as nightmare only
brings.
Asps, and spread eagles without beak or
feet,
Sirens and mermaids here and dragons
meet,
And antlered stags and fabled unicorn,
And fearful things of monstrous fancy
born.
Upon the rigid form of morion's sheen
Winged lions and the Cerberus are seen,
And serpents winged and finned; things
made to fright
That timid foe, alone by sense of sight.
Some leaning forward and the others
back,
They looked a growing forest that did
lack
No form of terror; but these things of
dread
That once on barons' helms the battle
led
Beneath the giant banners, now are still,
As if they gaped and found the time
but ill,
Wearied the ages passed so slowly by,
And that the gory dead no more did lie
Beneath their feet—pined for the battle-
cry,
The trumpet's clash, the carnage and
the strife,
Yawning to taste again their dreadful
life.
Like tears upon the palfreys' muzzles
were
The hard reflections of the metal there;
From out these spectres, ages past ex-
humed,

Of hideous biers have not their joints
  more strong
Than are the joinings of these legs; the
  long
Scaled gauntlet fingers look like worms
  that shine,
And battle robes to shroud-like folds in-
  cline.
The heads are skull-like, and the stony
  feet
Seem for the charnal house but only
  meet.
The pikes have death's-heads carved, and
  seem to be
Too heavy; but the shapes defiantly
Sit proudly in the saddle—and perforce
The rider looks united to the horse
Upon whose flanks the mail and harness
  cross.
The cap of Marquis beams near Ducal
  wreath,
And on the helm and gleaming shield
  beneath
Alternate triple pearls with leaves dis-
  played
Of parsley, and the royal robes are made
So large that with the knightly hauberk
  they
Seem to o'erspread the palfrey every
  way.
To Rome the oldest armour might be
  traced,
And men and horses' armour interlaced
Blent horribly; the man and steed we
  feel
Made but one hydra with its scales of
  steel.

Yet is there history here. Each coat of
  mail
Is representant of some stirring tale.
Each delta-shaped escutcheon shines to
  show

A vision of the chief by it we know.
Here are the blood-stained Dukes' a
  Marquis' line,
Barbaric lords, who amid war's rapi
Bore gilded saints upon their banne
  still
Painted on fishes' skin with cunnin
  skill.
Here Geth, who to the Slaves cried
  "Onward go,"
And Mundiaque and Ottocar—Plato
And Ladislāus Kunne; and Welf who
  bore
These words upon his shield his foes
  before:
"Nothing there is I fear." Otho blear-
  eyed,
Zultan and Nazamustus, and beside
The later Spignus, e'en to Spartibor
Of triple vision, and yet more and more
As if a pause at every age were made,
And Antæus' fearful dynasty portrayed.

What do they here so rigid and erect?
What wait they for—and what do they
  expect?
Blindness fills up the helm 'neath iron
  brows;
Like sapless tree no soul the hero knows.
Darkness is now where eyes with flame
  were fraught,
And pierced visor serves for mask of
  nought.
Of empty void is spectral giant made,
And each of these all-powerful knights
  displayed
Is only rind of pride and murderous sin;
Themselves are held the icy grave
  within.
Rust eats the casques enamoured once
  so much
Of death and daring—which knew kiss-
  like touch

And as their shadows on the roof-beams
  loomed,
Cast by the trembling light, each figure
  wan
Seemed growing, and a monstrous shape
  to don,
So that the double range of horrors
  made
The darkened zenith clouds of blackest
  shade,
That shaped themselves to profiles terrible.

All motionless the coursers horrible,
That formed a legion lured by Death to
  war,
These men and horses masked, how
  dread they are!
Absorbed in shadows of the eternal
  shore,
Among the living all their tasks are o'er.
Silent, they seem all mystery to brave,
These sphynxes whom no beacon light
  can save
Upon the threshold of the gulf so near,
As if they faced the great enigma here;
Ready with hoofs, between the pillars
  blue,
To strike out sparks, and combats to
  renew,
Choosing for battle-field the shades be-
  low,
Which they provoked by deeds we can-
  not know,
In that dark realm thought dares not to
  expound
False masks from heaven lowered to
  depths profound.

A NOISE ON THE FLOOR

This is the scene on which now enters in
Eviradnus; and follows page Gasclin.

The outer walls were almost all decayed,
The door, for ancient Marquises once
  made—
Raised many steps above the courtyard
  near—
Commanded view of the horizon clear.
The forest looked a great gulf all
  around,
And on the rock of Corbus there were
  found
Secret and blood-stained precipices tall.
Duke Plato built the tower and banquet
  hall
Over great pits,—so was it Rumour said.
The flooring sounds 'neath Eviradnus'
  tread
Above abysses many.
                  "Page," said he,
"Come here, your eyes than mine can
  better see,
For sight is woman-like and shuns the
  old;
Ah! he can see enough, when years are
  told,
Who backward looks. But, boy, turn
  towards the glade
And tell me what you see."
                      The boy obeyed,
And leaned across the threshold, while
  the bright,
Full moon shed o'er the glade its white,
  pure light.
"I see a horse and woman on it now,"
Said Gasclin, "and companions also
  show."
"Who are they?" asked the seeker of
  sublime
Adventures. "Sir, I now can hear like
  chime
The sound of voices, and men's voices
  too,
Laughter and talk; two men there are
  in view,

Across the road the shadows clear I mark
Of horses three."
        "Enough. Now, Gasclin, hark!"
Exclaimed the knight, "you must at once return
By other path than that which you discern,
So that you be not seen. At break of day
Bring back our horses fresh, and every way
Caparisoned; now leave me, boy, I say."
The page looked at his master like a son,
And said to him, "Oh, if I might stay on,
For they are two."
        "Go—I suffice alone!"

THE SPECTRAL KNIGHT

And lone the hero is within the hall
And nears the table where the glasses all
Show in profusion; all the vessels there,
Goblets and glasses gilt, or painted fair,
Are ranged for different wines with practised care.
He thirsts; the flagons tempt; but there must stay
One drop in emptied glass, and 'twould betray
The fact that some one living had been here.
Straight to the horses goes he, pauses near
That which is next the table shining bright,
Seizes the rider — plucks the phantom knight
To pieces—all in vain its panoply
And pallid shining to his practised eye;
Then he conveys the severed iron remain

To corner of the hall where darkness reigns;
Against the wall he lays the armour low
In dust and gloom like hero vanquished now—
But keeping pond'rous lance and shield so old,
Mounts to the empty saddle, and behold!
A statue Eviradnus has become,
Like to the others in their frigid home.
With visor down scarce breathing seemed maintained.

Throughout the hall a death-like silence reigned.

KISS FOR FODDER

Listen! like hum from unseen nests we hear
A mirthful buzz of voices coming near,
Of footsteps—laughter—from the trembling trees.
And now the thick-set forest all receives
A flood of moonlight—and there gently floats
The sound of a guitar of Innsbruck; notes
Which blend with chimes—vibrating to the hand—
Of tiny bell—where sounds a grain of sand.
A man's voice mixes with the melody,
And vaguely melts to song in harmony.

"If you like we'll dream a dream.
   Let us mount on palfreys two;
Birds are singing,—let it seem
   You lure me—and I take you.

"Let us start—'tis eve, you see,
   I'm thy master and thy prey.

My bright steel shall pleasure be;
   Yours, it shall be love, I say.

"Journeying leisurely we go,
   We will make our steeds touch
      heads,
Kiss for fodder,—and we so
   Satisfy our horses' needs.

"Come! the two delusive things
   Stamp impatiently it seems,
Yours has heavenward soaring wings,
   Mine is of the land of dreams.

"What's our baggage? only vows,
   Happiness, and all our care.
And the flower that sweetly shows
   Nestling lightly in your hair.

"Come, the oaks all dark appear,
   Twilight now will soon depart,
Railing sparrows laugh to hear
   Chains thou puttest round my
      heart.

"Not my fault 'twill surely be
   If the hills should vocal prove,
And the trees when us they see,
   All should murmur—let us love!

"Oh, be gentle!—I am dazed,
   See the dew is on the grass,
Wakened butterflies amazed
   Follow thee as on we pass.

"Envious night-birds open wide
   Their round eyes to gaze awhile,
Nymphs that lean their urns beside
   From their grottoes softly smile,

"And exclaim, by fancy stirred,
   'Hero and Leander they;

We in listening for a word
   Let our water fall away.'

"Let us journey Austrian way,
   With the daybreak on our brow;
I be great, and you I say
   Rich, because we love shall know.

"Let us over countries rove,
   On our charming steeds content,
In the azure light of love,
   And its sweet bewilderment.

"For the charges at our inn,
   You with maiden smiles shall pay;
I the landlord's heart will win
   In a scholar's pleasant way.

"You, great lady—and I, Count—
   Come, my heart has opened quite.
We this tale will still recount,
   To the stars that shine at night."

The melody went on some moments
      more
Among the trees the calm moon glis-
      tened o'er,
Then trembled and was hushed; the
      voice's thrill
Stopped like alighting birds, and all was
      still.

THREE HEADS

Quite suddenly there showed across the
      door,
Three heads which all a festive aspect
      wore.
Two men were there; and, dressed in
      cloth of gold,
A woman. Of the men one might have
      told

Some thirty years, the other younger
  seemed,
Was tall and fair, and from his shoulder
  gleamed
A gay guitar with ivy leaves enlaced.
The other man was dark, but pallid-
  faced
And small. At the first glance they
  seemed to be
But made of perfume and frivolity.
Handsome they were, but through their
  comely mien
A grinning demon might be clearly
  seen.
April has flowers where lurk the slugs
  between.

"Big Joss and little Zeno, pray come
  here;
Look now—how dreadful! can I help
  but fear!"
Madame Mahaud was speaker. Moon-
  light there
Caressingly enhanced her beauty rare,
Making it shine and tremble, as if she
So soft and gentle were of things that be
Of air created, and are brought and ta'en
By heavenly flashes. Now, she spoke
  again:
"Certes, 'tis heavy purchase of a throne,
To pass the night here utterly alone.
Had you not slyly come to guard me
  now,
I should have died of fright outright I
  know."
The moonbeams through the open door
  did fall,
And shine upon the figure next the wall.
Said Zeno, "If I played the Marquis
  part,
I'd send this rubbish to the auction
  mart;

Out of the heap should come the finest
  wine,
Pleasure and gala-fêtes, were it all
  mine."
And then with scornful hand he touched
  the thing,
And made the metal like a soul's cry
  ring.
He laughed—the gauntlet trembled at
  his stroke.
"Let rest my ancestors"—'twas Mahaud
  spoke;
Then murmuring added she, "For you
  are much
Too small their noble armour here to
  touch."
And Zeno paled, but Joss with laugh ex-
  claimed,
"Why, all these good black men so
  grandly named
Are only nests for mice. By Jove, al-
  though
They lifelike look and terrible, we know
What is within; just listen, and you'll
  hear
The vermins' gnawing teeth, yet 'twould
  appear
These figures once were proudly named
  Otho,
And Ottocar, and Bela, and Plato.
Alas! the end's not pleasant—puts one
  out;
To have been kings and dukes—made
  mighty rout—
Colossal heroes filling tombs with slain,
And, Madame, this to only now remain;
A peaceful nibbling rat to calmly pierce
A prince's noble armour proud and
  fierce."

"Sing, if you will—but do not speak so
  loud:

Besides, such things as these," said fair
    Mahaud,
"In your condition are not understood."
"Well said," made answer Zeno, " 'tis a
    place
Of wonders—I see serpents, and can
    trace
Vampires, and monsters swarming, that
    arise
In mist, through chinks, to meet the
    gazer's eyes."
Then Mahaud shuddered, and she said:
    "The wine
The Abbé made me drink as task of
    mine,
Will soon enwrap me in the soundest
    sleep—
Swear not to leave me—that you here
    will keep."
"I swear," cried Joss, and Zeno, "I also;
But now at once to supper let us go."

A MINSTREL WITHOUT SHAME

With laugh and song they to the table
    went.
Said Mahaud gaily: "It is my intent
To make Joss chamberlain. Zeno shall
    be
A constable supreme of high degree."
All three were joyous, and were fair to
    see.
Joss ate—and Zeno drank; on stools the
    pair,
With Mahaud musing in the regal chair.
The sound of separate leaf we do not
    note—
And so their babble seemed to idly
    float,
And leave no thought behind. Now
    and again
Joss his guitar made trill with plaintive
    strain

Or Tyrolean air; and lively tales they
    told
Mingled with mirth all free, and frank,
    and bold.
Said Mahaud: "Do you know how
    fortunate
You are?" "Yes, we are young at any
    rate—
Lovers half crazy—this is truth at
    least."
"And more, for you know Latin like a
    priest,
And Joss sings well."
        "Ah, yes, our master true,
Yields us these gifts beyond the measure
    due."
"Your master!—who is he?" Mahaud
    exclaimed.
"Satan, we say—but Sin you'd think
    him named,"
Said Zeno, veiling words in raillery.
"Do not laugh thus," she said with dig-
    nity;
"Peace, Zeno. Joss, you speak, my
    chamberlain."
"Madame, Viridis, Countess of Milan,
Was deemed superb; Diana on the
    mount
Dazzled the shepherd boy; ever we
    count
The Isabel of Saxony so fair,
And Cleopatra's beauty all so rare—
Aspasia's, too, that must with theirs
    compare—
That praise of them no fitting language
    hath.
Divine was Rhodope—and Venus' wrath
Was such at Erylesis' perfect throat,
She dragged her to the forge where Vul-
    can smote
Her beauty on his anvil. Well, as much
As star transcends a sequin, and just
    such

As temple is to rubbish-heap, I say
You do eclipse their beauty every way.
Those airy sprites that from the azure
    smile
Peris and elfs the while they men be-
    guile,
Have brows less youthful pure than
    yours; besides
Dishevelled they whose shaded beauty
    hides
In clouds."
            "Flatt'rer," said Mahaud, "you
            but sing
Too well."
        Then Joss more homage sought
        to bring;
"If I were angel under heav'n," said he,
"Or girl or demon, I would seek to be
By you instructed in all art and grace,
And as in school but take a scholar's
    place.
Highness, you are a fairy bright, whose
    hand
For sceptre vile gave up your proper
    wand."
Fair Mahaud mused—then said, "Be
    silent now;
You seem to watch me; little 'tis I
    know,
Only that from Bohemia Joss doth
    come,
And that in Poland Zeno hath his home.
But you amuse me; I am rich, you
    poor—
What boon shall I confer and make se-
    cure?
What gift? ask of me, poets, what you
    will
And I will grant it—promise to fulfil."
"A kiss," said Joss.
        "A kiss!" quick anger wrought
In Mahaud at the minstrel's shameless
    thought,

And flush of indignation warmed her
    cheek.
"You do forget to whom it is you
    speak,"
She cried.
            "Had I not known your high
            degree,
Should I have asked this royal boon,"
    said he,
"Obtained or given, a kiss must ever be.
No gift like king's—no kiss like that of
    queen!"
Queen! And on Mahaud's face a smile
    was seen.

THE ODOUR OF CRIME

But now the potion proved its subtle
    power,
And Mahaud's heavy eyelids 'gan to
    lower.
Zeno, with finger on his lip, looked on—
Her head next drooped, and conscious-
    ness was gone.
Smiling she slept, serene and very fair,
He took her hand, which fell all una-
    ware.

"She sleeps," said Zeno, "now let chance
    or fate
Decide for us which has the marquisate,
And which the girl."
            Upon their faces now
A hungry tiger's look began to show.
"My brother, let us speak like men of
    sense,"
Said Joss, "while Mahaud dreams in
    innocence,
We grasp all here—and hold the foolish
    thing—
Our Friend below to us success will
    bring.
He keeps his word; 'tis thanks to him
    I say.

No awkward chance has marred our
  plans to-day.
All has succeeded—now no human power
Can take from us this woman and her
  dower.
Let us conclude. To wrangle and to
  fight
For just a yes or no, or to prove right
The Arian doctrines, all the time the
  Pope
Laughs in his sleeve at you—or with the
  hope
Some blue-eyed damsel with a tender
  skin
And milkwhite dainty hands by force to
  win—
This might be well in days when men
  bore loss
And fought for Latin or Byzantine
  Cross;
When Jack and Rudolf did like fools
  contend,
And for a simple wench their valour
  spend—
When Pepin held a synod at Leptine,
And times than now were much less
  wise and fine.
We do no longer heap up quarrels thus,
But better know how projects to dis-
  cuss.
Have you the needful dice?"
          "Yes, here they wait
For us."
          "Who wins shall have the
              Marquisate;
Loser, the girl."
          "Agreed."
          "A noise I hear?"
"Only the wind that sounds like some
  one near—
Are you afraid?" said Zeno.
          "Naught I fear

Save fasting—and that solid earth
  should gape.
Let's throw and fate decide—ere time
  escape."
Then rolled the dice.
          " 'Tis four."
              'Twas Joss to throw.
"Six!—and I neatly win, you see; and
  lo!
At bottom of this box I've found Lu-
  sace,
And henceforth my orchestra will have
  place;
To it they'll dance. Taxes I'll raise,
  and they
In dread of rope and forfeit well will
  pay;
Brass trumpet-calls shall be my flutes
  that lead,
Where gibbets rise the imposts grow
  and spread."
Said Zeno, "I've the girl and so is best."
"She's beautiful," said Joss.
          "Yes, 'tis confess'd."
"What shall you do with her?" asked
  Joss.
          "I know.
Make her a corpse," said Zeno;
  "marked you how
The jade insulted me just now! Too
  small
She called me—such the words her lips
  let fall.
I say, that moment ere the dice I threw
Had yawning Hell cried out, 'My son,
  for you
The chance is open still: take in a heap
The fair Lusace's seven towns, and reap
The corn, and wine, and oil of counties
  ten,
With all their people diligent, and then
Bohemia with its silver mines, and now

The lofty land whence mighty rivers
    flow
And not a brook returns; add to these
    counts
The Tyrol with its lovely azure mounts
And France with her historic fleurs-de-
    lis;
Come now, decide, what 'tis your choice
    must be?'
I should have answered, 'Vengeance!
    give to me
Rather than France, Bohemia, or the
    fair
Blue Tyrol! I my choice, O Hell! de-
    clare
For government of darkness and of
    death,
Of grave and worms.'   Brother, this
    woman hath
As marchioness with absurdity set forth
To rule o'er frontier bulwarks of the
    north.
In any case to us a danger she,
And having stupidly insulted me
'Tis needful that she die. To blurt all
    out—
I know that you desire her; without
    doubt
The flame that rages in my heart warms
    yours;
To carry out these subtle plans of ours,
We have become as gipsies near this
    doll,
You as her page—I dotard to control—
Pretended gallants changed to lovers
    now.
So, brother, this being fact for us to
    know
Sooner or later, 'gainst our best intent
About her we should quarrel. Evident
Is it our compact would be broken
    through.
There is only one thing for us to do,

And that is, kill her."
        "Logic very clear,"
Said musing Joss, "but what of blood
    shed here?"
Then Zeno stooped and lifted from the
    ground
An edge of carpet—groped until he
    found
A ring, which, pulled, an opening did
    disclose,
With deep abyss beneath; from it there
    rose
The odour rank of crime. Joss walked
    to see
While Zeno pointed to it silently.
But eyes met eyes, and Joss, well
    pleased, was fain
By nod of head to make approval plain.

HELL'S PARTITION

If sulphurous light had shone from this
    vile well
One might have said it was a mouth of
    hell,
So large the trap that by some sudden
    blow
A man might backward fall and sink be-
    low.
Who looked could see a harrow's threat-
    ening teeth,
But lost in night was everything be-
    neath.
Partitions blood-stained have a reddened
    smear,
And Terror unrelieved is master here.
One feels the place has secret histories
Replete with dreadful murderous mys-
    teries,
And that this sepulchre, forgot to-day,
Is home of trailing ghosts that grope
    their way

Along the walls where spectre reptiles
  crawl.
"Our fathers fashioned for us after all
Some useful things," said Joss; then
  Zeno spoke:
"I know what Corbus hides beneath its
  cloak,
I and the osprey know its ancient walls
And how was justice done within its
  halls."
"And are you sure that Mahaud will not
  wake?"
"Her eyes are closed as now my fist I
  make;
She is in mystic and unearthly sleep;
The potion still its power o'er her must
  keep."
"But she will surely wake at break of
  day?"
"In darkness."
   "What will all the courtiers
  say
When in the place of her they find two
  men?"
"To them we will declare ourselves—
  and then
They at our feet will fall."
   "Where leads this hole?"
"To where the crow makes feast and
  torrents roll,
To desolation. Let us end it now."

These young and handsome men had
  seemed to grow
Deformed and hideous—so doth foul
  black heart
Disfigure man, till beauty all depart.
So too the hell within the human face
Transparent is. They nearer move
  apace;
And Mahaud soundly sleeps as in a bed.
"To work."

Joss seizes her and holds her
  head
Supporting her beneath her arms, in his;
And then he dared to plant a monstrous
  kiss
Upon her rosy lips,—while Zeno bent
Before the massive chair, and with in-
  tent
Her robe disordered as he raised her
  feet;
Her dainty ankles thus their gaze to
  meet.
And while the mystic sleep was all pro-
  found,
The pit gaped wide like grave in burial
  ground.

SPIRIT OF THE ABYSS

Bearing the sleeping Mahaud they
  moved now
Silent and bent with heavy step and
  slow.
Zeno faced darkness—Joss turned towards the light—
So that the hall to Joss was quite in
  sight.
Sudden he stopped—and Zeno, "What
  now!" called,
But Joss replied not, though he seemed
  appalled,
And made a sign to Zeno, who with
  speed
Looked back. Then seemed they changed
  to stone indeed,
For both perceived that in the vaulted
  hall
One of the grand old knights ranged by
  the wall
Descended from his horse. Like phantom he
Moved with a horrible tranquillity.
Masked by his helm towards them he
  came; his tread

Made the floor tremble—and one might
have said
A spirit of th' abyss was here; between
Them and the pit he came—a barrier
seen;
Then said, with sword in hand and visor
down,
In measured tones that had sepulchral
grown
As tolling bell. "Stop, Sigismond, and
you,
King Ladislāus;" at those words, though
few,
They dropped the Marchioness, and in
such a way
That at their feet like rigid corpse she
lay.

The deep voice speeking from the vi-
sor's grate
Proceeded—while the two in abject state
Cowered low. Joss paled, by gloom and
dread o'ercast.
And Zeno trembled like a yielding mast.
"You two who listen now must recollect
The compact all your fellow-men sus-
pect.
'Tis this: 'I, Satan, god of darkened
sphere,
The king of gloom and winds that bring
things drear,
Alliance make with my two brothers
dear,
The Emperor Sigismond and Polish
King
Named Ladislāus. I to surely bring
Aid and protection to them both alway,
And never to absent myself or say
I'm weary. And yet more—I, being lord
Of sea and land, to Sigismond award
The earth; to Ladislāus all the sea.
With this condition that they yield to
me

When I the forfeit claim—the King his
head,
But shall the Emperor give his soul instead.' "

Said Joss, "Is't he?—Spectre with flash-
ing eyes,
And art thou Satan come us to sur-
prise?"
"Much less am I and yet much more.
Oh, kings of crimes and plots! your day
is o'er,
But I your lives will only take to-day;
Beneath the talons black your souls
let stay
To wrestle still."
                    The pair looked stupefied
And crushed. Exchanging looks 'twas
Zeno cried,
Speaking to Joss, "Now who—who can
it be?"
Joss stammered, "Yes, no refuge can I
see;
The doom is on us. But oh, spectre!
say
Who are you?"
                    "I'm the judge."
                    "Then mercy, pray."
The voice replied: "God guides His
chosen hand
To be th' Avenger in your path to stand.
Your hour has sounded, nothing now in-
deed
Can change for you the destiny decreed,
Irrevocable quite. Yes, I looked on.
Ah! little did you think that any one
To this unwholesome gloom could
knowledge bring
That Joss a kaiser was, and Zeno king.
You spoke just now—but why?—too
late to plead.
The forfeit's due and hope should all be
dead.

Incurables! For you I am the grave.
Oh, miserable men! whom naught can
save.
Yes, Sigismond a kaiser is, and you
A king, O Ladislāus!—it is true.
You thought of God but as a wheel to
roll
Your chariot on; you who have king's
control
O'er Poland and its many towns so
strong,
You, Milan's Duke, to whom at once
belong
The gold and iron crowns. You, Em-
peror made
By Rome, a son of Hercules, 'tis said;
And you of Spartibor. And your two
crowns
Are shining lights; and yet your shadow
frowns
From every mountain land to trembling
sea.
You are at giddy heights twin powers
to be
A glory and a force for all that's great—
But 'neath the purple canopy of state,
Th' expanding and triumphant arch you
prize,
'Neath royal power that sacred veils
disguise,
Beneath your crowns of pearls and
jewelled stars,
Beneath your exploits terrible and wars,
You, Sigismond, have but a monster
been,
And, Ladislāus, you are scoundrel seen.
Oh, degradation of the sceptre's might
And sword's—when Justice has a hand
like night,
Foul and polluted; and before this thing,
This hydra, do the Temple's hinges
swing—

The throne becomes the haunt of all
things base!
Oh, age of infamy and foul disgrace!
Oh, starry heavens looking on the
shame,
No brow but reddens with resentful
flame—
And yet the silent people do not stir!
Oh, million arms! what things do you
deter—
Poor sheep, whom vermin-majesties de-
vour,
Have you not nails with strong desiring
power
To rend these royalties, that you so
cower?
But two are taken,—such as will amaze
E'en hell itself, when it on them shall
gaze.
Ah, Sigismond and Ladislāus, you
Were once triumphant, splendid to the
view,
Stifling with your prosperity—but now
The hour of retribution lays you low.
Ah, do the vulture and the crocodile
Shed tears! At such a sight I fain must
smile.
It seems to me 'tis very good some-
times
That princes, conquerors stained with
bandits' crimes,
Sparkling with splendour, wearing
crowns of gold,
Should know the deadly sweat endured
of old,
That of Jehoshaphat; should sob and
fear,
And after crime th' unclean be brought
to bear.
'Tis well—God rules—and thus it is
that I
These masters of the world can make to
lie

In ashes at my feet. And this was he
Who reigned—and this a Cæsar known
   to be!
In truth, my old heart aches with very
   shame
To see such cravens with such noble
   name.
But let us finish—what has just passed
   here
Demands thick shrouding, and the time
   is near.
Th' accursed dice that rolled at Calvary
You rolled a woman's murder to decree:
It was a dark disastrous game to play;
But not for me a moral to essay.
This moment to the misty grave is due,
And far too vile and little human you
To see your evil ways. Your fingers
   lack
The human sense to test your actions
   black.
What use in darkness mirror to uphold?
What use that now your deeds should be
   retold?
Drink of the darkness—greedy of the
   ill
To which from habit you're attracted
   still,
Not recognizing in the draught you take
The stench that your atrocities must
   make.
I only tell you that this burthened age
Tires of your Highnesses, that soil its
   page,
And of your villainies—and this is why
You now must swell the stream that
   passes by
Of refuse filth. Oh, horrid scene to
   show
Of these young men and that young
   girl just now!
Oh! can you really be of human kind

Breathing pure air of heaven? Do we
   find
That you are men? Oh, no! for when
   you laid
Foul lips upon the mouth of sleeping
   maid,
You seemed but ghouls that had come
   furtively
From out the tombs; only a horrid lie
Your human shape; of some strange
   frightful beast
You have the soul. To darkness I at
   least
Remit you now. Oh, murderer Sigis-
   mond
And Ladislāus pirate, both beyond
Release—two demons that have broken
   ban!
Therefore 'tis time their empire over
   man,
And converse with the living, should be
   o'er;
Tyrants, behold your tomb your eyes
   before;
Vampires and dogs, your sepulchre is
   here.
Enter."
               He pointed to the gulf so near.

All terrified upon their knees they fell.
"Oh! take us not in your dread realm
   to dwell,"
Said Sigismond. "But, phantom! do us
   tell
What thou wouldst have from us—we
   will obey.
Oh, mercy!—'tis for mercy now we
   pray."
"Behold us at your feet, oh, spectre
   dread!"
And no old crone in feebler voice could
   plead
Than Ladislāus did.

But not a word
Said now the figure motionless, with
    sword
In hand. This sovereign soul seemed to
    commune
With self beneath his metal sheath; yet
    soon
And suddenly, with tranquil voice said
    he,
"Princes, your craven spirit wearies me.
No phantom—only man am I. Arise!
I like not to be dreaded otherwise
Than with the fear to which I'm used;
    know me,
For it is Eviradnus that you see!"

COLOSSAL HANDS

As from the mist a noble pine we tell
Grown old upon the heights of Appen-
    zel,
When morning freshness breathes round
    all the wood,
So Eviradnus now before them stood,
Opening his vizor, which at once re-
    vealed
The snowy beard it had so well con-
    cealed.
Then Sigismond was still as dog at
    gaze,
But Ladislāus leaped, and howl did
    raise,
And laughed and gnashed his teeth, till,
    like a cloud
That sudden bursts, his rage was all
    avowed.
" 'Tis but an old man after all!" he
    cried.

Then the great knight, who looked at
    both, replied,
"Oh, kings! an old man of my time can
    cope

With two much younger ones of yours,
    I hope.
To mortal combat I defy you both
Singly; or, if you will, I'm nothing loth
With two together to contend; choose
    here
From out the heap what weapon shall
    appear
Most fit. As you no cuirass wear, I
    see,
I will take off my own, for all must be
In order perfect—e'en your punish-
    ment."

Then Eviradnus, true to his intent,
Stripped to his Utrecht jerkin; but the
    while
He calmly had disarmed—with dexter-
    ous guile
Had Ladislāus seized a knife that lay
Upon the damask cloth, and slipped
    away
His shoes; then barefoot, swiftly, sil-
    ently
He crept behind the knight, with arm
    held high.
But Eviradnus was of all aware,
And turned upon the murderous weapon
    there,
And twisted it away; then in a trice
His strong colossal hand grasped like
    a vice
The neck of Ladislāus, who the blade
Now dropped; over his eyes a misty
    shade
Showed that the royal dwarf was near
    to death.

"Traitor!" said Eviradnus in his wrath,
"I rather should have hewn your limbs
    away,
And left you crawling on your stumps;

I say,—
But now die fast."

Ghastly, with starting eyes,
The King without a cry or struggle dies.
One dead—but lo! the other stands
  bold-faced,
Defiant; for the knight, when he un-
  laced
His cuirass, had his trusty sword laid
  down,
And Sigismond now grasps it as his
  own.
The monster youth laughed at the sil-
  v'ry beard,
And, sword in hand, a murderer glad
  appeared.
Crossing his arms, he cried, " 'Tis my
  turn now!"
And the black mounted knights in
  solemn row
Were judges of the strife. Before them
  lay
The sleeping Mahaud—and not far away
The fatal pit, near which the champion
  knight
With evil Emperor must contend for
  right,
Though weaponless he was. And yawned
  the pit
Expectant which should be engulphed in
  it.
"Now we shall see for whom this ready
  grave,"
Said Sigismond, "you dog, whom nought
  can save!"
Aware was Eviradnus that if he
Turned for a blade unto the armoury,
He would be instant pierced—what can
  he do?
The moment is for him supreme. But,
  lo!
He glances now at Ladisläus dead,

And with a smile triumphant and yet
  dread,
And air of lion caged to whom is shown
Some loophole of escape, he bends him
  down.
"Ha! ha! no other club than this I
  need!"
He cried, as seizing in his hands with
  speed
The dead King's heels, the body lifted
  high,
Then to the frightened Emperor he came
  nigh,
And made him shake with horror and
  with fear,
The weapon all so ghastly did appear.
The head became the stone to this
  strange sling,
Of which the body was the potent
  string;
And while 'twas brandished in a deadly
  way,
The dislocated arms made monstrous
  play
With hideous gestures, as now upside
  down
The bludgeon corpse a giant force had
  grown.
" 'Tis well!" said Eviradnus, and he
  cried,
"Arrange between yourselves, you two
  allied;
If hell-fire were extinguished, surely it
By such a contest might be all relit;
From kindling spark struck out from
  dead King's brow,
Batt'ring to death a living Emperor
  now."

And Sigismond, thus met and horrified,
Recoiled to near the unseen opening
  wide:

The human club was raised, and struck
again . . .
And Eviradnus did alone remain
All empty-handed—but he heard the
sound
Of spectres two falling to depths profound;
Then, stooping o'er the pit, he gazed below,
And, as half-dreaming now, he murmured low
"Tiger and jackal meet their portion
here,
'Tis well together they should disappear!"

. . . .

Then lifts he Mahaud to the ducal chair,
And shuts the trap with noiseless, gentle
care;
And puts in order everything around,
So that, on waking, nought should her
astound.

NO BAPTISM

FINDING that earthquakes far too much
prevailed,
The Spanish kings with sacred rites as-
sailed
Volcanic mountains of the New World
land,
Baptising them; and to the priestly hand
They all submitted, saving only one,
But Momotombo would not have it
done.
Divers the surpliced priests who—choice
of Rome—
Essayed to reach the frowning moun-
tain's dome,

Bearing the Sacrament the Church decrees,
With eyes on Heaven fixed, but of all
these—
And many were they—none were heard
of more.

"Oh Momotombo, thou colossus hoar,
Who ponderest by the sea, whilst thou
hast made
Tiara of thy crater's flame and shade,
Why, when thy dreadful threshold we
draw near,
And bring thee God, why wilt thou not
us hear?"
Stayed was the belching of its lava tide,
While gravely Momotombo thus replied:

"I liked not much the god you chased
away,
His jaws were black with gory rot al-
way.
Eater of human flesh was he, this god,
And miser hiding gold beneath the sod.
His cave, the porch to frightful yard,
was made
Sepulchral Temple where his Pontiff
stayed,
The slaughterer deaf, deformed, of hide-
ous mien,
Bleeding between his teeth was ever
seen
A corpse, while round his wrists the ser-
pents twined;
And horrid skeletons of human kind
Grinn'd at his feet. Oh cruel were the
ways
Of shocking murder in those dreadful
days,
Blackening of the firmament sublime.
At this
I groaned from out the depths of my
abyss.

Thus when came proudly o'er the trem-
bling sea
White men, from that side whence un-
failingly
The morning ever breaks, it seemed to
me
That to receive them well were only
wise.
'White men,' said I, 'resemble azure
skies,
Surely the colour of their souls we
trace,
It must be like the colour of their face,
The god that these men worship must
be good;
Murders will cease,' and I in happy
mood
Rejoiced—the ancient priest I hated so;
But when the new one's work began to
show,
When I could see the Inquisition flame,
That ne'er was quenched, taking the
Holy name,
A mournful torch that to my level
reached,
Just Heaven! when thus you daily
taught and preached,
And Torquemada tried with fiery might
To dissipate the darkness of the night
Of savage heathendom—when I saw then
How He would civilize—at Lima, when
I saw the osier giants, in the strife,
Filled to the brim with childish baby
life
Crackling above the mighty furnace
heat,
And curls of smoke round burning
women meet,
Choked by the stench of every horrid
deed,
Auto-da-fé according to your creed,
I—who but shadow brightly burn
away—

Repented of my gladness, forced to say,
When looking at the strangers' god more
near,
'To change is not worth while it doth
appear!' "

MARCH OF THE HALBERDIERS

WHEN the regiment of Halberdiers
Is proudly marching by,
The eagle of the mountain screams
From out his stormy sky;
Who speaketh to the precipice,
And to the chasm sheer;
Who hovers o'er the thrones of kings,
And bids the caitiffs fear.
King of the peak and glacier,
King of the cold, white scalps—
He lifts his head, at that close tread,
The eagle of the Alps.

O shame! those men that march below—
O ignominy dire!
Are the sons of my free mountains
Sold for imperial hire.
Ah! the vilest in the dungeon!
Ah! the slave upon the seas—
Is great, is pure, is glorious,
Is grand compared with these,
Who, born amid my holy rocks
In solemn places high,
Where the tall pines bend like rushes
When the storm goes sweeping by;

Yet give the strength of foot they
learned
By perilous path and flood,
And from their blue-eyed mothers won,
The old, mysterious blood;
The daring that the good south wind
Into their nostrils blew,

And the proud swelling of the heart
　With each pure breath they drew;
The graces of the mountain glens,
　With flowers in summer gay;
And all the glories of the hills
　To earn a lackey's pay.

Their country free and joyous—
　She of the rugged sides—
She of the rough peaks arrogant
　Whereon the tempest rides:
Mother of the unconquered thought
　And of the savage form,
Who brings out of her sturdy heart
　The hero and the storm;
Who giveth freedom unto man,
　And life unto the beast;
Who hears her silver torrents ring
　Like joy-bells at a feast;

Who hath her caves for palaces,
　And where her châlets stand—
The proud, old archer of Altorf,
　With his good bow in his hand.
Is she to suckle gaolers?
　Shall shame and glory rest,
Amid her lakes and glaciers,
　Like twins upon her breast?
Shall the two-headed eagle,
　Marked with her double blow,
Drink of her milk through all those
　hearts
Whose blood he bids to flow?

Say, was it pomp ye needed,
　And all the proud array
Of courtly joust and high parade
　Upon a gala day?
Look up; have not my valleys
　Their torrents white with foam—
Their lines of silver bullion
　On the blue hillocks of home?
Doth not sweet May embroider

My rocks with pearls and flowers?
Her fingers trace a richer lace
　Than yours in all my bowers.

Are not my old peaks gilded
　When the sun arises proud,
And each one shakes a white mist plume
　Out of the thunder-cloud?
O neighbour of the golden sky—
　Sons of the mountain sod—
Why wear a base king's colours
　For the livery of God?
O shame! despair! to see my Alps
　Their giant shadows fling
Into the very waiting-room
　Of tyrant and of king!

O thou deep heaven, unsullied yet,
　Into thy gulfs sublime—
Up azure tracks of flaming light—
　Let my free pinion climb;
Till from my sight, in that clear light,
　Earth and her crimes be gone—
The men who act the evil deeds—
　The caitiffs who look on.
Far, far into that space immense,
　Beyond the vast white veil,
Where distant stars come out and shine.
　And the great sun grows pale.

———————

HERO OF GENTLE MIEN

My father, hero of benignant mien,
On horseback visited the gory scene,
After the battle as the evening fell,
And took with him a trooper loved
　right well,
Because of bravery and presence bold.
The field was covered with the dead,
　all cold,

And shades of night were deepening:
     came a sound,
Feeble and hoarse, from something on
     the ground;
It was a Spaniard of the vanquished
     force,
Who dragged himself with pain beside
     their course;
Wounded and bleeding, livid and half
     dead,
"Give me to drink—in pity, drink!" he
     said.
My father, touched, stretched to his fol-
     lower now,
A flask of rum that from his saddle-bow
Hung down: "The poor soul—give him
     drink," said he.
But while the trooper prompt, obediently
Stooped towards the other, he of Moor-
     ish race
Pointed a pistol at my father's face,
And with a savage oath the trigger
     drew;
The hat flew off, a bullet passing
     through.
As swerved his charger in a backward
     stride,
"Give him to drink the same," my
     father cried.

NIGHT AND A CABIN

'Tis night—within the close stout cabin
     door,
     The room is wrapped in shade save
          where there fall
Some twilight rays that creep along the
     floor,
     And show the fisher's nets upon the
          wall.

In the dim corner, from the oaken
     chest,
     A few white dishes glimmer; through
          the shade
Stands a tall bed with dusky curtains
     dressed,
     And a rough mattress at its side is
          laid.

Five children on the long low mattress
     lie—
     A nest of little souls, it heaves with
          dreams;
In the high chimney the last embers
     die,
     And redden the dark room with crim-
          son gleams.

The mother kneels and thinks, and pale
     with fear,
     She prays alone, hearing the billows
          shout:
While to wild winds, to rocks, to mid-
     night drear,
     The ominous old ocean sobs without.

.   .   .   .   .

Poor wives of fishers! Ah! 'tis sad to
     say,
     Our sons, our husbands, all that we
          love best,
Our hearts, our souls, are on those
     waves away,
     Those ravening wolves that know not
          ruth, nor rest.

Think how they sport with these be-
     loved forms;
     And how the clarion-blowing of the
          wind unties
Above their heads the tresses of the
     storms:
     Perchance even now the child, the
          husband dies

For we can never tell where they may
  be
  Who, to make head against the tide
    and gale,
Between them and the starless, soulless
  sea
  Have but one bit of plank, with one
    poor sail.

Terrible fear! We seek the pebbly
  shore,
  Cry to the rising billows, "Bring them
    home."
Alas! what answer gives their troubled
  roar,
  To the dark thought that haunts us
    as we roam.

Janet is sad: her husband is alone,
  Wrapped in the black shroud of this
    bitter night:
His children are so little, there is none
  To give him aid. "Were they but old,
    they might."
Ah, mother! when they too are on the
  main,
  How wilt thou weep: "Would they
    were young again!"

She takes his lantern—'tis his hour at
  last:
  She will go forth, and see if the day
    breaks,
And if his signal-fire be at the mast;
  Ah, no—not yet—no breath of morn-
    ing wakes.

No line of light o'er the dark water lies;
  It rains, it rains, how black is rain at
    morn:
The day comes trembling, and the young
    dawn cries—
  Cries like a baby fearing to be born.

Sudden her humane eyes that peer and
  watch
  Through the deep shade, a moulder-
    ing dwelling find,
No light within—the thin door shakes—
  the thatch
  O'er the green walls is twisted of the
    wind.

Yellow, and dirty, as a swollen rill,
  "Ah, me," she saith, "here does that
    widow dwell;
Few days ago my good man left her ill:
  I will go in and see if all be well."

She strikes at the door, she listens, none
  replies,
  And Janet shudders. "Husbandless,
    alone,
And with two children—they have scant
  supplies.
  Good neighbour! She sleeps heavy
    as a stone."

She calls again, she knocks, 'tis silence
  still;
  No sound—no answer—suddenly the
    door,
As if the senseless creature felt some
  thrill
  Of pity, turned—and open lay before.

She entered, and her lantern lighted all
  The house so still, but for the rude
    waves' din.
Through the thin roof the plashing rain-
    drops fall,
  But something terrible is couched
    within.

.   .   .   .   .   .

"So, for the kisses that delight the
  flesh,

For mother's worship, and for children's bloom,
For song, for smile, for love so fair and
fresh,
For laugh, for dance, there is one
goal—the tomb."

And why does Janet pass so fast away?
What hath she done within that house
of dread?
What foldeth she beneath her mantle
grey?
And hurries home, and hides it in her
bed:
With half-averted face, and nervous
tread,
What hath she stolen from the awful
dead?

The dawn was whitening over the sea's
verge
As she sat pensive, touching broken
chords
Of half-remorseful thought, while the
hoarse surge
Howled a sad concert to her broken
words.

"Ah, my poor husband! we had five before,
Already so much care, so much to
find,
For he must work for all. I give him
more.
What was that noise? His step! Ah,
no! the wind.

"That I should be afraid of him I love!
I have done ill. If he should beat
me now,
I would not blame him. Did not the
door move?

Not yet, poor man." She sits with
careful brow
Wrapped in her inward grief; nor hears
the roar
Of winds and waves that dash against
his prow,
Nor the black cormorant shrieking on
the shore.

Sudden the door flies open wide, and
lets
Noisily in the dawn-light scarcely
clear,
And the good fisher, dragging his damp
nets,
Stands on the threshold, with a joyous cheer.

" 'Tis thou!" she cries, and, eager as a
lover,
Leaps up and holds her husband to
her breast;
Her greeting kisses all his vesture cover;
" 'Tis I, good wife!" and his broad face
expressed

How gay his heart that Janet's love
made light.
"What weather was it?"   "Hard."
"Your fishing?"   "Bad.
The sea was like a nest of thieves to-
night;
But I embrace thee, and my heart is
glad.

"There was a devil in the wind that
blew;
I tore my net, caught nothing, broke
my line,
And once I thought the bark was broken
too;
What did you all the night long, Janet
mine?"

She, trembling in the darkness, answered, "I!
Oh, nought—I sew'd, I watch'd, I was
afraid,
The waves were loud as thunders from
the sky;
But it is over." Shyly then she said—

"Our neighbour died last night; it must
have been
When you were gone. She left two
little ones,
So small, so frail—William and Made-
line;
The one just lisps, the other scarcely
runs."

The man looked grave, and in the corner cast
His old fur bonnet, wet with rain and
sea,
Muttered awhile, and scratched his
head,—at last:
"We have five children, this makes
seven," said he.

"Already in bad weather we must sleep
Sometimes without our supper. Now!
Ah, well—
'Tis not my fault. These accidents are
deep;
It was the good God's will. I cannot
tell.

"Why did he take the mother from
those scraps,
No bigger than my fist. 'Tis hard to
read;
A learned man might understand, perhaps—
So little, they can neither work nor
need.

"Go fetch them, wife; they will be
frightened sore,
If with the dead alone they waken
thus.
That was the mother knocking at our
door,
And we must take the children home
to us.

"Brother and sister shall they be to
ours,
And they will learn to climb my knee
at even;
When He shall see these strangers in
our bowers,
More fish, more food, will give the
God of Heaven.

"I will work harder; I will drink no
wine—
Go fetch them. Wherefore dost thou
linger, dear?
Not thus were wont to move those feet
of thine."
She drew the curtain, saying, "They
are here!"

SONG OF THE GILDERS

We are the gilders of the prows.
Wheel-like awhirl, strong winds arouse
The verdant sea's rotundity,
Mingling the shadows and the gleams,
And 'mid the folds of sombre streams
Drawing slant vessels steadfastly.

The shrilling squall close-circling flies,
The tortuous winds deep guiles devise,
The Archer black in his horn doth blow;
These sounds bode death's dark mys-
tery,

And through these prodigies 'tis we
That make the golden spectres go.

For the ship's prow is like a ghost.
Still wave-engirdled, tempest-tossed;
Proudly from our bazaars she sails
To serve the lightnings with a mark,
And midst the hazards of the dark
To be an eye that never fails.

King, 'neath the plane-trees pleasure
    thee;
Sultan to the Sultanas see,
And hide beneath long veils the grace
Of myriad girls with names untold
Who yestermorn stark-bare were sold
By auction on the market-place.

What cares the wave? What cares the
    air!
This girl is dark and that is fair,
Of Halep she, or Ispahan;
Before thy face they all make quake;
What heed thereof forsooth should take
The vast mysterious ocean!

Ye have each one your revelry.
Be thou the prince, the tempest he.
He lightning hath, the yataghan
Thou, to chastise your multitudes;
Beneath its lord the people broods,
The wave beneath the hurricane.

For one and the other do we strive.
This double task is ours alive;—
And thus we sing: O stern Emir,
Thine eyes of steel, thy heart of ice
Keep not the little swallow's eyes
From trustful sleep when night is near.

For holy Nature is eterne
And tranquil; living souls that yearn
God sheltereth beneath His wing;

Amid the all-serene sweet shade,
With hearts for ever undismayed
By spectral terrors, do we sing.

Unto our lords we leave the palm
And statelier laurel! We are calm
And steadfast while within their hand
They have not ta'en the minished stars,
And the swift flight of the cloud-cars
Depends not on a king's command.

The summer glows, the flowers bloom
    bright,
Small rose-buds tip the bosoms white;
One hunts, one laughs; the craftsmen
    still
Sing, and the priests still sigh and sleep;
Slight shadowy fawns through copses
    deep
Fleeing, make greyhounds strain and
    thrill.

If soothly, Sultan, thou hadst quaffed
All proffered pleasures, the sweet
    draught
Would surely quickly poison thee!
Live thou and reign,—thy life is sweet.
Couched on the moss the roebuck fleet
In forest slumbers dreamfully.

Who mounts aloft must needs descend;
The hours are flame, dust is their end;
The tomb saith, unto man: "Be-
    hold!"—
Times change, blithe birds not alway
    sing,
Waves lisp, and straight are thundering,
While aye around are omens rolled:

The hour is sultry; women bare
Lave lovely limbs nigh blooms less fair;
All lightest sorrows now repose;

O'er blue tranced lakes white clouds are
    driven;
With the most golden star of heaven;
Crowneth itself earth's reddest rose.

Thy galley we have gold-arrayed
By sixty pairs of oars is swayed
Which from Lepanto, 'mid the surge,
Subdue the tempest and the tide,
And each of which is hotly plied
By four slaves shackled, 'neath the
    scourge.

SAGA OF THE BEAST

THE BABE

A LION in his jaws caught up a child—
Not harming it—and to the woodland,
    wild
With secret streams and lairs, bore off
    his prey;
The beast, as one might cull a flower in
    May,
Had plucked this bud, not thinking
    wrong or right,
Mumbling its stalk, too proud or kind
    to bite,—
A lion's way, roughly compassionate.
Yet truly dismal was the victim's fate;
Thrust in a cave that rumbled with each
    roar,
His food wild herbs, his bed the earthly
    floor,
He lived, half-dead with daily frighten-
    ing.
It was a rosy boy, son of a king;
A ten-year lad with bright eyes shining
    wide,
And save this son his majesty beside
Had but one girl—two years of age—
    and so

The monarch suffered, being old, much
    woe,
His heir the monster's prey, while the
    whole land
In dread both of the beast and king did
    stand;
Sore terrified were all:—
        By came a Knight
That road, who halted, asking "What's
    the fright?"
They told him, and he spurred straight
    for the den:
Oh, such a place, the sunlight entering
    in
Grew pale and crept, so grim a sight
    was shown
Where the gaunt Lion on the rock lay
    prone:
The wood, at this part thick of growth
    and wet,
Barred out the sky with black trunks
    closely set;
Forest and forester matched wondrous
    well!
Great stones stood near, with ancient
    tales to tell—
Such as make moorlands weird in Brit-
    tany—
And at its edge a mountain you might
    see,
One of those iron walls which shut off
    heaven;
The Lion's den was a deep cavern driven
Into the granite ridge, fenced round
    with oaks:
Cities and caverns are discordant folks,
They bear each other grudges! this did
    wave
A leafy threat to trespasser,—"Hence,
    knave!
Or meet my Lion!"
        In the champion went.
The den had all the sombre sentiment

Which palaces display—deaths—mur-
derings—
Terrors—you felt "here lives one of the
kings:"
Bones strewn around showed that this
mighty lord
Denied himself nought which his woods
afford.
A rock-rift pierced by stroke of lightning
gave
Such misty glimmer as a den need have:
What eagles might think dawn and owls
the dusk
Makes day enough for kings of claw and
tusk.
All else was regal, though! you under-
stood
Why the majestic brute slept, as he
should,
On leaves, with no lace curtains to his
bed;
And how his wine was blood—nay, or
instead,
Spring-water lapped *sans* napkin, spoon,
or cup,
Or lackeys:—
Being from spur to crest
mailed up,
The champion enters.
In the den he spies
Truly a Mighty One! Crowned to the
eyes
With shaggy golden fell—the Beast!—
it muses
With look infallible; for, if he chooses,
The master of a wood may play at
Pope,
And this one had such claws, there was
small hope
To argue with him on the point of creed!
The Knight approached—yet not too
fast, indeed;

His footfall clanged, flaunted his rose-
red feather,
None the more notice took the Beast of
either,
Still in his own reflections plunged pro-
found;
Theseus a-marching upon that black
ground
Of Sisyphus, Ixion, and dire hell,
Saw such a scene, murk and implacable:
But duty whispered "Forward!" so the
Knight
Drew out his sword: the Lion at that
sight
Lifted his head in slow wise, grim to
see;

The Knight said: "Greeting! mon-
strous brute! to thee;
In this foul hole thou hast a child in
keeping,—
I search its noisome nooks with glances
sweeping
But spy him not. That child I must
reclaim,
Friends are we if thou renderest up the
same;
If not—I too am lion, thou wilt find;
The king his lost son in his arms shall
bind;
While here thy wicked blood runs, smok-
ing-hot,
Before another dawn."
"I fancy not,"
Pensive the Lion said.
The Knight strode near,
Brandished his blade and cried: "Sire!
have a care!"
The Beast was seen to smile—ominous
sight!—
Never make lions smile! Then joined
they fight,

The man and monster, in most desperate duel,
Like warring giants, angry, huge, and cruel;
Like tigers crimsoning an Indian wood,
The man with steel, the beast with claws as good;
Fang against falchion, hide to mail, that lord
Hurled himself foaming on the flashing sword:
Stout though the Knight, the Lion stronger was,
And tore that brave breast under its cuirass,
And striking blow on blow with ponderous paw,
Forced plate and rivet off, until you saw
Through all the armour's cracks the bright blood spirt,
As when clenched fingers make a mulberry squirt;
And piece by piece he stripped the iron sheath,
Helm, armlets, greaves—gnawed bare the bones beneath
Scrunching that hero, till he sprawled—alas!
Beneath his shield, all blood, and mud, and mess:
Whereat the Lion feasted:—then it went
Back to its rocky couch and slept content.

THE HERMIT

Next came a hermit:
    He found out the cave;
With girdle, gown, and cross—trembling and grave—
He entered. There that Knight lay, out of shape,

Mere pulp: the Lion waking up did gape,
Opened his yellow orbs, heard some one grope,
And—seeing the woollen coat bound with a rope,
A black peaked cowl, and inside that a man—
He finished yawning and to growl began:
Then, with a voice like prison-gates which creak,
Roared, "What would'st thou?"
    "My King"
      "King?"
        "May I speak?"
"Of whom?"
      "The Prince."
        "Is that what makes a King?"
The monk bowed reverence, "Majesty! I bring
A message—wherefore keep this child?"
    "For that
Whene'er it rains I've some one here to chat."
"Return him."
    "Not so."
      "What then wilt thou do?
Would'st eat him?"
      "Ay—if I have naught to chew!"
"Sire! think upon His Majesty in woe!"
"They killed my dam," the Beast said, "long ago."
"Bethink thee, sire, a king implores a king."
"Nonsense—he talks—he's man! when my notes ring
A Lion's heard!"
    "His only boy!"
      "Well, well!
He hath a daughter."

"She's no heir."
    "I dwell
Alone in this my home, 'mid wood and
    rock,
Thunder my music, and the lightning-
    shock
My lamp;—let his content him."
        "Ah! show pity."
"What means that word? is't current in
    your city?"
"Lion thou'dst wish to go to heaven—
    see here!
I offer thee indulgence, and, writ clear,
God's passport to His paradise!"
        "Get forth,
Thou holy rogue," thundered the Beast
    in wrath:
The hermit disappeared.

THE HOUNDS

Thereat left free,
Full of a lion's vast serenity
He slept again, leaving still night to
    pass:
The moon rose, starting spectres on the
    grass,
Shrouding the marsh with mist, blotting
    the ways,
And melting the black woodland to grey
    maze;
No stir was seen below, above no mo-
    tion
Save of the white stars trooping to the
    ocean:
And while the mole and cricket in the
    brake
Kept watch, the Lion's measured breath
    did make
Slow symphony that kept all creatures
    calm.
Sudden—loud cries and clamours! strik-
    ing qualm

Into the heart of the quiet, horn and
    shout
Causing the solemn wood to reel with
    rout,
And all the nymphs to tremble in their
    trees.
The uproars of a midnight chase are
    these
Which shakes the shades, the marsh,
    mountain and stream,
And breaks the silence of their sombre
    dream.
The thicket flashed with many a lurid
    spark
Of torches borne 'mid wild cries through
    the dark;
Hounds, nose to earth, ran yelping
    through the wood,
And armed groups, gathering in the
    alleys, stood.
Terrific was the noise that rolled be-
    fore;
It seemed a squadron; nay, 'twas some-
    thing more —
A whole battalion, sent by that sad king
With force of arms his little Prince to
    bring,
Together with the Lion's bleeding hide.

Which here was right or wrong? who
    can decide?
Have beasts or men most claim to live?
    God wots!
He is the unit, we the cypher-dots.

Well warmed with meat and drink those
    soldiers were,
Good hearts they bore—and many a
    bow and spear;
Their number large, and by a captain
    led
Valiant, whilst some in foreign wars had
    bled,

And all were men approved and firm in
  fight;
The Lion heard their cries, affronting
  night,
For by this time his awful lids were
  lifted;
But from the rock his chin he never
  shifted,
And only his great tail wagged to and
  fro.

Meantime, outside the cavern, startled
  so,
Came close the uproar of this shouting
  crowd.
As round a web flies buzzing in a cloud,
Or hive-bees swarming o'er a bear en-
  snared,
This hunter's legion buzzed, and
  swarmed, and flared.
In battle order all their ranks were set:
'Twas understood the Beast they came
  to get,
Fierce as a tiger's cunning—strong to
  seize—
Could munch up heroes as an ape cracks
  fleas,
Could with one glance make Jove's own
  bird look down;
Wherefore they laid him siege as to a
  town.
The spearmen followed in close array,
The archers held their arrows on the
  string;
Silence was bid, lest any chattering
Should mask the Lion's footstep in the
  wood;
The dogs—who know the moment when
  'tis good
To hold their peace—went first, nose
  to the ground,
Giving no tongue; the torches all around

Hither and thither flickered, their long
  beams
Through sighing foliage sending ruddy
  gleams;—
Such is the order a great hunt should
  have:
And soon between the trunks they spy
  the cave,
A black, dim-outlined hole, deep in the
  gloom,
Gaping, but blank and silent as the
  tomb,
Wide open to the night, as though it
  feared
As little all that clamour as it heard.
There's smoke where fire smoulders, and
  a town,
When men lay siege, rings tocsin up and
  down;
Nothing so here! therefore with vague
  dismay
Each stood, and grasp on bow or blade
  did lay,
Watching the sombre stillness of that
  chasm:
The dogs among themselves whimpered:
  a spasm
From the horror lurking in all voiceless
  places—
Worse than the rage of tempests—
  blanched all faces:
Yet they were there to find and fight
  this Thing,
So they advance, each bush examining,
Dreading full sore the very prey they
  sought;
The pioneers held high the lamps they
  brought:
"There! that is it! the very mouth of
  the den!"
The trees all round it muttered, warning men:

Still they kept step and neared it—look
  you now,
Company's pleasant, and there were a
  thou—
Good Lord! all in a moment, there's its
  face!
Frightful!—they saw the Lion! Not
  one pace
Further stirred any man; the very trees
Grew blacker with his presence, and the
  breeze
Blew shudders into all hearts present
  there:
Yet, whether 'twas from valour or wild
  fear,
The archers drew—and arrow, bolt, and
  dart
Made target of the Beast. He, on his
  part—
As calm as Pelion in the rain or hail—
Bristled majestic from the nose to tail,
And shook full fifty missiles from his
  hide;
Yet any meaner brute had found be-
  side
Enough still sticking fast to make him
  yell
Or fly; the blood was trickling down his
  fell,
But no heed took he, glaring stead-
  fastly;
And all those men of war, amazed to
  be
Thus met by so stupendous might and
  pride,
Thought him no beast, but some god
  brutified.
The hounds, tail down, slunk back be-
  hind the spears;
And then the Lion, 'mid the silence,
  rears
His awful face, and over wood and
  marsh

Roared a vast roar, hoarse, vibrant,
  vengeful, harsh,—
A rolling, raging peal of wrath, which
  spread
From the quaking earth to the echoing
  vault o'erhead,
Making the half-awakened thunder cry
"Who thunders there?" from its black
  bed of sky.

This ended all!—sheer horror cleared
  the coast:
As fogs are driven by wind, that valor-
  ous host
Melted, dispersed to all the quarters
  four,
Clean panic-stricken by that monstrous
  roar;
Each with one impulse—leaders, rank
  and file,
Deeming it haunted ground, where Earth
  somewhile
Is wont to breed marvels of lawless
  might—
They scampered, mad, blind, reckless,
  wild with fright.
Then quoth the Lion, "Woods and
  mountains! see,
A thousand men enslaved fear one
  Beast free!'
As lava to volcanoes, so a roar
Is to these creatures; and, the eruption
  o'er
In heaven-shaking wrath, they mostly
  calm.
The gods themselves to lions yield the
  palm
For magnanimity. When Jove was king,
Hercules said, "Let's finish off the thing,
Not the Nemæan merely; every one
We'll strangle—all the lions." Where-
  upon

The lions yawned a "much obliged!"
his way.

But this Beast, being whelped by night,
not day—
Offspring of glooms—was sterner; one
of those
Who go down slowly when their storm's
at close;
His anger had a savage ground-swell
in it:
He loved to take his naps, too, to the
minute,
And to be roused up thus with horn
and hound,—
To find an ambush sprung—to be
hemmed round—
Targetted—'twas an insult to his grove!
He paced towards the hill, climbed high
above,
Lifted his voice, and, as the sowers sow
The seeds down wind, thus did that
Lion throw
His message far enough the town to
reach.

"King! your behaviour really passes
speech!
Thus far no harm I've wrought to him
your son;
But now I give you notice—when night's
done
I will make entry at your city-gate,
Bringing the Prince alive; and those
who wait
To see him in my jaws—your lackey-
crew—
Shall see me eat him in your palace
too!"

Quiet the night passed, while the stream-
lets bubbled,

And the clouds sailed across the vault
untroubled.

Next morning this is what was viewed
in town:

Dawn coming — people going — some
adown
Praying, some crying; pallid cheeks,
swift feet,
And a huge Lion stalking through the
street.

OUT OF RED JAWS

The quaking townsmen in the cellars
hid;
How make resistance? briefly, no one
did;
The soldiers left their posts, the gates
stood wide;
'Twas felt the Lion had upon his side
A majesty so godlike, such an air—
That den, too, was so dark and grim a
lair—
It seemed scarce short of rash impiety
To cross its path as the fierce Beast
went by.
So to the palace and its gilded dome
With stately steps unchallenged did he
roam,
In many a spot with those vile darts
scarred still,
As you may note an oak scored with
the bill,
Yet nothing recks that giant-trunk; so
here
Paced this proud wounded Lion, free of
fear,
While all the people held aloof in dread,
Seeing the scarlet jaws of that great
head

Hold up the princely boy—aswoon.
　　Is't true
Princes are flesh and blood?　Ah, yes!
　　and you
Had wept with sacred pity, seeing him
Swing in the Lion's mouth, body and
　　limb:
The tender captive gripped by those
　　grim fangs,
On either side the jowl helplessly hangs,
Deathlike, albeit he bore no wound of
　　tooth.
And for the brute thus gagged it was,
　　in sooth,
A grievous thing to wish to roar, yet be
Muzzled and dumb, so he walked sav-
　　agely,
His pent heart blazing through his burn-
　　ing eyes,
While not one bow is stretched, no ar-
　　row flies;
They dreaded, peradventure, lest some
　　shaft
Shot with a trembling hand and falter-
　　ing craft
Might miss the Beast and pierce the
　　Prince:
　　　　So, still
As he had promised, roaring from his
　　hill,
This Lion, scorning town and towns-
　　folk sick
To view such terror, goes on straight
　　and quick
To the King's house, hoping to meet
　　there one
Who dares to speak with him:—outside
　　is none!
The door's ajar, and flaps with every
　　blast;
He enters it — within those walls at
　　last!—
No man!

For, certes, though he raged
　　and wept,
His Majesty, like all, close shelter kept,
Solicitous to live, holding his breath
Specially precious to the realm: now
　　death
Is not thus viewed by honest beasts of
　　prey,
And when the Lion found him fled away,
Ashamed to be so grand, man being so
　　base,
He muttered to himself in that dark
　　place
Where lions keep their thoughts: "This
　　wretched King!
'Tis well, I'll eat his boy!"　Then, wan-
　　dering,
Lordly he traversed courts and corri-
　　dors,
Paced beneath vaults of gold on shining
　　floors,
Glanced at the throne deserted, stalked
　　from hall
To hall—green, yellow, crimson—empty
　　all!
Rich couches void, soft seats unoccu-
　　pied!
And as he walked he looked from side
　　to side
To find some pleasant nook for his re-
　　past,
Since appetite was come to munch at
　　last
The princely morsel:—Ah! what sight
　　astounds
That grisly lounger?
　　　　In the palace grounds
An alcove on a garden gives, and there
A tiny thing—forgot in the general fear,
Lulled in the flower-sweet dreams of
　　infancy,
Bathed with soft sunlight falling
　　brokenly

Through leaf and lattice—was that mo-
    ment waking;
A little lovely maid, most dear and
    taking,
The Prince's sister; all alone—un-
    dressed—
She sate up singing: children sing so
    best.

A voice of joy, than silver lute-string
    softer!
A mouth all rose-bud, blossoming in
    laughter!
A baby-angel hard at play! a dream
Of Bethlehem's cradle, or what nests
    would seem
If girls were hatched!—all these! Eyes,
    too, so blue
That sea and sky might own their
    sapphire new!
Neck bare, arms bare, pink legs and
    stomach bare!
Nought hid the roseate satin skin, save
    where
A little white-laced shift was fastened
    free;
She looked as fresh, singing thus peace-
    fully,
As stars at twilight or as April's
    heaven;
A floweret — you had said — divinely
    given,
To show on earth how God's own lilies
    grow;
Such was this beauteous baby-maid;
    and so
The Beast caught sight of her and
    stopped—

          And then
Entered:—the floor creaked as he
    stalked straight in.

Above the playthings by the little bed
The Lion put his shaggy massive head,
Dreadful with savage might and lordly
    scorn,
More dreadful with that princely prey
    so borne;
Which she, quick spying, "Brother!
    brother!" cried,
"Oh, my own brother!" and, unterri-
    fied—
Looking a living rose that made the
    place
Brighter and warmer with its fearless
    grace—
She gazed upon that monster of the
    wood,
Whose yellow balls not Typhon had
    withstood.
And—well! who knows what thoughts
    these small heads hold?
She rose up in her cot—full height, and
    bold,
And shook her pink fist angrily at him.
Whereon—close to the little bed's white
    rim,
All dainty silk and laces—this huge
    Brute
Set down her brother gently at her
    foot,
Just as a mother might, and said to
    her—

*"Don't be put out, now! there he is,
    Dear!—there!"*

The Hunchback of Notre-Dame

BOOK I

THE PLAY

CHAPTER I

THE GREAT HALL

THREE hundred and forty-eight years, six months, and nineteen days ago to-day the Parisians were wakened by the sound of loud peals from all the bells within the triple precincts of the City, the University, and the Town.

And yet the 6th of January, 1482, is not a day of which history takes much note. There was nothing extraordinary about the event which thus set all the bells and the citizens of Paris agog from early dawn. It was neither an attack from the Picards or the Burgundians, nor some shrine carried in procession, nor was it a student revolt in the Ville de Laas, nor an entry of "our greatly to be dreaded lord the king," nor even the wholesale slaughter of a band of thieves before the Palace of Justice. Neither was it the arrival, so frequent during the fifteenth century, of some plumed and laced embassy. It was scarcely two days since the last cavalcade of this sort, that of the Flemish ambassadors empowered to arrange a marriage between the Dauphin and Margaret of Flanders, had entered Paris, to the great annoyance of Cardinal Bourbon, who, to please the king, was forced to smile upon all this rustic rout of Flemish burgomasters, and to entertain them at his own mansion with "a very fine morality and farce," while a driving rain-storm drenched the splendid tapestries at his door.

That which "stirred the emotions of the whole populace of Paris," as Jehan de Troyes expresses it, on January 6, was the double festival, celebrated from time immemorial, of Epiphany and the Feast of Fools.

Upon that day there was to be a bonfire at the Grève, a Maypole at the Braque chapel, and a mystery or miracle play at the Palace of Justice. All these things had been proclaimed at the cross-roads, to the sound of trumpets, by the provost's men, in fine coats of purple camlet, with big white crosses on the breast.

A crowd of citizens with their wives and daughters had therefore been making their way from every quarter, towards the places named, ever since early dawn. Each had decided for himself, in favour of the bonfire, the Maypole, or the mystery. It must be confessed, to the glory of the proverbial good sense of Parisian idlers, that the majority of the crowd turned towards the bonfire, which was most seasonable, or towards the miracle play which was to be performed in the great hall of the law courts, well roofed in and between four walls; and that most of the pleasure-seekers agreed to leave the poor Maypole with its scanty blossoms to shiver alone beneath the January sky, in the cemetery of the Braque chapel.

The people swarmed most thickly in the avenues leading to the law courts, because it was known that the Flemish ambassadors who arrived two nights before proposed to be present at the performance of the miracle play and election of the Lord of Misrule, which was also to take place in the great hall.

It was no easy matter to make a way into the great hall upon that day, although it was then held to be the largest enclosure under cover in the world (to be sure, Sauval had not yet measured the great hall of the castle at Montargis). The courtyard, filled with people, looked to the spectators at the windows like a vast sea into which five or six streets, like the mouths of so many rivers, constantly disgorged new waves of heads. The billowing crowd, growing ever greater, dashed against houses projecting here and there like so many promontories in the irregular basin of the court. In the middle of the lofty Gothic façade of the Palace was the great staircase, up and down which flowed an unending double stream, which, after breaking upon the intermediate landing, spread in broad waves over its two side slopes; the great staircase, I say, poured a steady stream into the courtyard, like a waterfall into a lake. Shouts, laughter, and the tramp of countless feet made a great noise and a great hubbub. From time to time the hubbub and the noise was redoubled; the current which bore this throng towards the great staircase was turned back, eddied, and whirled. Some archer had dealt a blow, or the horse of some provost's officer had administered a few kicks to restore order,—an admirable tradition, which provost has bequeathed to constable, constable to marshalsea, and marshalsea to our present Parisian police.

At doors, windows, in garrets, and on roofs swarmed thousands of good plain citizens, quiet, honest people, gazing at the Palace, watching the throng, and asking nothing more; for many people in Paris are quite content to look on at others, and there are plenty who regard a wall behind which something is happening as a very curious thing.

If it could be permitted to us men of 1830 to mingle in fancy with those fifteenth-century Parisians, and to enter with them, pushed, jostled, and elbowed, the vast hall of the Palace of Justice, all too small on the 6th of January, 1482, the sight would not be without interest or charm, and we should have about us only things so old as to seem brand-new.

With the reader's consent we will endeavour to imagine the impression he would have received with us in crossing the threshold of that great hall amidst that mob in surcoats, cassocks, and coats of mail.

And first of all there is a ringing in our ears, a dimness in our eyes. Above our heads, a double roof of pointed arches, wainscotted with carved wood, painted in azure, sprinkled with golden *fleurs-de-lis;* beneath our feet, a pavement of black and white marble laid in alternate blocks. A few paces from us, a huge pillar, then another,—in all seven pillars down the length of the hall, supporting the spring of the double arch down the centre. Around the first four columns are tradesmen's booths, glittering with glass and tinsel; around the last three, oaken benches worn and polished by the breeches of litigants and the gowns of attorneys. Around the hall, along the lofty wall, between the doors, between the casements, between the pillars, is an unending series of statues of all the kings of France, from Pharamond down,—the sluggard kings, with loosely hanging arms and downcast eyes; the brave and warlike kings, with head and hands boldly raised to heaven. Then in the long pointed windows, glass of a thousand hues; at the wide portals of the hall, rich doors finely carved; and the whole—arches, pillars, walls, cornices, wainscot, doors, and statues— covered from top to bottom with a gorgeous colouring of blue and gold, which, somewhat tarnished even at the date when we see it, had almost disappeared under dust and cobwebs in the year of grace 1549, when Du Breuil admired it from tradition.

Now, let us imagine this vast oblong hall, lit up by the wan light of a January day, taken possession of by a noisy motley mob who drift along the walls and ebb and flow about the seven columns, and we may have some faint idea of the general effect of the picture, whose strange details we will try to describe somewhat more minutely.

It is certain that if Ravaillac had not assassinated Henry IV., there would have been no documents relating to his case laid away in the Rolls Office in the Palace of Justice; no accomplices interested to make away with the said documents, accordingly no incendiaries, forced for want of better means to burn the Rolls Office in order to burn up the documents, and to burn the Palace of Justice in order to burn the Rolls Office; consequently, therefore, no fire in 1618. The old Palace would still be standing, with its great hall; I might say to my reader, "Go and look at it," and we should thus both of us be spared the need,—I of writing, and he of reading, an indifferent description; which proves this novel truth,—that great events have incalculable results.

True, Ravaillac may very possibly have had no accomplices; or his accomplices, if he chanced to have any, need have had no hand in the fire of 1618. There are two other very plausible explanations: first, the huge "star of fire, a foot broad and a foot and a half high," which fell, as every one knows, from heaven upon the Palace after midnight on the 7th of March; second, Théophile's verses:—

"In Paris sure it was a sorry game
When, fed too fat with fees, the
        frisky Dame
Justice set all her palace in a
        flame."

Whatever we may think of this triple explanation,—political, physical, and poetical,—of the burning of the Palace of Justice in 1618, one unfortunate fact remains: namely, the fire. Very little is now left, thanks to this catastrophe, and thanks particularly to the various and successive restorations which have finished what it spared,—very little is now left of this first home of the King of France, of this palace, older than the Louvre, so old even in the time of Philip the Fair that search had to be made for traces of the magnificent buildings erected by King Robert and described by Helgaldus. Almost everything is gone. What has become of the chancery office, Saint Louis' bridal chamber; the garden where he administered justice, "clad in a camlet coat, a sleeveless surcoat of linsey-woolsey, and over it a mantle of black serge, reclining upon carpets, with Joinville?" Where is the chamber of the Emperor Sigismond, that of Charles IV., and that of John Lackland? Where is the staircase from which Charles VI. issued his edict of amnesty; the flag-stone upon which Marcel slew, in the dauphin's presence, Robert of Clermont and the Marshal of Champagne; the wicket-gate where the bulls of Benedict the antipope were destroyed, and through which departed those who brought them, coped and mitred in mockery, thus doing public penance throughout Paris; and the great hall, with its gilding, its azure, its pointed arches, its statues, its columns, its great vaulted roof thickly covered with carvings; and the golden room; and the stone lion, which stood at the door, his head down, his tail between his legs, like the lions around Solomon's throne, in the humble attitude that befits strength in the presence of justice; and the beautiful doors; and the gorgeous windows; and the wrought-iron work which discouraged Biscornette; and Du Hancy's dainty bits of carving? What has time done, what have men done with these marvels? What has been given us in exchange for all this,— for all this ancient French history, all this Gothic art? The heavy elliptic arches of M. de Brosse, the clumsy architect of the St. Gervais portal,—so

much for art; and for history we have the gossipy memories of the big pillar still echoing and re-echoing with the tittle-tattle of the Patrus.

This is not much. Let us go back to the genuine great hall of the genuine old Palace.

The two ends of this huge parallelogram were occupied, the one by the famous marble table, so long, so broad, and so thick, that there never was seen, as the old Court Rolls express it in a style which would give Gargantua an appetite, "such another slice of marble in the world;" the other by the chapel in which Louis XI. had his statue carved kneeling before the Virgin, and into which, wholly indifferent to the fact that he left two vacant spaces in the procession of royal images, he ordered the removal of the figures of Charlemagne and Saint Louis, believing these two saints to be in high favour with Heaven as being kings of France. This chapel, still quite new, having been built scarcely six years, was entirely in that charming school of refined and delicate architecture, of marvellous sculpture, of fine, deep chiselling, which marks the end of the Gothic era in France, and lasts until towards the middle of the sixteenth century in the fairy-like fancies of the Renaissance. The small rose-window over the door was an especial masterpiece of delicacy and grace; it seemed a mere star of lace.

In the centre of the hall, opposite the great door, a daïs covered with gold brocade, placed against the wall, to which a private entrance was arranged by means of a window from the passage to the gold room, had been built for the Flemish envoys and other great personages invited to the performance of the mystery.

This mystery, according to custom, was to be performed upon the marble table. It had been prepared for this at dawn; the superb slab of marble, scratched and marked by lawyers' heels, now bore a high wooden cage-like scaffolding, whose upper surface, in sight of the entire hall, was to serve as stage, while the interior, hidden by tapestry hangings, was to take the place of dressing-room for the actors in the play. A ladder placed outside with frank simplicity formed the means of communication between the dressing-room and stage, its rough rounds doing service for entrance as well as exit. There was no character however unexpected, no sudden change, and no dramatic effect, but was compelled to climb this ladder. Innocent and venerable infancy of art and of machinery!

Four officers attached to the Palace, forced guardians of the people's pleasures on holidays as on hanging days, stood bolt upright at the four corners of the marble table.

The play was not to begin until the twelfth stroke of noon rang from the great Palace clock. This was doubtless very late for a theatrical performance; but the ambassadors had to be consulted in regard to the time.

Now, this throng had been waiting since dawn. Many of these honest sightseers were shivering at earliest daylight at the foot of the great Palace staircase. Some indeed declared that they had spent the night lying across the great door, to be sure of getting in first. The crowd increased every moment, and, like water rising above its level, began to creep up the walls, to collect around the columns, to overflow the entablatures, the cornices, the window-sills, every projection of the architecture, and every bit of bold relief in the carvings. Then, too, discomfort, impatience, fatigue, the day's license of satire and folly, the quarrels caused ever and anon by a sharp elbow or a hobnailed shoe, the weariness of waiting lent, long before the hour when the ambassadors were due, an acid, bitter tone to the voices of these people, shut up, pent in, crowded, squeezed, and stifled as they were. On every hand were heard curses and complaints against the Flemish, the mayor of Paris, Cardinal Bourbon, the Palace bailiff, Madame Margaret of Austria, the ushers, the cold, the heat, the bad weather, the Lord of Misrule, the columns, the statues, this closed door, that open window,—all to the vast amusement of the groups of students and lackeys scattered through the crowd, who mingled their mischief and their malice with all this discontent, and administered, as it were, pin-pricks to the general bad humour.

Among the rest there was one group of these merry demons who, having broken the glass from a window, had boldly seated themselves astride the sill, distributing their glances and their jokes by turns, within and without, between the crowd in the hall and the crowd in the courtyard. From their mocking gestures, their noisy laughter, and the scoffs and banter which they exchanged with their comrades, from one end of the hall to the other, it was easy to guess that these young students felt none of the weariness and fatigue of the rest of the spectators, and that they were amply able, for their own private amusement, to extract from what they had before their eyes a spectacle quite diverting enough to make them wait patiently for that which was to come.

"By my soul, it's you, Joannes Frollo de Molendino!" cried one of them to a light-haired little devil with a handsome but evil countenance, who was clinging to the acanthus leaves of a capital; "you are well named, Jehan du Moulin, for your two arms and your two legs look like the four sails fluttering in the wind. How long have you been here?"

"By the foul fiend!" replied Joannes Frollo, "more than four hours, and I certainly hope that they may be deducted from my time in purgatory. I heard the King of Sicily's eight choristers intone the first verse of high mass at seven o'clock in the Holy Chapel."

"Fine choristers they are!" returned the other; "their voices are sharper than the points of their caps. Before he endowed a Mass in honour of Saint John, the king might well have inquired whether Saint John liked his Latin sung with a southern twang."

"He only did it to give work to these confounded choristers of the King of Sicily!" bitterly exclaimed an old woman in the crowd beneath the window. "Just fancy! a thousand pounds Paris for a Mass! and charged to the taxes on all salt-water fish sold in the Paris markets too!"

"Silence, old woman!" said a grave and reverend personage who was holding his nose beside the fishwoman; "he had to endow a Mass. You don't want the king to fall ill again, do you?"

"Bravely spoken, Master Gilles Lecornu, sir furrier of the king's robes!" cried the little scholar clinging to the capital.

"Lecornu! Gilles Lecornu!" said some.

"*Cornutus et hirsutus,*" replied another.

"Oh, no doubt!" continued the little demon of the capital. "What is there to laugh at? An honourable man is Gilles Lecornu, brother of Master Jehan Lecornu, provost of the king's palace, son of Master Mahiet Lecornu, head porter of the Forest of Vincennes,—all good citizens of Paris, every one of them married, from father to son!"

The mirth increased. The fat furrier, not answering a word, strove to escape the eyes fixed on him from every side, but he puffed and perspired in vain; like a wedge driven into wood, all his efforts only buried his broad apoplectic face, purple with rage and spite, the more firmly in the shoulders of his neighbours.

At last one of the latter, fat, short, and venerable as himself, came to his rescue.

"Abominable! Shall students talk thus to a citizen! In my day they would have been well whipped with the sticks which served to burn them afterwards."

The entire band burst out:—

"Hollo! who sings that song? Who is this bird of ill omen?"

"Stay, I know him," said one; "it's Master Andry Musnier."

"He is one of the four copyists licensed by the University!" said another.

"Everything goes by fours in that shop," cried a third,— "four nations, four faculties, four great holidays, four proctors, four electors, four copyists."

"Very well, then," answered Jehan Frollo; "we must play the devil with them by fours."

"Musnier, we'll burn your books."

"Musnier, we'll beat your servant."

"Musnier, we'll hustle your wife."

"That good fat Mademoiselle Oudarde."

"Who is as fresh and as fair as if she were a widow."

"Devil take you!" growled Master Andry Musnier.

"Master Andry," added Jehan, still hanging on his capital, "shut up, or I'll fall on your head!"

Master Andry raised his eyes, seemed for a moment to be measuring the height of the column, the weight of the rascal, mentally multiplied that weight by the square of the velocity, and was silent.

Jehan, master of the field of battle, went on triumphantly:—

"I'd do it, though I am the brother of an archdeacon!"

"Fine fellows, our University men are, not even to have insisted upon our rights on such a day as this! For, only think of it, there is a Maypole and a bonfire in the Town; a miracle play, Lord of Misrule, and Flemish embassy in the City; and at the University—nothing!"

"And yet Maubert Square is big enough!" answered one of the scholars established on the window-seat.

"Down with the rector, the electors, and the proctors!" shouted Joannes.

"We must build a bonfire to-night in the Gaillard Field," went on the other, "with Master Andry's books."

"And the desks of the scribes," said his neighbour.

"And the beadles' maces!"

"And the deans' spittoons!"

"And the proctors' cupboards!"

"And the electors' bread-bins!"

"And the rector's footstools!"

"Down with them!" went on little Jehan, mimicking a droning psalm-tune; "down with Master Andry, the beadles, and the scribes; down with theologians, doctors, and decretists; proctors, electors, and rector!"

"Is the world coming to an end?" muttered Master Andry stopping his ears as he spoke.

"Speaking of the rector, there he goes through the square!" shouted one of those in the window.

Every one turned towards the square.

"Is it really our respectable rector, Master Thibaut?" asked Jehan Frollo du Moulin, who, clinging to one of the inner columns, could see nothing of what was going on outside.

"Yes, yes," replied the rest with one accord, "it is really he, Master Thibaut, the rector."

It was indeed the rector and all the dignitaries of the University going in procession to meet the embassy, and just at this moment crossing the Palace yard. The scholars, crowding in the window, greeted them, as they passed, with sarcasms and mock applause. The rector, who walked at the head of his company, received the first volley, which was severe:—

"Good-morning, Sir Rector! Hollo there! Good-morning, I say!"

"How does he happen to be here, the old gambler? Has he forsaken his dice?"

"How he ambles along on his mule! The animal's ears are not so long as his."

"Hollo there! Good-day to you, Master Rector Thibaut! *Tybalde alea-tor!* old fool! old gambler!"

"God keep you! did you throw many double sixes last night?"

"Oh, look at his lead-coloured old face, wrinkled and worn with love of cards and dice!"

"Whither away so fast, Thibaut, *Ty-balde ad dados,* turning your back on the University and trotting straight towards town?"

"He's probably going to look for a lodging in Tybaldy Street," shouted Jehan du Moulin.

The entire band repeated the silly joke in a shout like thunder, and with frantic clapping of hands.

"You're going to look for a lodging in Tybaldy Street, are you not, Sir Rector, you devil's advocate?"

Then came the turn of the other officials.

"Down with the beadles! down with the mace-bearers!"

"Say, you Robin Poussepain, who's that fellow yonder?"

"That's Gilbert de Suilly, *Gilbertus de Soliaco,* Chancellor of the College of Autun."

"Stay, here's my shoe; you've got a better place than I; fling it in his face."

"*Saturnalitias mittimus ecce nuces.*"

"Down with the six theologians in the white surplices!"

"Are those theologians? I thought they were six white geese given to the city by Saint Geneviève for the fief of Roogny."

"Down with the doctors!"

"Down with all cardinal and jocose disputations."

"Take my cap, Chancellor of St. Geneviève! You did me an injustice,— and that's the truth; he gave my place in the nation of Normandy to little Ascanio Falzaspada, who belongs to the province of Bourges, being an Italian."

"Rank injustice," exclaimed all the students. "Down with the Chancellor of St. Geneviève."

"Ho there, Master Joachim de Lade-hors! Ho there, Louis Dahuille! Hollo, Lambert Hoctement!"

"May the devil smother the proctor of the German nation!"

"And the chaplains of the Holy Chapel, with their grey amices, *cum tunicis grisis!*"

"*Seu de pellibus grisis fourratis!*"

"Ho there! you Masters of Arts! See all the fine black copes! See all the fine red copes!"

"That makes a fine tail for the rector!"

"You would think it was a Venetian doge on his way to wed the sea."

"I say, Jehan! look at the Canons of St. Geneviève!"

"Deuce take all Canons!"

"Abbot Claude Choart! Doctor Claude Choart! Are you looking for Marie la Giffarde?"

"She lives in Glatigny Street."

"She's bedmaker to the king of scamps."

"She's paying her four farthings, *qua-tuor denarios.*"

"*Aut unum bombum.*"

"Would you like her to pay you in the nose?"

"Comrades! there goes Master Simon

Sanguin the Elector from Picardy, with his wife behind him!"

"*Post equitem sedet atra cura.*"

"Cheer up, Master Simon!"

"Good-day to you, Sir Elector!"

"Good-night to you, Madame Electress!"

"How lucky they are to see so much!" sighed Joannes de Molendino, still perched among the foliage of his column.

Meanwhile, the licensed copyist to the University, Master Andry Musnier, leaned towards the ear of the furrier of the king's robes, Master Gilles Lecornu.

"I tell you, sir, this is the end of the world. The students never were so riotous before; it's the cursed inventions of the age that are ruining us all,—artillery, bombards, serpentines, and particularly printing, that other German pest. No more manuscripts, no more books! Printing is death to bookselling. The end of the world is at hand."

"So I see by the rage for velvet stuffs," said the furrier.

At this instant the clock struck twelve.

"Ha!" cried the entire throng with but a single voice.

The students were silent. Then began a great stir; a great moving of feet and heads; a general outbreak of coughing and handkerchiefs; everybody shook himself, arranged himself, raised himself on tiptoe, placed himself to the best advantage. Then came deep silence; every neck was stretched, every mouth was opened wide, every eye was turned towards the marble table. Nothing was to be seen there. The four officers still stood stiff and motionless as four coloured statues. Every eye turned towards the daïs reserved for the Flemish ambassadors. The door was still shut and the daïs empty. The throng has been waiting since dawn for three things: noon, the Flemish embassy, and the mystery. Noon arrived punctually.

Really it was too bad.

They waited one, two, three, five minutes, a quarter of an hour; nothing happened. The daïs was still deserted, the theatre mute. Rage followed in the footsteps of impatience. Angry words passed from mouth to mouth, though still in undertones, to be sure. "The mystery! the mystery!" was the low cry. Every head was in a ferment. A tempest, as yet but threatening, hung over the multitude. Jehan du Moulin drew forth the first flash.

"The mystery! and to the devil with the Flemish!" he shouted at the top of his voice, writhing and twisting around his capital like a serpent.

The crowd applauded.

"The mystery!" repeated the mob; "and deuce take Flanders!"

"We insist on the mystery at once," continued the student; "or else it's my advice to hang the Palace bailiff by way of a comedy and morality."

"Well said," cried the people; "and let us begin the hanging with his men."

Loud cheers followed. The four poor devils began to turn pale and to exchange glances. The mob surged towards them, and the frail wooden railing parting them from the multitude bent and swayed beneath the pressure.

It was a critical moment.

"To the sack with them! to the sack!" was the cry from every side.

At that instant the hangings of the

dressing-room, which we have already described, were raised, giving passage to a personage the mere sight of whom suddenly arrested the mob, changing rage to curiosity as if by magic.

"Silence! Silence!"

This person, but little reassured, and trembling in every limb, advanced to the edge of the table, with many bows, which, in proportion as he approached, grew more and more like genuflections. However, peace was gradually restored. There remained only that slight murmur always arising from the silence of a vast multitude.

"Sir citizens," said he, "and fair citizenesses, we shall have the honour to declaim and perform before his Eminence the Cardinal a very fine morality entitled, 'The Wise Decision of Mistress Virgin Mary.' I am to enact Jupiter. His Eminence is at this moment escorting the very honourable embassy of his Highness the Duke of Austria, which is just now detained to listen to the speech of the Rector of the University at the Donkeys' Gate. As soon as the most eminent Cardinal arrives, we will begin."

It is plain that it required nothing less than the intervention of Jupiter himself to save the poor unfortunate officers of the bailiff. If we had had the good luck to invent this very truthful history, and consequently to be responsible for it to our lady Criticism, the classic rule, *Nec deus intersit,* could not be brought up against us at this point. Moreover, Lord Jupiter's costume was very handsome, and contributed not a little to calm the mob by attracting its entire attention. Jupiter was clad in a brigandine covered with black velvet,

with gilt studs; on his head was a flat cap trimmed with silver-gilt buttons; and had it not been for the paint and the big beard which covered each half of his face, had it not been for the roll of gilded cardboard, sprinkled with spangles and all bristling with shreds of tinsel, which he carried in his hand, and in which practised eyes readily recognized the thunder, had it not been for his flesh-coloured feet bound with ribbons in Greek fashion, he might have stood favourable comparison, for severity of bearing, with any Breton archer in the Duke of Berry's regiment.

CHAPTER II

PIERRE GRINGOIRE

BUT as he spoke, the satisfaction, the admiration excited by his dress, were destroyed by his words; and when he reached the fatal conclusion "as soon as the most eminent Cardinal arrives, we will begin," his voice was drowned in a storm of hoots.

"Begin at once! The mystery! the mystery at once!" screamed the people. And over all the other voices was heard that of Johannes de Molendino piercing the uproar, like the fife in a *charivari* at Nismes. "Begin at once!" shrieked the student.

"Down with Jupiter and Cardinal Bourbon!" shouted Robin Poussepain and the other learned youths perched in the window.

"The morality this instant!" repeated the mob; "instantly! immediately! To the sack and the rope with the actors and the Cardinal!"

Poor Jupiter, haggard, terrified, pale

beneath his paint, let his t.. inderbolt fall, and seized his cap in his hand. Then he bowed, trembled, and stammered out: "His Eminence—the ambassadors—Madame Margaret of Flanders—" He knew not what to say. In his secret heart he was mightily afraid of being hanged.

Hanged by the populace for waiting, hanged by the Cardinal for not waiting, —on either hand he saw a gulf; that is to say, a gallows.

Luckily, some one appeared to extricate him from his embarrassing position and assume the responsibility.

An individual, standing just within the railing, in the vacant space about the marble table, and whom nobody had as yet observed,—so completely was his long slim person hidden from sight by the thickness of the pillar against which he leaned,—this individual, we say, tall, thin, pale, fair-haired, still young, although already wrinkled in brow and cheeks, with bright eyes and a smiling mouth, clad in black serge, worn and shining with age, approached the table and made a sign to the poor victim. But the latter, in his terror and confusion, failed to see him.

The new-comer took another step forward.

"Jupiter!" said he, "my dear Jupiter!"

The other did not hear him.

At last the tall fair-haired fellow, growing impatient, shouted almost in his ear,—

"Michel Giborne!"

"Who calls me?" said Jupiter, as if suddenly wakened.

"I," replied the person dressed in black.

"Ah!" said Jupiter.

"Begin directly," continued the other. "Satisfy the public; I take it upon myself to pacify the bailiff, who will pacify the Cardinal."

Jupiter breathed again.

"Gentlemen and citizens," he shouted at the top of his lungs to the crowd who continued to hoot him, "we will begin at once."

"*Evoe, Jupiter! Plaudite, cives!*" cried the students.

"Noël! Noël!" cried the people.

Deafening applause followed, and the hall still trembled with the plaudits when Jupiter had retired behind the hangings.

But the unknown person who had so miraculously changed "the tempest to a calm," as our dear old Corneille says, had modestly withdrawn into the shadow of his pillar, and would doubtless have remained there invisible, motionless, and mute as before, had he not been drawn forward by two young women, who, placed in the foremost rank of the spectators, had observed his colloquy with Michel Giborne-Jupiter.

"Master," said one of them, beckoning him to come nearer.

"Be quiet, my dear Liénarde," said her neighbour, pretty, fresh, and emboldened by all her Sunday finery. "That is no scholar, he is a layman; you must not call him *Master*, but *Sir*."

"Sir," said Liénarde.

The stranger approached the railing.

"What do you wish of me, young ladies?" he asked eagerly.

"Oh, nothing!" said Liénarde, much confused; "it is my neighbour Gisquette la Gencienne who wants to speak to you."

"Not at all," replied Gisquette, blushing; "it was Liénarde who called you Master; I told her that she should say Sir."

The two young girls cast down their eyes. The stranger, who desired nothing better than to enter into conversation with them, looked at them with a smile.

"Then you have nothing to say to me, young ladies?"

"Oh, nothing at all!" answered Gisquette.

The tall fair-haired youth drew back a pace; but the two curious creatures had no idea of losing their prize.

"Sir," said Gisquette hastily, and with the impetuosity of water rushing through a floodgate or a woman coming to a sudden resolve, "so you know that soldier who is to play the part of Madame Virgin in the mystery?"

"You mean the part of Jupiter?" replied the unknown.

"Oh, yes," said Liénarde, "isn't she silly? So you know Jupiter?"

"Michel Giborne?" replied the unknown. "Yes, madame."

"He has a fine beard!" said Liénarde.

"Will it be very interesting—what they are going to recite up there?" asked Gisquette, shyly.

"Very interesting indeed," replied the stranger, without the least hesitation.

"What is it to be?" said Liénarde.

" 'The Wise Decision of Madame Virgin Mary,' a morality, if you please, madame."

"Ah, that's another thing," replied Liénarde.

A short pause followed. The stranger first broke the silence:—

"It is quite a new morality, which has never yet been played."

"Then it is not the same," said Gisquette, "that was given two years ago, on the day of the legate's arrival, and in which three beautiful girls took the part of—"

"Sirens," said Liénarde.

"And all naked," added the young man. Liénarde modestly cast down her eyes; Gisquette looked at her, and did the same. He continued with a smile,—

"That was a very pretty sight. This, now, is a morality, written expressly for the young Flemish madame."

"Will they sing pastorals?" asked Gisquette.

"Fie!" said the stranger, "in a morality! You must not mix up different styles. If it were a farce, that would be another thing."

"What a pity!" replied Gisquette. "That day there were wild men and women at the Ponceau Fountain, who fought together and made all sorts of faces, singing little motets and pastorals all the while."

"What suits a legate," said the stranger, somewhat drily, "will hardly suit a princess."

"And close by them," added Liénarde, "were several bass instruments which played grand melodies."

"And to refresh the passers-by," continued Gisquette, "the fountain streamed wine, milk and hippocras, from three mouths, for all to drink who would."

"And a little way beyond that fountain," went on Liénarde, "at the Trinity, there was a passion-play, performed by mute characters."

"How well I remember it!" exclaimed

Gisquette,—"God on the cross, and the two thieves to right and left."

Here the young gossips, growing excited at the recollection of the arrival of the legate, both began to talk at once.

"And farther on, at the Painters' Gate, there were other persons richly dressed."

"And at the Fountain of the Holy Innocents, that hunter chasing a doe, with a great noise of dogs and hunting-horns!"

"And at the Paris shambles, those scaffolds representing the fortress at Dieppe!"

"And when the legate passed by, you know, Gisquette, there was an attack, and all the English had their throats cut."

"And over against the Châtelet Gate there were very fine persons!"

"And on the Money-brokers' Bridge, which was hung all over with tapestries!"

"And when the legate passed by, they let loose more than two hundred dozen of all sorts of birds; it was very fine, Liénarde."

"It will be finer to-day," replied their listener at last, seeming to hear them with some impatience.

"Then you promise us that this play will be a fine one?" said Gisquette.

"To be sure," he answered. Then he added with a certain emphasis: "Young ladies, I am the author of it."

"Really?" said the young girls, much amazed.

"Really!" replied the poet, drawing himself up; "that is, there are two of us: Jehan Marchand, who sawed the planks and built the frame and did all the carpenter's work, and I, who wrote the piece. My name is Pierre Gringoire."

The author of the "Cid" could not have said "Pierre Corneille" with any greater degree of pride.

Our readers may have noticed that some time had already passed since Jupiter had gone behind the hangings, and before the author of the new morality revealed himself so abruptly to the simple admiration of Gisquette and Liénarde. Strange to say, all that multitude, which a few instants previous was so furiously uproarious, now waited calmly for the fulfillment of the actor's promise, which proves that enduring truth, still verified in our own theatres, that the best way to make your audience wait patiently is to assure them that you will begin directly.

However, student Joannes was not asleep.

"Hollo, ho!" he cried out suddenly, in the midst of the calm expectation which followed on confusion. "Jupiter, Madame Virgin, devilish mountebanks! are you mocking us? The play! the play! Begin, or we will stir you up again!"

This was quite enough.

The sound of musical instruments pitched in various keys was heard from the interior of the scaffolding. The tapestry was raised; four characters painted and clad in motley garb came out, climbed the rude stage ladder, and gaining the upper platform, ranged themselves in line before the public, bowing low; then the symphony ceased. The mystery was about to begin.

These four personages, having been abundantly repaid for their bows by applause, began, amid devout silence, a prologue which we gladly spare the reader. Moreover, as happens even nowadays, the audience was far more interested in the costumes of the actors than in the speeches which they recited; and, to tell the truth, they were quite right. They were all four dressed in gowns partly yellow and partly white, which only differed from each other in material; the first was of gold and silver brocade, the second of silk, the third of wool, the fourth of linen. The first of these characters had a sword in his right hand, the second two golden keys, the third a pair of scales, the fourth a spade; and to aid those indolent understandings which might not have penetrated the evident meaning of these attributes, might be read embroidered in big black letters—on the hem of the brocade gown, "I AM NOBILITY;" on the hem of the silk gown, "I AM RELIGION," on the hem of the woolen gown, "I AM TRADE;" and on the hem of the linen gown, "I AM LABOUR." The sex of the two male allegories was clearly shown to every sensible beholder by their shorter gowns and by their peculiar headdress,—a flat cap called a *cramignole*; while the two feminine allegories, clad in longer garments, wore hoods.

One must also have been wilfully dull not to gather from the poetical prologue that Labour was wedded to Trade, and Religion to Nobility, and that the two happy pairs owned in common a superb golden dolphin, which they desired to bestow only on the fairest of the fair. They were therefore journeying through the world in search of this beauty; and having in turn rejected the Queen of Golconda, the Princess of Trebizond, the daughter of the Cham of Tartary, etc., Labour and Religion, Nobility and Trade, were now resting on the marble table in the Palace of Justice, spouting to their simple audience as many long sentences and maxims as would suffice the Faculty of Arts for all the examinations, sophisms, determinances, figures, and acts required of all the bachelors in taking their degrees. All this was indeed very fine.

But in the crowd upon whom the four allegorical personages poured such floods of metaphor, each trying to outdo the other, there was no more attentive ear, no more anxious heart, no more eager eye, no neck more outstretched, than the eye, the ear, the neck, and the heart of the author, the poet, the worthy Pierre Gringoire, who could not resist, a moment previous, the delight of telling his name to two pretty girls. He had withdrawn some paces from them, behind his pillar; and there he listened, looked, and enjoyed. The kindly plaudits which greeted the opening lines of his prologue still rang in his innermost soul, and he was completely absorbed in that kind of ecstatic contemplation with which an author watches his ideas falling one by one from the actor's lips amid the silence of a vast assembly. Good Pierre Gringoire!

We regret to say that this first ecstasy was very soon disturbed. Gringoire had scarcely placed his lips to this intoxicating draught of joy and triumph, when a drop of bitterness was blended with it.

A ragged beggar, who could reap no harvest, lost as he was in the midst of the crowd, and who doubtless failed to find sufficient to atone for his loss in the pockets of his neighbours, hit upon the plan of perching himself upon some conspicuous point, in order to attract eyes and alms. He therefore hoisted himself, during the first lines of the programme, by the aid of the columns of the daïs, up to the top of the high railing running around it; and there he sat, soliciting the attention and the pity of the multitude, by the sight of his rags, and a hideous sore which covered his right arm. Moreover, he uttered not a word.

His silence permitted the prologue to go on without interruption, and no apparent disorder would have occurred if ill luck had not led the student Joannes to note the beggar and his grimaces, from his own lofty post. A fit of mad laughter seized upon the young rogue, who, regardless of the fact that he was interrupting the performance and disturbing the general concentration of thought, cried merrily,—

"Just look at that impostor asking for alms!"

Any one who has thrown a stone into a frog-pond or fired a gun into a flock of birds, can form some idea of the effect which these incongruous words produced in the midst of the universal attention. Gringoire shuddered as at an electric shock. The prologue was cut short, and every head was turned, in confusion, towards the beggar, who, far from being put out of countenance, regarded this incident as a good occasion for a harvest, and began to whine, with an air of great distress, his eyes half closed, "Charity, kind people!"

"Why, upon my soul," continued Joannes, "it is Clopin Trouillefou! Hollo there, my friend! Did you find

the wound on your leg inconvenient, that you have transferred it to your arm?"

So saying, with monkey-like skill he flung a small silver coin into the greasy felt hat which the beggar held with his invalid arm. The beggar accepted the alms and the sarcasm without wincing, and went on in piteous tones, "Charity, kind people!"

This episode greatly distracted the attention of the audience; and many of the spectators, Robin Poussepain and all the students at their head, joyfully applauded the odd duet, improvised, in the middle of the prologue, by the student with his shrill voice and the beggar with his imperturbable whine.

Gringoire was much displeased. Recovering from his first surprise, he began shouting to the characters on the stage: "Go on! What the deuce! Go on!" not even condescending to cast a look of scorn at the two interrupters.

At this moment he felt himself pulled by the hem of his surtout; he turned, in rather an ill-humour, and had hard work to force a smile, as he needs must do. It was the fair arm of Gisquette la Gencienne, which, passed through the rails, thus entreated his attention.

"Sir," said the young girl, "will they go on?"

"Of course," replied Gringoire, quite shocked at the question.

"In that case, sir," she went on, "would you have the kindness to explain to me—"

"What they are going to say?" interrupted Gringoire. "Well! listen."

"No," said Gisquette, "but what they have already said."

Gringoire started violently, like a man touched on a sensitive spot.

"Plague take the foolish, stupid little wench!" he muttered between his teeth. From that moment Gisquette was lost in his estimation.

However, the actors had obeyed his command, and the public, seeing that they had begun to speak again, again began to listen, not without necessarily losing many beauties from this kind of rough joining of the two parts of the piece, so abruptly dissevered. Gringoire brooded bitterly over this fact in silence. Still, quiet was gradually restored, the student was silent, the beggar counted a few coins in his hat, and the play went on.

It was really a very fine work, and one which it seems to us might well be made use of to-day, with a few changes. The plot, somewhat long and somewhat flat,—that is, written according to rule, —was simple; and Gringoire, in the innocent sanctuary of his innermost soul, admired its clearness. As may be imagined, the four allegorical characters were rather fatigued after traversing three quarters of the globe without managing to dispose of their golden dolphin creditably. Thereupon ensued fresh eulogies of the marvellous fish, with a thousand delicate allusions to the young lover of Margaret of Flanders, then very sadly secluded at Amboise, and little suspecting that Labour and Religion, Nobility and Trade, had just travelled around the world for his sake. The aforesaid dauphin was young, was handsome, was strong, and especially (magnificent source of all royal virtues!) he was the son of the Lion of France. I declare that this bold metaphor is ad-

mirable; and that the natural history of the theatre, on a day of allegories and royal epithalamia, is not to be alarmed at the thought of a dolphin being the son of a lion. It is just these rare and Pindaric mixtures which prove the degree of enthusiasm. Nevertheless, to play the critic, we must confess that the poet might have managed to develop this beautiful idea in less than two hundred lines. True, the mystery was to last from noon until four o'clock, by the order of the provost; something must be done to fill up the time. Besides, the people listened patiently.

All at once, in the very middle of a quarrel between Mademoiselle Trade and Madame Nobility, just as Master Labour pronounced this wonderful line,—

"Ne'er saw the woods a beast more beautiful."

the door leading to the platform, which had hitherto remained so inopportunely closed, was still more inopportunely opened, and the ringing voice of the usher abruptly announced "His Eminence, Cardinal Bourbon!"

CHAPTER III

THE CARDINAL

POOR Gringoire! The noise of all the big cannon crackers fired on St. John's day, the discharge of twenty crooked arquebuses, the report of that famous serpentine of the Tower of Billy, which, during the siege of Paris, on Sunday, Sept. 29, 1465, killed seven Burgundians at one shot, the explosion of all the gunpowder stored at the Temple Gate, would have rent his ears less rudely, at that solemn and dramatic moment, than did those few words dropping from the mouth of an usher: "His Eminence, Cardinal Bourbon!"

Not that Pierre Gringoire feared the Cardinal or scorned him; he was neither so weak nor so conceited. A genuine eclectic, as he would be called nowadays, Gringoire was one of those firm and lofty, calm and temperate souls, who always contrive to choose a happy medium (*stare in dimidio rerum*), and who are full of sense and liberal philosophy, although they have a high regard for cardinals. Precious and perpetual race of philosophers, to whom, as to another Ariadne, wisdom seems to have given a guiding clew which they have gone on unwinding from the beginning of the world, as they journeyed through the labyrinth of human things! They are to be found in every age, ever the same; that is, always in harmony with the age. And, to say nothing of our Pierre Gringoire, who would represent them in the fifteenth century if we could succeed in portraying him as he deserves, it is assuredly their spirit which animated Father du Breuil in the sixteenth, when he wrote these simple and sublime words, worthy of all the ages: "I am a Parisian in nationality and a Parrhisian in speech; *Parrhisia* being a Greek word signifying 'freedom of speech;' the which I have used even towards the cardinals, uncle and brother to the Prince of Conty; always with due respect to their greatness, and without offending any man among their followers, which is much."

The disagreeable effect which the Cardinal produced on Pierre Gringoire, therefore, partook neither of hatred nor of scorn. Quite the contrary; our poet had too much good sense and too threadbare a coat not to attach especial value to the fact that many an allusion in his prologue, and particularly those in glorification of the dauphin, son of the Lion of France, might be heard by a most eminent ear. But interest is not all-powerful in the noble nature of poets. Let us suppose the entity of the poet to be represented by the number ten: it is certain that a chemist, who should analyze and pharmacopœize it, as Rabelais says, would find it to be composed of one part self-interest to nine parts of self-esteem. Now, at the moment that the door was thrown open to admit the Cardinal, Gringoire's nine parts of self-esteem, swollen and inflated by the breath of public admiration, were in a state of abnormal development, before which the imperceptible molecule of self-interest, which we just now discovered in the constitution of poets, vanished and faded into insignificance, precious ingredient though it was,—the ballast of reality and humanity, without which they would never descend to earth. Gringoire enjoyed feeling, seeing, handling, as it were, an entire assembly, —of rascals, it is true, but what did that matter? They were stupefied, petrified, and almost stifled by the incommensurable tirades with which every portion of his epithalamium bristled. I affirm that he himself partook of the general beatitude, and that, unlike La Fontaine, who, on witn ssing a performance of his own comedy, "The Florentine," inquired, "What clown wrote that rhapsody?" Gringoire would fain have asked his neighbour, "Whose is this masterpiece?" You may judge of the effect produced on him by the abrupt and untimely arrival of the Cardinal.

His fears were but too soon realized. The entrance of his Eminence distracted the audience. Every head was turned towards the platform. No one listened. "The Cardinal! the Cardinal!" repeated every tongue. The unfortunate prologue was a second time cut short.

The Cardinal paused for a moment on the threshold. While he cast an indifferent glance over the assembly, the uproar increased. Every one wished to get a better view of him. Every one tried to see who could best stretch his neck over his neighbour's shoulders.

He was indeed a great personage, and one the sight of whom was well worth any other spectacle. Charles, Cardinal Bourbon, Archbishop and Count of Lyons, Primate of the Gauls, was at the same time allied to Louis XI. through his brother, Pierre, Lord of Beaujeu, who had married the eldest daughter of the king, and allied to Charles the Bold through his mother, Agnes of Burgundy. Now, the dominant feature, the characteristic and distinctive trait in the character of the Primate of the Gauls, was his courtier-like spirit and his devotion to those in power. It is easy to imagine the countless difficulties in which his double kinship had involved him, and all the temporal reefs between which his spiritual bark had been forced to manœuvre lest it should founder upon either Louis or Charles,—that Charybdis and that Scylla which had swallowed up the Duke of Nemours and the Constable of Saint-Pol. Heaven be thanked, he had escaped tolerably well from the voyage, and had reached Rome without accident. But although he was safe in

port, and indeed because he was safe in port, he never recalled without a tremor the various haps and mishaps of his political life, so long full of alarms and labours. He was therefore wont to say that the year 1476 had been to him both black and white; meaning that in one and the same year he had lost his mother, the Duchess of Bourbonnais, and his cousin, the Duke of Burgundy, and that one loss had consoled him for the other.

However, he was a very good fellow; he led a joyous life as cardinal, cheered himself willingly with the royal wine of Chaillot, was not averse to Richarde lo Garmoise and Thomasse la Saillarde, preferred to bestow alms upon pretty maids rather than aged matrons, and for all these reasons was very agreeable to the populace of Paris. He always went surrounded by a small court of bishops and priests of lofty lineage, gallant, jovial, and fond of feasting on occasion; and more than once the good devotees of St. Germain d'Auxerre, as they passed by night beneath the brightly lighted windows of Bourbon's house, had been scandalized on hearing the same voices which had sung vespers for them that day, now chanting to the clink of glasses the Bacchic adage of Benedict III.,—that pope who added a third crown to the tiara,—*"Bibamus papaliter."*

It was undoubtedly this popularity, so justly acquired, which saved him, on his entrance, from any unpleasant reception on the part of the mob, so malcontent but a moment before, and but little inclined to respect a cardinal on the very day when they were to elect a pope. But Parisians are not given to hoarding up grudges; and then, by insisting that the play should begin, the good citizens had shown their authority, thus getting the better of the Cardinal: and this triumph sufficed them. Besides, Cardinal Bourbon was a remarkably handsome man; he had a very gorgeous red robe which was most becoming; which is as much as to say that all the women, and consequently the better half of the audience, were on his side. Certainly, it would have been unjust, and in very bad taste, to hoot a cardinal for being late at the play, when he is handsome and wears his red robe gracefully.

He entered, therefore, bowed to the assembly with the hereditary smile of the grandee to the people, and walked slowly towards his scarlet velvet armchair with an air of being absorbed in thoughts of far other things. His escort, or what we should now call his staff of bishops and priests, flocked after him upon the daïs, not without renewed curiosity and confusion on the part of the groundlings. Every man tried to point them out and name them; every man knew at least one among them: this one, the Bishop of Marseilles, Alaudet, if I remember rightly; that one, the Dean of St. Denis; another, Robert de Lespinasse, Abbot of St. Germain des Prés, the libertine brother of one of the mistresses of Louis XI.,—all with endless mistakes and mispronunciations. As for the students, they swore roundly. It was their day, their Feast of Fools, their saturnalia, the annual orgies of the basoche and the schools. No iniquity but was allowable and sacred upon that day. And then there were plenty of giddy girls in the crowd,—Simone Qua-trelivres, Agnès la Gadine, Robine Piédebou. Was it not the least that they could do to swear at their ease and blaspheme a little on so fine a day, in so goodly a company of churchmen and courtesans? Neither were they slow to seize the opportunity; and in the midst of the uproar came a terrific outburst of oaths and obscenities from their lawless lips,—the lips of a set of students and scholars restrained all the rest of the year by their dread of the hot iron of Saint Louis. Poor Saint Louis! how they set him at defiance in his own Palace of Justice! Each of them selected from the new-comers on the daïs a black or grey, a white or purple gown for his own especial victim. As for Joannes Frollo de Molendino, in his quality of brother to an archdeacon he boldly attacked the red cassock, and bawled at the top of his voice, fixing his impudent eyes full on the Cardinal, *"Cappa repleta mero!"*

All these details, boldly set down here for the edification of the reader, were so covered by the general noise and confusion, that they were lost before they reached the daïs; besides which, the Cardinal would have paid but little heed to them, had he heard them, the license of that particular day was so well established a fact in the history of public morals. He had, moreover,—and his countenance showed how fully it absorbed him,—quite another care following him closely, and stepping upon the platform almost at the same moment as himself; namely, the Flemish embassy.

Not that he was much of a politician, or that he troubled himself much about the possible results of the marriage of his cousin, Lady Margaret of Burgundy, with his cousin Charles, Dauphin of Vienna; he cared very little about the duration of the friendship patched up between the Duke of Austria and the King of France, or about the King of England's opinion of the slight put upon his daughter! and he tested the royal vintage of Chaillot every evening, without suspecting that a few flasks of that same wine (slightly doctored and improved by Doctor Coictier, to be sure), cordially presented to Edward IV. by Louis XI. would one fine day rid Louis XI. of Edward IV. The very honourable embassy of the Duke of Austria brought none of these cares to the Cardinal's mind, but it troubled him in another way. It was indeed rather hard, and we have already spoken a word in regard to it in an earlier page of this book, to be forced to welcome and entertain—he, Charles of Bourbon—these nondescript citizens; he, a cardinal, to condescend to aldermen; he, a Frenchman and a boon companion, to befriend Flemish beer-drinkers, and that in public too! This was assuredly one of the most painful farces he had ever been compelled to play for the king's pleasure.

Still, he turned to the door with the best grace in the world (so well had he trained himself) when the usher announced in ringing tones, "The envoys from the Duke of Austria!" Needless to say that the entire audience did the same.

Then entered, two by two, with a gravity in vivid contrast to the lively ecclesiastical escort of Charles of Bourbon, the forty-eight ambassadors of Maximilian of Austria, headed by the reverend father in God, Jehan, Abbot of Saint-Bertin, Chancellor of the Golden Fleece, and Jacques de Goy, Lord of Dauby, high bailiff of Ghent. A profound silence fell upon the assembly, followed by stifled laughter at all the absurd names and all the commonplace titles which each of these personages calmly transmitted to the usher, who instantly hurled names and titles pell-mell, and horribly mangled, at the heads of the crowd. There were Master Loys Roelof, alderman of the city of Louvain; Master Clays d'Etuelde, alderman of Brussels; Master Paul de Baeurst, Lord of Voirmizelle, president of Flanders; Master Jehan Coleghens, burgomaster of the city of Antwerp; Master George de la Moere, head sheriff of the *kuere* of the town of Ghent; Master Gheldolf van der Hage, head sheriff of the court of equity of the same town; and the Lord of Bierbecque, and Jehan Pinnock, and Jehan Dymaerzelle, etc., etc., etc.: bailiffs, aldermen, burgomasters; burgomasters, aldermen, bailiffs; all stiff, starched, and strait-laced, dressed in their Sunday best of velvet and damask, wearing flat black velvet caps on their heads, with large tassels of gold thread from Cyprus; honest Flemish figures after all, severe and dignified faces, of the race of those whom Rembrandt portrayed so gravely and forcibly against the dark background of his "Night Watch,"—personages every one of whom bore it written upon his brow that Maximilian of Austria was right in "confiding fully," as his proclamation had it, "in their good sense, valour, experience, loyalty, and good qualities."

But there was one exception. This

was a man with a cunning, intelligent, crafty face, the face of a monkey combined with that of a diplomatist, to meet whom the Cardinal stepped forward three paces, bowing low, and yet who bore a name no more high sounding than "Guillaume Rym, councillor and pensionary of the town of Ghent."

Few persons there knew what Guillaume Rym was,—a rare genius, who in time of revolution would have appeared with renown in the foremost rank, but who in the fifteenth century was reduced to the lowest intrigues, and to "living by sapping and mining" as the Duke of St. Simon expresses it. However, he was appreciated by the greatest "sapper" in Europe; he planned and plotted with Louis XI. on familiar terms, and often laid his hand on the king's secret necessities.

All these things were utterly unknown to this throng, who marvelled at the politeness shown by the Cardinal to this scurvy Flemish bailiff.

CHAPTER IV

MASTER JACQUES COPPENOLE

As the pensionary of Ghent and his Eminence were exchanging very low bows, and a few words in still lower voices, a tall, broad-faced, square-shouldered man entered boldly after Guillaume Rym; he reminded one of a dog in pursuit of a fox. His felt hat and leather jerkin looked very shabby in the midst of the velvet and silk which surrounded him. Supposing him to be some groom who had lost his way, the usher stopped him.

"Hollo, my friend! there's no passing here."

The man in the leather coat shouldered him aside.

"What does the fellow mean?" he said in a tone which made the entire hall aware of this strange colloquy. "Don't you see that I belong to the party?"

"Your name?" asked the usher.

"Jacques Coppenole."

"Your titles?"

"Hosier at the sign of the Three Little Chains, at Ghent."

The usher started back. It was bad enough to have to announce aldermen and burgomasters; but a hosier, that was hard indeed! The Cardinal was on thorns. Every one was looking and listening. For two days past his Eminence had been labouring to lick these Flemish bears into some presentable shape, and this outburst was hard upon him. However, Guillaume Rym, with his crafty smile, leaned towards the usher.

"Announce Master Jacques Coppenole, clerk to the aldermen of the town of Ghent," he whispered softly.

"Usher," added the Cardinal in a loud voice, "announce Master Jacques Coppenole, clerk to the aldermen of the illustrious town of Ghent."

This was a mistake. Guillaume Rym, if left to himself, would have evaded the difficulty; but Coppenole had overheard the Cardinal.

"No, by God's cross!" he cried in his voice of thunder. "Jacques Coppenole, hosier. Do you hear me, usher? Nothing more, nothing less. By God's cross! a hosier is good enough for me. The archduke himself has more than once sought his gauntlet in my hose."

There was a burst of laughter and applause. A pun is always instantly appreciated in Paris, and consequently always applauded.

Let us add that Coppenole was a man of the people, and that the audience about him consisted of the people only; thus the sympathy between them was prompt, electric, and they were at once on an equal footing. The proud exclamation of the Flemish hosier, while it mortified the courtiers, stirred in every humble soul a certain sense of dignity still vague and indistinct in the fifteenth century. This hosier, who had just bearded the Cardinal himself, was their equal! A very pleasant thought for poor devils who were want to respect and obey the servants of the officers of the bailiff of the Abbot of St. Geneviève, train-bearer to the Cardinal.

Coppenole bowed haughtily to his Eminence, who returned the salutation of the all-powerful citizen dreaded by Louis XI. Then, while Guillaume Rym, "a wise and wily man," as Philippe de Comines has it, watched them both with a smile full of raillery and superiority, they took each his place,— the Cardinal troubled and disconcerted, Coppenole calm and erect, doubtless thinking that after all his title of hosier was quite as good as any other, and that Mary of Burgundy, mother of that Margaret whose marriage he was now negotiating, would have feared him less as cardinal than as hosier; for no cardinal would have led on the men of Ghent against the favourites of the daughter of Charles the Bold; no cardinal could have hardened the hearts of the masses against her tears and her prayers, by a single word, when the heiress of Flanders besought her people to grant their pardon, at the very foot of their scaffold; while the hosier had but to lift his leathern elbow to cause both your heads to fall, O ye illustrious lords, Guy d'Hymbercourt and Chancellor Guillaume Hugonet!

But all was not over yet for the poor Cardinal, who must needs drink to the dregs the bitter cup of compassion with such low company.

The reader may perhaps recall the impudent beggar who clung to the fringes of the Cardinal's daïs at the opening of the prologue. The arrival of the distinguished guests did not cause him to relax his hold; and while prelates and ambassadors were packed as close as Dutch herrings in the seats upon the platform, he made himself quite comfortable, and coolly crossed his legs upon the architrave. Such insolence was unusual, and no one noted it at the moment, attention being -fixed elsewhere. He for his part saw nothing in the hall; he swayed his head to and fro with the careless ease of a Neapolitan, repeating ever and anon amid the din, as if mechanically, "Charity, kind people!" and certainly he was the only one in the entire audience who did not deign to turn his head to listen to the altercation between Coppenole and the usher. Now, as chance would have it, the master hosier of Ghent, with whom the people already sympathized strongly, and upon whom all eyes were fixed, seated himself in the front row upon the platform, just above the beggar; and they were not a little amazed to see the Flemish ambassador, after glancing at the rascal beneath him, give him a friendly slap upon his tattered shoulder.

The beggar turned; surprise, recognition, delight, were visible in both faces, then, without paying the slightest heed to the throng of spectators, the hosier and the scurvy knave fell to talking in low tones, clasping each other's hands; while the rags of Clopin Trouillefou, displayed against the cloth of gold of the daïs, produced the effect of a caterpillar upon an orange.

The novelty of this strange scene excited such an outburst of mirth in the hall that the Cardinal quickly perceived it; he bent forward, and, unable from his position to catch more than a glimpse of Trouillefou's disgraceful garments, he quite naturally supposed that the beggar was asking alms, and indignant at his audacity, he exclaimed, "Sir Bailiff of the Palace, throw me that rascal into the river!"

"By God's cross! Sir Cardinal," said Coppenole, without releasing Clopin's hand, "he is my friend."

"Noël! Noël" cried the mob. From that instant Master Coppenole was "in high favour with the people," in Paris as in Ghent; "for men of his cut always are," says Philippe de Comines, "when they are thus disorderly."

The Cardinal bit his lip. He bent towards his neighbour, the Abbot of St. Geneviève, and said in an undertone:—

"Pleasant ambassadors are these sent us by the archduke to announce the coming of Lady Margaret!"

"Your Eminence," replied the abbot, "wastes his courtesies upon these Flemish grunters,—*Margaritas ante porcos.*"

"Say rather," replied the Cardinal with a smile, "*Porcos ante Margaritam.*"

All the little court in priestly robes went into ecstasies over the joke. The Cardinal felt slightly comforted: he was quits with Coppenole; his pun also had been applauded.

Now, let those of our readers who have the power of generalizing an image and an idea, as it is the pleasant fashion to express it, allow us to ask them if they have a distinct conception of the spectacle afforded, at the moment that we claim their attention, by the vast parallelogram of the great hall of the Palace: In the centre of the hall, against the western wall, a broad and magnificent platform covered with gold brocade, upon which stepped in procession, through a small arched doorway, a number of grave and reverend personages successively announced by the nasal voice of an usher; on the foremost benches, already seated, various venerable figures wrapped in ermine, velvet, and scarlet; around the daïs, where all was dignity and silence, below, in front, everywhere, a great crowd and a great uproar; a thousand eyes from the crowd fixed upon every face on the platform, a thousand murmurs upon the announcement of every name. Certainly the sight is a strange one, and well worthy the attention of the spectators. But below there, at the extreme end, what is that kind of trestle-work with four motley puppets above and four more below? Who is that pale-faced man in a black coat beside the boards? Alas! dear reader, that is Pierre Gringoire and his prologue.

We had all entirely forgotten him.

This was precisely what he feared.

From the instant that the Cardinal entered, Gringoire had never ceased working for the salvation of his prologue. He at first enjoined the actors, who remained in suspense, to go on, and to raise their voices; then, seeing that no one was listening, he stopped them; and then, after the interruption had lasted nearly fifteen minutes, he began to stamp, to struggle, to question Gisquette and Liénarde, and to encourage his neighbours to call for the prologue. All in vain; not an eye would move from the Cardinal, the embassy, and the daïs,—the sole centre of that vast circle of visual rays. We must therefore believe, and we say it with regret, that the prologue was beginning to be somewhat tedious to the audience at the moment that his Eminence caused so terrible a diversion. After all, the spectacle was the same upon the daïs as upon the marble table,—the conflict between Labour and Religion, Nobility and Trade; and many people preferred to see them simply, in living, breathing reality, elbowing and pushing, in flesh and blood, in this Flemish embassy, in this Episcopal court, beneath the Cardinal's robe, beneath the jacket of Coppenole, rather than painted and decked out, speaking in artificial verse, and as it were stuffed with straw beneath the white and yellow tunics in which Gringoire had arrayed them.

However, when our poet saw that peace was beginning to reign once more, he hit upon a stratagem which might have saved all.

"Sir," said he, turning towards one of his neighbours, a good fat fellow with a patient face, "suppose they begin again?"

"Begin what?" said the neighbour.

"Why, the mystery!" said Gringoire.

"If you like," responded his neighbour.

This lukewarm approval was enough for Gringoire, and acting for himself he began to shout, mixing with the crowd as much as he could, "Go on with the miracle-play! Go on!"

"The devil!" said Joannes de Molendino, "what are they bawling about over there?" (For Gringoire made noise enough for four.) "Say, boys, isn't the play done? They want to have it all over again; it's not fair."

"No, no!" cried the students. "Down with the mystery! down with it!"

But Gringoire seemed ubiquitous, and shouted louder than before, "Go on, go on!"

These outcries attracted the attention of the Cardinal.

"Bailiff," he said to a tall dark man seated near him, "are those devils caught in a font of holy water, that they make such an infernal noise?"

The Bailiff of the Palace was a species of amphibious magistrate, a sort of bat of the judicial order, partaking at once of the nature of the rat and the bird, the judge and the soldier.

He approached his Eminence, and, not without serious fears of his displeasure, stammered out an explanation of the popular misconduct,—that noon had come before his Eminence, and that the actors were obliged to begin without awaiting his Eminence.

The Cardinal burst out laughing.

"Upon my word, the Rector of the University had better have done as much. What say you, Master Guillaume Rym?"

"My lord," replied Guillaume Rym, "let us be content that we have escaped half the play. It is just so much gained."

"May those rascals go on with their performance?" asked the bailiff.

"Go on, go on," said the Cardinal; "it's all the same to me. I will read my breviary meantime."

The bailiff advanced to the edge of the platform and cried aloud, after imposing silence by a wave of his hand: "Citizens, commoners, and residents: to satisfy those who wish the play to begin again and those who wish it to end, his Eminence orders that it be continued."

Both parties were forced to submit. However, the author and the audience long cherished a grudge against the Cardinal.

The characters on the stage accordingly resumed their recital, and Gringoire hoped that the rest of his work at least would be heard. This hope soon proved as illusory as all the rest. Silence was indeed restored to a certain extent among the audience; but Gringoire had not remarked that, at the moment when the Cardinal gave the order to go on, the daïs was far from being filled, and that in the train of the Flemish embassy came other personages forming part of the procession, whose names and titles, shouted out in the midst of his prologue by the intermittent cry of the usher, made many ravages in it. Imagine the effect, in the midst of a play, of the shrill voice of an usher uttering between two rhymes, and often between two hemistichs, such parentheses as these:—

"Master Jacques Charmolue, king's attorney in the Ecclesiastical Court!"

"Jehan de Harlay, esquire, keeper of the office of captain of the watch of the city of Paris!"

"Master Galiot de Genoilhac, knight, Lord of Brussac, chief of the king's ordinance!"

"Master Dreux-Raguier, inspector of the woods and waters of our lord the king, in the lands of France, Champagne, and Brie!"

"Master Louis de Graville, knight, councillor, and chamberlain to the king, admiral of France, keeper of the forest of Vincennes!"

Master Denis le Mercier, guardian of the Home for the Blind of Paris!" etc.

This at last became unendurable.

This strange accompaniment, which made it very hard to follow the play, enraged Gringoire all the more because he could not blind himself to the fact that the interest was constantly increasing, and that all his work needed was to be heard. It was indeed difficult to conceive of a more ingenious and more dramatic context. The four characters of the prologue were lamenting their terrible embarrassment, when Venus in person (*vera incessu patuit dea*) appeared before them, clad in a fine coat of mail, emblazoned with the ship from the seal of the city of Paris. She came herself to claim the dolphin promised to the fairest of the fair. Jupiter, whose thunder was heard muttering in the dressing-room below, supported her claim, and the goddess was about to triumph,—that is, speaking without metaphor, to marry the Dauphin,—when a young child, habited in white damask and holding a daisy (an obvious allusion to the Lady of Flanders), came to contest the prize with Venus. Theatrical effect and sudden change of affairs! After some controversy, Venus, Margaret, and those behind the scenes agreed to refer the matter to the wise decision of the Holy Virgin. There was also another fine part, that of Don Pedro, King of Mesopotamia; but amid so many interruptions it was difficult to discover the object of his introduction. All these characters came up the ladder.

But it all was in vain; none of these beauties were appreciated or understood. With the Cardinal's entrance, an invisible and magical cord seemed suddenly to draw all eyes from the marble table to the daïs, from the southern to the western portion of the hall. Nothing could free the audience from the spell; every eye was fixed, and the new-comers and their accursed names, and their faces and their dresses, were a perpetual source of distraction. It was heartrending. Save for Gisquette and Liénarde, who occasionally turned away when Gringoire pulled them by the sleeve; save for the patient fat neighbour, no one listened to, no one looked at, the poor forsaken morality. Gringoire saw nothing but profiles.

With what bitterness he saw his whole framework of fame and poetry crumble away bit by bit! And to think that this very mob had been on the point of revolting against the bailiff, from sheer impatience to hear his work! Now that they had it, they cared nothing for it,—this same performance which began amid such universal applause! Eternal ebb and flow of popular favour! To think that they had come so near hanging the bailiff's men! What would he not have given to recover that golden hour!

The usher's brutal monologue ceased at last; every one had arrived, and Gringoire breathed again; the actors went bravely on.

But then what should Master Coppenole, the hosier, do but rise suddenly; and Gringoire heard him utter, amid universal attention, this abominable speech:—

"Citizens and squires of Paris, I know not, by God's cross! what we are doing here. I do indeed see in yonder corner, upon those boards, people who look as if they were spoiling for a fight. I don't know whether that is what you call a 'mystery,' but it is not at all amusing: they abuse one another, and get no farther. For full fifteen minutes I have been waiting for the first blow; nothing comes; they are cowards, who deal in no other weapons than insults. You ought to fetch a few wrestlers from London or Rotterdam, and then you'd have a treat! You would see blows that could be heard all over the place; but those fellows yonder are a disgrace. They might at least give us a Morris-dance or some other mummery! This is not what I was told I should see; I was promised a Feast of Fools and the election of a Lord of Misrule. We have our Lord of Misrule in Ghent, too; and we're not behind you in that, by God's cross! But this is how we do it: we collect a crowd, as you do here; then every man in his turn puts his head through a hole and pulls a face at the rest; he who makes the ugliest is chosen pope by popular acclaim; there! It's very amusing. Would you like to choose your pope after the fashion of my country? At least it would be better than listening to those chatterboxes. If they will come and make their grimaces through the window, they can join the game. What say you, Sir Citizens? There are quite enough absurd specimens of both sexes here to give us a good Flemish laugh, and we have ugly mugs enough to hope for some fine grimaces."

Gringoire longed to answer; but amazement, anger, indignation, robbed him of speech. Moreover, the proposal of the popular hosier was greeted with such enthusiasm by those plain citizens who were flattered at being dubbed "Squires," that all opposition was useless. Nothing remained but to follow the current. Gringoire hid his face in his hands, not being lucky enough to have a cloak to cover his head, like Agamemnon of Timanthes.

CHAPTER V

QUASIMODO

In the twinkling of an eye, all was ready for the execution of Coppenole's idea. Citizens, students, and lawyers' clerks set briskly to work. The little chapel opposite the marble table was chosen as the stage for the grimaces. A broken pane in the pretty rose-window over the door left free a circle of stone, through which it was agreed that the contestants should thrust their heads. To reach it, all were obliged to climb upon a couple of casks, which had been discovered somewhere and set one upon the other. It was settled that all candidates, men or women (for a papess might be chosen), lest the effect of their grimaces should be weakened, should cover their faces and remain hidden in the chapel until the proper moment to appear. In less than an instant the chapel was filled with aspirants, upon whom the door was closed.

Coppenole, from his seat, directed everything, arranged everything. During the confusion the Cardinal, no less disconcerted than Gringoire, withdrew with all his train, feigning business and vespers; the same crowd which had been so stirred by his coming, showing not the least emotion at his departure. Guillaume Rym was the only one who observed his Eminence's flight. Popular attention, like the sun, pursued its course; starting from one end of the hall, after pausing for some time in the centre, it was now at the other end. The marble table, the brocaded daïs, had had their day; it was the turn of Louis XI.'s chapel. The field was now clear for every kind of folly. No one remained but the Flemings and the vulgar herd.

The wry faces began. The first to appear at the window, with eyelids inverted until they showed the red, a cavernous mouth, and a forehead wrinkled like the boots of a hussar under the Empire, produced such inextinguishable laughter, that Homer would have taken all these clowns for gods. And yet, the great hall was anything but an Olympus, and Gringoire's poor Jupiter knew this better than any one. A second, a third wry face followed, then another, and another; and still the shouts of laughter and stamps of delight increased. There was a certain peculiar intoxication in the spectacle, a certain potent ecstasy and fascination which it would be hard to explain to the reader of our own day and society. Let him imagine a series of faces presenting in turn every geometric form, from the triangle to the trapezium, from the cone to the polyhedron; every human expression, from rage to lust; every age, from the wrinkles of the new-born babe to the furrows of the old and dying; every religious phantasmagoria, from Faunus to Beelzebub; every animal profile, from the jaws of the dog to the beak of the bird, from the boar's head to the pig's snout. Let him picture to himself all the grotesque heads carved on the Pont Neuf, those petrified nightmares from the hand of Germain Pilon, taking breath and life, and coming in turn to gaze at you with fiery eyes; all the masks from a Venetian carnival passing before your glass,— in one word, a human kaleidoscope.

The revelry became more and more Flemish. Téniers could have given but an imperfect idea of it! Imagine Salvator Rosa's battle-piece turned into a bacchanal feast. There were no longer students, ambassadors, townspeople, men, or women; no longer a Clopin Trouillefou, a Gilles Lecornu, a Simone Quatrelivres, or a Robin Poussepain. All distinctions died in the common license. The great hall ceased to be anything but a vast furnace of effrontery and mirth, wherein every mouth was a cry, every face a grimace, every individual a posture; the sum total howled and yelled. The strange faces which took their turn in gnashing their teeth through the rose-window were like so many brands cast into the flames; and from this effervescent mob arose, like steam from a furnace, a sharp, shrill, piercing sound, like the buzz of a gnat's wings.

"Oh, confound it!"

"Just look at that face!"

"That's nothing!"

"Let's have another!"

"Guillemette Maugerepuis, do look at that bull's head! it only lacks horns. It is not your husband."

"Another!"

"By the Pope's head! what's the meaning of that contortion?"

"Hollo there! that's not fair. You should show only your face."

"That damned Perrette Callebotte! She is just capable of such a thing."

"Noël! Noël!"

"I'm smothering!"

"There's a fellow whose ears are too big to go through!"

But we must do justice to our friend Jehan. Amidst this uproar he was still to be seen perched upon his pillar, like a cabin-boy on a topsail. He exerted himself with incredible fury. His mouth was opened wide, and there issued from it a yell which no one heard,—not that it was drowned by the general clamour, tremendous though it was; but because it undoubtedly reached the limit of audible shrillness,—the twelve thousand vibrations of Sauveur or the eight thousand of Biot.

As for Gringoire, the first moment of depression over, he recovered his composure. He braced himself to meet adversity. "Go on!" he cried for the third time to his actors, whom he regarded as mere talking-machines; then, as he strode up and down in front of the marble table, he was seized with a desire to appear in his turn at the chapel window, were it only for the pleasure of making faces at that ungrateful mob. "But no, that would be unworthy of us; no vengeance. Let us struggle on to the end," he murmured; "the power of poetry over the people is great; I will bring them back. Let us see whether wry faces or polite learning will triumph."

Alas! he was left the only spectator of his play.

It was even worse than before. Now he saw nothing but people's backs.

I am wrong. The patient fat man, whom he had already consulted at a critical moment, was still turned towards the theatre. As for Gisquette and Liénarde, they had long since deserted.

Gringoire was touched to the heart by the fidelity of his only listener. He went up to him and addressed him, shaking him slightly by the arm; for the worthy man was leaning against the railing in a light doze.

"Sir," said Gringoire, "I thank you."

"Sir," replied the fat fellow with a yawn, "for what?"

"I see what annoys you," resumed the poet; "it is all this noise which prevents you from hearing readily. But be calm! your name shall be handed down to posterity. Your name, if you please?"

"Renauld Château, Keeper of the Seals of the Châtelet, at Paris, at your service."

"Sir, you are the sole representative of the muses here," said Gringoire.

"You are too kind, sir," replied the Keeper of the Seals of the Châtelet.

"You are the only man," added Gringoire, "who has paid proper attention to the play. How do you like it?"

"Ha, ha!" replied the fat magistrate, who was but half awake, "jolly enough, in truth!"

Gringoire was forced to content himself with this eulogy; for a storm of applause, mingled with prodigious shouts,

cut short their conversation. The Lord of Misrule was elected.

"Noël! Noël! Noël!" shouted the people on all sides.

That was indeed a marvellous grin which now beamed through the hole in the rose-window. After all the pentagonal, hexagonal, and heteroclitic faces which had followed one another in quick succession at the window without realizing that ideal of the grotesque constructed by imagination exalted by revelry, it required nothing less to gain the popular vote than the sublime grimace which had just dazzled the assembly. Master Coppenole himself applauded; and Clopin Trouillefou, who had competed for the prize (and Heaven knows to what intensity of ugliness his features could attain), confessed himself conquered. We will do the same. We will not try to give the reader any idea of that tetrahedron-like nose, of that horse-shoe-shaped mouth; of that small left eye overhung by a bushy red eyebrow, while the right eye was completely hidden by a monstrous wart; of those uneven, broken teeth, with sad gaps here and there like the battlements of a fortress; of that callous lip, over which one of these teeth projected like an elephant's tusk; of that forked chin; and especially of the expression pervading all this,—that mixture of malice, amazement, and melancholy. Imagine, if you can, that comprehensive sight.

The vote was unanimous; the crowd rushed into the chapel. They returned leading the fortunate Lord of Misrule in triumph. But it was then only that surprise and admiration reached their highest pitch; the grimace was his natural face.

Or rather the entire man was a grimace. A large head bristling with red hair; between his shoulders an enormous hump, with a corresponding prominence in front; legs and thighs so singularly crooked that they touched only at the knees, and, seen from the front, resembled two reaping-hooks united at the handle; broad feet, huge hands; and, with all this deformity, a certain awe-inspiring air of vigour, agility, and courage; strange exception to the rule which declares power, as well as beauty, to be the result of harmony,—such was the pope whom the fools had chosen to reign over them.

He looked like a giant broken to pieces and badly cemented together.

When this species of Cyclop appeared upon the threshold of the chapel, motionless, thickset, almost as broad as he was long, "the square of his base," as a great man once expressed it, the people recognized him instantly, by his partly-coloured red and purple coat spangled with silver, and particularly by the perfection of his ugliness, and cried aloud with one voice:—

"It is Quasimodo, the bell-ringer! It is Quasimodo, the humpback of Notre-Dame! Quasimodo, the one-eyed! Quasimodo, the handy-legged! Noël! Noël!"

The poor devil evidently had an abundance of nicknames to choose from.

"Let all pregnant women beware!" cried the students.

"Or all those who hope to be so," added Joannes.

In fact, the women hid their faces.

"Oh, the ugly monkey!" said one of them.

"As wicked as he is ugly," added another.

"He's the very devil," added a third.

"I am unlucky enough to live near Notre-Dame. I hear him prowling among the gutters by night."

"With the cats."

"He's always on our roofs."

"He casts spells upon us through the chimneys."

"The other evening he came and pulled a face at me through the window. I thought it was a man. He gave me such a fright!"

"I'm sure he attends the Witches' Sabbath. Once he left a broomstick on my leads."

"Oh, what a disagreeable humpback's face he has!"

"Oh, the villainous creature!"

"Faugh!"

The men, on the contrary, were charmed, and applauded.

Quasimodo, the object of this uproar, still stood at the chapel door, sad and serious, letting himself be admired.

A student (Robin Poussepain, I think) laughed in his very face, and somewhat too close. Quasimodo merely took him by the belt and cast him ten paces away through the crowd; all without uttering a word.

Master Coppenole, lost in wonder, approached him.

"By God's cross and the Holy Father! you are the most lovely monster that I ever saw in my life. You deserve to be pope of Rome as well as of Paris."

So saying, he laid his hand sportively upon his shoulder. Quasimodo never budged. Coppenole continued:—

"You're a rascal with whom I have a longing to feast, were it to cost me a new douzain of twelve pounds Tours. What say you?"

Quasimodo made no answer.

"By God's cross!" said the hosier, "you're not deaf, are you?"

He was indeed deaf.

Still, he began to lose his temper at Coppenole's proceedings, and turned suddenly towards him, gnashing his teeth so savagely that the Flemish giant recoiled, like a bull-dog before a cat.

Then a circle of terror and respect, whose radius was not less than fifteen geometric paces, was formed about the strange character. An old woman explained to Master Coppenole that Quasimodo was deaf.

"Deaf!" said the hosier, with his hearty Flemish laugh. "By God's cross! but he is a perfect pope!"

"Ha! I know him now," cried Jehan, who had at last descended from his capital to view Quasimodo more closely; "it's my brother the archdeacon's bellringer. Good-day, Quasimodo!"

"What a devil of a fellow!" said Robin Poussepain, till aching from his fall. "He appears: he's a humpback; he walks: he's bandy-legged; he looks at you: he is blind of one eye; you talk to him: he is deaf. By the way, what use does this Polyphemus make of his tongue?"

"He talks when he likes," said the old woman; "he grew deaf from ringing the bells. He is not dumb."

"That's all he lacks," remarked Jehan.

"And he has one eye too many," said Robin Poussepain.

"Not at all," judiciously observed Jehan. "A one-eyed man is far more incomplete than a blind one. He knows what he lacks."

But all the beggars, all the lackeys, all the cutpurses, together with the students, had gone in procession to fetch, from the storeroom of the basoche, the pasteboard tiara and mock robes of the Pope of Fools, or Lord of Misrule. Quasimodo submitted to be arrayed in them without a frown, and with a sort of proud docility. Then he was seated upon a barrow painted in motley colours. Twelve officers of the fraternity of fools raised it to their shoulders; and a sort of bitter, scornful joy dawned upon the morose face of the Cyclop when he saw beneath his shapeless feet the heads of so many handsome, straight, and well-made men. Then the howling, tatterdemalion train set out, as was the custom, to make the tour of the galleries within the Palace before parading the streets and public squares.

CHAPTER VI

ESMERALDA

WE are delighted to be able to inform our readers that during the whole of this scene Gringoire and his play had stood their ground. His actors, spurred on by him, had not stopped spouting his verses, and he had not given over listening. He had resigned himself to the uproar, and was determined to go on to the bitter end, not despairing of recovering some portion of public attention. This ray of hope revived when he saw Quasimodo, Coppenole, and the deafening escort of the Lord of Misrule leave the hall with a tremendous noise. The crowd followed eagerly on their heels. "Good!" said he to himself; "now we have got rid of all the marplots." Unfortunately, all the marplots meant the whole audience. In the twinkling of an eye, the great hall was empty.

To be exact, there still remained a handful of spectators, some scattered, others grouped around the pillars, women, old men, or children, who had had enough of the tumult and the hurly-burly. Some few students still lingered, astride of the window-frames, gazing into the square.

"Well," thought Gringoire, "here are still enough to hear the end of my mystery. There are but few, but it is a picked public, an intellectual audience."

A moment later, a melody meant to produce the greatest effect at the appearance of the Holy Virgin was missing. Gringore saw that his musicians had been borne off by the procession of the Lord of Misrule. "Proceed," he said stoically.

He went up to a group of townspeople who seemed to him to be talking about his play. This is the fragment of conversation which he caught:—

"You know, Master Cheneteau, the Hôtel de Navarre, which belonged to M. de Nemours?"

"Yes, opposite the Braque Chapel."

"Well, the Treasury Department has just let it to Guillaume Alexandre, the painter of armorial bearings, for six pounds and eight pence Paris a year."

"How high rents are getting to be!"

"Well, well!" said Gringoire with a sigh; "the rest are listening."

"Comrades!" shouted one of the young scamps in the window; "Esmeralda! Esmeralda is in the square!"

This cry had a magical effect. Every one in the hall rushed to the windows, climbing up the walls to get a glimpse, and repeating, "Esmeralda! Esmeralda!"

At the same time a great noise of applause was heard outside.

"What do they mean by their 'Esmeralda'?" said Gringoire, clasping his hands in despair. "Oh, heavens! I suppose it's the turn of the windows now!"

He turned back again to the marble table, and saw that the play had stopped. It was just the moment when Jupiter should have appeared with his thunder. Now Jupiter stood motionless at the foot of the stage.

"Michel Giborne!" cried the angry poet, "what are you doing there? Is that put down in your part? Go up, I tell you!"

"Alas!" said Jupiter, "one of the students has taken away the ladder."

Gringoire looked. It was but too true. All communication was cut off between his plot and its solution.

"The rascal!" he muttered; "and why did he carry off that ladder?"

"That he might see Esmeralda," piteously responded Jupiter. "He said, 'Stay, there's a ladder which is doing no one any good!' and he took it."

This was the finishing stroke. Gringoire received it with submission.

"May the devil seize you!" said he to the actors; "and if I am paid, you shall be too."

Then he beat a retreat, with drooping head, but last to leave, like a general who has fought a brave fight.

And as he descended the winding Palace staircase, he muttered between his teeth: "A pretty pack of donkeys and clowns these Parisians are! They come to hear a miracle play, and then pay no heed to it! Their whole minds are absorbed in anybody and everybody,— in Clopin Trouillefou, the Cardinal, Coppenole, Quasimodo, the devil! but in Madame Virgin Mary not a whit. If I had known, I'd have given you your fill of Virgin Marys, you boobies! And I,—to come to see faces, and to see nothing but backs! to be a poet, and to have the success of an apothecary! True, Homer begged his way through Greek villages, and Naso died in exile among the Muscovites. But may the devil flay me if I know what they mean by their 'Esmeralda'! What kind of a word is that, anyhow? It must be Egyptian!"

BOOK II

LOVE

CHAPTER I

FROM CHARYBDIS TO SCYLLA

NIGHT comes on early in January. The streets were already dark when Gringoire left the Palace. This nightfall pleased him. He longed to find some dark and solitary alley where he might meditate at his ease, and let the philosopher apply the first healing balm to the poet's wounds. Besides, philosophy was his only refuge; for he knew not where to find shelter. After the total failure of his first theatrical effort he durst not return to the lodging which he had occupied, opposite the Hay-market, in the Rue Grenier-sur-l'Eau, having reckoned upon what the provost was to give him for his epithalamium to pay Master Guillaume Doulx-Sire, farmer of the taxes on cloven-footed animals in Paris, the six months' rent which he owed him, namely, twelve Paris pence, —twelve times the worth of everything that he owned in the world, including his breeches, his shirt, and his hat.

After a moment's pause for reflection, temporarily sheltered under the little gateway of the prison of the treasurer of the Sainte-Chapelle, as to what refuge he should seek for the night, having all the pavements of Paris at his disposition, he remembered having noticed, the week before in the Rue de la Savaterie, at the door of a Parliamentary Councillor, a stone block for mounting a mule, and having said to himself that this stone would, on occasion, make a very excellent pillow for a beggar or a poet. He thanked Providence for sending him so good an idea; but as he prepared to cross the Palace courtyard on his way to the crooked labyrinth of the city, formed by the windings of all those antique sisters, the Rues de la Barillerie, de la Vieille-Draperie, de la Savaterie, de la Juiverie, etc., still standing at the present day with their nine-story houses, he saw the procession of the Lord of Misrule, which was also just issuing from the Palace and rushing across the courtyard, with loud shouts, an abundance of glaring torches, and his (Gringoire's) own music. This sight opened the wound to his self-esteem; he fled. In the bitterness of dramatic misfortune, all that recalled the day's festival incensed him, and made his wound bleed afresh.

He meant to cross St. Michael's Bridge; some children were careering up and down there with rockets and crackers.

"A plague on all fireworks!" said Gringoire; and he turned towards Exchange Bridge. The houses at the head of the bridge were adorned with three large banners representing the king, the dauphin, and Margaret of Flanders, and six little bannerets with portraits of the Duke of Austria, Cardinal Bourbon, M. de Beaujeu, and Madame Jeanne de France, the Bastard of Bourbon, and I know not who besides,—all lighted up by torches. The mob gazed in admiration.

"Lucky painter, Jehan Fourbault!" said Gringoire, with a heavy sigh; and he turned his back on banners and bannerets. A street opened directly before him: it looked so dark and deserted that he hoped it would afford a way of escape from every echo as well as every reflection of the festival: he plunged down it. In a few moments he struck his foot against something, stumbled, and fell. It was the big bunch of hawthorn which the members of the basoche had that morning placed at the door of a president of the Parliament, in honour of the day. Gringoire bore this new misfortune bravely; he rose and walked to the bank of the river. Leaving behind him the civil and criminal towers, and passing by the great walls of the royal gardens, along the

unpaved shore where the mud was ankle-deep, he reached the western end of the city, and for some time contemplated the islet of the Passeur aux Vaches, which has since vanished beneath the bronze horse on the Pont Neuf. The islet lay before him in the darkness,—a black mass across the narrow strip of whitish water which lay between him and it. The rays of a tiny light dimly revealed a sort of beehive-shaped hut in which the cows' ferryman sought shelter for the night.

"Lucky ferryman!" thought Gringoire; "you never dream of glory, and you write no wedding songs! What are the marriages of kings and Burgundian duchesses to you? You know no Marguerites save those which grow upon your turf in April for the pasturage of your cows! and I, poet that I am, am hooted, and I shiver, and I owe twelve pence, and the soles of my shoes are so thin that you might use them for glasses in your lantern. Thanks, ferryman! Your hut rests my eyes and makes me forget Paris."

He was roused from his almost lyric ecstasy by a huge double-headed St. John's cracker, which was suddenly sent up from the blessed cabin. The ferryman was taking his part in the festivities of the day, and setting off a few fireworks.

The explosion set Gringoire's teeth on edge.

"Accursed festival!" he exclaimed, "will you pursue me forever,—oh, my God! even to the ferryman's house?"

He gazed at the Seine at his feet and a horrible temptation overcame him.

"Ah!" said he, "how cheerfully 1

would drown myself if the water were not so cold!"

Then he took a desperate resolve. It was, since he could not escape from the Lord of Misrule, Jehan Fourbault's flags, the bunches of hawthorn, the rockets, and squibs, to plunge boldly into the very heart of the gaiety and go directly to the Grève.

"At least," thought he, "I may find some brands from the bonfire to warm myself and I may sup on some crumbs from the three great sugar escutcheons which were to be served on the public sideboard."

CHAPTER II

THE GRÈVE

BUT very slight traces now remain of the Grève as it existed at the time of which we write; all that is left is the picturesque little tower at the northern corner of the square; and that, already buried beneath the vulgar whitewash which incrusts the sharp edges of its carvings, will soon disappear perhaps, drowned in that flood of new houses which is so rapidly swallowing up all the old fronts in Paris.

People who, like ourselves, never pass through the Grève without giving a glance of sympathy and pity to the poor little tower, choked between two hovels of the time of Louis XV., may readily reconstruct in fancy the entire mass of buildings to which it belonged, and as it were restore the old Gothic square of the fifteenth century.

It was, as it still is, an irregular square, bounded on one side by the quay, and on the other three by a number of tall, narrow, gloomy houses. By day one might admire the variety of its edifices, all carved in stone or wood, and presenting perfect specimens of the various kinds of mediæval domestic architecture, going back from the fifteenth to the eleventh century, from the casement window which was beginning to supersede the pointed arch, to the semicircular arch of the Romance period, which gave way to the pointed arch, and which still occupied below it the first story of that old house called Roland's Tower, on the corner of the square nearest the Seine, close to the Rue de la Tannerie. At night, nothing could be seen of this mass of buildings but the dark indented line of the roofs stretching their chain of acute angles round the square. For it is one of the radical differences between the modern and ancient towns, that nowadays the fronts of the houses face upon the squares and streets, and in old times it was the gable ends. In two centuries the houses have turned round.

In the middle of the eastern side of the square stood a heavy and hybrid construction composed of three houses together. It was known by three names, which explain its history, its purpose, and its architecture. The Dauphin's House, because Charles V. occupied it while dauphin; the Trades House, because it was used as Town Hall; the Pillar House (*domus ad piloria*), on account of a series of thick columns which supported its three stories. There the city found everything required for a well-to-do town like Paris—a chapel in which to pray to God; a court of special pleas, where audience was given, and if necessary "the king's men put down;" and in the garrets an "arsenal" full of artillery. For the citizens of Paris, knowing that it is not always enough to pray and plead for the liberties of the town, always had a good rusty arquebus or two in reserve in an attic of the Town Hall.

Even then the Grève had the same forbidding aspect which the detestable ideas clinging about it awaken, and the gloomy Town Hall built by Dominique Bocador, which has taken the place of the Pillar House, still gives it. It must be confessed that a permament gibbet and pillory,—"a justice and a ladder," as they were then called,—standing side by side in the middle of the flagstones, largely contributed to make men turn away from that fatal square where so many beings full of life and health have died in agony; where the Saint Vallier's fever was destined to spring to life some fifty years later,—that disease which was nothing but dread of the scaffold, the most monstrous of all maladies, because it came not from God, but from man.

It is a consoling thought (let us say in passing) that the death penalty, which three hundred years ago still cumbered the Grève, the Markets, the Place Dauphine, the Cross du Trahoir, the Pigmarket, the hideous Montfaucon, the Sergeants' Barrier, Cats' Square, St. Denis Gate, Champeaux, Baudet Gate, and St. Jacques Gate, with its iron wheels, its stone gibbets and all its machinery of torture, permanently built into the pavement; not to mention the countless pillories belonging to provosts, bishops, chapters, abbots, and priors administering justice; to say nothing of the legal drownings in the river Seine,—

it is a consolation that in the present day, having successively lost all the pieces of her armour, her refinements of torture, her purely capricious and wilful penal laws, her torture for the administration of which she made afresh every five years a leather bed at the Grand-Châtelet, that ancient sovereign of feudal society, almost outlawed and exiled from our cities, hunted from code to code, driven from place to place, now possesses in one vast Paris but one dishonoured corner of the Grève, but one wretched guillotine, furtive, timid, and ashamed, seeming ever in dread of being taken in the very act, so swiftly does it vanish after it has dealt its deadly stroke!

CHAPTER III

BESOS PARA GOLPES

WHEN Pierre Gringoire reached the Grève, he was benumbed. He had come by way of the Millers' Bridge to avoid the mob on Exchange Bridge and Jehan Fourbault's flags; but the wheels of all the bishop's mills had bespattered him as he crossed, and his coat was soaked; moreover, it seemed to him that the failure of his play had made him more sensitive to cold than ever. He therefore made haste to draw near the bonfire which still blazed gloriously in the middle of the square; but a considerable crowd formed a circle round about it.

"Damned Parisians!" said he to himself (for Gringoire, like all true dramatic poets, was given to monologues), "there they stand blocking my way to the fire! and yet I greatly need a good warm chimney-corner; my shoes leak, and all those cursed mills have dripped upon me! Deuce take the Bishop of Paris and his mills! I would really like to know what a bishop wants with a mill! does he expect to turn miller? If he is merely waiting for my curse, I give it to him cheerfully, and to his cathedral and his mills into the bargain! Now just let's see if any of those boors will disturb themselves for me! What on earth are they doing there? Warming themselves indeed; a fine amusement! Watching to see a hundred fagots burn; a fine sight, truly!"

Looking more closely, he saw that the circle was far larger than was necessary for the crowd to warm themselves at the royal bonfire, and that the large number of spectators was not attracted solely by the beauty of the hundred blazing fagots.

In the vast space left free between the crowd and the fire a young girl was dancing.

Whether this young girl was a human being, or a fairy, or an angel, was more than Gringoire, cynic philosopher and sarcastic poet though he was, could for a moment decide, so greatly was he fascinated by the dazzling vision.

She was not tall, but seemed to be, so proudly erect did she hold her slender figure. She was brown, but it was evident by daylight her skin must have that lovely golden gleam peculiar to Spanish and Roman beauties. Her tiny foot was Andalusian too, for it fitted both snugly and easily into its dainty shoe. She danced, she turned, she twirled, upon an antique Persian carpet thrown carelessly beneath her feet; and every time her radiant figure passed, as she turned, her great black eyes sent forth lightning flashes.

Upon her every eye was riveted, every mouth gaped wide; and in very truth, as she danced to the hum of the tambourine which her round and graceful arms held high above her head, slender, quick and active as any wasp, with smoothly fitting golden bodice, her many-coloured full skirts, her bare shoulders, her shapely legs, from which her skirts now and then swung away, her black hair, her eyes of flame, she seemed more than mortal creature.

"Indeed," thought Gringoire, "she is a salamander, a nymph, a goddess, a bacchante from Mount Mænalus!"

At this moment one of the salamander's tresses was loosened, and a bit of brass which had been fastened to it fell to the ground.

"Alas, no!" said he, "she's a gipsy."

All illusion had vanished.

She began to dance once more. She picked up two swords, and balancing them by their points on her forehead, she twirled them in one direction while she herself revolved in another; she was indeed but a gipsy girl. But great as was Gringoire's disenchantment, the picture was far from being destitute of all charm and beauty; the bonfire lit it up with a crude red light, which flickered brightly upon the circle of surrounding figures and the young girl's brown face, casting wan reflections, blended with alternating shadows, into the farthest corners of the square,—on one side upon the black and weather-beaten front of the Pillar House, and on the other upon the cross-beam of the stone gibbet.

Among the myriad faces dyed scarlet by the flames, there was one which seemed absorbed even beyond all the rest in gazing at the dancer. It was the face of a man, austere, calm, and sombre. This man, whose dress was hidden by the crowd about him, seemed not more than thirty-five years old, and yet he was bald; he had but a few grey and scanty locks of hair about his temples; his broad, high forehead was already beginning to be furrowed with wrinkles, but in his deep-set eyes sparkled an extraordinary spirit of youth, an ardent love of life and depth of passion. He kept them fixed on the gipsy; and while the giddy young damsel danced and fluttered to the delight of all, his thoughts seemed to become more and more melancholy. From time to time a smile and a sigh met upon his lips, but the smile was far sadder than the sigh.

The young girl stopped at last, breathless, and the people applauded eagerly.

"Djali!" said the gipsy.

Then Gringoire saw a pretty little white goat, active, alert, and glossy, with gilded horns, gilded hoofs, and a gilded collar, which he had not before observed, and which had hitherto remained quietly crouching on a corner of the carpet, watching its mistress as she danced.

"Djali," said the dancer. "it's your turn now."

And sitting down, she gracefully offered the goat her tambourine.

"Djali," she added, "what month in the year is this?"

The goat raised its fore-foot and struck once upon the tambourine. It was indeed the first month of the year. The crowd applauded.

"Djali," resumed the young girl, turning her tambourine another way, "what day of the month is it?"

Djali lifted his little golden hoof and struck it six times upon the tambourine.

"Djali," continued the daughter of Egypt, with still another twist of the tambourine, "what time of day is it?"

Djali gave seven blows, and at the same instant the clock on the Pillar House struck seven.

The people were lost in wonder.

"There is sorcery in this," said a forbidding voice from the throng. It was the voice of the bald man, who had never taken his eyes from the gipsy.

She trembled, and turned towards him; but fresh plaudits broke out, and drowned the surly exclamation.

They even effaced it so completely from her mind that she went on questioning her goat.

"Djali, how does Master Guichard Grand-Remy, the captain of the city pistoleers, walk in the procession at Candlemas?"

Djali rose on his hind-legs and began to bleat, walking as he did so with an air of polite gravity that the whole ring of spectators burst into a laugh at this parody of the selfish devotion of the captain of pistoleers.

"Djali," continued the young girl, encouraged by her increasing success, "show us how Master Jacques Charmolue, king's attorney in the Ecclesiastical Court, preaches."

The goat sat up and began to bleat, waving his fore-feet in so strange a fashion that, except for the bad French and the bad Latin, Jacques Charmolue himself stood before you,—gesture, accent, and attitude.

And the crowd applauded louder than before.

"Sacrilege! Profanation!" exclaimed the voice of the bald-headed man.

The gipsy turned again.

"Ah!" said she, "it is that ugly man!" Then projecting her lower lip beyond the upper one, she made a little face which seemed habitual with her, pirouetted on her heel, and began to collect the gifts of the multitude in her tambourine.

Big pieces of silver, little pieces of silver, pennies, and farthings, rained into it. Suddenly she passed Gringoire. He put his hand in his pocket so heedlessly that she stopped. "The devil!" said the poet, as he found reality at the bottom of his pocket,—that is to say, an empty void. But there stood the pretty girl, looking at him with her big eyes, holding out her tambourine, and waiting. Gringoire was in agony.

If he had had the wealth of Peru in his pocket, he would certainly have given it to the dancing-girl; but Gringoire did not possess the wealth of Peru, and moreover America had not then been discovered.

Luckily an unexpected event came to his rescue.

"Will you be gone, you gipsy grasshopper?" cried a sharp voice from the darkest corner of the square.

The young girl turned in terror. This was not the voice of the bald-headed man; it was a woman's voice,—the voice of a malicious and bigoted person.

However, the cry which alarmed the gipsy delighted a band of roving children.

"It's the recluse of the Tour-Roland," they shouted with riotous laughter.

"It's the nun scolding! Hasn't she had her supper? Let's carry her some bits from the city sideboard!"

All rushed towards the Pillar House.

Gringoire seized the occasion of the dancer's distress to disappear. The children's shouts reminded him that he too had not supped. He therefore hastened to the sideboard. But the little scamps had better legs than he; when he arrived, they had swept the table clear. There was not even a paltry cake at five cents the pound remaining. Nothing was left on the wall but the delicate *fleurs-de-lis,* twined with rose branches, painted in 1434 by Mathieu Biterne. That was a meagre repast.

It's a tiresome matter to go to bed without supper; it is still less agreeable to have no supper and not to know where to find a bed. This was Gringoire's condition. No bread, no shelter; he was goaded on every hand by necessity, and he found necessity very crabbed and cross. He had long since discovered the truth that Jupiter created mankind in a fit of misanthropy, and that throughout a wise man's life fate keeps his philosophy in a state of siege. As for himself, the blockade had never been so complete. He heard his stomach sounding a parley, and he thought it very improper for an evil destiny to overcome his philosophy by famine.

He was becoming more and more absorbed in these melancholy reflections, when a peculiar although melodious song suddenly roused him from them. The young gipsy girl was singing.

Her voice was like her dancing, like her beauty. It was charming, and not to be defined,—possessing a pure and sonorous quality, something ethereal and airy. There was a constant succession of bursts of melody, of unexpected cadences, then of simple phrases mingled with shrill sibilant notes: now runs and trills which would have baffled a nightingale, but which never ceased to be harmonious; then softly undulating octaves rising and falling like the bosom of the youthful singer.

Her fine features expressed every caprice of her song with singular flexibility, from the most lawless inspiration to the chastest dignity. At one instant she seemed a mad woman, at the next a queen.

The words which she sang were in a language unknown to Gringoire, and apparently one with which she was not herself familiar, so little connection had the expression which she lent her song with the meaning of the words. Thus these four lines in her mouth became wildly gay:—

"Un cofre de gran riqueza
    Hallaron dentro un pilar,
    Dentro del, nuevas banderas
    Con figuras de espantar."

And a moment later, the tone in which she uttered the words,—

"Alarabes de cavallo
    Sin poderse menear,
    Con espadas, y los cuellos,
    Ballestas de buen echar."

brought the tears into Gringoire's eyes. And yet her song was full of joy, and she seemed to sing like a bird, from sheer happiness and freedom from care.

The gipsy's song had troubled Gringoire's reverie, but as the swan troubles the water. He listened in a sort of ecstasy which rendered him oblivious of all else. It was the first instant, for some hours, in which he had felt no pain.

The moment was brief.

The same woman's voice which had cut short the girl's dance now interrupted her song.

"Will you hold your tongue, you infernal cricket?" she cried, still from the dark corner of the square.

The poor "cricket" stopped short. Gringoire clapped his hands to his ears.

"Oh," he exclaimed, "cursed be that rusty saw, which breaks the lyre!"

And the other listeners grumbled with him.

"Deuce take the nun!" said more than one. And the invisible old marplot might have had reason to repent of her aggressions had not their thoughts been diverted at that very moment by the procession of the Lord of Misrule, which, having traversed many a street and square, now appeared in the Grève with all its torches and all its noise.

This procession, which our readers saw as it started from the Palace, had taken shape as it marched, enlisting all the available vagabonds and scamps and idle thieves in Paris; so that it presented quite a respectable appearance when it reached the Grève.

First came the barn-stormers, the chief cackling cove at the head, on horseback, with his aids on foot, holding his stirrup and bridle. Behind walked the rest of the barn-stormers, male and female, with their little ones clamouring on their backs; all, men, women, and children, in rags and tatters. Then came the thieves' brotherhood: that is, all the robbers in France, ranged according to their degree, the least expert coming first. Thus they filed along four by four, armed with the various insignia of their degrees. In this singular faculty, most of them maimed, some halt, some with but one arm, were shoplifters, mock pilgrims, tramps who pretended to have been bitten by wolves, dummy chuckers, thimble-riggers, sham Abrams, Jeremy Diddlers, sham cripples, mumpers, pall-yards, show-fall pitchers, rogues pretending to have been burned out, cadgers, old soldiers, high-flyers, swell mobsmen, gonnofs, flash coves,— a list long enough to weary Homer himself. In the centre of the conclave of gonnofs and flash coves might dimly be distinguished the head of the thieves' brotherhood, the "Grand Coëre," or king of rogues, squatting in a small cart, drawn by two big dogs. After the fraternity of thieves came the Empire of Galilee. Guillaume Rousseau, Emperor of the Galilees, marched majestic in his purple robes stained with wine, preceded by mountebanks fighting and dancing Pyrrhic dances, surrounded by his mace-bearers, tools, and the clerks of the Court of Exchequer. Last came the basoche (the corporation of lawyers' clerks), with their sheaves of maize crowned with flowers, their black gowns, their music worthy of a Witches' Sabbath, and their huge yellow wax candles. In the midst of this throng the high officials of the fraternity of fools bore upon their shoulders a barrow more heavily laden with tapers than the shrine of St. Geneviève in time of plague; and upon this barrow rode resplendent, with crosier, cope, and mitre, the new Lord of Misrule, the bell-ringer of Notre-Dame, Quasimodo the Humpback.

Each division of this grotesque procession had its own peculiar music. The barn-stormers drew discordant notes from their balafos and their African tabours. The thieves, a far from musical race, were still using the viol, the cowherd's horn, and the quaint rubeb of the twelfth century. Nor was the Empire of Galilee much more advanced; their music was almost wholly confined to some wretched rebec dating back to the infancy of the art, still imprisoned within the *re-la-mi*. But it was upon the Lord of Misrule that all the musical riches of the period were lavished in one magnificent cacophony. There were treble rebecs, counter-tenor rebecs, tenor rebecs, to say nothing of flutes and brass instruments. Alas! our readers may remember that this was Gringoire's orchestra.

It is difficult to convey any idea of the degree of proud and sanctimonious rapture which Quasimodo's hideous and painful face had assumed during the journey from the Palace to the Grève. This was the first thrill of vanity which he had ever felt. Hitherto he had known nothing but humiliation, disdain of his estate, and disgust for his person. Therefore, deaf as he was, he enjoyed, like any genuine pope, the plaudits of that mob which he had hated because he felt that it hated him. What mattered it to him that his subjects were a collection of fools, cripples, thieves, and beggars! They were still subjects and he a sovereign! And he took seriously all the mock applause, all the satirical respect with which, it must be confessed, there was a slight mixture of very real fear in the hearts of the throng. For the humped back was strong; for the bandy legs were nimble;

for the deaf ears were malicious,—three qualities which tempered the ridicule.

Moreover, we are far from fancying that the new Lord of Misrule realized clearly either his own feelings or those which he inspired. The spirit lodged in that imperfect body was necessarily something dull and incomplete. Therefore what he felt at this instant was absolutely vague, indistinct, and confused to him. Joy only pierced the cloud; pride prevailed. The sombre and unhappy face was radiant.

It was not therefore without surprise and fright that, at the moment when Quasimodo in his semi-intoxication passed triumphantly before the Pillar House, the spectators saw a man dart from the crowd and snatch from his hands, with a gesture of rage, his gilded crosier, the badge of his mock papacy.

This man, this rash fellow, was no other than the bald-headed character who, the instant before, mingling with the group about the gipsy girl, had chilled her blood with his words of menace and hatred. He was clad now in ecclesiastical garb. Just as he stepped forward from the crowd, Gringoire, who had not noticed him until then, recognized him. "Why!" said he with an exclamation of amazement, "it is my master in Hermes, Don Claude Frollo, the archdeacon! What the devil does he want with that ugly one-eyed man? He'll be swallowed up alive!"

Indeed, a cry of terror rose. The terrible Quasimodo flung himself headlong from his barrow, and the women turned away their eyes that they might not see the archdeacon rent limb from limb.

He made but one bound towards the priest, gazed at him, and fell on his knees.

The priest tore from him his tiara, broke his crosier and rent his tinsel cope.

Quasimodo still knelt, with bowed head and clasped hands.

Then followed between them a strange dialogue in signs and gestures, for neither spoke,—the priest, erect, angry, threatening, imperious; Quasimodo, prostrate, humble, suppliant. And yet it is very certain that Quasimodo could have crushed the priest with his thumb.

At last the archdeacon, rudely shaking Quasimodo's powerful shoulder, signed to him to rise and follow.

Quasimodo rose.

Then the fraternity of fools, their first stupor over, strove to defend their pope, so abruptly dethroned. The thieves, the Galilees, and all the lawyers' clerks yelped about the priest.

Quasimodo placed himself before the priest, put the muscles of his fists into play, and glared at his assailants, gnashing his teeth like an enraged bear.

The priest resumed his wonted sombre gravity, beckoned to Quasimodo, and withdrew silently.

Quasimodo walked before him, scattering the crowd as he passed.

When they had made their way through the people and the square, a swarm of curious idlers attempted to follow them. Quasimodo then took up the position of rearguard, and followed the archdeacon backwards, short, thickset, crabbed, monstrous, bristling, gathering himself together, licking his tusks, growling like a wild beast, and driving the crowd before him in waves, with a gesture or a look.

They vanished down a dark, narrow street, where none dare venture after them; so effectually did the mere image of Quasimodo grinding his teeth bar the way.

"Strange enough!" said Gringoire; "but where the deuce am I to find supper?"

CHAPTER IV

THE INCONVENIENCES OF FOLLOWING A PRETTY WOMAN IN THE STREET AT NIGHT

GRINGOIRE determined to follow the gipsy girl at any risk. He had seen her go down the Rue de la Coutellerie with her goat; he therefore went down the Rue de la Coutellerie.

"Why not?" said he to himself.

Gringoire, being a practical philosopher of the streets of Paris, had observed that nothing is more favourable to reverie than the pursuit of a pretty woman when you don't know where she is going. In this voluntary surrender of your own free will, this caprice yielding to another caprice, all unconscious of submission, there is a mixture of odd independence and blind obedience, a certain happy medium between slavery and liberty, which pleased Gringoire, a mind essentially mixed, undetermined, and complex, carrying everything to extremes, forever wavering betwixt all human propensities, and neutralizing them the one by the other. He frequently compared himself to Mahomet's tomb, attracted in opposite directions by two loadstones, and perpetually trembling between top and bottom, between the ceiling and the pavement, between descent

and ascent, between the zenith and the nadir.

If Gringoire were living now, what a golden mean he would observe between the classic and romantic schools!

But he was not sufficiently primitive to live three hundred years, and 't is a pity. His absence leaves a void but too deeply felt to-day.

However, nothing puts a man in a better mood for following people in the street (especially when they happen to be women), a thing Gringoire was always ready to do, than not knowing where he is to sleep.

He accordingly walked thoughtfully along behind the young girl, who quickened her pace and urged on her pretty goat, as she saw the townspeople were all going home, and the taverns—the only shops open upon this general holiday—were closing.

"After all," thought he, "she must have a lodging somewhere; gipsies are generous. Who knows—"

And there were some very pleasant ideas interwoven with the points of suspension that followed this mental reticence.

Still, from time to time, as he passed the last belated groups of citizens shutting their doors, he caught fragments of their talk, which broke the chain of his bright hypotheses.

Now, it was two old men chatting together.

"Master Thibaut Fernicle, do you know it is cold?"

(Gringoire had known this since the winter first set in.)

"Yes, indeed, Master Boniface Disome! Are we going to have another winter like the one we had three years ago, in '80, when wood cost eight pence the measure?"

"Bah! that's nothing, Master Thibaut, to the winter of 1407, when it froze from St. Martin's Day to Candlemas, and with such fury that the parliamentary registrar's pen froze, in the Great Chamber, between every three words, which was a vast impediment to the registration of justice!"

Farther on, two neighbour women gossiped at their windows; the candles in their hands flickered faintly through the fog.

"Did your husband tell you of the accident, Mademoiselle la Boudraque?"

"No. What was it, Mademoiselle Turquant?"

"The horse of M. Gilles Godin, the notary from the Châtelet, took fright at the Flemish and their procession, and knocked down Master Philippot Avrillot, lay brother of the Celestines."

"Is that really so?"

"Indeed it is."

"And such a plebeian animal! It's a little too much. If it had only been a cavalry horse, it would not be so bad!"

And the windows were closed. But Gringoire had already lost the thread of his ideas.

Luckily, he soon recovered and readily resumed it, thanks to the gipsy girl, thanks to Djali, who still went before him,—two slender, delicate, charming creatures, whose tiny feet, pretty forms, and graceful manners he admired, almost confounding them in his contemplation; thinking them both young girls from their intelligence and close friendship; considering them both goats from the lightness, agility, and grace of their step.

But the streets grew darker and more deserted every instant. The curfew had long since sounded and it was only at rare intervals that a passenger was seen upon the pavement or a light in any window. Gringoire had involved himself, by following in the footsteps of the gipsy, in that inextricable labyrinth of lanes, cross-streets, and blind alleys, which encircles the ancient sepulchre of the Holy Innocents, and which is much like a skein of thread tangled by a playful kitten.

"Here are streets with but little logic!" said Gringoire, lost in the myriad windings which led back incessantly to their original starting-point, but amid which the damsel pursued a path with which she seemed very familiar, never hesitating, and walking more and more swiftly. As for him, he would not have had the least idea where he was, if he had not caught a glimpse, at the corner of a street, of the octagonal mass of the pillory of the Markets, whose pierced top stood out in sharp, dark outlines against a window still lighted in the Rue Verdelet.

A few moments before, he had attracted the young girl's attention; she had several times turned her head anxiously towards him; once she had even stopped short, and taken advantage of a ray of light which escaped from a half-open bake-shop, to study him earnestly from head to foot; then, having cast that glance, Gringoire saw her make the little grimace which he had already noted, and then she passed on.

It gave Gringoire food for thought. There was certainly a leaven of scorn and mockery in that dainty grimace. He therefore began to hang his head, to count the paving-stones, and to follow the young girl at a somewhat greater distance, when at the turn of a street which hid her from his sight, he heard her utter a piercing scream.

He hastened on.

The street was full of dark shadows. Still, a bit of tow soaked in oil, which burned in an iron cage at the foot of the image of the Holy Virgin at the street corner enabled Gringoire to see the gipsy girl struggling in the arms of two men who were trying to stifle her cries. The poor little goat, in great alarm, lowered its horns and bleated piteously.

"This way, gentlemen of the watch!" shouted Gringoire; and he rushed boldly forward. One of the men who held the girl turned towards him. It was the formidable figure of Quasimodo.

Gringoire did not take flight, but neither did he advance another step.

Quasimodo approached him, flung him four paces away upon the pavement with a single back stroke, and plunged rapidly into the darkness, bearing the girl, thrown over one arm like a silken scarf. His companion followed him, and the poor goat ran behind, with its plaintiff bleat.

"Murder! murder!' shrieked the unfortunate gipsy.

"Halt, wretches, and let that wench go!" abruptly exclaimed, in a voice of thunder, a horseman who appeared suddenly from the next cross-street.

It was a captain of the king's archers, armed from head to foot, and broadsword in hand.

He tore the gipsy girl from the arms of the astonished Quasimodo, laid her across his saddle, and just as the redoubtable humpback, recovering from his surprise, rushed upon him to get back his prey, some fifteen or sixteen archers, who were close behind their captain, appeared, two-edged swords in hand. They were a squadron of the royal troops going on duty as extra watchmen, by order of Master Robert d'Estouteville, provost's warden of Paris.

Quasimodo was surrounded, seized, garotted. He roared, he foamed at the mouth, he bit; and had it been daylight, no doubt his face alone, made yet more hideous by rage, would have routed the whole squadron. But by night he was stripped of his most tremendous weapon,—his ugliness.

His companion had disappeared during the struggle.

The gipsy girl sat gracefully erect upon the officer's saddle, placing both hands upon the young man's shoulders, and gazing fixedly at him for some seconds, as if charmed by his beauty and the timely help which he had just rendered her.

Then breaking the silence, she said, her sweet voice sounding even sweeter than usual:

"What is your name, Mr. Officer?"

"Captain Phœbus de Châteaupers, at your service, my pretty maid!" replied the officer, drawing himself up.

"Thank you," said she.

And while Captain Phœbus twirled his moustache, cut in Burgundian fashion, she slipped from the horse like an arrow falling to the earth, and fled.

A flash of lightning could not have vanished more swiftly.

"By the Pope's head!" said the captain, ordering Quasimodo's bonds to be tightened, "I had rather have kept the wench."

"What would you have, Captain?" said one of his men; "the bird has flown, the bat remains."

CHAPTER V

THE REST OF THE INCONVENIENCES

GRINGOIRE, still dizzy from his fall, lay stretched on the pavement before the figure of the Blessed Virgin at the corner of the street. Little by little he regained his senses; at first he was for some moments floating in a sort of half-drowsy reverie which was far from unpleasant, in which the airy figures of the gipsy and her goat were blended with the weight of Quasimodo's fist. This state of things did not last long. A somewhat sharp sensation of cold on that part of his body in contact with the pavement roused him completely, and brought his mind back to realities once more.

"Why do I feel so cold?" said he, abruptly. He then discovered that he was lying in the middle of the gutter.

"Deuce take the humpbacked Cyclop!" he muttered; and he tried to rise. But he was too dizzy and too much bruised; he was forced to remain where he was. However, his hand was free; he stopped his nose and resigned himself to his fate.

"The mud of Paris," thought he (for he felt very sure that the gutter must be his lodging for the night).

"And what should we do in a lodging if we do not think?"

"the mud of Paris is particularly foul; it must contain a vast amount of vola-

tile and nitrous salts. Moreover, such is the opinion of Master Nicolas Flamel and of the Hermetics—"

The word "Hermetics" suddenly reminded him of the archdeacon, Claude Frollo. He recalled the violent scene which he had just witnessed,—how the gipsy struggled with two men, how Quasimodo had a companion; and the morose and haughty face of the archdeacon passed confusedly through his mind. "That would be strange!" he thought. And he began to erect, upon these data and this basis, the fantastic edifice of hypothesis, that card-house of philosophers; then suddenly returning once more to reality, "But there! I am freezing!" he exclaimed.

The situation was in fact becoming more and more unbearable. Every drop of water in the gutter took a particle of heat from Gringoire's loins, and the temperature of his body and the temperature of the gutter began to balance each other in a very disagreeable fashion.

An annoyance of quite another kind all at once beset him.

A band of children, those little barefoot savages who have haunted the streets of Paris in all ages under the generic name of "gamins," and who, when we too were children, threw stones at us every day as we hastened home from school because our trousers were destitute of holes,—a swarm of these young scamps ran towards the crossroads where Gringoire lay, with shouts and laughter which seemed to show but little regard for their neighbour's sleep. They dragged after them a shapeless sack, and the mere clatter of their wooden shoes would have been enough to rouse the dead. Gringoire, who was not quite lifeless yet, rose to a sitting position.

"Hollo, Hennequin Dandèche! Hollo there, Jehan-Pincebourde!" they bawled at the top of their voices; "old Eustache Moubon, the junk-man at the corner, has just died; we've got his mattress; we're going to build a bonfire. This is the Flemings' day!"

And lo, they flung the mattress directly upon Gringoire, near whom they stood without seeing him. At the same time one of them snatched up a wisp of straw which he lighted at the good Virgins lamp.

"Christ's body!" groaned Gringoire, "am I going to be too hot next?"

It was a critical moment. He would soon be caught betwixt fire and water. He made a supernatural effort,—such an effort as a coiner of false money might make when about to be boiled alive and struggling to escape. He rose to his feet, hurled the mattress back upon the little rascals, and fled.

"Holy Virgin!" screamed the boys; "the junk-dealer has returned!"

And they too took to their heels.

The mattress was left mistress of the battlefield. Belleforêt, Father le Juge, and Corrozet affirm that it was picked up next day with great pomp by the clergy of the quarter, and placed in the treasury of the Church of the Holy Opportunity, where the sacristan earned a handsome income until 1789 by his tales of the wonderful miracle performed by the statue of the Virgin at the corner of the Rue Mauconseil, which had by its mere presence, on the memorable night of Jan. 6, 1482, exorcised the spirit of the defunct Eustache Moubon, who, to outwit the devil, had, in dying, maliciously hidden his soul in his mattress.

CHAPTER VI

THE BROKEN JUG

AFTER running for some time as fast as his legs would carry him, without knowing whither, plunging headlong around many a street corner, striding over many a gutter, traversing many a lane and blind alley, seeking to find escape and passage through all the windings of the old streets about the markets, exploring in his panic fear what the elegant Latin of the charters calls *tota via, cheminum et viaria,* our poet came to a sudden stop, partly from lack of breath, and partly because he was collared as it were by a dilemma which had just dawned upon his mind. "It strikes me, Pierre Gringoire," said he to himself, laying his finger to his forehead, "that you are running as if you had lost your wits. Those little scamps were quite as much afraid of you as you were of them. It strikes me, I tell you, that you heard the clatter of their wooden shoes as they fled to the south, while you took refuge to the north. Now, one of two things: either they ran away, and then the mattress, which they must have forgotten in their fright, is just the hospitable bed which you have been running after since morning, and which Our Lady miraculously sends you to reward you for writing a morality in her honour, accompanied by triumphal processions and mummeries; or else the boys did not run away, and in that case they have set fire to the mattress; and there you have just exactly the good fire that you need to cheer, warm, and dry you. In either case, whether as a good fire or a good bed, the mattress is a gift from Heaven. The Blessed Virgin Mary, at the corner of the Rue Mauconseil, may have killed Eustache Moubon for this very purpose; and it is sheer madness in you to betake yourself to such frantic flight, like a Picard running before a Frenchman, leaving behind what you are seeking before you; and you are a fool!"

Then he retraced his steps, and fumbling and ferreting his way, snuffing the breeze, and his ear on the alert, he strove to find the blessed mattress once more, but in vain. He saw nothing but intersecting houses, blind alleys, and crossings, in the midst of which he doubted and hesitated continually, more hindered and more closely entangled in this confusion of dark lanes than he would have been in the very labyrinth of the Hôtel des Tournelles. At last he lost patience, and exclaimed solemnly: "Curse all these crossings! The devil himself must have made them in the likeness of his pitchfork."

This outburst comforted him somewhat, and a sort of reddish reflection which he observed at this instant at the end of a long, narrow lane, quite restored his wonted spirits. "Heaven be praised!" said he; "yonder it is! There's my mattress burning briskly." And comparing himself to the boatman foundering by night, he added piously: "*Salve, salve, maris stella!*"

Did he address this fragment of a litany to the Holy Virgin, or to the mattress? That we are wholly unable to say.

He had taken but a few steps down the long lane, which was steep, unpaved, and more and more muddy and sloping, when he remarked a very strange fact. It was not empty: here and there, along its length, crawled certain vague and shapeless masses, all proceeding towards the light which flickered at the end of the street, like those clumsy insects which creep at night from one blade of grass to another towards a shepherd's fire.

Nothing makes a man bolder than the sense of an empty pocket. Gringoire continued to advance, and had soon overtook that larva which dragged itself most lazily along behind the others. As he approached, he saw that it was nothing but a miserable cripple without any legs, strapped into a bowl, and hopping along as best he might on his hands, like a wounded spider which has but two legs left. Just as he passed this kind of human insect, it uttered a piteous appeal to him; "*La buona mancia, signor! la buona mancia!*"

"Devil fly away with you," said Gringoire, "and with me too, if I know what you're talking about!"

And he passed on.

He came up with another of these perambulating masses, and examined it. It was another cripple, both lame and one-armed, and so lame and so armless that the complicated system of crutches and wooden limbs which supported him made him look like a mason's scaffolding walking off by itself. Gringoire, who loved stately and classic similes, compared the fellow, in fancy, to Vulcan's living tripod.

The living tripod greeted him as he

passed, by holding his hat at the level of Gringoire's chin, as if it had been a barber's basin, and shouting in his ears: *"Señor caballero, para comprar un pedaso de pan!"*

"It seems," said Gringoire, "that he talks too; but it's an ugly language, and he is better off than I am if he understands it."

Then, clapping his hand to his head with a sudden change of idea: "By the way, what the devil did they mean this morning by their 'Esmeralda'?"

He tried to quicken his pace; but for the third time something blocked the way. This something, or rather this some one, was a blind man, a little blind man, with a bearded Jewish face, who, feeling about him with a stick, and towed by a big dog, snuffled out to him with a Hungarian accent: *"Facitote caritatem!"*

"That's right!" said Pierre Gringoire; "here's one at last who speaks a Christian tongue. I must have a very charitable air to make all these creatures come to me for alms when my purse is so lean. My friend (and he turned to the blind man), I sold my last shirt last week; that is to say, since you understand the language of Cicero, *'Von didi hebdomade nuper transita meam ultimam chemisam!'*"

So saying, he turned his back on the blind man and went his way. But the blind man began to mend his steps at the same time; and lo and behold! the cripple and the man bound into the bowl hurried along after them with a great clatter of bowl and crutches over the pavement.

Then all three, tumbling over each other in their haste at the heels of poor Gringoire, began to sing their several songs:

"Caritatem!" sang the blind man.

"La buona mancia!" sang the man in the bowl.

And the lame man took up the phrase with, *"Un pedaso de pan!"*

Gringoire stopped his ears, exclaiming, "Oh, tower of Babel!"

He began to run. The blind man ran. The lame man ran. The man in the bowl ran.

And then, the farther he went down the street, the more thickly did cripples, blind men, and legless men swarm around him, with armless men, one-eyed men, and lepers with their sores, some coming out of houses, some from adjacent streets, some from cellar-holes, howling, yelling, bellowing, all hobbling and limping, rushing towards the light, and wallowing in the mire like slugs after a shower.

Gringoire, still followed by his three persecutors and not knowing what would happen next, walked timidly through the rest, going around the lame, striding over the cripples, his feet entangled in this ant-hill of deformity and disease, like that English captain caught fast by an army of land-crabs.

He thought of retracing his steps; but it was too late. The entire legion had closed up behind him, and his three beggars pressed him close. He therefore went on, driven alike by this irresistible stream, by fear, and by a dizzy feeling which made all this seem a horrible dream.

At last he reached the end of the street. It opened into a vast square where a myriad scattered lights twinkled through the dim fog of night. Gringoire hurried forward, hoping by the swiftness of his legs to escape the three infirm spectres who had fastened themselves upon him.

"*Onde vas, hombre?*" cried the lame man, throwing away his crutches, and running after him with the best pair of legs that ever measured a geometric pace upon the pavements of Paris.

Then the man in the bowl, erect upon his feet, clapped his heavy iron-bound bowl upon Gringoire's head, and the blind man glared at him with flaming eyes.

"Where am I?" asked the terrified poet.

"In the Court of Miracles," replied a fourth spectre, who had just accosted them.

"By my soul!" replied Gringoire; "I do indeed behold blind men seeing and lame men running; but where is the Saviour?"

They answered with an evil burst of laughter.

The poor poet glanced around him. He was indeed in that fearful Court of Miracles, which no honest man had ever entered at such an hour; the magic circle within whose lines the officers of the Châtelet, and the provost's men who ventured to penetrate it, disappeared in morsels; a city of thieves, a hideous wart upon the face of Paris; the sewer whence escaped each morning, returning to stagnate at night, that rivulet of vice, mendicity, and vagrancy, perpetually overflowing the streets of every great capital; a monstrous hive, receiving nightly all the drones of the social order with their booty; the lying hospital, where the gipsy, the unfrocked monk, the ruined scholar, the scape-

grace of every nation, Spanish, Italian, and German, and of every creed, Jew, Christian, Mahometan, and idolater, covered with painted sores, beggers by day, were transformed into robbers by night,—in short, a huge cloak-room, used at this period for the dressing and undressing of all the actors in the everlasting comedy enacted in the streets of Paris by theft, prostitution, and murder.

It was a vast square, irregular and ill-paved, like every other square in Paris at that time. Fires, around which swarmed strange groups, gleamed here and there. People came and went, and shouted and screamed. There was a sound of shrill laughter, of the wailing of children and the voices of women. The hands, the heads of this multitude, black against the luminous background, made a thousand uncouth gestures. At times, a dog which looked like a man, or a man who looked like a dog, passed over the space of ground lit up by the flames, blended with huge and shapeless shadows. The limits of race and species seemed to fade away in this city as in some pandemonium. Men, women, beasts, age, sex, health, disease, all seemed to be in common among these people; all was blended, mingled, confounded, superimposed; each partook of all.

The feeble flickering light of the fires enabled Gringoire to distinguish, in spite of his alarm, all around the vast square a hideous framing of ancient houses whose worm-eaten, worn, misshapen fronts, each pierced by one or two lighted garret windows, looked to him in the darkness like the huge heads of old women ranged in a circle, monstrous and malign, watching and winking at the infernal revels.

It was like a new world, unknown, unheard of, deformed, creeping, swarming, fantastic.

Gringoire, more and more affrighted, caught by the three beggars, as if by three pairs of pincers, confused by the mass of other faces which snarled and grimaced about him,—the wretched Gringoire tried to recover sufficient presence of mind to recall whether it was Saturday or not. But his efforts were in vain; the thread of his memory and his thoughts was broken; and doubting everything, hesitating between what he saw and what he felt, he asked himself the unanswerable questions: "If I be I, are these things really so? If these things be so, am I really I?"

At this instant a distinct cry arose from the buzzing mob which surrounded him: "Take him to the king! take him to the king!"

"Holy Virgin!" muttered Gringoire, "the king of this region should be a goat."

"To the king! to the king!" repeated every voice.

He was dragged away. Each one vied with the other in fastening his claws upon him. But the three beggars never loosed their hold, and tore him from the others, howling, "He is ours!"

The poet's feeble doublet breathed its last in the struggle.

As they crossed the horrid square his vertigo vanished. After walking a few steps, a sense of reality returned. He began to grow accustomed to the atmosphere of the place. At first, from his poetic head, or perhaps, quite simply and quite prosaically, from his empty stomach, there had arisen certain fumes, a vapour as it were, which, spreading itself between him and other objects, prevented him from seeing anything save through a confused nightmare mist, through those dreamlike shadows which render every outline vague, distort every shape, combine all objects into exaggerated groups, and enlarge things into chimeras and men into ghosts. By degrees this delusion gave way to a less wild and less deceitful vision. Reality dawned upon him, blinded him, ran against him, and bit by bit destroyed the frightful poetry with which he had at first fancied himself surrounded. He could not fail to see that he was walking, not in the Styx, but in the mire; that he was pushed and elbowed, not by demons but by thieves; that it was not his soul, but merely his life which was in danger (since he lacked that precious conciliator which pleads so powerfully with the bandit for the honest man,—a purse). Finally, examining the revels more closely and with greater calmness, he descended from the Witches' Sabbath to the pot-house.

The Court of Miracles was indeed only a pot-house, but a pot-house of thieves, as red with blood as with wine.

The spectacle presented to his eyes when his tattered escort at last landed him at his journey's end was scarcely fitted to bring him back to poetry, even were it the poetry of hell. It was more than ever the prosaic and brutal reality of the tavern. If we were not living in the fifteenth century, we should say that Gringoire had fallen from Michael Angelo to Callot.

Around a large fire burning upon a great round flagstone, and lapping with its flames the rusty legs of a trivet empty for the moment, stood a number of worm-eaten tables here and there, in dire confusion, no lackey of any geometrical pretensions having deigned to adjust their parallelism, or at least to see that they did not cross each other at angles too unusual. Upon these tables glittered various pots and jugs dripping with wine and beer, and around these jugs were seated numerous Bacchanalian faces, purple with fire and wine. One big-bellied man with a jolly face was administering noisy kisses to a brawny, thickset woman. A rubbie, or old vagrant, whistled as he loosed the bandages from his mock wound, and rubbed his sound, healthy knee, which had been swathed all day in ample ligatures. Beyond him was a mumper, preparing his "visitation from God"—his sore leg—with suet and ox-blood. Two tables farther on, a sham pilgrim, in complete pilgrim dress, was spelling out the lament of Sainte-Reine, not forgetting the snuffle and the twang. In another place a young scamp who imposed on the charitable by pretending to have been bitten by a mad dog, was taking a lesson of an old dummy chucker in the art of frothing at the mouth by chewing a bit of soap. By their side a dropsical man was reducing his size, making four or five doxies hold their noses as they sat at the same table, quarrelling over a child which they had stolen during the evening,—all circumstances which, two centuries later, "seemed so ridiculous to the court," as Sauval says, "that they served as diversion to the king, and as the opening to a royal ballet entitled 'Night,' divided into four parts, and danced at the Petit Bourbon Theatre." "Never," adds an eye-witness in 1653, "have the sudden changes of the Court of Miracles been more happily hit off. Benserade prepared us for them by some very fine verses."

Coarse laughter was heard on every hand, with vulgar songs. Every man expressed himself in his own way, carping and swearing, without heeding his neighbour. Some hobnobbed, and quarrels arose from the clash of their mugs, and the breaking of their mugs was the cause of many torn rags.

A big dog squatted on his tail, gazing into the fire. Some children took their part in the orgies. The stolen child cried and screamed; while another, a stout boy of four, sat on a high bench, with his legs dangling, his chin just coming above the table, and not speaking a word. A third was gravely smearing the table with melted tallow as it ran from the candle. Another, a little fellow crouched in the mud, almost lost in a kettle which he was scraping with a potsherd, making a noise which would have distracted Stradivarius.

A cask stood near the fire, and a beggar sat on the cask. This was the king upon his throne.

The three who held Gringoire led him up to his cask, and all the revellers were hushed for a moment, except the caldron inhabited by the child.

Gringoire dared not breathe or raise his eyes.

"Hombre, quita tu sombrero!" said one of the three scoundrels who held him; and before he had made up his mind what this meant, another snatched his hat,—a shabby headpiece, to be sure,

but still useful on sunny or on rainy days. Gringoire sighed.

But the king, from the height of his barrel, addressed him,—

"Who is this varlet?"

Gringoire started. The voice, although threatening in tone, reminded him of another voice which had that same morning dealt the first blow to his mystery by whining out from the audience, "Charity, kind souls!" He lifted his head. It was indeed Clopin Trouillefou.

Clopin Trouillefou, decked with his royal insignia, had not a tatter more or less than usual. The wound on his arm had vanished.

In his hand he held one of those whips with whit-leather thongs then used by serjeants of the wand to keep back the crowd, and called "boullayes." Upon his head he wore a circular coif closed at the top; but it was hard to say whether it was a child's pad or a king's crown, so similar are the two things.

Still, Gringoire, without knowing why, felt his hopes revive when he recognized this accursed beggar of the Great Hall in the king of the Court of Miracles.

"Master," stuttered he, "My lord— Sire— How shall I address you?" he said at last, reaching the culminating point of his crescendo, and not knowing how to rise higher or to redescend.

"My lord, your Majesty, or comrade. Call me what you will; but make haste. What have you to say in your defence?"

"'In your defence,'" thought Gringoire; "I don't like the sound of that." He resumed stammeringly, "I am he who this morning—"

"By the devil's claws!" interrupted Clopin, "your name, varlet, and nothing more. Hark ye. You stand before three mighty sovereigns: me, Clopin Trouillefou, King of Tunis, successor to the Grand Coëre, the king of rogues, lord paramount of the kingdom of Cant; Mathias Hungadi Spicali, Duke of Egypt and Bohemia, that yellow old boy you see yonder with a clout about his head, Guillaume Rousseau, Emperor of Galilee, that fat fellow who pays no heed to us, but caresses that wanton. We are your judges. You have entered the kingdom of Cant, the land of thieves, without being a member of the confraternity; you have violated the privileges of our city. You must be punished, unless you be either prig, mumper, or cadger; that is, in the vulgar tongue of honest folks, either thief, beggar, or tramp. Are you anything of the sort? Justify yourself; state your character."

"Alas!" said Gringoire, "I have not that honour. I am the author—"

"Enough!" cried Trouillefou, not allowing him to finish his sentence. "You must be hanged. Quite a simple matter, my honest citizens! As you treat our people when they enter your domain, so we treat yours when they intrude among us. The law which you mete out to vagabonds, the vagabonds mete out to you. It is your own fault if it be evil. It is quite necessary that we should occasionally see an honest man grin through a hempen collar; it makes the thing honourable. Come, friend, divide your rags cheerfully among these young ladies. I will have you hanged to amuse the vagabonds, and you shall give them your purse to pay for a drink. If you have any mummeries to perform, over yonder in that mortar there's a capital God the Father, in stone, which we stole from the Church of Saint-Pierre-aux-Bœufs. You have four minutes to fling your soul at his head."

This was terrible speech.

"Well said, upon my soul! Clopin Trouillefou preaches as well as any pope!" exclaimed the Emperor of Galilee, smashing his jug to prop up his table.

"Noble emperors and kings," said Gringoire with great coolness (for his courage had mysteriously returned, and he spoke firmly), "you do not consider what you're doing. My name is Pierre Gringoire; I am the poet whose play was performed this morning in the Great Hall of the Palace."

"Oh, is it you, sirrah?" said Clopin. "I was there, God's wounds! Well, comrade, because you bored us this morning, is that any reason why we should not hang you to-night?"

"I shall have hard work to get off," thought Gringoire. But yet he made one more effort. "I don't see," said he, "why poets should not be classed with vagabonds. Æsop was a vagrant; Homer was a beggar; Mercury was a thief—"

Clopin interrupted him: "I believe you mean to cozen us with your lingo. Good God! be hanged, and don't make such a row about it!"

"Excuse me, my lord King of Tunis," replied Gringoire, disputing every inch of the ground. "Is it worth while— An instant— Hear me— You will not condemn me unheard—"

His melancholy voice was indeed lost in the uproar around him. The little boy scraped his kettle more vigorously than ever; and, to cap the climax, an old woman had just placed a frying-pan full of fat upon the trivet, and it crackled over the flames with a noise like the shouts of an army of children in chase of some masquerader.

However, Clopin Trouillefou seemed to be conferring for a moment with the Duke of Egypt and the Emperor of Galilee, the latter being entirely drunk. Then he cried out sharply, "Silence, I say!" and as the kettle and the frying-pan paid no heed, but kept up their duet, he leaped from his cask, dealt a kick to the kettle, which rolled ten paces or more with the child, another kick to the frying-pan, which upset all the fat into the fire, and then gravely reascended his throne, utterly regardless of the little one's stifled sobs and the grumbling of the old woman whose supper had vanished in brilliant flames.

Trouillefou made a sign, and the duke, the emperor, the arch thieves, and the gonnofs ranged themselves around him in the form of a horseshoe, Gringoire, still roughly grasped by the shoulders, occupying the centre. It was a semicircle of rags, of tatters, of tinsel, of pitchforks, of axes, of staggering legs, of bare brawny arms, of sordid, dull, stupid faces. In the middle of this Round Table of beggary Clopin Trouillefou reigned pre-eminent, as the doge of this senate, the king of this assembly of peers, the pope of this conclave,—pre-eminent in the first place by the height of his cask, then by a peculiarly haughty, savage, and tremendous air, which made his eyes flash, and amended in his fierce profile the bestial type of the vagrant. He seemed a wild boar among swine.

"Hark ye," he said to Gringoire, caressing his shapeless chin with his horny hand; "I see no reason why you should not be hanged. To be sure, you seem to dislike the idea, and it's very plain that you worthy cits are not used to it; you've got an exaggerated idea of the thing. After all, we wish you no harm. There is one way of getting you out of the difficulty for the time being. Will you join us?"

My reader may fancy the effect of this proposal upon Gringoire, who saw his life escaping him, and had already begun to lose his hold upon it. He clung to it once more with vigour.

"I will indeed, with all my heart," said he.

"Do you agree," resumed Clopin, "to enroll yourself among the gentry of the chive."

"Of the chive, exactly," answered Gringoire.

"Do you acknowledge yourself a member of the rogues' brigade?" continued the King of Tunis.

"Of the rogues' brigade."

"A subject of the kingdom of Cant?"

"Of the kingdom of cant."

"A vagrant?"

"A vagrant."

"At heart?"

"At heart."

"I would call your attention to the fact," added the king, "that you will be hanged none the less."

"The devil!" said the poet.

"Only," continued Clopin, quite unmoved, "you will be hanged later, with more ceremony, at the cost of the good city of Paris, on a fine stone gallows, and by honest men. That is some consolation."

"As you say," responded Gringoire.

"There are other advantages. As a member of the rogues' brigade you will have to pay no taxes for pavements, for the poor, or for lighting the streets, to all of which the citizens of Paris are subject."

"So be it," said the poet, "I consent. I am a vagrant, a Canter, a member of the rogues' brigade, a man of the chive,—what you will; and I was all this long ago, Sir King of Tunis, for I am a philosopher; *et omnia in philosophia, omnes in philosopho continentur,* as you know."

The King of Tunis frowned.

"What do you take me for, mate? What Hungarian Jew's gibberish are you giving us? I don't know Hebrew. I'm no Jew, if I am a thief. I don't even steal now; I am above that; I kill. Cut-throat, yes; cutpurse, no."

Gringoire tried to slip in some excuse between these brief phrases which anger made yet more abrupt.

"I beg your pardon, my lord. It is not Hebrew, it is Latin."

"I tell you," replied Clopin, furiously, "that I am no Jew, and that I will have you hanged,—by the synagogue, I will! —together with that paltry Judean cadger beside you, whom I mightily hope I may some day see nailed to a counter, like the counterfeit coin that he is!"

So saying, he pointed to the little Hungarian Jew with beard, who had accosted Gringoire with his *"Facitote caritatem,"* and who, understanding no other language, was amazed at the wrath which the King of Tunis vented upon him.

At last my lord Clopin became calm.

"So, varlet," said he to our poet, "you wish to become a vagrant?"

"Undoubtedly," replied the poet.

"It is not enough merely to wish," said the surly Clopin; "good-will never added an onion to the soup, and is good for nothing but a passport to paradise; now, paradise and Cant are two distinct things. To be received into the kingdom of Cant, you must prove that you are good for something; and to prove this you must fumble the snot."

"I will fumble," said Gringoire, "as much as ever you like."

Clopin made a sign. A number of Canters stepped from the circle and returned immediately, bringing a couple of posts finished at the lower end with broad wooden feet, which made them stand firmly upon the ground; at the upper end of the two posts they arranged a crossbeam, the whole forming a very pretty portable gallows, which Gringoire had the pleasure of seeing erected before him in the twinkling of an eye. Nothing was wanting, not even the rope, which swung gracefully from the crossbeam.

"What are they going to do?" wondered Gringoire with some alarm. A sound of bells which he heard at the same moment put an end to his anxiety; it was a manikin, or puppet, that the vagrants hung by the neck to the cord, —a sort of scarecrow, dressed in red, and so loaded with little bells and hollow brasses that thirty Castilian mules might have been tricked out with them. These countless tinklers jingled for some time with the swaying of the rope, then the sound died away by degrees, and finally ceased when the manikin had been restored to a state of complete im-mobility by that law of the pendulum which has superseded the clepsydra and the hour-glass.

Then Clopin, showing Gringoire a rickety old footstool, placed under the manikin, said,—

"Climb up there!"

"The devil!" objected Gringoire; "I shall break my neck. Your stool halts like one of Martial's couplets; one foot has six syllables and one foot has but five."

"Climb up!" repeated Clopin.

Gringoire mounted the stool, and succeeded, though not without considerable waving of head and arms, in recovering his centre of gravity.

"Now," resumed the King of Tunis, "twist your right foot round your left leg, and stand on tiptoe with your left foot."

"My lord," said Gringoire, "are you absolutely determined to make me break a limb?"

Clopin tossed his head.

"Hark ye, mate; you talk too much. I will tell you in a couple of words what I expect you to do: you are to stand on tiptoe, as I say; in that fashion you can reach the manikin's pockets; you are to search them; you are to take out a purse which you will find there; and if you do all this without ringing a single bell, it is well: you shall become a vagrant. We shall have nothing more to do but to baste you with blows for a week."

"Zounds! I shall take good care," said Gringoire. "And if I ring the bells?"

"Then you shall be hanged. Do you understand?"

"I don't understand at all," answered Gringoire.

"Listen to me once more. You are to search the manikin and steal his purse; if but a single bell stir in the act, you shall be hanged. Do you understand that?"

"Good," said Gringoire, "I understand that. What next?"

"If you manage to get the purse without moving the bells, you are a vagrant, and you shall be basted with blows for seven days in succession. You understand now, I suppose?"

"No, my lord; I no longer understand. Where is the advantage? I shall be hanged in the one case, beaten in the other?"

"And as a vagrant," added Clopin, "and as a vagrant; does that count for nothing? It is for your own good that we shall beat you, to harden you against blows."

"Many thanks," replied the poet.

"Come, make haste," said the king, stamping on his cask, which re-echoed like a vast drum.

"Fumble the snot, and be done with it! I warn you, once for all, that if I hear but one tinkle you shall take the manikin's place."

The company of Canters applauded Clopin's words, and ranged themselves in a ring around the gallows, with such pitiless laughter that Gringoire saw that he amused them too much not to have everything to fear from them. His only hope lay in the slight chance of succeeding in the terrible task imposed upon him; he decided to risk it, but not without first addressing a fervent prayer to the manikin whom he was to plunder, and who seemed more easily

moved than the vagrants. The myriad little bells with their tiny brazen tongues seemed to him like so many vipers with gaping jaws, ready to hiss and sting.

"Oh," he murmured, "is it possible that my life depends upon the slightest quiver of the least of these bells! Tinkle not, ye tinklers! Jingle not, ye jinglers!"

He made one more attempt to melt Trouillefou.

"And if a breeze spring up?" he asked.

"You will be hanged," answered the other, without hesitating.

Seeing that neither respite, delay, nor subterfuge was possible, he made a desperate effort; he twisted his right foot round his left leg, stood tiptoe on his left foot, and stretched out his arm, but just as he touched the manikin, his body, now resting on one foot, tottered upon the stool, which had but three; he strove mechanically to cling to the figure, lost his balance, and fell heavily to the ground, deafened and stunned by the fatal sound of the myriad bells of the manikin, which, yielding to the pressure of his hand, first revolved upon its own axis, then swung majestically to and fro between the posts.

"A curse upon it!" he cried as he fell; and he lay as if dead, face downwards.

Still he heard the fearful peal above his head, and the devilish laughs of the vagrants, and the voice of Trouillefou, as it said, "Lift up the knave, and hang him with a will."

He rose. The manikin had already been taken down to make room for him.

The Canters made him mount the

stool. Clopin stepped up to him, passed the rope round his neck, and clapping him on the shoulder, exclaimed,—

"Farewell, mate. You can't escape now, though you have the digestion of the Pope himself."

The word "mercy" died on Gringoire's lips. He gazed around him, but without hope; every man was laughing.

"Bellevigne de l'Etoile," said the King of Tunis to a huge vagrant who started from the ranks, "climb upon the crossbeam."

Bellevigne de l'Etoile nimbly climbed the crossbeam, and in an instant Gringoire, raising his eyes, with terror beheld him squatting upon it, above his head.

"Now," continued Clopin Trouillefou, "when I clap my hands, do you, Andry le Rouge, knock away the footstool from under him; you, François Chant-Prune, hang on to the knave's feet; and you, Bellevigne, jump down upon his shoulders; and all three at once, do you hear?"

Gringoire shuddered.

"Are you ready?" said Clopin Trouillefou to the three Canters prepared to fall upon Gringoire. The poor sufferer endured a moment of horrible suspense, while Clopin calmly pushed into the fire with his foot a few vine-branches which the flame had not yet kindled. "Are you ready?" he repeated; and he opened his hands to clap. A second more, and all would have been over.

But he paused, as if struck by a sudden thought.

"One moment," said he; "I forgot! It is our custom never to hang a man without asking if there be any woman who'll have him. Comrade, it's your last chance. You must marry a tramp or the rope."

This gipsy law, strange as it may seem to the reader, is still written out in full in the ancient English code. (See "Burington's Observations.")

Gringoire breathed again. This was the second time that he had been restored to life within the half-hour; so he dared not feel too confident.

"Hollo!" cried Clopin, remounting his cask; "hollo there, women, females! is there among you, from the old witch to her cat, a wench who'll take this scurvy knave? Hollo, Colette la Charonne! Elisabeth Trouvain! Simone Jodouyne! Marie Piédebou! Thonne la Longue! Bérarde Fanouel! Michelle Genaille! Claude Ronge-Oreille! Mathurine Girorou! Hollo! Isabeau la Thierrye! Come and look! a man for nothing! who'll take him?"

Gringoire, in his wretched plight, was doubtless far from tempting. The vagabond women seemed but little moved by the offer. The luckless fellow heard them answer: "No! no! hang him; that will make sport for us all."

Three, however, stepped from the crowd to look him over. The first was a stout, square-faced girl. She examined the philosopher's pitiable doublet most attentively. The stuff was worn, and more full of holes than a furnace for roasting chestnuts. The girl made a wry face. "An old clout!" she grumbled, and, addressing Gringoire, "Let's look at your cloak?"

"I have lost it," said Gringoire.

"Your hat?"

"Some one took it from me.'

"Your shoes?"

"The soles are almost worn through."

"Your purse?"

"Alas!" faltered Gringoire, "I have not a penny."

"Be hanged to you then, and be thankful!" replied the tramp, turning her back on him.

The second, old, weather-beaten, wrinkled, and ugly, hideous enough to be conspicuous even in the Court of Miracles, walked round and round Gringoire. He almost trembled lest she should accept him. But she muttered, "He's too thin," and took her leave.

The third was a young girl, quite rosy and not very ugly. "Save me!" whispered the poor devil.

She looked at him a moment with a compassionte air, then looked down, began to plait up her skirt, and seemed uncertain. He watched her every motion; this was his last ray of hope. "No," said the young woman at last; "no! Guillaume Longuejoue would lick me," and she went back to the crowd.

"Comrade," said Clopin Trouillefou, "you're down on your luck."

Then, standing erect upon his cask, he cried, "Will no one take this lot?" mimicking the tone of an auctioneer, to the great entertainment of all; "will no one take it? Going, going, going!" and turning to the gallows with a nod, "Gone!"

Bellevigne de l'Etoile, Andry le Rouge, and François Chant-Prune approached Gringoire.

At this instant a shout rose from the thieves: "Esmeralda! Esmeralda!"

Gringoire trembled, and turned in the direction of the cry. The crowd opened and made way for a pure and radiant figure.

It was the gipsy girl.

"Esmeralda!" said Gringoire, astounded, amidst his contending emotions, at the suddenness with which that magic word connected all the various recollections of his day.

This rare creature seemed to exercise sovereign sway through her beauty and her charm even in the Court of Miracles. Thieves, beggars, and harlots stood meekly aside to let her pass, and their brutal faces brightened at her glance.

She approached the victim with her light step. Her pretty Djali followed her. Gringoire was more dead than alive. She gazed at him an instant in silence.

"Are you going to hang this man?" she gravely asked Clopin.

"Yes, sister," replied the King of Tunis, "unless you'll take him for your husband."

She pouted her pretty lower lip.

"I'll take him," said she.

Gringoire here firmly believed that he had been dreaming ever since morning, and that this was the end of the dream.

In fact, the sudden change of fortune, though charming, was violent.

The slip-noose was unfastened, the poet was helped from his stool. He was obliged to seat himself, so great was his agitation.

The Duke of Egypt, without uttering a word, brought forward an earthen jug. The gipsy girl offered it to Gringoire. "Throw it down," she said to him.

The jug was broken into four pieces.

"Brother," then said the Duke of Egypt, laying his hands on their heads, "she is your wife; sister, he is your husband. For four years. Go!"

Chapter VII

A WEDDING NIGHT

A FEW moments later our poet found himself in a small room with a vaulted roof, very snug, very warm, seated before a table which seemed to ask nothing better than to borrow a few stores from a hanging cupboard close by; with a good bed in prospect, and alone with a pretty girl. The adventure partook of the nature of magic. He began seriously to think himself the hero of some fairy-tale; now and then he gazed about him as if in search of the fairy chariot, drawn by two winged steeds, which could alone have transported him so swiftly from Tartarus to Paradise. Occasionally his eyes were riveted on the holes in his doublet, to bring himself back to actual things, and lest he should quite lose sight of land. His reason, floating in imaginary realms, had only this thread to cling to.

The young girl apparently took no notice of him: she came and went, moved a stool, chatted with her goat, smiled, and pouted. Finally she seated herself at the table, and Gringoire could study her at his leisure.

You were once a child, reader, and you may be lucky enough to be one still. You must more than once (and for my part I spent whole days at it,— the best days of my life) have pursued from bush to bush, on the brink of some brisk stream, in bright sunshine, some lovely green or azure dragon-fly, which checked its flight at sharp angles, and kissed the tip of every twig. You will remember the loving curiosity with which your mind and your eye followed that buzzing, whizzing little whirlwind, with blue and purple wings, between which floated an intangible form, veiled by the very swiftness of its motion. The airy creature, vaguely seen amid the quivering wings, seemed to you chimerical, imaginary, impossible to touch, impossible to see. But when the dragon-fly at last rested on the tip of a reed, and you could examine, holding your breath meanwhile, its slender gauzy wings, its long enamelled robes, its crystal globe-like eyes, what amazement you felt, and what fear lest it should again fade to a shadow and the creature turn to a chimera! Recall these sensations, and you will readily appreciate what Gringoire felt as he beheld in visible, palpable form that Esmeralda of whom he had hitherto had but a glimpse amidst the eddying dance and song, and a confused mass of people.

Becoming more and more absorbed in his reverie, he thought: "This, then, is 'Esmeralda'! a celestial creature! a street dancer! So much and so little! It was she who put the finishing stroke to my play this morning; it was she who saved my life this evening. My evil genius! my good angel! A pretty woman, upon my word! And she must love me to distraction to take me in this fashion. By-the-by," said he, rising suddenly with that sense of truth which formed the basis of his character and his philosophy, "I don't quite know how it came about, but I am her husband!"

With this idea in mind and in his eyes, he approached the young girl in so military and lover-like fashion that she shrank away from him.

"What do you want?" she said.

"Can you ask me, adorable Esmeralda?" replied Gringoire in such impassioned tones that he himself was astounded at his own accents.

The gipsy girl stared at him. "I don't know what you mean."

"Oh, come now!" added Gringoire, becoming more and more excited, and thinking that after all he was only dealing with the ready-made virtue of the Court of Miracles; "am I not yours, sweet friend? Are you not mine?"

And, quite innocently, he clasped her by the waist.

The girl's bodice slipped through his hands like a snake's skin. She leaped from one end of the little cell to the other, stooped, and rose with a tiny dagger in her hand, before Gringoire had time to see whence this dagger came,—proud, angry, with swelling lips, dilated nostrils, cheeks red as crabapples, and eyes flashing lightning. At the same time the white goat placed itself before her, and presented a battlefront to Gringoire, bristling with two pretty, gilded, and very sharp horns. All this took place in the twinkling of an eye.

The damsel had turned wasp, and asked nothing better than to sting.

Our philosopher stood abashed, glancing alternately at the girl and the goat in utter confusion. "Holy Virgin!" he exclaimed at last, when surprise allowed him to speak, "here's a determined pair!"

The gipsy girl broke the silence in her turn. "You must be a very bold rascal!"

"Forgive me, mademoiselle," said Gringoire with a smile. "But why did you marry me, then?"

"Was I to let them hang you?"

"So," replied the poet, somewhat disappointed in his amorous hopes, "you had no other idea in wedding me than to save me from the gibbet?"

"And what other idea should I have had?"

Gringoire bit his lips. "Well," said he, "I am not quite such a conquering hero as I supposed. But then, what was the use of breaking that poor jug?"

But Esmeralda's dagger and the goat's horns still remained on the defensive.

"Mademoiselle Esmeralda," said the poet, "let us come to terms. I am not clerk of the Châtelet, and I shall not pick a quarrel with you for carrying concealed weapons in Paris, in the face of the provost's orders and prohibition. Yet you must know that Noël Lescrivain was sentenced to pay ten Paris pence only a week ago for wearing a broadsword. Now, that is none of my business, and I will come to the point. I swear to you, by all my hopes of paradise, that I will not come near you without your sovereign leave and permission; but give me some supper."

To tell the truth, Gringoire, like Despréaux, was "very little of a Don Juan." He was not one of the chivalric, musketeering kind who take girls by storm. In the matter of love, as in all other matters, he was always for temporizing and compromising; and a good supper, in friendly society, struck him, especially when he was hungry, as an excellent interlude between the prologue and the issue of an intrigue.

The gipsy made no answer. She gave her usual scornful little pout, cocked her head like a bird, then burst out laughing, and the dainty dagger disappeared as it came, Gringoire being still unable to discover where the bee hid her sting.

A moment late, a rye loaf, a slice of bacon, a few withered apples, and a jug of beer were on the table. Gringoire began to eat greedily. Judging by the fierce clatter of his iron fork against his earthen-plate, all his love had turned to hunger.

The young girl seated near him looked on in silence, evidently absorbed in other thoughts, at which she occasionally smiled, while her gentle hand caressed the intelligent head of the goat as it rested idly against her knee.

A yellow wax candle lit up this scene of voracity and reverie.

However, the first cravings of hunger appeased, Gringoire felt somewhat ashamed to find that there was but one apple left. "You don't eat, Mademoiselle Esmeralda?"

She answered by a shake of the head, and her pensive gaze was fixed on the arched roof of the cell.

"What the deuce is she thinking about?" thought Gringoire; and, looking to see what she was looking at: "It can't be the wry face of that stone dwarf carved upon yonder keystone which so absorbs her attention. What the devil! I'm sure I can stand the comparison!"

He raised his voice: "Mademoiselle!"

She did not seem to hear him.

He spoke still louder: "Mademoiselle Esmeralda!"

Labour lost. The girl's mind was elsewhere, and Gringoire's voice had no power to call it back. Luckily the goat interfered, by softly pulling her mistress by the sleeve.

"What do you want, Djali?" said the gipsy, hastily, as if roused suddenly.

"The creature is hungry," said Grin-goire, delighted to open the conversation.

Esmeralda began to crumble some bread, which Djali nibbled daintily from the hollow of her hand.

However, Gringoire gave her no time to resume her reverie. He risked a delicate question:—

"Then you don't want me for your husband?"

The young girl looked steadily at him, and replied, "No."

"For your lover?" continued Gringoire.

She pouted, and answered, "No."

"For your friend?" went on Gringoire.

She looked at him fixedly once more, and after an instant's reflection said, "Perhaps."

This "perhaps," so dear to philosophers, emboldened Gringoire.

"Do you know what friendship is?" he asked.

"Yes," answered the gipsy; "it is to be brother and sister; two souls which meet without mingling, two fingers of one hand."

"And love?" continued Gringoire.

"Oh, love!" said she, and her voice trembled and her eye brightened. "That is to be two and yet but one. A man and a woman blended into an angel. It is heaven itself."

The street dancer assumed a beauty, as she spoke, which struck Gringoire strangely, and seemed to him in perfect harmony with the almost Oriental exaltation of her words. Her pure rosy lips half smiled; her serene and innocent brow was clouded for the moment by her thought, as when a mirror is dimmed by a breath; and from her long, dark, drooping lashes flashed an ineffable light, which lent her profile that ideal sweetness which Raphael has since found at the mystic meeting-point of the virgin, the mother, and the saint.

Nevertheless, Gringoire kept on,—

"What must one be to please you, then?"

"He must be a man."

"And I," said he,—"what am I?"

"A man with a helmet on his head, a sword in his hand, and golden spurs on his heels."

"Good!" said Gringoire; "dress makes the man. Do you love any one?"

"As a lover?"

"As a lover."

She looked pensive for a moment; then she said with a peculiar expression, "I shall know soon."

"Why not to-night?" said the poet, tenderly; "why not me?"

She cast a serious glance at him.

"I can only love a man who can protect me."

Gringoire flushed, and was silent. It was evident that the young girl alluded to the slight assistance which he had afforded her in the critical situation in which she had found herself a couple of hours previous. This memory, blotted out by the other adventures of the evening, returned to him. He struck his brow.

"By-the-by, mademoiselle, I ought to have begun there. Forgive me my foolish distractions. How did you manage to escape from Quasimodo's claws?"

This question made the gipsy shudder.

"Oh, the horrid hunchback!" she cried, hiding her face in her hands.

And she shivered as if icy cold.

"Horrid, indeed," said Gringoire, not

dropping the subject; "but how did you contrive to escape him?"

Esmeralda smiled, sighed, and was silent.

"Do you know why he pursued you?" continued Gringoire, trying to get an answer by a roundabout way.

"I don't know," said the girl. And she added quickly, "But you followed me too; why did you follow me?"

"In good faith," replied Gringoire, "I have forgotten."

There was a pause. Gringoire slashed the table with his knife. The girl smiled, and seemed to be gazing at something through the wall. All at once she began to sing in a voice which was scarcely articulate,—

"Quando las pintadas aves
Mudas estan, y la tierra—"

She broke off abruptly, and began to fondle Djali.

"That's a pretty creature of yours," said Gringoire.

"It is my sister," she replied.

"Why do they call you 'Esmeralda'?" the poet ventured to ask.

"I've no idea."

"But why do they?"

She drew from her bosom a small oblong bag fastened to her neck by a string of beads made of some sweet-scented gum. This bag gave forth a strong smell of camphor; it was made of green silk, and had in the centre a large bit of green glass, in imitation of an emerald.

"Perhaps it is on account of that," said she.

Gringoire tried to take the bag. She drew back.

"Don't touch it! It's an amulet. You

will injure the charm, or the charm you."

The poet's curiosity was more and more eagerly aroused.

"Who gave it to you?"

She put her finger to her lip and hid the amulet in her bosom. He tried her with other questions, but she scarcely answered him.

"What does the word 'Esmeralda' mean?"

"I don't know," said she.

"To what language does it belong?"

"I think it is a gipsy word."

"So I suspected," said Gringoire; "you are not a native of France?"

"I know nothing about it."

"Are your parents living?"

She began to sing, to an ancient air:—

"A bird is my mother,
My father another.
Nor boat nor bark need I
As over the sea I fly;
A bird is my mother,
My father another."

"Very good," said Gringoire. "At what age did you come to France?"

"When I was very small."

"To Paris?"

"Last year. Just as we entered the Papal Gate, I saw the reed warbler skim through the air; it was the last of August. I said: It will be a hard winter."

"So it has been," said Gringoire, charmed at this beginning of conversation; "I have spent it in blowing on my fingers to keep them warm. So you have the gift of prophecy?"

She fell back into her laconicism.

"No."

"Is that man whom you call the Duke of Egypt, the head of your tribe?"

"Yes."

"But it was he who married us," timidly remarked the poet.

She made her usual pretty grimace.

"I don't even know your name."

"My name? You shall have it, if you wish: Pierre Gringoire."

"I know a nicer one," said she.

"Cruel girl!" replied the poet. "Never mind, you shall not vex me. Stay; perhaps you will love me when you know me better; and then you told me your history so confidingly that I owe you somewhat of mine. You must know, then, that my name is Pierre Gringoire, and that I am the son of the notary of Gonesse. My father was hanged by the Burgundians and my mother ripped up by the Picards, at the time of the siege of Paris, now twenty years ago. At the age of six years, therefore, I was left an orphan, with no sole to my foot but the pavement of Paris. I don't know how I managed to exist from six to sixteen. A fruit-seller would give me a plum, a baker would throw me a crust; at nightfall I would contrive to be caught by the watch, who put me in prison, and there I found a bundle of straw. All this did not hinder me from growing tall and thin, as you see. In winter time I warmed myself in the sun, under the portico of the Hôtel de Sens, and I thought it very absurd that the bale-fires of St. John should be deferred until the dog-days. At the age of sixteen I wished to learn a trade. I tried everything in turn. I became a soldier, but I was not brave enough. I turned monk, but I was not pious enough; and then, I'm no drinker. In despair, I became a carpenter's apprentice, but I was not strong enough. I had more liking for the schoolmaster's trade; true, I did not know how to read but that was no hindrance. After a time, I discovered that I lacked some necessary quality for everything; and seeing that I was good for nothing, I became a poet and composer of rhymes, of my own free will. That is a trade that one can always take up when one is a vagabond; and it is better than stealing, as certain thievish young friends of mine advised. By good luck, I one fine day encountered Don Claude Frollo, the reverend archdeacon of Notre-Dame. He took an interest in me, and it is to him I owe it that I am now a genuine man of letters, knowing Latin, from Cicero's Offices to the necrology of the Celestine Fathers, and being ignorant of neither scholastics, poetry, nor rhythm, that sophism of sophisms. I am the author of the miracle-play performed to-day with great triumph, and before a great concourse of people, in the hall of the Palace. I have also written a book which will make six hundred pages, on the wonderful comet of 1465, which drove one man mad. I have also had other successes. Being somewhat of an engineer, I worked on Jean Maugue's great bomb, which you know burst on Charenton Bridge the day that it was to be tested, and killed twenty-four of the curious spectators. You see that I am by no means a bad match. I know a great many sorts of delightful tricks which I will teach your goat; for instance, how to take off the Bishop of Paris, that accursed Parisian whose mills bespatter all those who pass over the Millers' Bridge. And then, my miracle-play will bring me in plenty of ready money if they pay me. Finally, I am at your service, I and my wit and my science and my learning,—ready to live with you, lady, as it may please you: soberly or merrily; as husband and wife if you see fit; as brother and sister if you prefer."

Gringoire ceased, awaiting the effect of this speech upon the young girl. Her eyes were bent on the floor.

"'Phœbus,'" she said in an undertone. Then, turning to the poet, "'Phœbus;' what does that mean?"

Gringoire, scarcely comprehending the connection between his words and this question, was nothing loath to display his erudition. He answered, drawing himself up,—

"It is a Latin word signifying 'sun.'"

"'Sun'?" she repeated.

"It is the name of a certain handsome archer who was a god," added Gringoire.

"A god!" repeated the gipsy; and there was something pensive and passionate in her tone.

At this moment, one of her bracelets became unfastened and fell. Gringoire stooped quickly to pick it up; when he rose, the girl and the goat had disappeared. He heard a bolt slide across a small door, doubtless communicating with a neighbouring cell, which was fastened on the other side.

"At least, I hope she has left me a bed!" said our philosopher.

He walked around the room. There was nothing fit to sleep upon except a long wooden chest; and even that had a carved lid, which gave Gringoire a feeling, when he stretched himself out upon it, very like that experienced by Micromegas when he slept at full length upon the Alps.

"Come," said he, making himself as comfortable as he could, "I must submit to fate. But this is an odd wedding night. It is a pity; there was something simple and antediluvian about this marriage with a broken jug, which I liked."

BOOK III

THE CATHEDRAL

CHAPTER I

NOTRE-DAME

THE Church of Notre-Dame at Paris is doubtless still a sublime and majestic building. But, much beauty as it may retain in its old age, it is not easy to repress a sigh, to restrain our anger, when we mark the countless defacements and mutilations to which men and Time have subjected that venerable monument, without respect for Charlemagne, who laid its first stone, or Philip Augustus, who laid its last.

Upon the face of this aged queen of French cathedrals, beside every wrinkle we find a scar. *"Tempus edax, homo edacior;"* which I would fain translate thus: "Time is blind, but man is stupid."

Had we leisure to study with the reader, one by one, the various marks of destruction graven upon the ancient church, the work of Time would be the lesser, the worse that of Men, especially of "men of art," since there are persons who have styled themselves architects during the last two centuries.

And first of all, to cite but a few glaring instances, there are assuredly few finer pages in the history of architecture than that façade where the three receding portals with their pointed arches, the carved and denticulated plinth with its twenty-eight royal niches, the huge central rose-window flanked by its two lateral windows as is the priest by his deacon and subdeacon, the lofty airy gallery of trifoliated arcades supporting a heavy platform upon its slender columns, and lastly the two dark and massive towers with their penthouse roofs of slate, harmonious parts of a magnificent whole, one above the other, five gigantic stages, unfold themselves to the eye, clearly and as a whole, with their countless details of sculpture, statuary, and carving, powerfully contributing to the calm grandeur of the whole; as it were, a vast symphony in stone; the colossal work of one man and one nation, one and yet complex, like the Iliad and the old Romance epics, to which it is akin; the tremendous sum of the joint contributions of all the forces of an entire epoch, in which every stone reveals, in a hundred forms, the fancy of the workman disciplined by the genius of the artist,—a sort of human creation, in brief, powerful and prolific as the Divine creation, whose double characteristics, variety and eternity, it seems to have acquired.

And what we say of the façade, we

must also say of the whole church; and what we say of the cathedral church of Paris must also be said of all the Christian churches of the Middle Ages. Everything is harmonious which springs from that spontaneous, logical, and well-proportioned art. To measure a toe, is to measure the giant.

Let us return to the façade of Notre-Dame as we see it at the present day, when we make a pious pilgrimage to admire the solemn and mighty cathedral, which, as its chroniclers declare, inspires terror: *"Quœ mole sua terrorem incutit spectantibus."*

This façade now lacks three important things: first, the eleven steps which formerly raised it above the level of the ground; next, the lower series of statues which filled the niches over the doors; and lastly, the upper row of the twenty-eight most ancient kings of France, which adorned the gallery of the first story, from Childebert down to Philip Augustus, each holding in his hand "the imperial globe."

The stairs were destroyed by Time, which, with slow and irresistible progress, raised the level of the city's soil; but while this flood-tide of the pavements of Paris swallowed one by one the eleven steps which added to the majestic height of the edifice, Time has perhaps given to the church more than it took away, for it is Time which has painted the front with that sober hue of centuries which makes the antiquity of churches their greatest beauty.

But who pulled down the two rows of statues? Who left those empty niches? Who carved that new and bastard pointed arch in the very centre of the middle door? Who dared to insert that clumsy, tasteless wooden door, carved in the style of Louis XV., side by side with the arabesques of Biscornette? Who but men, architects, the artists of our day?

And if we step into the interior of the edifice, who overthrew that colossal figure of Saint Christopher, proverbial among statues by the same right as the Great Hall of the Palace among halls, as the spire of Strasburg among steeples? And those myriad statues which peopled every space between the columns of the choir and the nave, kneeling, standing, on horseback, men, women, children, kings, bishops, men-at-arms,—of stone, of marble, of gold, of silver, of copper, nay, even of wax,— who brutally swept them away? It was not the hand of Time.

And who replaced the old Gothic altar, with its splendid burden of shrines and reliquaries, by that heavy marble sarcophagus adorned with clouds and cherubs, looking like a poor copy of the Val-de-Grâce or the Hôtel des Invalides? Who was stupid enough to fasten that clumsy stone anachronism into the Carlovingian pavement of Hercandus? Was it not Louis XIV., fulfilling the vow of Louis XIII.?

And who set cold white panes in place of that stained glass of gorgeous hue, which led the wondering gaze of our fathers to roam uncertain 'twixt the rose-window of the great door and the ogives of the chancel? And what would a precentor of the sixteenth century say if he could see the fine coat of yellow wash with which our Vandal archbishops have smeared their cathedral? He would remember that this was the colour with which the executioner formerly painted those buildings judged "infamous;" he would recall the hotel of the Petit-Bourbon, dedaubed with yellow in memory of the Constable's treason; " a yellow of so fine a temper," says Sauval, "and so well laid on, that more than a hundred years have failed to wash out its colour." He would fancy that the sacred spot had become accursed, and would turn and flee.

And if we climb higher in the cathedral, without pausing to note a thousand barbarous acts of every kind, what has become of that delightful little steeple which rested upon the point of intersection of the transept, and which, no less fragile and no less daring than its neighbour, the spire of the Sainte-Chapelle (also destroyed), rose yet nearer heaven than the towers, slender, sharp, sonorous, and daintily wrought? An architect of good taste (1787) amputated it, and thought it quite enough to cover the wound with that large leaden plaster which looks like the lid of a stewpan. Thus was the marvellous art of the Middle Ages treated in almost every land, but particularly in France. We find three sorts of injury upon its ruins, these three marring it to different depths: first, Time, which has made insensible breaches here and there, mildewed and rusted the surface everywhere; then, political and religious revolutions, which, blind and fierce by nature, fell furiously upon it, rent its array of sculpture and carving, shivered its rose-windows, shattered its necklaces of arabesques and quaint figures, tore down its statues,—sometimes because of their mitre, sometimes because of their crown; lastly, changing fashion, ever more grotesque and absurd, from the anarchic and splendid deviations of the Renaissance down to the necessary decline of architecture. Fashion did more harm than revolutions. Fashion cut into the living flesh, attacked the very skeleton and framework of art; it chopped and hewed, dismembered, slew the edifice, in its form as well as in its symbolism, in its logic no less than in its beauty. But fashion restored,—a thing which neither time nor revolution ever pretended to do. Fashion, on the plea of "good taste," impudently adapted to the wounds of Gothic architecture the paltry gewgaws of a day,—marble ribbons, metallic plumes, a veritable leprosy of egg-shaped mouldings, of volutes, wreaths, draperies, spirals, fringes, stone flames, bronze clouds, lusty cupids, and bloated cherubs, which began to ravage the face of art in the oratory of Catherine de Médicis, and destroyed it, two centuries later, tortured and distorted, in the Dubarry's boudoir.

There are thus, to sum up the points to which we have alluded, three sorts of scars now disfiguring Gothic architecture,—wrinkles and warts upon the epidermis (these are the work of time); wounds, brutal injuries, bruises, and fractures (these are the work of revolution from Luther to Mirabeau); mutilations, amputations, dislocations of the frame, "restorations" (these are the Greek, Roman, Barbaric work of professors according to Vitruvius and Vignole). Academies have murdered the magnificent art which the Vandals produced. To centuries, to revolutions which at least laid waste with impartiality and grandeur, are conjoined the host of scholastic architects licensed and sworn, degrading all they touch with the discernment and selection of bad taste, substituting the tinsel of Louis XV. for Gothic lace-work, for the greater glory of the Parthenon. This is the donkey's kick at the dying lion. It is the old oak, decaying at the crown, pierced, bitten, and devoured by caterpillars.

How different from the time when Robert Cenalis, comparing Notre-Dame at Paris to the famous temple of Diana at Ephesus, "so loudly boasted by the ancient pagans," which immortalized Erostrates, held the cathedral of the Gauls to be "more excellent in length, breadth, height, and structure!"

Notre-Dame at Paris is not, however, what can be called a complete, definite monument, belonging to a class. It is neither a Roman nor a Gothic church. The edifice is not a typical one. It has not, like the abbey at Tournus, the sober massive breadth, the round expansive arch, the icy bareness, the majestic simplicity of those buildings based on the semicircular arch. It is not, like the cathedral at Bourges, the magnificent, airy, multiform, bushy, sturdy, efflorescent product of the pointed arch. It is impossible to class it with that antique order of dark, mysterious, low-studded churches, apparently crushed by the semicircular arch,—almost Egyptian, save for the ceiling; all hieroglyphic, all sacerdotal, all symbolic, more loaded in their ornamentation with lozenges and zig-zags than with flowers, with flowers than with animals, with animals than with men: less the work of the architect than of the bishop; the first transformation of the art, bearing the deep impress of theocratic and military discipline, taking root in the Lower Empire, and ceasing with William the Conqueror. It is impossible to place our cathedral in that other family of lofty, aerial churches, rich in stained glass and sculpture; of pointed forms and daring attitudes; belonging to the commoners and plain citizens, as political symbols; free, capricious, lawless, as works of art; the second transformation of architecture, no longer hieroglyphic, unchangeable, sacerdotal, but artistic, progressive, and popular, beginning with the close of the Crusades and ending with Louis XI. Notre-Dame at Paris is not of purely Roman race like the former, nor of purely Arab breed like the latter.

It is a building of the transition period. The Saxon architect had just reared the pillars of the nave, when the pointed arch, brought back from the Crusades, planted itself as conqueror upon those broad Roman capitals which were never meant to support anything but semicircular arches. The pointed arch, thenceforth supreme, built the rest of the church. And still, inexperienced and shy at first, it swelled, it widened, it restrained itself, and dared not yet shoot up into spires and lancets, as it did later on in so many marvellous cathedrals. It seemed sensible of the close vicinity of the heavy Roman columns.

Moreover, these buildings of the transition from Roman to Gothic are no less valuable studies than the pure types. They express a gradation of the art which would otherwise be lost. They represent the ingrafting of the pointed arch upon the semicircular.

Notre-Dame at Paris, in particular, is a curious example of this variety. Every face, every stone of the venerable monument is a page not only of the history of the country, but also of the history of science and art. Thus, to allude only to leading details, while the little Porte Rouge attains almost the extreme limit of the Gothic refinements of the fifteenth century, the pillars of the nave, in their size and gravity of style, go back to the Carlovingian Abbey of Saint-Germain des Prés. One would say that there was an interval of six centuries between that door and those pillars. Even the Hermetics find among the symbols of the great door a satisfactory epitome of their science, of which the Church of Saint-Jacques de la Boucherie formed so complete a hieroglyph. Thus, the Roman abbey, the philosophers' church, Gothic art, Saxon art, the clumsy round pillar, which recalls Gregory VII., the hermetic symbolism by which Nicolas Flamel paved the way for Luther, papal unity, schism, Saint-Germain des Prés, Saint-Jacques de la Boucherie, are all confounded, combined, and blended in Notre-Dame. This central and generative church is a kind of chimera among the old churches of Paris; it has the head of one, the limbs of another, the trunk of a third, something of all.

We repeat it; these hybrid constructions are by no means the least interesting to the artist, the antiquary, and the historian. They show us to how great an extent architecture is a primitive thing, in that they demonstrate (as the Cyclopean remains, the pyramids of Egypt, the vast pagodas of India demonstrate) that the greatest products of architecture are not so much individual as they are social works; rather the children of nations in labour than the inspired efforts of men of genius; the legacy of a race; the accumulated wealth of centuries; the residuum of the successive evaporations of human society, —in a word, a species of formation. Every wave of time adds its alluvium, every race leaves a fresh layer on the monument, every individual brings his stone. Thus the beavers work, thus work the bees, thus works man. The great symbol of architecture, Babel, is a beehive.

Great buildings, like great mountains, are the work of centuries. Art is often transformed while they are still pending, —pendent opera interrupta; they go on quietly, in harmony with the changes in the art. The new form of art takes up the monument where it finds it, becomes a part of it, assimilates it to itself, develops it according to its fancy, and finishes it if it can. The thing is done without effort, without reaction, in accordance with a natural and tranquil law. It is like a budding graft, like circulating sap, like renewed vegetation. Certainly, there is matter for many big books, and often for the universal history of humanity, in these successive weldings of various forms of art at various levels upon one and the same structure. The man, the artist, and the individual are obliterated in these huge anonymous piles; they represent the sum total of human intelligence. Time is the architect, the nation is the mason.

Considering here Christian European architecture only, that younger sister of the grand piles of the Orient, we may say that it strikes the eye as a vast formation divided into three very distinct zones or layers, one resting upon the other; the Roman zone, the Gothic zone, the zone of the Renaissance, which may be called the Greco-Roman. The

Roman stratum, which is the oldest and the lowest, is occupied by the semicircular arch, which reappears, together with the Greek column, in the modern and uppermost stratum of the Renaissance. The pointed arch is between the two. The buildings belonging to any one of these three strata are perfectly distinct, uniform, and complete. Such are the Abbey of Jumiéges, the Cathedral of Rheims, the Church of the Holy Cross at Orleans. But the three zones are blended and mingled at the edges, like the colours in the solar spectrum. Hence, we have certain complex structures, buildings of gradation and transition, which may be Roman at the base, Gothic in the middle, and Greco-Roman at the top. This is caused by the fact that it took six hundred years to build such a fabric. This variety is rare. The donjon-keep at Etampes is a specimen. But monuments of two formations are more frequent. Such is Notre-Dame at Paris, a structure of the pointed arch, its earliest columns leading directly to that Roman zone, of which the portal of Saint-Denis and the nave of Saint-Germain des Prés are perfect specimens. Such is the charming semi-Gothic chapter-house of Bocherville, where the Roman layer reaches midway. Such is the cathedral of Rouen, which would be wholly Gothic if the tip of its central spire did not dip into the zone of the Renaissance.

However, all these gradations and differences affect the surface only of an edifice. Art has but changed its skin. The construction itself of the Christian church is not affected by them. The interior arrangement, the logical order of the parts, is still the same. Whatever may be the carved and nicely wrought exterior of a cathedral, we always find beneath it, if only in a rudimentary and dormant state, the Roman basilica. It rises forever from the ground in harmony with the same law. There are invariably two naves intersecting each other in the form of a cross, the upper end being rounded into a chancel or choir; there are always side aisles, for processions and for chapels, a sort of lateral galleries or walks, into which the principal nave opens by means of the spaces between the columns. This settled, the number of chapels, doors, steeples, and spires may be modified indefinitely according to the fancy of the century, the people, and the art. The performance of divine service once provided for and assured, architecture acts its own pleasure. Statues, stained glass, rose-windows, arabesques, denticulations, capitals, and bas-reliefs,—it combines all these flowers of the fancy according to the logarithm that suits it best. Hence the immense variety in the exteriors of those structures within which dwell such unity and order. The trunk of the tree is fixed; the foliage is variable.

CHAPTER II

A BIRD'S-EYE VIEW OF PARIS

In the last chapter we strove to restore the wonderful Church of Notre-Dame at Paris for the reader's pleasure. We briefly pointed out the greater part of the charms which it possessed in the fifteenth century and which it now lacks; but we omitted the chief beauty, —the view of Paris then to be had from the top of its towers.

It was, indeed, when after long fumbling in the gloomy spiral staircase which pierces perpendicularly the thick wall of the steeples you finally emerged suddenly upon one of the two lofty platforms bathed in sunshine and daylight, —it was, indeed, a fine picture which lay unrolled before you on every hand; a spectacle *sui generis,* as those of our readers can readily imagine who have been so fortunate as to see one of the few Gothic cities still left entire, complete, and homogeneous, such as Nuremberg in Bavaria, and Vittoria in Spain; or even smaller examples, if they be but well preserved, like Vitré in Brittany, and Nordhausen in Prussia.

The Paris of three hundred and fifty years ago, the Paris of the fifteenth century, had already attained to vast dimensions. We modern Parisians are apt to deceive ourselves in regard to the ground which we imagine we have gained since then. Paris has not grown much more than a third larger since the days of Louis XI. It has certainly lost far more in beauty than it has gained in size.

Paris was born, as every one knows, on that island of the City which is shaped like a cradle. The shores of that island were her first enclosure, the Seine her first moat. Paris remained for several centuries in the state of an island, with two bridges, one on the north, the other on the south, and two bridge-heads, at once her gates and her fortresses: the Grand-Châtelet on the right bank, the Petit Châtelet on the left. With the first line of kings, being pressed for room in her island, back of which she no longer could return, Paris crossed the water. Then, beyond the two Châtelets, the first enclosing line of walls and towers began to encroach upon the country region on either side the Seine. Some traces of this ancient boundary wall still existed in the last century; now, nothing but the memory of it survives, and here and there a local tradition, like the Porte des Baudets or Baudoyer, *Porta Bagauda.* Little by little the flood of houses, perpetually driven from the centre of the city, overflowed, made breaches in, and wore away this enclosure. Philip Augustus made a new embankment, and confined Paris within a circular chain of great towers, tall and solid. For more than a hundred years the houses pressed one upon the other, accumulated and raised their level within this basin, like water in a reservoir. They began to grow higher; they added story to story; they climbed one upon the other; they leaped up in height like any repressed fluid, vying each with the other in raising its head above its neighbour's to get a little air. The streets became deeper and narrower; every vacant space was filled up and disappeared. The houses at last leaped the wall of Philip Augustus, scattered merrily over the plain irregularly and all awry, like so many school-boys let loose. There they strutted proudly about, cut themselves gardens from the fields, and took their ease. By 1367 the city had extended so far into the suburbs that a new boundary wall was needed, particularly on the right bank of the river; Charles V. built it. But a city like Paris is in a perpetual state of growth. It is only such cities which ever become capitals. They are funnels into which flow all the geographical, political, and intellectual watersheds of a country, all the natural tendencies of a nation; wells of civilization, as it were, and also sewers, into which trade, commerce, intellect, population, all the vigour, all the life, all the soul of a nation unceasingly filter and collect, drop by drop, century after century. Charles V.'s boundary wall followed in the footsteps of that of Philip Augustus. By the end of the fifteenth century, it was overtaken, left behind, and the suburbs advanced yet farther. In the sixteenth, the wall seemed to recede visibly, and to be more and more deeply buried in the old city, so thickly did the new town spring up outside it. Thus, in the fifteenth century, to stop there, Paris had already worn out the three concentric circles of walls, which in the time of Julian the Apostate were, as we may say, in the germ, in the Grand-Châtelet and the Petit-Châtelet. The mighty city rent asunder its four girdles of ramparts in succession, like a child outgrowing his last year's clothes. Under Louis XI., groups of the ruined towers belonging to the old enclosure rose here and there from the sea of houses like hill-tops after a flood,—archipelagoes, as it were, of the old Paris submerged beneath the new.

Since then Paris has, unfortunately for us, undergone another transformation, but has crossed only one more wall, that of Louis XV.,—that miserable rampart of lath and plaster, worthy of the king who built it, worthy of the poet who celebrated it in a verse defying translation:—

"Le mur murant Paris rend
    Paris murmurant."

In the fifteenth century, Paris was still divided into three quite distinct and separate cities, each possessing its own physiognomy, peculiar features, manners, customs, privileges, and history,—the City, the University, and the Town. The City, which occupied the island, was the oldest, the smallest, and the mother of the other two, crowded in between them (if we may be allowed the comparison) like a little old woman between two tall, handsome daughters. The University covered the left bank of the Seine, from the Tournelle to the Tour de Nesle,—points corresponding in the Paris of to-day to the Wine-market and the Mint. Its precincts infringed boldly upon the region where Julian built his baths. St. Geneviève's Mount was included in this division. The culminating point of this curve of walls was the Porte Papale; that is, just about where the Pantheon now stands. The Town, which was the largest of the three parts of Paris, held possession of the right bank of the river. Its quay, broken and interrupted at various points, ran along the Seine, from the Tour de Billy to the Tour du Bois; that is, from the present site of the Public Granaries to the present site of the Tuileries. These four points, at which the river intersected the precincts of the capital; the Tournelle and the Tour de Nesle on the left, the Tour de Billy and the Tour du Bois on the right, were called the "Four Towers of Paris," by way of distinction. The Town extended even farther into the country than the University. The extreme limits of the Town (in the time of Charles V.) were the Portes Saint-Denis and Saint-Martin, the situation of which has not been changed.

As we have just observed, each of

these three great divisions of Paris was a city in itself, but a city too individual to be complete,—a city which could not dispense with the aid of the other two. Thus, they were utterly unlike in aspect. Churches abounded in the City, palaces in the Town, and colleges in the University. To pass over the minor eccentricities of old Paris and the caprices of those persons holding right of road, we may make the general statement—speaking only of the great masses in the chaos of communal jurisdictions —that the island was subject to the bishop, the right bank of the river to the provost, and the left bank to the rector; the Provost or Mayor of Paris, a royal and not a municipal officer, having authority over them all. The City contained Notre-Dame, the Town the Louvre and the Hôtel de Ville, and the University the College of the Sorbonne. The Town contained the Markets, the City the Hospital, the University the Pré-aux-Clercs. For any offence committed by a student on the left bank of the river, he was tried upon the island at the Palace of Justice, or law courts, and punished on the right bank, at Montfaucon, unless the rector, finding the University strong and the king weak, interfered; for it was one of the privileges of the students to be hanged in their own domain.

(The majority of these privileges, it may be noted in passing,—and there were many more desirable than this,— had been extorted from various kings by riots and revolts. This is the traditional course of things: a French proverb declares that the king only grants what the people wrest from him. There is an ancient charter which states the

fact with much simplicity; speaking of loyalty, it says: *"Civibus fidelitas in reges, quæ tamen aliquoties seditionibus interrupta, multa peperit privilegia."*)

In the fifteenth century, the Seine washed the shores of five islets within the precincts of Paris: the Ile Louviers, where there were then trees, and where there is now nothing but wood; the Ile aux Vaches and the Ile Notre-Dame, both deserted, save for a single structure, both held in fee by the bishop (in the seventeenth century, these two islands were made into one, now known as the Ile Saint-Louis); and lastly, the City, and at its extreme end the islet of the Passeur aux Vaches, since submerged beneath the platform of the Pont-Neuf. The City had then five bridges: three on the right,—the Pont Notre-Dame and Pont au Change, of stone, the Pont aux Meuniers, of wood; two on the left side,—the Petit-Pont, of stone, the Pont Saint-Michel, of wood: all built over with houses. The University had six gates, built by Philip Augustus; starting from the Tournelle, there were the Porte Saint-Victor, the Porte Bordelle, the Porte Papale, the Porte Saint-Jacques, the Porte Saint-Michel, the Porte Saint-Germain. The Town had six gates, built by Charles V.; starting from the Tour de Billy, there were the Porte Saint-Antoine, the Porte du Temple, the Porte Saint-Martin, the Porte Saint-Denis, the Porte Montmartre, and the Porte Saint-Honoré. All these gates were strong, and handsome also, which does not detract from strength. A broad, deep moat, whose waters ran rapidly during winter floods, washed the foot of the walls all around Paris, the Seine providing the water. At night the gates were closed, the river barred at each end of the town by great iron chains, and Paris slept in peace.

A bird's-eye view of these three boroughs—the City, the University, and the Town—presented an inextricable network of streets strangely entangled. But still, even at first sight, it was apparent that these three fragments of a city formed but one body. One saw at once two long parallel streets, without break or deviation, running almost in a straight line, and traversing the three towns from end to end, from north to south, perpendicular to the Seine, connecting them, uniting them, infusing, pouring, and incessantly decanting the people of the one into the precincts of the other, and making of the three but one. One of these two streets led from the Porte Saint-Jacques to the Porte Saint-Martin; it was known as Rue Saint-Jacques in the University, Rue de la Juiverie in the City, Rue Saint-Martin in the Town; it crossed the water twice under the name of the Petit-Pont and the Pont Notre-Dame.

The other, known as Rue de la Harpe on the left bank of the river, Rue de la Barillerie on the island, Rue Saint-Denis on the right bank, Pont Saint-Michel over one arm of the Seine, Pont au Change over the other, ran from the Porte Saint-Michel in the University to the Porte Saint-Denis in the Town. And yet, under all these various names, they were still the same two streets, the two parent streets, the two original streets, the two arteries of Paris. All the other veins of the triple town proceeded from or emptied into them.

Independently of these two diametrical main streets, traversing the entire breadth of Paris, and common to the whole capital, the University and Town had each its individual street, traversing its length, parallel to the Seine, and crossing the two arterial streets at right angles. Thus, in the Town, one could go in a straight line from the Porte Saint-Antoine to the Porte Saint-Honoré; in the University, from the Porte Saint-Victor the the Porte Saint-Germain. These two great roads, crossing the two first mentioned, made the canvas upon which was wrought the knotted and tangled Dædalian web of the streets of Paris. By careful study of the unintelligible design of this network, one might also distinguish—like two sheaves of wheat stretching, one into the University, the other into the Town—two bunches of great streets leading from the bridges to the gates. Something of this geometric plan still exists.

We shall now attempt to give some idea of the general view seen from the top of the towers of Notre-Dame.

To the spectator who reached this pinnacle in a breathless condition, all was at first a dazzling sea of roofs, chimneys, streets, bridges, squares, spires, and steeples. Everything burst upon his vision, at once,—the carved gable, the steep roof, the turret hanging from the angles of the walls, the eleventh-century stone pyramid, the fifteenth-century slate obelisk, the round bare tower of the donjon-keep, the square elaborately wrought tower of the church, the great, the small, the massive, and the light. The eye wandered for a time, plunging deep down into this labyrinth, where there was no one thing destitute of originality, purpose, genius, and beauty, nothing uninspired by art, from the tiniest house with carved and painted front, outside timbers, surbased door, and overhanging stories, to the royal Louvre, which then had a colonnade of towers. But the principal masses to be seen when the eye became wonted to this medley of buildings were as follows:—

First, the City. "The island of the City," as says Sauval, who, in spite of his nonsense, sometimes hits upon a happy phrase,—"the island of the City is shaped like a huge ship buried in the mud and stranded in the current towards the middle of the Seine." We have just explained that in the fifteenth century this ship was moored to the shores of the stream by five bridges. This likeness to a vessel also struck the heraldic scribes; for it is thence, and not from the Norman siege, say Favyn and Pasquier, that the ship blazoned on the ancient shield of Paris is taken. To him who can decipher it, the science of heraldry is another algebra, the science of heraldry is a language. The whole history of the second half of the Middle Ages is written out in heraldry, as is the history of the first half in the symbolism of the Roman Church. The hieroglyphs of feudalism follow those of theocracy.

The City, then, first fell upon the eye with its stern to the east and its prow to the west. Facing the prow, the spectator saw a countless collection of ancient roofs, above which rose, broad and round, the leaden bolster of the Sainte-Chapelle, like an elephant's back laden with its tower. Only in this case the tower was the most daring, the most daintily wrought, the most delicately carved spire that ever gave glimpses of the sky through its lace-like cone. In front of Notre-Dame, close at hand, three streets emptied into the space in front of the cathedral,—a beautiful square lined with old houses. Over the southern side of this square hung the wrinkled and frowning front of the Hospital, or Hôtel-Dieu, and its roof, which seemed covered with warts and pimples. Then to the left, to the right, to the east, to the west, throughout the City limits, narrow as they were, rose the steeples of its one-and-twenty churches of every age, of every form and every size, from the low, worm-eaten Roman campanile of Saint-Denis du Pas (*carcer Glaucini*) to the slender spires of Saint-Pierre aux Bœufs and Saint-Landry. Behind Notre-Dame were revealed, on the north, the cloisters with their Gothic galleries; on the south, the semi-Roman palace of the bishop; on the east, the borders of the Terrain, a plot of waste land. Amid this accumulation of houses, by the tall mitres made of openwork stone, which crowned the highest windows of the palace, then placed even in the very roof, the eye could also distinguish the hotel given by the town in the reign of Charles VI. to Juvénal des Ursins; a little farther away, the tarred booths of the Palus Market; elsewhere, again, the new chancel of Saint-Germain le Vieux, pieced out in 1458 with a bit of the Rue aux Febves; and then, at intervals, a square crowded with people; a pillory set up at some street corner; a fine fragment of the pavement of Philip Augustus,—superb flagging laid in the middle of the road, and furrowed to prevent horses from slipping, which was so ill replaced in the sixteenth century by the wretched flints and pebbles known as the "pavement of the League;" a deserted back yard with one of those open turret staircases which were common in the fifteenth century, and an example of which may still be seen in the Rue des Bourdonnais. Finally, to the right of the Sainte-Chapelle, towards the west, the Palace of Justice reared its group of towers on the water's edge. The tall trees of the king's gardens, which covered the western end of the City, hid the Ile du Passeur. As for the water, from the top of the towers of Notre-Dame it was barely visible on either side of the City: the Seine was concealed by bridges, the bridges by houses.

And if the spectator looked beyond those bridges, the roofs of which were of a greenish tint, mouldy before their time by the damp vapours rising from the water, if he turned to the left in the direction of the University, the first building which attracted him was a broad, low group of towers, the Petit-Châtelet, whose wide-mouthed porch swallowed up the end of the Petit-Pont; then, if his eye followed the shore from east to west, from the Tournelle to the Tour de Nesle, he saw a long line of houses with carved beams and stained-glass windows, overhanging the pavement story upon story, an endless zigzag of homely gables, often interrupted by the mouth of some street, and sometimes also by the front or the projecting corner of a huge stone mansion, spreading out its courtyards and gardens, its wings and its main buildings, quite at its ease amid this mob of narrow crowded houses, like a great lord in a rabble of rustic clowns. There were five

or six of these mansions on the quay, from the house of Lorraine, which shared the great monastery enclosure next the Tournelle with the Bernardines, to the family mansion of the de Nesles, the main tower of which bounded Paris on that side, and whose painted roofs for three months in the year slivered the scarlet disk of the setting sun with their dark triangles.

This side of the Seine, moreover, was the less commercial of the two; students were noisier and more numerous than labourers, and, properly speaking, the quay extended only from the Pont Saint-Michel to the Tour de Nesle. The rest of the river-bank was now a bare beach, as beyond the Bernardine monastery, and then again a mass of houses washed by the water, as between the two bridges.

There was a vast clamour of washer-women; they shouted, chattered, and sang from morning till night along the shore, and beat the linen hard, as they do in our day. This is not the least part of the gaiety of Paris.

The University presented a huge mass to the eye. From one end to the other it was a compact and homogeneous whole. The myriad roofs, close-set, angular, adherent, almost all composed of the same geometrical elements, looked from above like a crystallization of one substance. The fantastic hollows of the streets divided this pasty of houses into tolerably equal slices. The forty-two colleges were distributed about quite evenly, there being some in every quarter. The delightfully varied pinnacles of these fine structures were the product of the same art as the simple roofs which they crowned, being really but a multiplication of the square or cube of the same geometrical figure. In this way they made the sum total more intricate without rendering it confused, and completed without overloading the general effect. Geometry is harmony. Certain handsome mansions here and there stood out superbly among the picturesque garrets on the left bank of the river, —the Nevers house, the house of Rome, the Rheims house, which have all disappeared; the Hôtel de Cluny, still standing for the consolation of artists, and the tower of which was so stupidly lowered some years since. That Roman palace near Cluny, with its beautiful arches, was formerly the Baths of Julian. There were also a number of abbeys of a beauty more religious, a grandeur more severe, than the mansions, but no less splendid, no less spacious. Those first attracting the eye were the monastery of the Bernardines, with its three spires; Sainte-Geneviève, whose square tower, still standing, makes us regret the rest so much; the Sorbonne, half college, half monastery, of which the fine nave still remains; the elegant quadrangular cloister of the Mathurin friars; its neighbour, the cloister of St. Benedict, within the walls of which a theatre has been knocked up in the interval between the seventh and eighth editions of this book; the Franciscan abbey, with its three enormous gables side by side; the house of the Austin friars, whose graceful spire was, after the Tour de Nesle, the second lofty landmark on this side of Paris, looking westward. The colleges, which are in fact the connecting link between the convent and the world, formed the central point in the series of buildings be-

tween secular and religious houses, with a severity full of elegance, their sculptures being less meaningless than those of the palaces, their architecture not so sober as that of the monasteries. Unfortunately, scarcely anything is left of these monuments in which Gothic art hit so happy a medium between richness and economy; the churches (and they were many and splendid in the University quarter, representing every period of architecture, from the semicircular arches of St. Julian to the painted arches of St. Severius) predominated over everything else; and, like one harmony the more in that mass of harmonies, they broke through the varied sky-line of gables ever and anon with their sharp spires, their open steeples, and their slender pinnacles, whose line was but a magnificent exaggeration of the steep pitch of the roofs.

The ground on which the University stood was hilly. St. Geneviève's Mount formed a huge wen to the southeast; and it was a sight well worth seeing, to look down from the top of Notre-Dame upon that crowd of narrow, winding streets (now the Latin Quarter), and those close clusters of houses which, scattered in every direction from the summit of the height, seemed hurrying haphazard and almost perpendicularly down its sides to the water's edge, some apparently falling, others climbing up again, all clinging together for mutual support. The constant ebb and flow of a myriad black dots crossing and recrossing each other on the pavement lent a shimmering and indistinct look to everything; these were the people seen from a height and a distance.

Lastly, in the spaces between these

roofs, these spires, these unnumbered and irregular structures which curved and twisted and indented the outline of the University in so odd a fashion, might be seen at intervals a big bit of mossy wall, a thick round tower, or an embattled city gate, representing the fortress: this was the wall of Philip Augustus. Beyond were the green fields, and beyond these ran the roads, along which stretched a few suburban houses, becoming fewer in number as the distance increased. Some of these suburbs were of considerable importance: there was first, starting from the Tournelle, the borough of Saint-Victor, with its single arched bridge across the Bièvre; its abbey, where one might read the epitaph of Louis the Fat,—*epitaphium Ludovici Grossi;* and its church with an octagonal steeple flanked by four eleventh-century belfries (there is a similar one at Etampes, which has not yet been destroyed); then the borough of Saint-Marceau, which possessed three churches and a convent; then, leaving the Gobelins factory and its four white walls on the left, came the suburb of Saint-Jacques, with the beautiful carved cross in the market-place; the Church of Saint-Jacques du Haut-Pas, which was then Gothic, pointed and delightful; Saint-Magloire, with a fine fourteenth-century nave, which Napoleon turned into a hayloft; Notre-Dame des Champs, where there were Byzantine mosaics; lastly, leaving in the open country the Carthusian monastery, a rich edifice of the same date as the Palace of Justice, with its little private gardens, and the ill-famed ruins of Vauvert, the eye fell, to the westward, upon the three Roman spires of Saint-Germain des Prés. The borough of Saint-Germain, even then a large parish, included fifteen or twenty streets in the rear; the sharp spire of Saint-Sulpice formed one of the boundaries of the borough. Close beside it might be seen the square enclosure of the Saint-Germain fair-ground, where the market now stands; then the abbot's pillory, a pretty little round tower neatly capped with a leaden cone; the tile-kiln was farther on, as were the Rue du Four, leading to the town ovens, the mill on its knoll, and the hospital for lepers, —a small isolated building shunned by all. But the thing which particularly attracted and held attention was the abbey itself. It is certain that this monastery which held high rank both as a church and as a manor, this abbatial palace where the bishops of Paris held themselves happy to be allowed to pass a night, that refectory to which the architect had given the air, the beauty, and the splendid rose-window of a cathedral, that elegant Lady Chapel, that vast dormitory, those great gardens, that portcullis, that drawbridge, the battlements which intrenched upon the verdure of the surrounding fields, the courtyards glittering with men-at-arms mingled with golden copes, all grouped and combined around the three tall spires with their semicircular arches, firmly planted upon a Gothic chancel, made a magnificent figure on the horizon.

When at length, after close study of the University, the spectator turned towards the Town, the character of the view changed abruptly. The Town, in fact, though much larger than the University, was less of a unity. At the first glance it seemed to be divided into several strangely distinct masses. First, to the east, in that part of the town which still retains the name of the Marais, derived from the marsh in which Camulogenes mired Cæsar, there were a number of palaces. The buildings extended to the water's edge. Four mansions, so close together as to be almost connected,—the homes of the Jouy, Sens, Barbeau families, and the queen's residence,—mirrored their slated roofs, broken by slender turrets, in the Seine. These four buildings occupied the region between the Rue des Nonaindières and the Celestine Abbey, whose spire formed a graceful contrast to their line of battlements and gables. Certain moss-grown structures, overhanging the water in front of these sumptuous mansions, did not hide the fine outlines of their façades, their broad square windows with stone casements, their porches with pointed arches overloaded with statues, the sharp clear-cut edges of their walls, and all those dainty architectural accidents which make Gothic art seem as if it began a fresh series of combinations with every new building. Behind these palaces, stretched on every hand, here broken, palisaded, and crenelated like a citadel, here concealed amid tall trees like a monastery, the vast and varied wall around that marvellous Hôtel Saint-Pol, where the king had sufficient space to lodge luxuriously twenty-two princes of the rank of the Dauphin and the Duke of Burgundy, with their servants and suites, to say nothing of great lords, and the Emperor himself when he visited Paris, and the lions, which had a separate residence in the royal establishment. Let us say here that the apartment of a prince at this period comprised no less than eleven

rooms, from the audience chamber to the oratory, not to mention the galleries, baths, stove-rooms, and other "superfluous places" with which each apartment was provided; not to mention the private gardens for each guest of the king; not to mention the kitchens, cellars, offices, and general refectories of the house; the servants' quarters, where there were twenty-two offices, from the bakehouse to the wine-cellars; the games of various sorts, mall, tennis, riding at the ring, etc.; aviaries, fish-ponds, poultry-yards, stables, cow-houses, libraries, arsenals, and foundries. Such was a royal palace of that period, a Louvre, a Hôtel Saint-Pol,—a city within a city.

From the tower where in fancy we stand, the Hôtel Saint-Pol, almost half concealed by the four great mansions just mentioned, was yet very vast and very wonderful to behold. Although skilfully joined to the main building by long glazed and columned galleries, the three residences which Charles V. had added to his palace were readily to be distinguished: the Hôtel du Petit-Muce, with the open-work balustrade so gracefully bordering its roof; the house of the Abbot of St. Maur, having the aspect of a stronghold, a great tower, bastions, loop-holes, iron cowls, and over the wide Saxon gateway, the abbot's escutcheon between the two grooves for the drawbridge; the residence of the Count d'Etampes, whose donjon-keep, in ruins at the top, was round and notched like a cock's comb; here and there three or four low bushy old oaktrees grew close together, looking like huge cauliflowers; swans sported in the clear waters of the fish-ponds, rippled with light and shade: numerous courtyards afforded picturesque glimpses; the Hôtel des Lions, with its low pointed arches resting upon short Saxon pillars, its iron portcullises and its never-ending roar; rising above all this, the scaly spire of the Ave-Maria; to the left, the house of the provost of Paris, flanked by four delicately designed turrets; in the centre, in the background, the Hôtel Saint-Pol itself, properly so called, with its myriad façades, its successive embellishments from Charles V.'s day down, the hybrid excrescences with which the caprice of architects had loaded it during the lapse of two centuries, with all the chancels of its chapels, all the gables of its galleries, its endless weathercocks, and its two tall adjacent towers, whose conical roofs, bordered with battlements at their base, looked like cocked hats.

Still climbing the various stages of this amphitheatre of palaces rising in the distance, after crossing a deep ravine cut through the house-roofs of the Town, which marked the passage of the Rue Saint-Antoine, the eye fell upon the D'Angoulême mansion, a vast structure built at different periods, and containing very new and shining portions, which harmonized with the general effect no better than a red patch with a blue doublet. Still, the oddly steep, high roof of the modern palace, bristling with carved gutters, covered with sheets of lead over which rolled sparkling incrustations of gilded copper in a thousand fanciful arabesques,—the curiously damascened roof soared airily and gracefully aloft in the midst of the dark ruins of the ancient edifice, whose antique towers, bulging like casks, from old age, were bowed down by the weight of years and rent asunder from top to

bottom. Behind them rose the forest of spires of the Palace of the Tournelles. No view in the world, not even from Chambord or the Alhambra, could be more magical, more airy, more enchanting than this wilderness of spires, steeples, chimneys, vanes, winding staircases, wrought lanterns which looked as if struck out with a die, pavilions and spindle-shaped turrets, or tournelles, all varying in form, height, and position. It might well be compared to a gigantic stone chess-board.

That group of enormous inky-black towers, one melting into the other, and as it were bound together by a circular moat; that donjon-keep more thickly pierced with loopholes than with windows; that drawbridge forever raised and that portcullis forever down, to the right of the Tournelles, is the Bastille. Those black muzzles peering from the battlements, and which from this distance might pass for gutter-spouts, are cannon.

Within gunshot, below the terrible edifice, is the Porte Saint-Antoine, quite hidden between its two towers.

Beyond the Tournelles, as far as the wall of Charles V., stretched an expanse of beds of shrubs and flowers, and velvety lawns, the royal parks, amidst which the Dædalus garden, given by Louis XI. to Coictier, was easily to be distinguished by its labyrinth of trees and winding walks. The doctor's laboratory rose from the maze like a great solitary column with a tiny house for capital. In this small dwelling dread predictions of astrology were concocted. The Place Royale now stands upon this spot.

As we have just observed, the region

of the Palace—some idea of which we have striven to give the reader, although alluding to its principal features only—filled up the angle formed on the east by the Seine and the boundary wall of Charles V. The heart of the Town was occupied by a group of common houses. There the three bridges leading from the City discharged themselves upon the right bank; and bridges lead to the building of houses rather than of palaces. This collection of ordinary houses, crowded together like cells in a hive, was not without a beauty of its own. The roofs of a great city have a certain grandeur, like the waves of the sea. In the first place, the streets, crossed and intertangled, formed a hundred droll figures; around the markets, they looked like a myriad-rayed star. The Rues Saint-Denis and Saint-Martin, with their endless ramifications, climbed the hill side by side, like two great trees with intermingling branches; and then crooked lines, like the Rues de la Plâtrerie, de la Verrerie, de la Tixeranderie, etc., twisted and wound in and out among the whole. There were also fine structures piercing through the fixed swell of this sea of gables. At the end of the Pont aux Changeurs, behind which the Seine foamed beneath the wheels of the Pont aux Meuniers, there was the Châtelet, no longer a Roman tower, as in the days of Julian the Apostate, but a feudal tower of the thirteenth century, and constructed of a stone so hard that three hours' work with the pick could not remove a piece the size of a man's fist; there was the superb square bell-tower of Saint-Jacques de la Boucherie, all its angles softened by sculptures, even then worthy of

admiration, although it was not finished in the fifteenth century. (It lacked particularly those four monsters which even yet, perched on the corners of its roof, look like four sphinxes giving modern Paris the riddle of the ancient Paris to solve. Rault the sculptor put them up in 1526, and he was paid only twenty francs for his pains!) There was the Pillar House, opening on the Grève, of which we have already given the reader some idea; there was Saint-Gervais, which a porch "in good taste" has since spoiled; Saint-Méry, whose old pointed arches were a close approach to the semicircular; Saint-Jean, whose magnificent spire had passed into a proverb; there were at least twenty other edifices, which did not disdain to bury their marvels in this wilderness of deep, dark, and narrow streets. Add to this the carved stone crosses, even more abundant at cross-roads than gibbets; the Cemetery of the Innocents, whose wall, a fine specimen of architecture, was visible from a distance, over the house-tops; the market pillory, the top of which peeped between two chimneys in the Rue de la Cossonnerie; the "ladder" of the Croix-du-Trahoir at the cross-roads, always black with people; the circular booths of the Corn-market; the remains of the ancient wall of Philip Augustus, visible here and there, lost among the houses, towers overgrown with ivy, ruined gates, crumbling, shapeless fragments of masonry; the quay with its countless shops and its bloody knackers' yards; the Seine, covered with boats, from the Port au Foin to For-l'Evêque, —and you will have a dim idea of what the central portion of the town was in 1482.

Together with these two quarters,—the one of princely mansions, the other of ordinary houses,—the third element in the view of the Town was a long belt of abbeys bordering almost its entire circumference from east to west, and forming a second inner circle of convents and chapels in addition to the circle of fortifications enclosing Paris. Thus, close beside the Tournelles Park, between the Rue Saint-Antoine and the old Rue du Temple, there was a Sainte-Catherine with its immense grounds, bounded only by the city walls. Between the old and the new Rue du Temple there was the Temple,—a gloomy group of towers, tall, straight, lonely in the midst of a vast battlement enclosure. Between the Rue Neuve du Temple and the Rue Saint-Martin there was the Abbey of Saint-Martin, in its gardens, a superb fortified church, whose engirdling towers, whose coronet of spires, only yielded in strength and splendour to those of Saint-Germain des Prés. Between the Rues Saint-Martin and Saint-Denis were the precincts of the Convent of the Trinity. Lastly, between the Rue Saint-Denis and the Rue Montorgueil was the Convent of the Daughters of God. Close by might be seen the rotting roofs and unpaved district of the Court of Miracles. This was the only profane link in this pious chain of convents.

Lastly, the fourth division clearly outlined in the conglomeration of house-tops on the right bank of the river, and occupying the western angle formed by the boundary wall and the shore down stream, was still another cluster of palaces and elegant residences, nestling in the shadow of the Louvre. The old Louvre of Philip Augustus, that overgrown structure around whose great tower were grouped twenty-three towers almost as large, to say nothing of smaller turrets, seemed from a distance to be framed in the Gothic summits of the Hôtel d'Alençon and of the Petit-Bourbon. This hydra of towers, the giant guardian of Paris, with its twenty-four heads always reared aloft, with its monstrous cruppers covered with lead or scaly with slates, all dimpling and rippling with metallic reflections, made a surprising finish to the outline of the Town on the west.

An immense mass, therefore,—what the Romans called an *insula*,—of plain, homely houses, flanked on either hand by blocks of palaces, crowned, the one by the Louvre, the other by the Tournelles, bounded on the north by a long line of abbeys and cultivated fields, blending and mingling together as one gazed at them; above these countless buildings, whose tiled and slated roofs stood out in such strange outlines one against the other, the crimped, twisted, ornamented steeples of the forty-four churches of the right bank of the river; myriads of crooked streets, bounded on one side by a line of high walls with square towers (that of the University had round towers), on the other by the Seine intersected by bridges, and bearing along a wilderness of boats,—such was the Town in the fifteenth century.

Outside the walls, some few suburbs crowded to the gates; but there were not so many houses, nor were they so close together, as in the University quarter. There were, behind the Bastille, some twenty huts, built close around the Cross of Faubin with its curious carvings, and the Abbey of Saint-Antoine des Champs with its buttresses; then came Popincourt, hidden in wheat-fields; then Courtille, a jolly village of taverns; the borough of Saint-Laurent, with its church, whose steeple at a distance seemed to be a part of the pointed towers of the Porte Saint-Martin; the Faubourg Saint-Denis, with the vast enclosure of Saint-Ladre; outside the Porte Montmartre, Grange - Batelière, surrounded by white walls; behind it, with its chalky slopes, Montmartre, which then held almost as many churches as windmills,—for society now prefers material to spiritual bread. Lastly, beyond the Louvre the Faubourg Saint-Honoré, even then of considerable extent, stretched away into the fields, and Little Britain looked green in the distance, and the Pig-market was plainly visible, in the midst of it the horrible caldron for boiling alive coiners of counterfeit money. Between Courtille and Saint-Laurent the eye noted, on the summit of a height situated in the midst of bare plains, a sort of structure looking from a distance like a ruined colonnade standing upon bare foundations. It was neither a Parthenon nor a temple to Olympian Jove; it was Montfaucon.

Now, if the list of so many buildings, brief as we have tried to make it, has not destroyed, as fast as we constructed it, in the reader's mind the general outlines of old Paris, we will sum up our description in a few words. In the centre, the island of the City, shaped like a huge turtle, and protruding its bridges, scaly with tiles, like feet, from under its grey shell of roofs. To the left. the close, compact. crowded, mono-

lithic trapezium of the University; to the right, the vast semicircle of the Town, where houses and gardens were much more mingled,—the three districts, City, University and Town, veined with countless streets. In and out, through the whole, ran the Seine,—"the nourishing Seine," as Father du Breuil calls it,—obstructed with islands, bridges, and boats; all around an immense plain, green with a thousand different crops, and sprinkled with lovely villages: to the left, Issy, Vanvres, Vaugirard, Montrouge, Gentilly with its round tower and its square tower, etc.; to the right, a score of others, from Conflans to Ville-l'Evêque; on the horizon, a line of hills arranged in a circle like the rim of the basin. Finally, in the distance, to the eastward, Vincennes and its seven quadrangular towers; to the south, Bicêtre, and its pointed turrets; to the north, Saint-Denis and its spire; to the west, Saint-Cloud and its donjon. Such was Paris as seen from the top of the towers of Notre-Dame by the ravens who lived in 1482.

And yet it was of this city that Voltaire said that "before the time of Louis XIV. it possessed but four handsome public buildings": the dome of the Sorbonne, the Val-de-Grâce, the modern Louvre, and the fourth I have forgotten, —possibly the Luxembourg. Fortunately, Voltaire wrote "Candide" all the same, and is still, in spite of this criticism, of all men who have succeeded one another in the long series of humanity, the one who was most perfect master of sardonic laughter. This proves, moreover, that one may be a great genius and yet understand nothing of other people's art. Did not

Molière think he honoured Raphael and Michael Angelo when he called them "those Mignards of their age"?

Let us return to Paris and the fifteenth century.

It was not only a beautiful city; it was a uniform, consistent city, an architectural and historic product of the Middle Ages, a chronicle in stone. It was a city formed of two strata only,—the bastard Roman and the Gothic; for the pure Roman stratum had long since disappeared, except in the Baths of Julian, where it still broke through the thick crust of the Middle Ages. As for the Celtic stratum, no specimen was now to be found even in the digging of wells.

Fifty years later, when the Renaissance added to this severe and yet varied unity the dazzling luxury of its fantasy and its systems, its riotous wealth of Roman semicircular arches, Greek columns, and Gothic foundations, its tender and ideal sculpture, its peculiar taste for arabesques and acanthus-leaves, its architectural paganism, contemporary with Luther, Paris was perhaps still more beautiful, although less harmonious to the eye and intellect. But this splendid moment was of brief duration, the Renaissance was not impartial; not content with building up, it desired to pull down: true, it needed space. Thus Gothic Paris was complete for an instant only. Saint-Jacques de la Boucherie was scarcely finished when the destruction of the old Louvre began.

Since then the great city has grown daily more and more deformed. Gothic Paris, which swallowed up the Paris of the bastard Roman period, vanished in

its turn; but who can say what manner of Paris has replaced it?

There is the Paris of Catherine de Médicis, at the Tuileries; the Paris of Henry II., at the Hôtel de Ville, or Town Hall,—two buildings still in the best taste; the Paris of Henry IV., at the Place Royale,—brick fronts, with stone corners and slated roofs, tricoloured houses; the Paris of Louis XIII., at the Val-de-Grâce,—a squat, dumpy style of architecture, basket-handle vaults, something corpulent about the columns, something crook-backed about the dome; the Paris of Louis XIV., at the Invalides,—grand, rich, gilded, and cold; the Paris of Louis XV., at Saint-Sulpice,—volutes, knots of ribbon, clouds, vermicelli, and chiccory, all in stone; the Paris of Louis XVI., at the Pantheon, —a poor copy of St. Peter's at Rome (the building has settled awkwardly, which has not corrected its lines); the Paris of the Republic at the Medical School,—a poor bit of Greek and Roman taste, no more like the Coliseum or the Parthenon than the Constitution of the year III. is like the laws of Minos; it is known in architecture as "the Messidor style;" the Paris of Napoleon, at the Place Vendôme: this is sublime,— a bronze column made from captured cannon; the Paris of the Restoration, at the Exchange,—a very white colonnade supporting a very smooth frieze; the whole thing is square, and cost twenty million francs.

For each of these characteristic structures we find a certain number of houses similar in taste, style, and attitude, scattered through different quarters of the city, and easily to be recognized and dated by a trained observer. Any one who has the art of seeing can trace the spirit of a century and the physiognomy of a king even in a door-knocker.

Paris of the present day, therefore, has no general character of its own. It is a collection of specimens of various ages, and the best ones have disappeared. The capital increases in houses only, and what houses! At the rate at which Paris moves, it will be renewed every fifty years. Thus the historic significance of its architecture dies daily. Monuments of art are becoming more and more rare, and it seems as if we saw them swallowed up by degrees, lost among the houses. Our fathers had a Paris of stone; our children will have a Paris of plaster.

As for the modern monuments of new Paris, we would gladly forbear to speak of them. This is not because we do not admire them as they deserve. M. Soufflot's Sainte-Geneviève is assuredly the best fancy cake that was ever made of stone. The Palace of the Legion of Honour is also a very elegant piece of confectionery. The dome of the Corn-market is an English jockey-cap on a large scale. The towers of Saint-Sulpice are two big clarionets, and that is a very good shape in its way; the telegraph wire, twisting and wriggling, makes a pretty diversity upon their roof. Saint-Roch has a doorway only comparable in magnificence to that of the church of Saint-Thomas d'Aquin. It has also a Calvary in high relief in a cellar, and a sun made of gilded wood. These are very marvellous matters. The lantern in the labyrinth of the Botanical Garden, too, is very ingenious. As for the Exchange, which has a Greek colonnade, Roman semicircular arches over its

doors and windows, and a great elliptic vault of the period of the Renaissance, it is undoubtedly a very correct and very pure piece of architecture: the proof being, that it is crowned with an attic such as Athens never saw,—a beautiful straight line gracefully broken here and there by chimney-pots. Let us add, that if it be the rule that the architectural design of a building should be adapted to its purpose, so that this purpose shall be self-evident from one look at the edifice, we cannot too much wonder at a public building which might be indifferently a royal palace, a House of Commons, a town-hall, a college, a riding-school, a warehouse, a courthouse, a museum, a barrack, a tomb, a temple, or a theatre. And, after all, it is an Exchange! Moreover, a building should be appropriate to the climate. This is evidently built for our cold and rainy sky. It has a roof almost as flat as if it were in the Orient, so that in winter, when it snows, the roof can be swept; and it is evident that roofs were made to be swept. As for that purpose to which we alluded just now, it fulfils it marvellously well; it is an Exchange in France, as it would have been a temple in Greece. True, the architect took great pains to hide the face of the clock, which would have destroyed the purity of the fine lines of the front; but, to make amends for this, there is that colonnade which runs round the building, and under which, on high holidays or religious festivals, the theories of stock-brokers and jobbers may be solemnly unfolded.

These are doubtless very superb structures. Add any number of fine streets, entertaining and diversified like the Rue de Rivoli, and I am not without hope that Paris, seen from a balloon, may yet present that richness of outline, that wealth of detail, that diversity of aspect, that union of the grandiose and simple, of the unexpected and the beautiful, which characterize a checker-board.

Nevertheless, admirable as Paris of the present day may seem to you, recall Paris of the fifteenth century; reconstruct it in imagination; gaze at the sky through that amazing thicket of spires, steeples, and towers; let the Seine flow through the centre of the vast city, interrupt its course with islands, let it curve around the arches of its bridges in broad pools of green and yellow more variable than a serpent's skin; draw distinctly on the blue horizon the Gothic profile of old Paris; let its outlines shimmer in the fog which clings about its many chimneys; drown it in profound darkness, and watch the strange play of lights and shadows in this gloomy labyrinth of buildings; throw a moonbeam upon it which shall reveal it dimly and lift the great heads of the towers above the fog; or recall that dark picture, light up the myriad sharp angles of spire and gable as they lurk in the shadow, and make them all stand out, more indented than a shark's jaw, against the coppery sunset sky,—and then compare the two.

And if you would receive an impression from the old city which the modern one can never give you, climb, some holiday morning, say at sunrise on Easter or Whitsunday,—climb to some high point whence you overlook the whole town, and listen to the call of the chimes. See, at a signal from the sky,—for it is the sun that gives it,—those count-less churches quiver simultaneously. At first a scattered tolling passes from church to church, as when musicians give notice that they are about to begin. Then, all at once, see,—for at certain moments it seems as if the ear had also its vision,—see as it were a column of sound, a vapour of harmony rise at one and the same moment from every tower. At first the vibrations of each bell ascend straight, pure, and as it were apart from the rest, into the clear morning sky; then, little by little, as they increase, they melt into one another, are blended, united, and combined into one magnificent harmony. It ceases to be anything but a mass of sonorous vibrations incessantly set loose from countless spires, floating, undulating, bounding, whirling over the city, and prolonging the deafening circle of its oscillations far beyond the horizon. Yet that sea of harmonies is not a chaos. Deep and wide as it may be, it has not lost its transparency; you may see each group of notes, as it escapes from the several chimes of bells, take its own meandering course. You may follow the dialogue, by turns solemn and shrill, between the small bell and the big bell; you may see the octaves bound from spire to spire; you watch them spring winged, light, and sibilant from the silver bell, fall maimed and halting from the wooden bell; you admire in their midst the rich gamut perpetually running up and down the seven bells of Saint-Eustache; you behold quick, clear notes dart through the whole in three or four luminous zigzags, and then vanish like lightning flashes. Yonder is the Abbey of Saint-Martin, shrill and cracked of voice; here is the surly, ominous voice of the Bastille; at the other end the great tower of the Louvre, with its counter-tenor. The royal peal of the Palace flings resplendent trills on every hand, without a pause; and upon them fall at regular intervals dull strokes from the belfry of Notre-Dame, which strike sparks from them as the hammer from the anvil. At intervals you see passing tones of every form, coming from the triple peal of Saint-Germain des Prés. Then again, from time to time this mass of sublime sounds half opens and makes way for the *stretto* of the Ave-Maria, which tinkles and flashes like a starry plume. Below, in the very heart of the harmony, you vaguely catch the inner music of the churches as it escapes through the vibrating pores of their vaulted roofs. Certainly, this is an opera worth hearing. Usually, the noise which rises up from Paris by day is the talking of the city; by night, it is the breathing of the city; but this,—this is the singing of the city. Hearken then to this *tutti* of the steeples; over all diffuse the murmur of half a million men, the never-ending murmur of the river, the endless sighing of the wind, the grave and distant quartet of the four forests ranged upon the hills in the horizon like huge organ-cases; drown, as in a demi-tint, all that would otherwise be too harsh and shrill in the central chime,— and then say if you know of anything on earth richer, more joyous, more mellow, more enchanting than this tumult of bells and chimes; than this furnace of music; than these ten thousand brazen voices singing together through stone flutes three hundred feet in length; than this city which is but an orchestra; than this symphony which roars like a tempest.

BOOK IV

GRATITUDE

CHAPTER I

KIND SOULS

IT was some sixteen years previous to the date of this story, on a fine morning of the first Sunday after Easter, known in France as Quasimodo Sunday, that a living creature was laid, after Mass, in the Church of Notre-Dame, upon the bedstead fixed in the square outside, to the left of the entrance, opposite that "great image" of Saint Christopher, which the carven stone figure of Master Antoine des Essarts, knight, had contemplated on his knees until the year 1413, when it was thought proper to pull down both saint and believer. Upon this bed it was customary to expose foundlings to public charity. Whoever chose to take them, did so. In front of the bedstead was a copper basin for alms.

The sort of living creature lying on the board upon this Sunday morning, in the year of our Lord 1467, seemed to excite in a high degree the curiosity of the somewhat numerous group of people who had gathered around the bed. This group was largely composed of members of the fair sex. They were almost all old women.

In the foremost rank, and bending over the bed, were four who by their grey hoods and gowns seemed to belong to some religious community. I know no reason why history should not hand down to posterity the names of these four discreet and venerable dames. They were Agnès la Herme, Jehanne de la Tarme, Henriette la Gaultière, and Gauchère la Violette, all four widows, all four good women from the Etienne Haudry Chapel, who had come out for the day by their superior's permission, and conformably to the statutes of Pierre d'Ailly, to hear the sermon. However, if these worthy Haudriettes were, for the time being, obeying the statutes of Pierre d'Ailly, they were certainly wilfully violating those of Michel de Brache and the Cardinal of Pisa, which so barbarously condemned them to silence.

"What on earth is it, sister?" said Agnès to Gauchère, gazing at the little foundling as it shrieked and writhed upon its bed, terrified by so many observers.

"What is the world coming to," said Jehanne, "if that is the way the children look nowadays?"

"I don't know much about children," added Agnès; "but it must surely be a sin to look at this thing."

"It's no child, Agnès."

"It's a deformed monkey," remarked Gauchère.

"It's a miracle," continued Henriette la Gaultière.

"Then," observed Agnès, "it's the third since Lætare Sunday; for it's not a week since we had the miracle of the

mocker of pilgrims divinely punished by Our Lady of Aubervilliers, and that was the second miracle of the month."

"This foundling, as they call it, is a regular monster of abomination," added Jehanne.

"He howls fit to deafen a chorister," said Gauchère. "Will you hold your tongue, you little screamer!"

"To think that the Bishop of Rheims should send this monstrosity to the Bishop of Paris," went on La Gaultière, clasping her hands.

"I believe," said Agnès la Herme, "that it's a beast, an animal, a cross between a Jew and a pig; something, in fact, which is not Christian, and should be burned or drowned."

"I'm sure I hope," exclaimed La Gaultière, "that no one will offer to take it."

"Oh, good gracious!" cried Agnès, "I pity those poor nurses in the Foundling Hospital at the end of the lane, as you go down to the river, just next door to his lordship the bishop, if this little monster is given to them to suckle. I'd rather nurse a vampire."

"What a simpleton you are, poor La Herme!" cried Jehanne; "don't you see, sister, that this little wretch is at least four years old, and that he would have less appetite for your breast than for a piece of roast meat."

In fact, "the little monster" (for we ourselves should find it hard to describe him otherwise) was no new-born baby. He was a very bony and very uneasy little bundle, tied up in a linen bag marked with the monogram of M. Guillaume Chartier, then Bishop of Paris, with a head protruding from one end. This head was a most misshapen thing; there was nothing to be seen of it but a shock of red hair, an eye, a mouth, and teeth. The eye wept, the mouth shrieked, and the teeth seemed only waiting a chance to bite. The whole body kicked and struggled in the bag, to the amazement of the crowd, which grew larger and changed continually around it.

Dame Aloïse de Gondelaurier, a rich and noble lady, leading a pretty girl of some six years by the hand, and trailing a long veil from the golden horn of her headdress, stopped as she passed the bed, and glanced for an instant at the miserable creature, while her lovely little daughter Fleur-de-Lys de Gondelaurier, arrayed in silk and velvet, spelled out with her pretty little finger the permanent inscription fastened to the bedstead: "For Foundlings."

"Really," said the lady, turning away in disgust, "I thought they only put children here!"

She turned her back, throwing into the basin a silver coin which jingled loudly among the copper pence, and made the four good women from the Etienne Haudry Home stare.

A moment later, the grave and learned Robert Mistricolle, prothonotary to the king, passed with a huge missal under one arm and his wife under the other (Damoiselle Guillemette la Mairesse), being thus armed on either hand with his spiritual and his temporal advisers.

"A foundling," said he, after examination, "found apparently on the shores of the river Phlegethon!"

"It sees with but one eye," remarked Damoiselle Guillemette; "there is a wart over the other."

"That is no wart," replied Master Robert Mistricolle; "that is an egg which holds just such another demon, who also bears another little egg containing another little demon, and so on *ad infinitum.*"

"How do you know?" asked Guillemette la Mairesse.

"I know it for very good reasons," answered the prothonotary.

"Mr. Prothonotary," inquired Gauchère la Violette, "what do you predict from this pretended foundling?"

"The greatest misfortunes," replied Mistricolle.

"Ah, good heavens!" said an old woman in the audience; "no wonder we had such a great plague last year, and that they say the English are going to land at Harfleur!"

"Perhaps it will prevent the queen from coming to Paris in September," added another; "and trade's so bad already!"

"It is my opinion," cried Jehanne de la Tarme, "that it would be better for the people of Paris if this little sorcerer here were laid on a fagot rather than a board,"

"A fine flaming fagot!" added the old woman.

"That would be more prudent," said Mistricolle.

For some moments a young priest had been listening to the arguments of the Haudriettes and the sententious decrees of the prothonotary. His was a stern face, with a broad brow and penetrating eye. He silently put aside the crowd, examined the "little sorcerer," and stretched his hand over him. It was high time; for all the godly old women were already licking their lips at the thought of the "fine flaming fagot."

"I adopt this child," said the priest. He wrapped it in his cassock and bore it away. The spectators looked after him with frightened eyes. A moment later he had vanished through the Porte Rouge, which then led from the church to the cloisters.

When their first surprise was over, Jehanne de la Tarme whispered in La Gaultière's ear,—

"I always told you, sister, that that young scholar Monsieur Claude Frollo was a wizard."

CHAPTER II

CLAUDE FROLLO

INDEED, Claude Frollo was no ordinary character. He belonged to one of those middle-class families called indifferently, in the impertinent language of the last century, the better class of citizens, or petty nobility. This family had inherited from the brothers Paclet the estate of Tirechappe, which was held of the Bishop of Paris, and the twenty-one houses belonging to which had been the subject of so many suits before the judge of the bishop's court during the thirteenth century. As holder of this fief, Claude Frollo was one of the one hundred and forty-one lords and nobles claiming quit-rents in Paris and its suburbs; and his name was long to be seen inscribed, in that capacity, between those of the Hôtel de Tancarville, belonging to Master François le Rez, and the College of Tours, in the cartulary deposited for safe keeping at Saint-Martin des Champs.

Claude Frollo had from early childhood been destined by his parents to enter the ranks of the clergy. He was taught to read in Latin; he was trained to look down and speak low. While still very young his father put him at the convent School of Torchi in the University. There he grew up on the missal and the lexicon.

He was moreover a sad, serious, sober, child, who loved study and learned quickly. He never shouted at play, took little part in the riotous frolics of the Rue du Fouarre, knew not what it was to *"dare alapas et capillos laniare,"* and had no share in the mutiny of 1463, which historians gravely set down as the "sixth disturbance at the University." It seldom occurred to him to tease the poor scholars of Montaigu about their capotes,—the little hoods from which they took their name,—or the bursars of the College of Dormans about their shaven pates, and their motley garb of grey, blue, and violet cloth, *"azurini coloris et bruni,"* as the charter of Cardinal des Quatre-Couronnes words it.

But, on the other hand, he was faithful to the great and little schools in the Rue Saint-Jean de Beauvais. The first scholar to be seen by the Abbot of Saint-Pierre de Val, as he began his lecture on canon law, was always Claude Frollo, glued to a column in the Saint-Vendregesile School, directly opposite the speaker's chair, armed with his inkhorn, chewing his pen, scribbling on his threadbare knee, and in winter blowing on his fingers to keep them warm. The first auditor whom Master Miles d'Isliers, doctor of decretals, saw hurrying up all out of breath every Monday morning at the opening of the doors of the Chef-Saint-Denis School, was Claude Frollo. Accordingly, at the age of sixteen the young scholar was quite able to argue matters of mystical theology with a father of the Church, of canonical theology with a father of the Councils, and of scholastic theology with a doctor of the Sorbonne.

Theology mastered, he plunged into decretals. After the "Master of Sentences," he fell upon the "Capitularies of Charlemagne;" and devoured in turn, in his appetite for knowledge, decretal after decretal,—those of Theodore, Bishop of Hispala; those of Bouchard, Bishop of Worms; those of Yves, Bishop of Chartres; then the decree of Gratian, which followed the "Capitularies of Charlemagne;" then the collection of Gregory IX.; then the epistle *"Super Specula,"* of Honorius III. He gained a clear idea of, he became familiar with, that vast and bewildering period when civil law and canon law were struggling and labouring amid the chaos of the Middle Ages,—a period beginning with Bishop Theodore in 618, and ending with Pope Gregory in 1227.

Decretals digested, he turned to medicine and the liberal arts. He studied the science of herbs, the science of salves; he became skilled in fevers and bruises, in wounds and sores. Jacques d'Espars would have given him the degree of doctor of medicine; Richard Hellain, that of surgeon. He also took all the degrees in all the other arts. He studied languages, Latin, Greek, and Hebrew,—a triple shrine then but little worshipped. His was a genuine thirst for acquiring and treasuring the facts of science. At eighteen, he had done with the four faculties; life seemed to the youth to have but one purpose,—to gain knowledge.

It was about this time that the excessive heat of the summer of 1466 caused an epidemic of the plague, which carried off more than forty thousand souls in the viscounty of Paris, and among others, says Jehan de Troyes, "Master Arnoul, astrologian to the king, who was a very virtuous, wise, and pleasant man." A rumour spread through the University that the Rue Tirechappe was especially subject to the disease. There Claude's parents lived, in the heart of their estate. The young scholar hastened in alarm to the paternal mansion. On entering, he found that his father and mother had died the night before. A baby brother was still living, and lay crying in his cradle. He was all that was left to Claude of his family. The youth took the child in his arms and walked thoughtfully away. Hitherto, he had lived for science only; he now began to live in the present.

This catastrophe marked an epoch in his existence. An orphan, the eldest, the head of a family at the age of nineteen, he was recalled from scholastic dreams to actual realities. Then, moved by pity, he was filled with love and devotion for this child, his brother; and a human affection was a strange sweet thing to him who had loved nothing but books before.

This affection grew to a singular degree; in so virgin a soul it was like a first love. Parted in infancy from his parents, whom he scarcely knew, cloistered and as it were immured among his books, eager to study and to learn everything, hitherto paying exclusive attention to his intellect, which delighted in literature, the poor student had had no time to learn that he had a heart. This little fatherless, motherless brother, this baby dropped unawares from heaven into his arms, made a new man of him. He saw that there were other things in the world than the speculations of the Sorbonne and the verses of Homer; that man required affection; that life without tenderness and without love was only a noisy, miserable, unfeeling machine. Only he fancied—for he was at the age when illusions are still replaced by illusions only—that the ties of family and kindred were all that was necessary, and that a little brother to love was enough to fill up a whole life.

He therefore yielded to his love for little Jehan with the passion of a character which was already energetic, ardent, and concentrated. The poor frail creature, a pretty, fair-haired, rosy, curly-locked child, an orphan, stirred him to the very soul; and like the serious thinker that he was, he began to meditate about Jehan with infinite compassion. He thought and cared for him as for something very fragile and very precious. He was more than a brother to the boy; he became a mother to him.

Little Jehan was not yet weaned when he lost his mother; Claude put him out to nurse. Besides the estate of Tirechappe, he had inherited from his father the fief of Moulin, which was held of the square tower of Gentilly; it consisted of a mill upon a hill, near the Château de Winchestre (now Bicêtre). The miller's wife was just then nursing a fine child; it was not far from the University. Claude himself carried little Jehan thither.

Henceforth, feeling that he had a burden to bear, he took life very soberly.

The thought of his little brother became not only the refreshment, but the object of his studies. He resolved to devote himself wholly to the future of one for whom he must be answerable to God, and to have no other wife, no other child, than the happiness and prosperity of his brother. He accordingly became more than ever attached to his clerical calling. His merits, his learning, his position as the direct vassal of the Bishop of Paris, opened wide all the doors of the Church to him. At the age of twenty, by a special dispensation from the Holy See, he was a priest, and served as the youngest of the chaplains of Notre-Dame at the altar called, from the lateness of the Mass said at it, *altare pigrorum.*

There, more than ever buried in his dear books, which he only left to make a hasty visit to the mill, this mixture of wisdom and austerity, so rare at his age, soon made him respected and admired by the cloisters. From the convent, his reputation as a learned man spread to the people, among whom it had been somewhat changed—a frequent occurrence in those days—to the renown of a sorcerer.

It was as he was returning, on Quasimodo, or Low Sunday, from saying the sluggards' mass at their altar, which was close by the gate of the choir leading into the nave, to the right, near the image of the Virgin, that his attention was aroused by the group of old women chattering round the bed for foundlings.

He approached the unfortunate little being who seemed to be so much hated and so much threatened. Its distress, its deformity, its desertion, the thought of his own little brother, the wild dread, which at once struck him, that if he should die his dear little Jehan might also be flung upon that board to suffer, —all this rushed into his heart at once; a great wave of pity swept over him and he carried off the child.

When he took the child from the sack, he found it terribly deformed indeed. The poor little imp had a wart over his left eye, his head was buried between his shoulders, his spine was curved, his breastbone prominent, his legs crooked; but he seemed lively; and although it was impossible to say in what language he babbled, his cries proclaimed a certain amount of health and vigour. Claude's pity increased at the sight of so much ugliness; and he vowed in his inmost soul that he would educate this child for love of his own brother, so that whatever faults little Jehan might in the future commit, he might always have to his credit this charitable deed done for his benefit. It was a sort of investment of good works in his little brother's name; it was part of the stock of good deeds which he decided to lay up for him in advance, in case the young rascal should one day run short of this sort of money,—the only coin which will be accepted at the toll-gate of paradise.

He baptized his adopted child, and named him Quasimodo, either because he wished to mark in this way the day upon which the child was found, or because he wished to show by this name how imperfect and incomplete the poor little creature was. Indeed, Quasimodo, one-eyed, humpbacked, and knock-kneed, was hardly more than an "apology."

CHAPTER III

IMMANIS PECORIS CUSTOS, IMMANIOR IPSE

Now, in 1482, Quasimodo had grown up. He had been made, some years previous, bell-ringer of Notre-Dame, thanks to his adopted father Claude Frollo, who had become archdeacon of Josas, thanks to his liege lord Sir Louis de Beaumont, who had become Bishop of Paris in 1472, on the death of Guillaume Chartier, thanks to his patron Olivier le Daim, barber to Louis XI., king by the grace of God.

Quasimodo, therefore, was ringer of Notre-Dame.

In time, a peculiar bond of intimacy grew up between the ringer and the church. Cut off forever from the world by the double faculty of his unknown birth and his deformity, confined from infancy in this doubly insuperable circle, the poor wretch became used to seeing nothing of the world outside the religious walls which had received him into their shadow. Notre-Dame had been to him by turns, as he grew and developed, egg, nest, home, country, universe.

And it is certain that there was a sort of mysterious and pre-existing harmony between this creature and the structure. When, still a child, he dragged himself tortuously and jerkingly along beneath its gloomy arches, he seemed, with his human face and animal-like limbs, to be some reptile native to that damp dark pavement upon which the Roman capitals cast so many grotesque shadows.

Later on, the first time that he mechanically grasped the bell-rope in the tower, and clung to it, and set the bell ringing, he seemed to Claude, his adopted father, like a child whose tongue is loosed, and who begins to talk.

It was thus, little by little, growing ever after the pattern of the cathedral, living there, sleeping there, seldom leaving its precincts, forever subject to its mysterious influence, he came to look like it, to be imbedded in it, to form, as it were, an integral part of it. His sharp angles (if we may be pardoned the simile) fitted into the re-entering angles of the building, and he seemed not only to inhabit it, but to be its natural tenant. He might almost be said to have assumed its form, as the snail assumes the form of its shell. It was his dwelling, his hole, his wrapper. There was so deep an instinct of sympathy between him and the old church, there were so many magnetic affinities between them, that he in some sort clung to it, as the tortoise to its shell. The rugged cathedral was his shell.

It is useless to warn the reader not to take literally the figures of speech which we are forced to use here to express this singular, symmetrical, direct, almost consubstantial union of a man and an edifice. It is also useless to speak of the degree of familiarity with the whole cathedral which he had acquired during so long and intimate a cohabitation. This dwelling was his own. It contained no deeps which Quasimodo had not penetrated, no heights which he had not scaled. He often climbed the façade several stories high by the mere aid of projecting bits of sculpture. The towers upon the outer face of which he was frequently seen crawling like a lizard gliding over a perpendicular wall

(those twin giants, so lofty, so threatening, so terrible) had no vertigoes, no terrors, no giddiness for him; they were so docile to his hand, so easily climbed, that he might be said to have tamed them. By dint of jumping, clambering, sporting amid the abysses of the huge cathedral, he had become, as it were, a monkey and a goat, like the calabrian child who swims before he walks, and plays with the sea while but an infant.

Moreover not only his body but also his spirit seemed to be moulded by the cathedral. What was the state of that soul? What bent had it assumed, what form had it taken under its knotty covering in this wild life? It would be hard to tell. Quasimodo was born blind of one eye, humpbacked, lame. It was only by great patience and great painstaking that Claude Frollo had succeeded in teaching him to speak. But a fatality followed the poor foundling. Bell-ringer of Notre-Dame at the age of fourteen, a new infirmity soon put the finishing touch to his misfortunes; the bells had broken the drums of his ears; he became deaf. The only avenue which Nature had left him open to the world was suddenly closed forever.

In closing, it shut off the only ray of joy and light which still reached Quasimodo's soul. That soul relapsed into utter darkness. The miserable lad's melancholy became as complete and as hopeless as his deformity. Add to this that his deafness made him in some sort dumb; for that he might not be an object of laughter to others, from the moment that he realized his deafness he firmly resolved to observe a silence which he scarcely ever broke save when alone. Of his own free will he bound that tongue which Claude Frollo had worked so hard to set free. Hence it resulted that, when necessity constrained him to speak, his tongue was stiff and awkward, like a door whose hinges have rusted.

If now we strive to penetrate Quasimodo's soul through this hard thick bark; could we sound the depths of that misshapen organism; could we hold a torch behind those non-transparent organs, explore the dark interior of that opaque being, illuminate its obscure corners, its absurd blind alleys, and cast a strong light suddenly upon the Psyche imprisoned at the bottom of this well, we should doubtless find the poor thing in some constrained attitude, stunted and rickety, like those prisoners under the leads of Venice, who grew old bent double in a stone coffer too short and too low for them either to lie down or to stand up.

The spirit certainly wastes away in a misshapen body. Quasimodo barely felt within him the blind stirring of a soul made in his own image. His impressions of objects underwent a considerable refraction before they reached his mind. His brain was a peculiar medium; the ideas which traversed it came forth greatly distorted. The reflection resulting from that refraction was necessarily divergent, and deviated from the right path.

Hence endless optical illusions, endless aberrations of opinion, endless digressions into which his thoughts, sometimes foolish, and sometimes idiotic, would wander.

The first effect of this unfortunate condition of things was to disturb his views of all outward objects. He had scarcely any direct perception of them. The external world seemed much farther away from him than it does from us.

The second effect of his misfortune was to make him mischievous.

He was mischievous because he was an untrained savage; he was a savage because he was ugly. There was a logic in his nature as in ours.

His strength, wonderfully developed as it was, was the cause of still greater mischief. *"Malus puer robustus,"* says Hobbes.

But we must do him the justice to say that this mischievous spirit was not innate. From his first intercourse with men he had felt, had seen himself despised, scorned, repulsed. To him, human speech meant nothing but mockery or curses. As he grew up, he encountered nothing but hate. He caught the infection. He acquired the universal malevolence. He adopted the weapon with which he had been wounded.

After all, he never turned his face to the world of men save with regret; his cathedral was enough for him. It was peopled with marble figures, kings, saints, and bishops who at least did not laugh at him, and never looked upon him otherwise than with peace and goodwill. The other statues, those of monsters and demons, did not hate Quasimodo; he looked too much like them for that. They rather mocked at other men. The saints were his friends, and blessed him. The monsters were his friends, and protected him. Thus he had long conversations with them. He would sometimes pass whole hours squatting before one of these statues, in solitary chat with it. If any one came by, he would fly like a lover surprised in his serenade.

And the cathedral was not only company for him, it was the universe; nay, more, it was Nature itself. He never dreamed that there were other hedge-rows than the stained-glass windows in perpetual bloom; other shade than that of the stone foliage always budding, loaded with birds in the thickets of Saxon capitals; other mountains than the colossal towers of the church; or other ocean than Paris roaring at their feet.

But that which he loved more than all else in the motherly building, that which awakened his soul and bade it spread its poor stunted wings folded in such misery where it dwelt in darkness, that which sometimes actually made him happy, was the bells. He loved them, he caressed them, he talked to them, he understood them. From the chime in the steeple over the transept to the big bell above the door, he had a tender feeling for them all. The belfry of the transept and the two towers were to him like three great cages, in which the birds, trained by him, sang for him alone; and yet it was these very bells which made him deaf. But mothers often love that child best which has cost them most pain.

To be sure, their voice was the only one which he could now hear. For this reason the big bell was his best beloved. She was his favourite of that family of noisy damsels who fluttered about his head on holidays. This big bell had been christened Marie. She hung alone in the south tower with her sister Jacqueline, a bell of less size enclosed in a smaller cage close beside her own. This Jacqueline was named for the wife of Jehan Montague, who gave the bell to the church; which did not prevent him from figuring at Montfaucon without a head. In the second tower there were six other bells; and lastly, the six smallest dwelt in the belfry over the transept with the wooden bell, which only rung from the afternoon of Maundy Thursday till the morning of Holy Saturday or Easter Eve. Thus Quasimodo had fifteen bells in his harem; but big Marie was his favourite.

It is impossible to give any idea of his joy on those days when full peals were rung. When the archdeacon dismissed him with the word "Go," he ran up the winding staircase more rapidly than any one else could have gone down. He reached the aerial chamber of the big bell, breathless; he gazed at it an instant with love and devotion, then spoke to it gently, and patted it, as you would a good horse about to take a long journey. He condoled with it on the hard work before it. After these initiatory caresses he called to his assistants, stationed on a lower story of the tower, to begin. They then hung upon the ropes, the windlass creaked, and the enormous mass of metal moved slowly. Quasimodo, panting with excitement, followed it with his eye. The first stroke of the clapper upon its brazen wall made the beam on which he stood quiver. Quasimodo vibrated with the bell. "Here we go! There we go!" he shouted with a mad burst of laughter. But the motion of the great bell grew faster and faster, and as it traversed an ever-increasing space, his eye grew bigger and bigger, more and more glittering and phosphorescent. At last the full peal began; the whole tower shook: beams, leads, broad stones, all rumbled together, from the piles of the foundation to the trefoils at the top. Then Quasimodo's rapture knew no bounds: he came and went; he trembled and shook from head to foot with the tower. The bell, let loose, and frantic with liberty, turned its jaws of bronze to either wall of the tower in turn,—jaws from which issued that whirlwind whose roar men heard for four leagues around. Quasimodo placed himself before those gaping jaws! he rose and fell with the swaying of the bell, inhaled its tremendous breath, gazed now at the abyss swarming with people like ants, two hundred feet below him, and now at the huge copper clapper which from second to second bellowed in his ear. That was the only speech which he could hear, the only sound that broke the universal silence reigning around him. He basked in it as a bird in the sunshine. All at once the frenzy of the bell seized him; his look became strange; he waited for the passing of the bell as a spider lies in wait for a fly, and flung himself headlong upon it. Then, suspended above the gulf, launched upon the tremendous vibration of the bell, he grasped the brazen monster by its ears, clasped it with his knees, spurred it with his heels, doubling the fury of the peal with the whole force and weight of his body. As the tower shook, he shouted and gnashed his teeth, his red hair stood erect, his chest laboured like a blacksmith's bellows, his eye flashed fire, the monstrous steed neighed and panted under him; and then the big bell of Notre-Dame and Quasimodo ceased to exist: they became a dream, a whirl-

wind, a tempest; vertigo astride of uproar; a spirit clinging to a winged crupper; a strange centaur, half man, half bell; a sort of horrid Astolpho, borne aloft by a prodigious hippogriff of living bronze.

The presence of this extraordinary being pervaded the whole cathedral with a peculiar breath of life. It seemed, at least in the opinion of the grossly superstitious mob, as if mysterious emanations issued from him, animating every stone in Notre-Dame and making the very entrails of the old church throb and palpitate. His mere presence there was enough to lead the vulgar to fancy that the countless statues in the galleries and over the doors moved and breathed. And in very truth the cathedral seemed a creature docile and obedient to his hand: it awaited his pleasure to lift up its mighty voice; it was possessed and filled with Quasimodo as with a familiar spirit. He might be said to make the vast edifice breathe. He was indeed omnipresent in it, he multiplied himself at every point of the structure. Sometimes the terrified spectator saw an odd dwarf on the extreme pinnacle of one of the towers, climbing, creeping, writhing, crawling on all fours, descending head-first into the abyss, leaping from one projection to another, and diving deep into the maw of some sculptured gorgon: it was Quasimodo hunting for daws' nests. Sometimes a visitor stumbled over a sort of living nightmare, crouching and scowling in a dark corner of the church; it was Quasimodo absorbed in thought. Sometimes an enormous head and a bundle of ill-adjusted limbs might be seen swaying frantically to and fro from a rope's end under a belfry: it was Quasimodo ringing the Vespers or the Angelus. Often by night a hideous form was seen wandering along the frail delicately wrought railing which crowns the towers and runs round the top of the chancel: it was still the hunchback of Notre-Dame. Then, so the neighbours said, the whole church took on a fantastic, supernatural, horrible air,—eyes and mouths opened wide here and there; the dogs and dragons and griffins of stone which watch day and night, with outstretched necks and gaping jaws, around the monstrous cathedral, barked loudly. And if it were a Christmas night, while the big bell, which seemed uttering its death-rattle, called the faithful to attend the solemn midnight mass, the gloomy façade assumed such an aspect that it seemed as if the great door were devouring the crowd while the rose-window looked on. And all this was due to Quasimodo. Egypt would have taken him for the god of the temple; the Middle Ages held him to be its demon: he was its soul.

So much so that to those who knew that Quasimodo once existed, Notre-Dame is now deserted, inanimate, dead. They feel that something has gone from it. That immense body is empty; it is a skeleton; the spirit has left it, the abode remains, and that is all. It is like a skull; the sockets of the eyes are still there, but sight is gone.

CHAPTER IV

THE DOG AND HIS MASTER

THERE was, however, one human being whom Quasimodo excepted from his malice and hatred of mankind in general, and whom he loved as much as, perhaps more than, his cathedral: this was Claude Frollo.

This was very natural. Claude Frollo had taken him, adopted him, fed him, brought him up. While still a child, it was between Claude Frollo's legs that he found shelter when dogs and boys barked at him and tormented him. Claude Frollo taught him to speak, to read, and to write. Claude Frollo even made him bell-ringer. Now, to give the big bell in marriage to Quasimodo was like giving Juliet to Romeo.

Therefore Quasimodo's gratitude was profound, passionate, boundless; and although the face of his adopted father was often clouded and severe, although his speech was usually brief, harsh, and imperative, this gratitude never for an instant failed him. In Quasimodo the archdeacon had the most submissive of slaves, the most docile of servants, the most watchful of guardians. When the poor bell-ringer became deaf, the two contrived a language of signs, mysterious and incomprehensible to every one else. Thus the archdeacon was the only human being with whom Quasimodo kept up any communication. He had relations with but two things in the world,—Notre-Dame and Claude Frollo.

There is nothing to which we can compare the archdeacon's empire over the ringer or the ringer's devotion to the archdeacon. One sign from Claude, and the idea that it would please him, would have been enough for Quasimodo to hurl himself from the top of the cathedral towers. It was wonderful to see so much physical strength brought to such rare development in Quasimodo, and blindly placed by him at the disposal of another. This was doubtless partly due to filial love, domestic affection; it was also due to the fascination exercised by one mind upon another. It was a poor, clumsy, awkward nature, with bowed head and suppliant eyes, before a profound and lofty, superior, and all-powerful intellect. Lastly, and above all, it was gratitude,—gratitude so pushed to its extremest limits that we know of nothing to which it may be compared. This virtue is not one of those which are to be found in the finest examples among men. Let us say therefore that Quasimodo loved the archdeacon as no dog, no horse, no elephant, ever loved its master.

CHAPTER V

MORE ABOUT CLAUDE FROLLO

IN 1482 Quasimodo was about twenty years old, Claude Frollo about thirty-six. The one had grown up, the other had grown old.

Claude Frollo was no longer the simple scholar of the College of Torchi, the tender protector of a little child, the dreamy young philosopher who knew many things and was ignorant of many more. He was now an austere, grave, morose priest; a keeper of other men's consciences; the archdeacon of Josas, second acolyte to the bishop, having charge of the two deaneries of Montlhéry and Châteaufort, and one hundred and seventy-four of the rural clergy. He was a gloomy and awe-inspiring personage, before whom choir-boys in alb and petticoat, the precentors, the monks of St. Augustine, and those clerks who officiated at the early service at Notre-Dame, trembled when he passed slowly by beneath the lofty arches of the choir, majestic, pensive, with folded arms, and head so bent upon his bosom that nothing of his face could be seen but the high bald forehead.

Now, Don Claude Frollo had not given up either science or the education of his younger brother,—those two occupations of his life. But time had imparted a slight bitterness to these things once so sweet. "The best bacon in the world," says Paul Diacre, "grows rancid at last." Little Jehan Frollo, surnamed "du Moulin," from the place where he was put to nurse, had not grown up in the path in which Claude would fain have led him. The big brother expected him to be a pious, docile, studious, honourable pupil. Now, the little brother, like those young trees which foil the gardener's every effort and turn obstinately towards the sun and air,— the little brother only grew and flourished, only put forth fine leafy and luxuriant branches, in the direction of idleness, ignorance, and debauchery. He was a perfect imp, utterly lawless, which made Don Claude frown; but very shrewd and witty, which made the big brother smile. Claude had confided him to that same College of Torchi where he had passed his own early years in study and meditation; and it cost him many a pang that this sanctuary once so edified by the name of Frollo should now be scandalized by it. He sometimes read Jehan very long and very severe lectures on this text, but the latter bore them without wincing. After all, the young scamp had a good heart, as every comedy shows us is always the case.

But the lecture over, he resumed his riotous ways with perfect tranquillity. Now it was a yellow beak (as new-comers at the University were called) whom he mauled for his entrance fee,— a precious tradition which has been carefully handed down to the present day. Now he headed a band of students who had fallen upon some tavern in classic style, *quasi classico excitati*, then beaten the landlord "with offensive cudgels," and merrily sacked the house, even to staving in the casks of wine in the cellar; and then it was a fine report in Latin which the submonitor of Torchi brought ruefully to Don Claude, with this melancholy marginal note: *"Rixa; prima causa vinum optimum potatum."* Lastly, it was reported—horrible to relate of a sixteen-year-old lad—that his excesses often took him even to the Rue de Glatigny.

Owing to all this, Claude, saddened and discouraged in his human affections, threw himself with all the greater ardour into the arms of Science,—that lady who at least does not laugh in your face, and always repays you, albeit in coin that is sometimes rather hollow, for the attentions that you have bestowed on her. He therefore became more and more learned, and at the same time, as a natural consequence, more and more rigid as a priest, more and more melancholy as a man. With each of us there are certain parallelisms between our intellect, our morals, and our character, which are developed continuously, and only interrupted by great upheavals in our life.

Claude Frollo having traversed in his youth almost the entire circle of human knowledge, positive, external, and legitimate, was forced, unless he stopped *ubi defuit orbis*, to go farther afield and seek other food for the insatiate activity of his mind. The antique symbol of the serpent biting its own tail is especially appropriate to science. It seemed that Claude Frollo had experienced this. Many worthy persons affirmed that having exhausted the *fas* of human knowledge, he had ventured to penetrate into the *nefas*. He had, so they said, successively tasted every apple on the tree of knowledge, and whether from hunger or disgust, had ended by biting into the forbidden fruit. He had taken his place by turns, as our readers have seen, at the conferences of the theologians of the Sorbonne, the assemblies of the philosophers at the image of Saint-Hilaire, at the disputes of the decretists at the image of Saint-Martin, at the meetings of the doctors at the holy-water font in Notre-Dame, *ad cupam Nostræ-Dominæ*. All the permissible and approved meats which those four great kitchens called the four faculties could prepare and serve up to the understanding he had devoured, and satiety had ensued before his hunger was appeased. Then he had dug farther and deeper, beneath all this finite, material, limited science; he had possibly risked his soul, and had seated himself in the cavern at that mysterious table of the alchemists, astrologers, and hermetics, headed by Averroës, Guillaume de Paris, and Nicolas Flamel, in the Middle Ages, and prolonged in the East, by the light of the seven-branched candlestick, to Solomon, Pythagoras, and Zoroaster.

At least this is what people imagined, whether rightly or wrongly.

Certain it is that the archdeacon often

visited the Cemetery of the Holy Innocents, where, to be sure, his father and mother were buried, with the other victims of the pest in 1466; but he seemed far less interested in the cross over their grave than in the strange characters carved upon the tomb of Nicolas Flamel and Claude Pernelle which stood close by.

Certain it was that he was often seen walking slowly along the Rue des Lombards and furtively entering a small house at the corner of the Rue des Ecrivains and the Rue Marivault. This was the house which Nicolas Flamel built, where he died about 1417, and which having remained empty ever since, was now beginning to fall into decay; so badly had the hermetics and alchemists of every nation injured the walls merely by writing their names upon them. Certain of the neighbours even declared that they had once seen, through a venthole, archdeacon Claude, digging, turning over, and spading the earth in those two cellars whose buttresses were scribbled all over with endless rhymes and hieroglyphics by Nicolas Flamel himself. It was supposed that Flamel had buried the philosopher's stone in these cellars; and alchemists, for two centuries back, from Magistri down to Father Pacificus, never ceased delving at the soil, until the house, so severely rummaged and ransacked, ended by crumbling into dust beneath their feet.

Certain it is also that the archdeacon was seized with a singular passion for the symbolical doorway of Notre-Dame, that page of conjury written in stone by Bishop Guillaume de Paris, who was undoubtedly damned for having added so infernal a frontispiece to the holy poem perpetually sung by the rest of the structure. Archdeacon Claude also passed for having fathomed the mystery of the colossal figure of Saint Christopher, and that tall enigmatical statue then standing at the entrance to the square in front of the cathedral, which people called in derision, "Monsieur Legris." But what every one might have observed, was the interminable hours which he often passed, sitting on the parapet of this same square, gazing at the carvings of the porch, sometimes studying the foolish virgins with their lamps turned upside down, sometimes the wise virgins with the lamps upright; at other times calculating the angle of vision of the daw to the left of the porch and gazing at a mysterious point inside the church where the philosopher's stone must assuredly be hidden, if it be not in the cellar of Nicolas Flamel. It was, let us say in passing, a singular fate for the Church of Notre-Dame at this period to be so loved, in different degrees and with such devotion, by two beings so dissimilar as Claude and Quasimodo. Loved by the one, a sort of instinctive and savage half-man, for its beauty, for its stature, for the harmonies that proceeded from its magnificent mass; loved by the other, a man of scholarly and impassioned fancy, for its significance, for its myth, for its hidden meaning, for the symbolism scattered throughout the sculptures of its front, like the first text under the second in a palimpsest—in short, for the riddle which it forever puts to the intellect.

Certain it is, lastly, that the archdeacon had arranged for himself, in that one of the two towers which looks upon the Grève, close beside the belfry a very secret little cell, where none might enter without his leave, not even the bishop, it was said. This cell, contrived in old times, had been almost at the very summit of the tower, among the daws' and ravens' nests, by Bishop Hugh of Besançon, who practised sorcery there in his time. What this cell contained, no one knew; but from the shore of the Terrain there was often seen at night, through a small dormer-window at the back of the tower, a strange, red, intermittent light, appearing, disappearing, and reappearing at brief and regular intervals, and seeming to follow the blasts of a bellows, and to proceed rather from the flame of a fire than from the light of a candle. In the darkness, at that height, it produced a singular effect; and the gossips would say, "There's the archdeacon blowing again! Hell is sparkling up there!"

After all, there was no great proof of sorcery in all this; but still there was so much smoke that it might well be supposed there was fire, and the archdeacon had quite a formidable fame. And yet we must say that Egyptian arts, necromancy, and magic, even of the whitest and most innocent kind, had no more relentless enemy, no more pitiless accuser than himself, before the officials of Notre-Dame. Whether this were genuine horror, or the game played by the robber who shouts, "Stop, thief!" it did not prevent the archdeacon from being considered by the wise heads of the chapter as a soul which had ventured into the outskirts of hell, as one lost in the dark caves of the Cabala,— groping in the obscurity of the occult sciences. Nor were the people deceived: with every one who had a grain of

sense, Quasimodo passed for the devil, Claude Frollo for the sorcerer. It was plain that the bell-ringer was bound to serve the archdeacon for a given time, at the end of which he would carry off his soul by way of payment. The archdeacon was therefore, in spite of the extreme austerity of his life, in very bad odour with pious people; and there was no devout nose so inexperienced as not to smell in him the magician.

And if, as he grew old, there were voids in his science, there were others in his heart. At least, so one was led to believe on looking at that face in which his soul never shone forth save through a dark cloud. Whence came that broad bald brow, that head forever bowed, that breast forever heaved by sighs? What secret thought made his lips smile so bitterly at the very moment that his frowning brows met like two bulls about to tussle? Why were his few remaining hairs already grey? What was that inward fire which sometimes broke forth in his eye to such a degree that it looked like a hole pierced in the wall of a furnace?

These signs of intense moral preoccupation had acquired a high pitch of intensity at the very time of this story. More than once a choir-boy had taken to his heels in alarm on finding him alone in the church, so strange and wild was his look. More than once, in the choir, during divine service, his neighbour in the stalls had heard him mingle unintelligible parentheses with the church music. More than once the laundress of the Terrain, employed "to wash the chapter," had remarked, not without terror, marks of nails and clinched fingers in the surplice of the archdeacon of Josas.

In other respects he redoubled his severity, and had never been more exemplary. From disposition as well as by profession he had always held himself aloof from women; he seemed now to hate them more than ever. The mere rustle of a silk petticoat made him pull his hood over his eyes. He was so jealous of his austerity and reserve upon this point that when Madame de Beaujeu, daughter of the king, came, in the month of December, 1481, to visit the convent of Notre-Dame, he gravely opposed her entrance, reminding the bishop of that statute in the Black Book, dated on the eve of St. Bartholomew, 1334, which forbids all access to the cloister to every woman "whatsoever, old or young, mistress or maid;" upon which the bishop was constrained to quote to him the ordinance of the legate Odo, which excepts certain great ladies, "*aliquæ magnates mulieres, quæ sine scandalo vitari non possunt*." And the archdeacon still protested, objecting that the legate's decree, which went back to 1207, antedated the Black Book by one hundred and twenty-seven years, and was consequently annulled by it; and he refused to appear before the princess.

It was moreover remarked that his horror of the gipsies seemed to have increased for some time past. He had solicited from the bishop an edict expressly forbidding the tribe from coming to dance and play the tambourine in the square before the cathedral; and he had also searched in the musty official papers, to collect all cases of witches and wizards condemned to be burned or hanged for complicity in conjury with goats, swine, or rams.

CHAPTER VI

UNPOPULARITY

THE archdeacon and the bell-ringer, as we have already observed, were not held in much favour by the great and little folk about the cathedral. When Claude and Quasimodo went forth together, as they frequently did, and were seen in company, the man behind the master, traversing the cool, narrow, shady streets about Notre-Dame, more than one malicious speech, more than one satirical exclamation and insulting jest stung them as they passed, unless Claude Frollo, as seldom happened, walked with head erect, displaying his stern and almost majestic brow to the abashed scoffers.

Both were in their district like the "poets" of whom Régnier speaks:—

"All sorts of folks will after poets
    hie,
As after owls our song-birds shriek
    and fly."

Now a sly brat would risk his bones for the ineffable delight of burying a pin in Quasimodo's hump: and now a lovely young girl, full of fun, and bolder than need be, would brush against the priest's black gown, singing in his ear the sarcastic song,—

"Hide, hide, for the devil is caught."
Sometimes a squalid group of old women, squatting in a row in the shade upon the steps of some porch, scolded roundly as the archdeacon and the bell-ringer went by, and flung after them with curses this encouraging greeting:

"Well, one of them has a soul as mis-shapen as the other one's body!" Or else it would be a band of students and beetle-crushers playing at hop-scotch, who jumped up in a body and hailed them in classic fashion with some Latin whoop and hoot: *"Eia! eia! Claudius cum Claudo!"*

But usually all insults were unheeded by both priest and ringer. Quasimodo was too deaf and Claude too great a dreamer to hear all these gracious speeches.

The Hunchback of Notre-Dame

BOOK V

THE NEW POWER

CHAPTER I

ABBAS BEATI MARTINI

Don Claude's renown had spread far and wide. It procured him, at about the period when he refused to see Madame de Beaujeu, the honour of a visit which he long remembered.

It was on a certain evening. He had just retired after divine service to his canonic cell in the convent of Notre-Dame. This apartment, aside from a few glass phials banished to a corner, and full of somewhat suspicious powder, which looked vastly like gunpowder, contained nothing strange or mysterious. There were inscriptions here and there upon the walls, but they were merely scientific statements, or pious extracts from well-known authors. The archdeacon had just seated himself, by the light of a three-beaked copper lamp, before a huge chest covered with manuscripts. His elbow rested on a wide-open book by Honorius d'Autun, *"De Prædestinatione et libero arbitrio,"* and he was very meditatively turning the leaves of a printed folio which he had brought upstairs with him,—the only product of the press which his cell contained. In the midst of his reverie there was a knock at the door. "Who is

there?" cried the sage in the gracious tone of a hungry dog disturbed while eating his bone.

A voice answered from without; "Your friend, Jacques Coictier." He at once opened the door.

It was indeed the king's physician,— a person of some fifty years of age, whose harsh expression was only corrected by a crafty look. Another man was with him. Both wore long slate-coloured robes furred with minever, belted and clasped, with caps of the same stuff and colour. Their hands were hidden in their sleeves, their feet under their gowns, their eyes beneath their bonnets.

"God help me, gentlemen!' said the archdeacon, showing them in; "I did not expect so honourable a visit at such an hour." And while speaking in this courteous fashion, he cast an anxious and searching glance from the physician to his companion.

"It is never too late to visit so distinguished a scholar as Don Claude Frollo de Tirechappe," replied Doctor Coictier, who, being a native of Franche-Comté, drawled all his sentences until they dragged as majestically as the long train of a lady's dress.

Then began between the doctor and the archdeacon one of those congratulatory prefaces with which it was at this period customary to precede every conversation between learned men, and which did not hinder them from hating each other most cordially. However, it is just so to-day: the lips of every learned man who compliments another scholar are like a cup of honeyed poison.

Claude Frollo's congratulations to Jacques Coictier dwelt particularly on the numerous worldly advantages which that worthy physician in the course of his much-envied career had contrived to extract from every royal malady,—the result of a better and surer alchemy than the search for the philosopher's stone.

"Truly, Doctor Coictier, I was delighted to hear of the bishopric of your nephew, my reverend lord Pierre Versé. Has he not been made Bishop of Amiens?"

"Yes, archdeacon; by the favour and mercy of God."

"Do you know that you cut a very fine figure on Christmas Day, at the head of your associates of the Court of Exchequer, Mr. President?"

"Vice-president, Don Claude. Nothing more, alas!"

"How is your superb house in the Rue Saint-André des Arcs getting on? It's another Louvre. I particularly admire the apricot-tree carved over the door, and the pleasing pun in the motto, 'A L'Abri Cotier.' "

"Alas! Master Claude, all that stonework costs me dear. I am being ruined as fast as the house grows."

"Pooh! Haven't you your revenues from the jail and the Palace bailiwick, and the rent of all the houses, butchers' stalls, booths, and shops within the boundary wall? That's a fine milch-cow for you."

"My Poissy castellany brought me in nothing this year."

"But your toll-gates at Triel, Saint-James, and Saint-Germain-en-Laye are still good."

"A hundred and twenty pounds, and not even Paris pounds at that."

"But you have your place as Councillor to the King. That's a permanent thing."

"Yes, Brother Claude; but that confounded manor of Poligny, which people make such a talk about, doesn't bring me in sixty crowns, take it one year with another."

In the compliments paid to Jacques Coictier by Don Claude there was the sarcastic, sour, slightly mocking tone, the cruel, acid smile of an unfortunate and superior person sporting for a moment, by way of amusement, with the fat prosperity of a vulgar fellow. The other did not observe this.

"By my soul," said Claude at last, pressing his hand, "I am glad to see you in such robust health!"

"Thank you, Master Claude."

"By the way," cried Don Claude, "how goes it with your royal patient?"

"He does not pay his doctor enough," answered the physician, casting a side glance at his comrade.

"Do you think so, friend Coictier?" said his comrade.

These words, uttered in tones of surprise and reproach, drew the archdeacon's attention to the stranger, although, to tell the truth, he had not been wholly unobservant of him for a single instant since he had crossed his threshold. Had there not been a thousand reasons for his conciliating Doctor Jacques Coictier, the all-powerful physician of King Louis XI., he would never have admitted him in such company. Therefore his mien was anything but cordial when Jacques Coictier said,—

"By the way, Don Claude, I bring you a brother worker, who was anxious to see you, being familiar with your fame."

"A gentleman of science?" inquired the archdeacon, fixing his piercing eye upon Coictier's companion. The stranger returned his gaze with an equally searching and defiant look.

As well as the feeble light of the lamp allowed one to judge, he was an elderly man of some sixty years, and of medium height, apparently quite ill and broken. His profile, although not at all aristocratic, was still strong and severe; his eye flashed from beneath a very prominent brow, like a light from the depths of a cave; and under the flat cap which drooped over his face, the broad forehead of a man of genius was visible.

He took upon himself to answer the archdeacon's question.

"Reverend sir," he said in grave tones, "your renown has reached me, and I desired to consult you. I am only a poor country gentleman, who takes off his shoes before venturing into the presence of learned men. You must know my name. I am Father Tourangeau."

"An odd name for a gentleman!" thought the archdeacon. Still, he felt that he had before him a strong and serious character. The instinct of his lofty intellect led him to guess that a spirit no less lofty lurked beneath the furred cap of Father Tourangeau; and as he studied his grave face, the ironical smile which the presence of Jacques

Coictier had forced to his sullen lips faded slowly, as twilight fades from the sky at night. He reseated himself silently and moodily in his great armchair, his elbow resumed its wonted place upon the table, and his head on his hand. After a few moments of meditation he signed to the two visitors to be seated, and addressed Father Tourangeau:—

"You came to consult me, sir; and upon what branch of science?"

"Your reverence," replied Father Tourangeau, "I am ill; very ill. You are said to be a great doctor, and I come to you for medical advice."

"Medical advice!" said the archdeacon, shaking his head. He seemed communing with himself an instant, then added: "Father Tourangeau, if that be your name, turn your head. You will find my answer ready written on the wall."

Father Tourangeau obeyed, and read this inscription on the wall above his head: "Medicine is the daughter of dreams.—JAMBLIQUE."

But Doctor Coictier listened to his comrade's question with a displeasure only increased by Don Claude's answer. He bent to Father Tourangeau's ear and said, low enough not to be overheard by the archdeacon, "I told you he was a madman; but you insisted on seeing him!"

"Because this madman may well be right, Doctor Jacques!" replied the stranger, in the same tone, and with a bitter smile.

"As you please," answered Coictier, drily. Then turning to the archdeacon: "You are an apt workman, Don Claude, and you handle Hippocrates as deftly as a monkey does a nut. Medicine a dream, indeed! I doubt me the druggists and the old masters would stone you well, were they here. Then you deny the influence of philters on the blood, of ointments on the flesh! You deny that everlasting pharmacy of flowers and metals which we call the world, made expressly for that eternal sufferer whom we call man!"

"I deny," said Don Claude, coldly, "neither drugs nor disease. I deny the physician."

"Then it is false," continued Coictier, with warmth, "that gout is an inward eruption, that a cannon-wound may be cured by the application of a roasted mouse, that young blood properly infused restores youth to old veins; it is false to say that two and two make four, and that emprostathonos follows opistathonos."

The archdeacon quietly replied, "There are certain things which I regard in a certain way."

Coictier turned red with rage.

"There, there, my good Coictier, don't be angry!" said Father Tourangeau. "The archdeacon is our friend."

Coictier calmed himself, muttering,—
"After all, he's a madman!"

"Odzooks, Master Claude!" continued Father Tourangeau, after a pause, "you embarrass me mightily. I had two pieces of advice to ask of you,—one concerning my health, the other concerning my star."

"Sir," responded the archdeacon, "if that be your object, you would have done as well not to waste your breath in climbing my stairs. I am no believer in medicine: I am no believer in astrology!"

"Indeed!" said the stranger with surprise.

Coictier laughed a forced laugh.

"You see now that he's mad," he whispered to Father Tourangeau. "He doesn't believe in astrology!"

"How can any-one imagine," continued Don Claude, "that every star-ray is a thread which leads to some man's head!"

"Pray, in what do you believe, then?" exclaimed Father Tourangeau.

The archdeacon for an instant seemed uncertain, then with a gloomy smile, which seemed to belie his answer, said: "credo in Deum."

"Dominum nostrum," added Father Tourangeau, making the sign of the cross.

"Amen," said Coictier.

"Reverend sir," resumed the stranger, "I am delighted to find you so good a Christian. But, great scholar that you are, have you reached such a point that you no longer believe in science?"

"No," said the archdeacon, seizing Father Tourangeau by the arm, while a lightning flash of enthusiasm kindled his dull eye,—"no, I do not deny science. I have not crawled flat on my face all these years, digging the earth with my nails, amid the countless mazes of the cavern, without seeing far before me, at the end of the dark tunnel, a light, a flame, something, doubtless the reflection of the dazzling central laboratory where sages and patient souls have taken God by surprise."

"Come, then," interrupted Tourangeau, "what do you consider true and certain?"

"Alchemy."

Coictier cried out: "Good God, Don

Claude! alchemy has its good points, no doubt; but why should you blaspheme against medicine and astrology?"

"Your science of mankind is naught; your science of heaven naught!" said the archdeacon, authoritatively.

"You treat Epidaurus and Chaldea very cavalierly," replied the doctor with a sneer.

"Hear me, Master Jacques. I speak in good faith. I am not the king's physician, and his Majesty did not give me the Dædalus garden as a convenient spot whence I might study the constellations. Don't be angry, and listen to me. What new truth did you ever derive,— I don't say from medicine, which is far too foolish a matter, but from astrology? Tell me the virtues of the vertical boustrophedon, the discoveries of the number Ziruph and the number Zephirod."

"Would you deny," said Coictier, "the sympathetic power of the clavicle, and that the Cabala is derived from it?"

"An error, Master Jacques! None of your formulæ lead to reality; while alchemy has its indubitable discoveries. Can you contest such results as these, —ice buried beneath the ground for a thousand years is transformed to rock crystal; lead is the progenitor of all the metals,—for gold is not metal, gold is light; lead requires but four periods of two hundred years each to pass successively from the state of lead to the state of red arsenic, from red arsenic to tin, from tin to silver? Are these facts or are they not? But to believe in clavicles, planets, and stars is as absurd as to believe with the natives of far Cathay that the golden oriole turns into

a mole, and grains of wheat into mollusks of the genus Cypræa!"

"I have studied hermetics," cried Coictier, "and I affirm—"

The fiery archdeacon did not permit him to finish his speech. "And I have studied medicine, astrology, and hermetics. Here alone is truth [as he spoke he took from the press a phial filled with the powder of which we spoke some pages back], here alone is light! Hippocrates is a dream; Urania is a dream; Hermes is a mere idea. Gold is the sun; to make gold, is to become God. This is the only wisdom. I have sounded the depths of medicine and astrology, I tell you. They are naught, naught! The human body is a mere shadow; the stars are shadows!"

And he fell back upon his seat in a striking and imposing attitude. Father Tourangeau watched him in silence. Coictier forced himself to sneer, shrugged his shoulders slightly, and repeated in a low voice,—

"A madman!"

"And," said Tourangeau suddenly, "the splendid goal,—have you attained that? Have you made gold?"

"Had I made it," replied the archdeacon, pronouncing his words slowly, like a man who is reflecting, "the King of France would be called Claude, and not Louis."

The stranger frowned.

"What do I say?" added Don Claude with a scornful smile. "What would the throne of France avail me when I could reconstruct the Empire of the East?"

"Well, well," said the stranger.

"Oh, poor fool!" muttered Coictier.

The archdeacon went on, apparently replying to his own thoughts only:—

"But no, I still crawl; I bruise my face and knees on the sharp stones of the subterranean way. I see dimly; I do not behold the full splendour! I do not read; I spell!"

"And when you can read," asked the stranger, "shall you make gold?"

"Who can doubt it?" said the archdeacon.

"In that case, Notre-Dame knows that I am in great need of money, and I would fain learn to read your books. Tell me, reverend master, is your science hostile or displeasing to Notre-Dame?"

To this question from the stranger Don Claude merely answered with a quiet dignity,—

"Whose archdeacon am I?"

"True, my master. Well; will it please you to initiate me? Let me spell with you?"

Claude assumed the majestic and pontifical attitude of a Samuel.

"Old man, it needs more years than still remain to you to undertake the journey through mysterious things. Your head is very grey! None ever leave the cavern without white hairs, but none enter save with dark hair. Science is skilled in furrowing, withering, and wrinkling human faces; it needs not that old age should bring to her faces ready wrinkled. Yet if you long to submit yourself to discipline at your age, and to decipher the dread alphabet of sages, come to me; it is well: I will try what I can do. I will not bid you, you poor old man, go visit the sepulchres in the Pyramids, of which ancient Herodotus speaks, nor the brick tower of Babylon, nor the huge white marble sanctuary of the Indian temple of Eklinga. Neither I nor you have seen the Chaldean edifices constructed after the sacred form of Sikra, or the Temple of Solomon, which is destroyed, or the stone doors of the tomb of the kings of Israel, which are shattered. We will be content with the fragments of the book of Hermes which we have at hand. I will explain to you the statue of Saint Christopher, the symbolism of the sower, and that of the two angels at the door of the Sainte-Chapelle, one of whom has his hand in a vase and the other in a cloud—"

Here Jacques Coictier, who had been disconcerted by the archdeacon's spirited replies, recovered himself, and interrupted in the triumphant tone of one wise man setting another right: "*Erras, amice Claudi.* The symbol is not the number. You take Orpheus for Hermes."

"It is you who err," gravely answered the archdeacon. "Dædalus is the basement; Orpheus is the wall; Hermes is the building itself,—is the whole. Come when you will," he added, turning to Tourangeau; "I will show you the particles of gold remaining in the bottom of Nicolas Flamel's crucible, and you may compare them with the gold of Guillaume de Paris. I will teach you the secret virtues of the Greek word *peristera*. But first of all, you must read in turn the marble letters of the alphabet, the granite pages of the book. We will go from the porch of Bishop Guillaume and of Saint-Jean le Rond to the Sainte-Chapelle, then to the house of Nicolas Flamel in the Rue Marivault, to his tomb, which is in the Cemetery of the Holy Innocents, to his

two almshouses in the Rue Mont-
morency. You shall read the hieroglyphics which cover the four great iron
andirons in the porch of the Saint-
Gervais Hospital, and those in the Rue
de la Ferronnerie. We will spell over
together once more the façades of Saint-
Côme, Sainte-Geneviève des Ardents,
Saint-Martin, Saint-Jacques de la Boucherie—"

For some time Tourangeau, intelligent though his appearance was, had
seemed as if he failed to follow Don
Claude. He now interrupted him with
the words,—

"Odzooks! What sort of books can
yours be?"

"Here is one of them," said the archdeacon.

And opening the window of his cell,
he pointed to the vast Church of Notre-
Dame, which, with its two towers outlined in black against a starry sky, its
stone sides and monstrous hiproof,
seemed like some huge double-headed,
sphinx crouching in the heart of the
town.

The archdeacon silently gazed at the
gigantic edifice; then with a sigh,
stretching his right hand towards the
printed book which lay open on the
table, and his left hand towards Notre-
Dame, with a melancholy glance from
book to church, he said, "Alas! the one
will kill the other."

Coictier, who had eagerly approached
the book, could not repress the words,
"Why! But what is there so terrible
about this: *'Glossa in epistolas D. Pauli.
Norimbergæ, Antonius Koburger. 1474.'*
This is nothing new. It is a book by
Pierre Lombard, the Master of Maxims.
Is it because it is printed?"

"That's it," replied Claude, who
seemed absorbed in deep meditation, and
stood with his forefinger on the folio
from the famous presses of Nuremberg.
Then he added these mysterious words:
"Alas! alas! Small things overcome
great ones: the Nile rat kills the crocodile, the swordfish kills the whale, the
book will kill the building."

The convent curfew rang just as
Doctor Jacques once more whispered
in his comrade's ear his perpetual refrain: "He is mad." To which his comrade now made answer, "I believe he
is."

No stranger was allowed to linger in
the convent at this hour. The two visitors withdrew. "Master," said Father
Tourangeau as he took leave of the
archdeacon, "I like scholars and great
minds, and I hold you in singular esteem.
Come to-morrow to the Palace of the
Tournelles, and ask for the Abbot of
Saint-Martin de Tours."

The archdeacon returned to his cell
in amazement, realizing at last who this
Father Tourangeau really was, and calling to mind this passage from the cartulary of Saint-Martin de Tours: *"Abbas
beati Martini,* SCILICET REX FRANCIÆ,
*est canonicus de consuetudine et habet
parvam præbendam quam habet sanctus
Venantius et debet sedere in sede the-
saurarii."*

It is said that from this time forth
the archdeacon held frequent meetings
with Louis XI., when his Majesty came
to Paris, and that Don Claude's credit
much eclipsed that of Olivier le Daim
and Jacques Coictier, the latter of
whom, as was his wont, roundly reproached the king on this score.

CHAPTER II

THE ONE WILL KILL THE OTHER

OUR fair readers will pardon us for pausing a moment to search for the hidden meaning of those enigmatical words of the archdeacon: "The one will kill the other. The book will kill the building."

In our opinion this thought had two phases. In the first place it was the thought of a priest. It was the terror of a true ecclesiastic at sight of a new agent,—printing. It was the fear and confusion of the man of the sanctuary at sight of Gutenberg's light-giving press. It was the pulpit and the manuscript, the spoken word and the written word, taking fright at the printed word; something similar to the stupor of a sparrow who should see the angel Legion spread his six million wings. It was the cry of the prophet who already hears the busy noise and stir of humanity set free, who sees in the future intellect undermining faith, opinion superseding belief, the world shaking off the yoke of Rome; the presage of the philosopher who sees human ideas, volatilized by the press, evaporated from the theocratic receiver; the dread of the soldier who examines the iron battering-ram and says: The tower must fall. It meant that one power was about to succeed another power. It meant: The press will kill the church.

But underlying this idea, doubtless the first and simplest, there was, to our thinking, another and more recent one, a corollary of the first, less easily seen and more easily contested; a point of view quite as philosophic, but not that of the priest alone,—that of the scholar and the artist as well. It was the presentiment that human thought, in changing its form, would also change its mode of expression; that the leading idea of each generation would no longer be written with the same material and in the same fashion; that the book of stone, so solid and so enduring, must make way for the book of paper, still more solid and enduring. Looked at in this light, the archdeacon's vague statement had another meaning; it meant that one art would dethrone another art. It meant: Printing will destroy architecture.

Indeed, from the beginning of things down to the fifteenth century of the Christian era inclusive, architecture was the great book of humanity, the chief expression of man in his various stages of development, whether as force or as intellect.

When the memory of the earliest races became surcharged, when mankind's burden of recollections became so great and so bewildering that mere speech, naked and winged, was in danger of losing a part on the road, men wrote them upon the ground in the way which was at once plainest, most enduring, and most natural. Every tradition was sealed beneath a monument.

The first monuments were mere fragments of rock "which the iron had not touched," says Moses. Architecture began like all writing. A stone was placed on end, and it was a letter, and each letter was a hieroglyph; and upon each hieroglyph rested a group of ideas, like the capital on a column. Thus did the first races, everywhere, at the same moment, over the entire surface of the world. We find the "cromlech" of the Celts in Asiatic Siberia and in American pampas.

Later on, words were formed; stone was added to stone, these granite syllables were coupled together, the verb essayed a few combinations. The Celtic dolmen and cromlech, the Etruscan tumulus, the Hebrew galgal, are words. Some of them, particularly the tumulus, are proper names. Sometimes, when there was plenty of stone and a vast stretch of coast, a phrase was written. The immense pile of Karnac is an entire formulary.

Finally, men made books. Traditions gave birth to symbols, which hid them as the leaves hide the trunk of a tree; all these symbols, in which humanity believed, grew, multiplied, crossed one another, became more and more complicated; the first monuments were no longer sufficient to contain them; they overflowed them on every side; these monuments barely sufficed to express the primitive tradition, as bare, as simple, and as plain as themselves. Symbolism must needs expand into an edifice. Architecture, therefore, was developed parallel with human thought; it became a thousand-headed, thousand-armed giantess, and fixed all that floating symbolism in an eternal, visible, palpable form. While Dædalus, that is, force, measured; while Orpheus, which is to say, intellect, sang, the column, which is a letter, the arcade, which is a syllable, the pyramid, which is a word, set in motion alike by a geometric and a poetic law, grouped, combined, blended, rose, fell, were juxtaposed upon the ground, placed in rows one above another in air, until they had written, at the dictation of the universal idea of an epoch, those marvellous books which were also marvellous buildings,—the pagoda at Eklinga, the Egyptian Rhamseïon, the Temple of Solomon.

The original idea, the word, was not only at the base of all these buildings, but also in their form. Solomon's Temple, for instance, was not merely the binding of the Holy Book, it was the Holy Book itself. In each of its concentric halls the priests could read the Word translated and made manifest; and thus they followed its transformations from sanctuary to sanctuary, until they grasped it in its innermost tabernacle in its most concrete form, which was again architectural,—the arch. Thus the Word was contained within the edifice; but its image was upon its exterior as the human figure is upon the case of a mummy.

And not only the form of the structure, but the site which was chosen for it, revealed the thought which it represented. According as the symbol to be expressed was graceful and pleasing or gloomy and severe, Greece crowned her mountains with a temple harmonious to the eye; India excavated hers, to carve within them those misshapen subterranean pagodas upborne by gigantic rows of granite elephants.

Thus, for the first six thousand years of the world's history, from the most immemorial pagoda of Hindustan to the Cologne Cathedral, architecture was the great writing of mankind. And this is so true that not only every religious symbol, but even each human thought, had its page and its monument in this vast book.

All civilization begins with theocracy

and ends with democracy. This law of liberty succeeding to unity is written in architecture. For,—let us dwell upon this point,—we must not suppose that the mason's work is only potent to build the temple, to express myth and priestly symbols, to transcribe the mysterious tables of the law in hieroglyphic characters upon its pages of stone. Were it so, as in every human society there comes a moment when the sacred symbol is worn away and obliterated by free thought, when the man slips away from the priest, when the excrescences of philosophies and systems eat away the face of religion, architecture could not reproduce this new state of the human mind; its leaves, closely written on the right side, would be blank upon the other, its work would be mutilated, its book would be imperfect. But it is not so.

Let us take for example the Middle Ages, which we see more clearly from their being nearer to us. During its first period, while theocracy was organizing Europe, while the Vatican rallied and reclassified around it the elements of a Rome made up from the Rome which lay crumbling about the Capitol, while Christianity was seeking the various stages of society amid the rubbish-heaps of previous civilizations, and was rebuilding from its ruins a new hierarchic universe whose high priest was the keystone of a vault, there was first heard springing into place amid this chaos, then little by little seen arising beneath the inspiration of Christianity, under the hand of the barbarians, fragments of dead schools of architecture, Greek and Roman,—that mysterious Roman architecture, the sister of the theocratic edifices of Egypt and India, the unalterable emblem of pure Catholicism, the unchanging hieroglyph of papal unity. All the thought of that time, in fact, is written in this sombre Roman style. Authority, unity, the impenetrable, the absolute, Gregory VII., are everywhere evident; everywhere we find the priest, never the man; everywhere the caste, never the people. Next came the Crusades. This was a great popular movement; and every great popular movement, whatever its cause and purpose, always releases the spirit of liberty from its final precipitate. Novelties are at hand. Here begins the stormy period of the Jacqueries, the Pragueries, and the Leagues. Authority is shaken, unity is divided. Feudality insists upon sharing with theocracy, until the people shall inevitably rise, and, as usual, seize the lion's portion; *Quia nominor leo.* The nobility then penetrate the ranks of the priesthood, the commonalty those of the nobility. The face of Europe is changed. Well! the face of architecture is also changed. Like civilization, it has turned the page, and the new spirit of the times finds architecture ready to write at its dictation. It returned from the Crusades with the pointed arch, as the nations did with liberty. Then, while Rome was being slowly dismembered, Roman architecture died. The hieroglyph forsook the cathedral, and went forth to emblazon the donjon and lend a glory to feudalism. The cathedral itself, that edifice once so dogmatic, henceforth invaded by the burghers, by the Commons, by liberty, escapes from the priest and falls into the power of the artist. The artist builds it in his own way.

Farewell to mystery, myth, and law! Fancy and caprice have full sway. If the priest have but his basilica and his altar, he has nothing to say; the four walls belong to the artist. The architectural book no longer belongs to the priesthood, to religion, to Rome; it is the property of the imagination, of poetry, of the people. Hence the rapid and innumerable changes in this style of architecture which has existed but for three centuries, and which are so striking after the stagnant immobility of the Roman school, which has lived through six or seven. But art advances with giant pace. The genius and originality of the people do the work formerly assigned to the bishops. Each race, as it passes, writes its line in the book; it erases the old Roman hieroglyphs from the frontispiece of the cathedrals, and barely permits the dogma to peep here and there from beneath the new symbolism overlying it. The popular drapery scarcely permits us to guess at the religious framework. No idea can be given of the liberties then taken by architects even in regard to the Church. We find capitals interwoven with monks and nuns in shameful attitudes, as in the Salle des Cheminées of the Palace of Justice at Paris; we find Noah's adventures carved at full length, as under the great porch at Bourges; or we find a tipsy monk, with the ears of an ass, and a glass in his hand, laughing in the face of an entire community, as in the lavatory of the Abbey of Bocherville. There was at this time a license for thoughts written in stone, comparable only to the present freedom of the press. It was the freedom of architecture.

This liberty was carried to great lengths. Sometimes a doorway, a façade, an entire church, offers a symbolic meaning absolutely foreign to religion, nay, even hostile to the Church. Guillaume de Paris in the thirteenth century, Nicolas Flamel in the fifteenth, wrote such seditious pages. Saint-Jacques de la Boucherie was a church of opposition throughout.

In those days thought was free in this direction only; it was therefore never written out in full except upon those books called buildings. Accepted in the form of a building, it would have been burned in the market-place by the executioner had any one been rash enough to risk it in the manuscript form; the thought expressed in the porch of a church would have witnessed the torture of the same thought expressed in the shape of a book. Thus, having only this one way, mason-work, to see the light, it bloomed forth in this way on every hand. Hence the vast quantity of cathedrals which once covered Europe,—a number so prodigious that we can hardly credit it even after verifying it. All the material and all the intellectual forces of society tended to one and the same end,—architecture. In this way, under pretext of building churches to God, the art grew to magnificent proportions.

Then, whoever was born a poet, turned architect. The genius scattered through the masses, repressed on every hand by feudalism as beneath a carapace of iron bucklers, finding no issue save in the direction of architecture, emerged through that art, and its Iliad took the form of cathedrals. All the other arts obeyed and submitted to the sway of architecture. They were the workmen who executed the great work. The architect, the poet, the master singer, summed up in his own person the sculpture which carved his façades, the painting which lit up his window-panes, the music which set his bells in motion and blew his organs. Even the poor poetry, properly so called, which persisted in vegetating in manuscript, was obliged to take some part, to enter into the structure in the form of canticle or prose hymn,—the same part, after all, played by the tragedies of Æschylus at the sacerdotal feasts of Greece, by the book of Genesis in Solomon's Temple.

So, down to the days of Gutenberg, architecture was the principal, the universal writing. In this granite volume, begun by the East, continued by Greek and Roman antiquity, the Middle Ages wrote the final page. Moreover, this phenomenon of an architecture of the people taking the place of an architecture of caste and rank, which we have observed in the Middle Ages, is reproduced with every analogous movement of the human intellect in the other great epochs of history. Thus, to state but briefly here a law which requires volumes for its development, in the Orient, the cradle of the primitive races, after Hindu architecture came Phœnician architecture, that opulent mother of Arab architecture; in antiquity, after Egyptian architecture, of which the Etruscan style and cyclopean monuments are but one variety, came Greek architecture, whose Roman style is but an overloaded prolongation of the Carthaginian dome; in modern times, after Roman architecture, came Gothic architecture. And by dividing these three series, we shall find in the three elder sisters (Hindu architecture, Egyptian architecture, Roman architecture) the same symbolism,—that is to say, theocracy, caste, unity, dogma, myth, God; and in the three younger sisters (Phœnician architecture, Greek architecture, Gothic architecture), whatever may be the diversity of form inherent in their nature, the meaning is always the same,—that is to say, liberty, humanity, mankind.

Whether he be known as Brahmin, Magian, or Pope, we are always conscious of the priest, nothing but the priest, in Hindu, Egyptian, or Roman structures. It is not so with the architecture of the people; their work is richer and less saintly. In the Phœnician school we are conscious of the tradesman; in the Grecian, of the republican; in the Gothic, of the burgher.

The general characteristics of all theocratic architecture are immutability, a horror of progress, a retention of traditional lines, a consecration of primitive types, a constant tendency of all human and natural forms towards the incomprehensible caprices of symbolism. These are obscure books, which only the initiated can decipher. Moreover, in them every form, every deformity even, has a meaning which makes it inviolable. Do not ask the Hindu, Egyptian, or Roman edifices to change their design or correct their statues. All perfection is to them impious. In these pieces of architecture the rigour of the dogma seems to overlie the stone like a second petrifaction. The general characteristics of popular edifices, on the contrary, should be variety, progress, originality, opulence, perpetual motion. They are sufficiently removed from religion to think of their beauty, to care for it, continually to alter and improve their adornment of statues or arabesques. They belong to this age. They have a human quality which they perpetually mingle with the divine symbolism under whose inspiration they are still produced. Hence edifices pervious to every soul, every intellect, and every imagination, still symbolical, but as easy to understand as Nature herself. Between theocratic architecture and this there is the difference that there is between a sacred language and a profane one, between hieroglyphics and art, between Solomon and Phidias.

If we sum up what we have thus far very hastily shown, omitting countless minor evidences and objections, we are led to these conclusions,—that architecture was, up to the fifteenth century, the chief register of humanity; that during this space of time no idea of any elaboration appeared in the world without being built into masonry; that every popular idea as well as every religious law has had its monument; in fact, that the human race has never had an important thought which it has not written in stone. And why? It is because every thought, whether religious or philosophic, is interested in its own perpetuation; because an idea which has stirred one generation desires to stir others, and to leave its trace. Now, what a precarious immortality is that of the manuscript! How far more solid, lasting, and enduring a book is a building! A torch and a Turk are enough to destroy the written words; it takes a social or a terrestrial revolution to destroy the constructed word. The barbarians passed over the Coli-

seum, the Deluge perhaps over the Pyramids.

In the fifteenth century everything changed.

Human thought discovered a means of perpetuation, not only more durable and more resisting than architecture, but also simpler and easier. Architecture was dethroned. To the stone letters of Orpheus succeeded the leaden letters of Gutenberg.

"The book will destroy the building."

The invention of printing was the greatest event in history. It was the primal revolution. It was the renewed and renovated form of expression of humanity; it is human thought laying off one form and assuming another; it is the entire and final changing of the skin of that symbolic serpent which ever since Adam has represented intellect.

Under the form of printing, thought is more imperishable than ever; it is volatile, intangible, indestructible. It is mingled with the air. In the day of architecture it became a mountain, and took armed possession of a century and a place. Now it becomes a flock of birds, is scattered to the four winds, and occupies at once all points of the horizon and all space.

We repeat it; who does not see that in this way it is far more indelible than before? From being solid, it has become perennial. It has passed from duration to immortality. A great body may be demolished, but how can ubiquity be rooted out? Had a flood come, the mountain would have disappeared beneath the waves long before the birds ceased to fly above it; and if but a single ark should float on the surface of the cataclysm, they would rest upon it, survive with it, watch with it the going down of the waters; and the new world which rose from that chaos would, on awakening, behold, hovering aloft, winged and living, the thought of the world which had been swallowed up.

And when we see that this mode of expression is not only the most preservative, but also the simplest, most convenient, and most practicable of all; when we consider that it entails no great amount of luggage, and requires no cumbrous apparatus; when we compare a thought obliged, in order to translate itself into an edifice, to set in motion four or five other arts, tons of gold, a whole mountain of stone, a whole forest of timber, a whole nation of workmen, —when we compare this with the thought which is made into a book, and which needs nothing but a little paper, a little ink, and a pen, why should we wonder that the human intellect gave up architecture for printing? Cross the original bed of a stream by a canal dug below its level, the stream will forsake its bed.

So, too, see how from the time of the discovery of printing, architecture gradually decayed, withered, and dried away. How plainly we can see the water sinking, the sap drying up, the thought of the time and of the people withdrawing from it! The sense of chill is almost imperceptible in the fifteenth century; the press was still too weak, and could only draw off somewhat of the superabundant life of mighty architecture. But with the dawn of the sixteenth century the disease of architecture becomes apparent; it has ceased to be the essential expression of society; in distress, it becomes classic art; from being Gal-

lican, European, indigenous, it becomes Greek and Roman; from being real and modern, it becomes pseudo-antique. It it this decline which is known as the Renaissance, or revival. And yet it is a magnificent decline; for the old Gothic genius, that sun which is setting behind the gigantic press of Mayence, for some time longer pierces with its last rays all this hybrid heap of Latin arcades and Corinthian columns.

It is this setting sun which we take for the light of dawn.

And yet, from the moment that architecture becomes an art, like any other art, that it ceases to be the sum total of art, the supreme, the tyrant art, it loses the power to hold the other arts. They therefore gain their liberty, break the yoke of the architect, and go each its own way. Each of them gains by this divorce. Isolation enlarges everything. Carving becomes sculpture, picture-making becomes painting, the canon becomes music. It might be compared to an empire torn limb from limb at the death of its Alexander, whose provinces become kingdoms.

Hence Raphael, Michael Angelo, Jean Goujon, Palestrina,—those splendours of the dazzling sixteenth century.

At the same time with the arts, thought gained freedom in all directions. The heresiarchs of the Middle Ages had already made large inroads upon Catholicism. The sixteenth century destroyed religious unity. Before the invention of printing, the Reformation would have been but a schism; the invention of printing made it a revolution. Take away the press, and heresy is unnerved. Whether it be due to Providence or to fate, Gutenberg was the precursor of Luther.

But when the sun of the Middle Ages had wholly set, when Gothic genius had forever faded from the horizon of art, architecture grew daily dimmer, duller, and fainter. The printed book, that undying worm of the great edifice, sucked its life-blood and devoured it. It grew visibly thinner, barer, and poorer. It was commonplace, it was paltry, it was null. It ceased to express anything, even the memory of the art of former ages. Reduced to itself, abandoned by the other arts because human thought has abandoned it, it calls in journeymen for lack of artists; plain glass takes the place of painted windows; the stonecutter succeeds the sculptor. Farewell to all vigour, originality, life, and intellect. Architecture now crawled, like a pitiful beggar of the studios, from copy to copy. Michael Angelo, who had doubtless foreseen its death from the dawn of the sixteenth century, had a last inspiration,—the in-inspiration of despair. That Titan of art piled the Pantheon upon the Parthenon, and created St. Peter's Church at Rome. It is a great work, which deserved to remain unique,—the last original creation of architecture, the signature of a colossal artist at the foot of the vast registry of stone which it closed. Michael Angelo dead, what did this wretched architecture do, which survived itself in a spectral, ghost-like state? It took St. Peter's at Rome, copied it, and parodied it. It was mere mania. It was pitiable. Every century had its St. Peter's; in the seventeenth century it was the Val-de-Grâce, in the eighteenth, Sainte-Geneviève.

Every country had its St. Peter's. London had its own; St. Petersburg had its own; Paris had two or three,— a worthless legacy, the last unmeaning drivel of a great art grown old and reduced to dotage before it died!

If in place of characteristic monuments, such as those to which we have just referred, we examine the general aspect of art from the sixteenth to the eighteenth centuries, we observe the same phenomena of decline and decay. From Francis II. down, the architectural form of the edifice becomes less and less apparent, the geometric form growing more and more prominent, like the skeleton of an emaciated invalid. The beautiful lines of art give way to the cold and inexorable lines of geometry. A building ceases to be a building; it is a polyhedron. Architecture, however, struggles to disguise this nakedness. We have the Greek pediment put down upon the Roman pediment, and *vice versa*. We still have the Pantheon within the Parthenon; we still have St. Peter's. We have the brick houses of the reign of Henry IV. with brick corners, as in the Place Royale and Place Dauphine. We have the churches of the reign of Louis XIII., heavy, clumsy, surbased, short, and broad, loaded with a dome as with a hump. We have the Mazarin architecture,—the wretched Italian Pasticcio of the "Four Nations." We have the palaces of the reign of Louis XIV., —long barracks built for courtiers, stiff, cold, and stupid. Lastly, we have the style of Louis XV., with its chiccory and vermicelli, and all the warts and fungi which disfigure that decrepit, toothless, coquettish old architecture. From the days of Francis II. to those of Louis XIV. the evil increased in geometrical ratio. Art was nothing but skin and bones. It was dying a wretched lingering death.

But what was printing doing? All the life which architecture lost, flushed its veins. In proportion as architecture degenerated, printing throve and flourished. The capital of forces which human thought had expended in building, it henceforth expended in books. So from the dawn of the sixteenth century onward, the press, grown to the level of the declining architecture, wrestled with it and slew it. In the seventeenth century it was already sufficiently supreme, sufficiently triumphant, sufficiently sure of victory, to give the world the spectacle of a great literary age. In the eighteenth century, after a long interval of rest at the court of Louis XIV., it once more grasped the old sword of Luther, armed Voltaire with it, and hastened tumultuously forth to attack that ancient Europe whose architectural expression it had already destroyed. When the eighteenth century closed, it had uprooted everything. In the nineteenth, it will reconstruct.

Now, we ask which of the two arts has really represented human thought for three centuries past? Which translates it? Which expresses, not only its literary and scholastic fancies, but its vast, profound, universal movement? Which constantly superposes itself, without rupture or void, upon mankind, which moves apace, a thousand-footed monster,—Architecture, or Printing?

Printing. Let no one be deceived: architecture is dead, irrevocably dead; killed by the printed book; killed because it was less enduring; killed because it was more costly. Every cathedral represents a thousand million francs. Think, then, what a capital would be required to rewrite the architectural book; to make thousands of structures once more cover the earth as thick as ant-hills; to bring back the days when the number of monumental works was such that, in the words of an eye-witness, "You would have thought that the world had shaken off her old garments, to clothe herself in a white array of churches," *Erat enim ut si mundus, ipse excutiendo semet, rejecta vetustate, candidam ecclesiarum vestem indueret."* —GLABER RADULPHUS.

A book is so soon made, costs so little, and may go so far! Why should we be surprised that all human thought flows that way? We do not mean to say that architecture may not yet produce a fine specimen here and there, a single masterpiece. We may still, I suppose, have from time to time, under the reign of printing, a column made by an entire army, of molten cannon, as during the reign of architecture we had Iliads and Romanceros, Mahâbhâratas, and Nibelungen-Lieds made by a whole nation, out of collected and blended rhapsodies.

The great accident of an architect of genius may occur in the twentieth century, as that of Dante did in the thirteenth; but architecture will never again be the social art, the collective art, the dominant art. The great poem, the great edifice, the great work of humanity, will no longer be built; it will be printed.

And in the future, should architecture accidentally revive, it will never again be supreme. It must bow to the sway of literature, formerly subject to it. The respective positions of the two arts will be reversed. It is certain that the rare poems to be found during the architectural period are like monuments. In India, Vyâsa was as manifold, strange, and impenetrable as a pagoda. In Egypt, poetry had, like the buildings, a grandeur and quietness of outline; in ancient Greece, beauty, serenity, and calm; in Christian Europe, the Catholic majesty, popular simplicity, the rich and luxuriant vegetation of a period of renewal. The Bible is like the Pyramids, the Iliad like the Parthenon, Homer like Phidias. Dante in the thirteenth century is the last Roman church; Shakspeare in the sixteenth the last Gothic cathedral.

Thus, to sum up what we have so far said in a manner necessarily brief and imperfect, mankind has two books, two registers, two testaments: architecture and printing,—the Bible of stone and the Bible of paper. Undoubtedly, when we examine these two Bibles, so widely opened during the lapse of centuries, we may be permitted to regret the visible majesty of the granite writing, of those gigantic alphabets formed into colonnades, pylons, and obelisks, of those human mountains which covered the world of the past, from the pyramid to the belfry, from Cheops to Strasburg. We should re-read the past upon those marble pages. We should admire and unceasingly re-turn the leaves of the book written by architecture; but we should not deny the grandeur of the structure reared by printing in its turn.

That structure is colossal. I know not what maker of statistics has calculated that by placing one upon another all the volumes issued from the press since the days of Gutenberg, we might fill up the space between the earth and the moon; but this is not the sort of grandeur which we mean. Still, when we try to form a mental image of all the products of printing down to our own day, does not the sum total seem a vast construction, resting upon the entire universe, at which humanity labours without respite, and whose monstrous summit is lost in the thick mists of the future? It is the ant-hill of intellects. It is the hive where all wit and imagination, those golden bees, store up their honey. The structure has a thousand stories. Here and there, opening on its staircases, we see the dark caves of learning intersecting one another within it. All over its surface art has woven its arabesques, its rose-windows, and its lace-work, to captivate the eye. There each individual work, fanciful and unique as it may seem, has its place and its purpose. Harmony results from the union of all. From the cathedral of Shakspeare to the mosque of Byron, a myriad spires are heaped pell-mell upon this metropolis of universal thought. At its base are inscribed some antique titles of humanity which architecture failed to register. At the left of the entrance is fastened the old white bas-relief of Homer; at the right the polyglot Bible rears its seven heads. The hydra of the Romancero bristles up beyond, with certain other hybrid forms, like the Vedas and the Nibelungen. Moreover, the vast edifice remains forever unfinished. The press, that gigantic machine which untiringly sucks up all the intellectual sap of society, unceasingly vomits forth fresh material for its work. All mankind are on the scaffolding. Every mind is a mason. The humblest stops up his hole or lays his stone. Every day a fresh course is laid. Independently of the original and individual contributions of each writer, there are collective supplies. The eighteenth century gave the "Encyclopædia," The French Revolution gave the "Moniteur." Assuredly, it is a structure which will gather and grow in unending spirals. Here, too, there is a confusion of tongues, an incessant activity, an indefatigable industry, a frantic co-operation of all humanity; it is the refuge promised to intellect against another deluge, against a flood of barbarians. It is the second Tower of Babel of the human race.

BOOK VI

The Pillory

CHAPTER I

AN IMPARTIAL GLANCE AT THE ANCIENT MAGISTRACY

A VERY lucky fellow, in the year of grace 1482, was that noble gentleman Robert d'Estouteville, knight, Lord of Beyne, Baron of Ivry and St. Andry in La Marche, councillor and chamberlain to the king, and keeper of the provosty of Paris. It was some seventeen years since he received from the king, Nov. 7, 1465, the year of the comet, the handsome appointment of provost of Paris, which was regarded rather as a dignity than an office. *"Dignitas,"* says Joannes Lœmnœus, *"quæ cum non exigua potestate politiam concernente, atque prærogativis multis et juribus conjuncta est."* It was an extraordinary thing in 1482 for a gentleman to hold a commission from the king; and a gentleman, too, whose appointment dated back to the time of the marriage of Louis XI.'s natural daughter to the Bastard of Bourbon. On the same day that Robert d'Estouteville succeeded Jacques de Villiers as provost of Paris, Master Jehan Dauvet took the place of Master Hélye de Thorrettes as first president of the court of Parliament, Jehan Jouvenel des Ursins supplanted Pierre de Morvilliers in the office of Lord Chancellor of France, Regnault des Dormans deprived Pierre Puy of his place as referendary in ordinary to the king's household. Now, through how many hands had the presidency, chancellorship, and referendaryship not passed since Robert d'Estouteville was made provost of Paris! The office was "granted into his keeping," said the letters-patent; and certainly he kept it well. He clung to it, he identified himself with it, he made himself so much a part of it that he escaped that passion for change which possessed Louis XI., the suspicious, stingy, industrious king, who insisted on keeping up the elasticity of his power by constant removals and appointments. Nay, more: the worthy knight had obtained the reversion of his office for his son, and for the last two years the name of the noble Jacques d'Estouteville, Esquire, had figured beside his own at the head of the ordinary of the provosty of Paris. Assuredly a rare and signal mark of favour! True, Robert d'Estouteville was a good soldier; he had loyally raised his standard against "the league of the public weal," and had offered the queen a very marvellous stag made of sweetmeats on the day she entered Paris, in 14—. Besides, he had a good friend in Master Tristan l'Hermite, provost of the marshals of the king's household. Master Robert, therefore, led a very smooth and pleasant life. In the first place, he had a capital salary, to which were attached and hung, like so many additional bunches of grapes to his vine, the revenues of the civil and criminal registries of the provostship, besides the civil and criminal revenues of the Inferior Courts of the Châtelet, not to mention some slight toll on the Pont de Mantes and Pont de Corbeil, the tax on all the onions, leeks, and garlic brought into Paris, and the tax on wood meters and salt measures. Add to this the pleasure of displaying his fine suit of armour within the city limits, and showing off among the party-coloured red and tan robes of the sheriffs and district police which you may still admire carved upon his tomb at the Abbey of Valmont in Normandy, as you may also see his embossed morion at Montlhéry. And then,—was it nothing to have supreme power over the twelve serjeants, the porter and warder of the Châtelet, the two auditors of the Châtelet, *auditores castelleti,* the sixteen commissaries of the sixteen quarters of

the city, the jailer of the Châtelet, the four enfeoffed serjeants, the hundred and twenty mounted police, the hundred and twenty vergers, the captain of the watch, his under-watch, counter-watch, and rear-watch? Was it nothing to administer high and low justice, to exercise the right to turn, hang, and draw, to say nothing of the minor jurisdiction "in the first instance" (*in prima instantia,* as the charters say) of that viscounty of Paris, so gloriously provided with seven noble bailiwicks? Can anything be imagined more agreeable than to give judgments and degrees, as Master Robert d'Estouteville did daily at the Grand-Châtelet, under the broad flat arches of Philip Augustus; and to return, as he was wont to do every evening, to that charming house in the Rue Galilée, within the precincts of the royal palace, which he held in right of his wife, Madame Ambroise de Loré, there to rest from the labour of sending some poor devil to pass his night in "that little lodge in the Rue de l'Escorcherie, wherein the provosts and sheriffs of Paris were used to make their prison, —the same measuring eleven feet in length, seven feet and four inches in width, and eleven feet in height?"

And not only had Master Robert d'Estouteville his private court as provost and viscount of Paris, but he also had his share, both active and passive, in the king's own high justice. There was no head of any note but had passed through his hands before falling into those of the executioner. It was he who went to the Bastille Saint-Antoine, in search of M. de Nemours, to take him to the Markets; and he who conducted M. de Saint-Pol to the Grève, the latter gentleman sulking and fretting, to the great delight of the provost, who had no love for the constable.

Here, certainly, was more than enough to make life happy and illustrious, and to justify in the future a memorable page in the interesting history of the provosts of Paris, wherein we learn that Oudard de Villeneuve had a house in the Rue des Boucheries, that Guillaume de Hangest bought big and little Savoy, that Guillaume Thiboust gave the nuns of Sainte-Geneviève his houses in the Rue Clopin, that Hugues Aubriot lived at Hôtel du Porc-Epic, and other domestic facts.

And yet, with all these motives for taking life patiently and pleasantly, Master Robert d'Estouteville waked on the morning of Jan. 7, 1482, in a very sulky and disagreeable mood. Whence came this ill-humour? He could not have told you himself. Was it because the sky was overcast; because the buckle of his old Montlhéry belt was fastened amiss, and girt his provostship's goodly portliness in too military a fashion; because he had seen a band of ragamuffins march through the street below his window, mocking him as they passed in double file, wearing doublets without shirts, crownless hats, and wallet and flask at their side? Was it a vague presentiment of the three hundred and seventy pounds, sixteen pence, and eight farthings which the future king, Charles VIII., was to cut off from the revenues of the provosty? The eader can take his choice; as for us, we incline to the belief that he was out of temper simply because he was out of temper.

Besides, it was the day after a holiday,—a stupid day for everybody, and especially for the magistrate, whose duty it was to sweep away all the dirt, actual and metaphorical, caused by a popular holiday in Paris. And then, he was to hold court at the Grand-Châtelet. Now, we have noticed that judges usually so arrange matters that the day upon which they hold court is also the day on which they are out of temper, in order that they may always have some one upon whom to vent their rage, in the name of the king, law, and justice.

However, the court had opened without him. His deputies, in the civil, criminal, and private courts, were doing his work for him, as was the custom; and ever since eight o'clock in the morning some scores of citizens, men and women, crowded and crammed into a dark corner of the lower court-room of the Châtelet, between a stout oaken railing and the wall, had blissfully looked on at the varied and attractive spectacle of the administration of civil and criminal law by Master Florian Barbedienne, auditor of the Châtelet, and provost's deputy, whose sentences were delivered pell-mell and somewhat at random.

The hall was small and low, with a vaulted roof. A table branded with *fleur-de-lis* stood at the back of it, with a large carved oaken arm-chair, which belonged to the provost and was empty, and a stool on the left for the auditor, Master Florian. Below sat the clerk, scribbling; opposite him were the people; and before the door and table were a number of the provost's officers, in frocks of purple camlet, with white crosses. Two officers from the Commonalty Hall, arrayed in party-coloured

red and blue kersey jackets, stood sentry before a half-open door, behind the table. A single arched window, deep set in the thick wall, cast a ray of pale January sunshine upon two grotesque figures,—the comical stone demon carved as a tailpiece to the keystone of the vaulted roof, and the judge seated at the end of the hall upon the *fleurs-de-lis.*

Now, picture to yourself at the provost's table, between two bundles of papers, leaning on his elbows, his feet on the train of his plain brown cloth gown, his face framed in its white lamb's-wool wig, of which his eyebrows seemed to be a fragment, red-faced, stern, winking and blinking, majestically bearing the burden of his fat cheeks, which met under his chin, Master Florian Barbedienne, auditor of the Châtelet.

Now, the auditor was deaf,—a slight defect for an auditor. Master Florian gave judgment, nevertheless, without appeal, and very properly too. It is certainly quite enough if a judge look as if he were listening; and the venerable auditor fulfilled this condition—the only one requisite to the due administration of justice—all the better for the fact that his attention was not to be distracted by any noise.

Moreover, he had a merciless comptroller of his sayings and doings, among the audience, in the person of our friend Jehan Frollo du Moulin, the little student of the previous day, that pedestrian who was sure to be found anywhere in Paris except in front of his professors' desk.

"Stay," he whispered to his comrade, Robin Poussepain, who was chuckling beside him while he commented on the scenes unrolled before them, "there's Jehanneton du Buisson,—the pretty daughter of that loafer from the New Market! Upon my soul, he has condemned her, the old wretch! Then his eyes can't be any better than his ears. Fifteen pence and four Paris farthings, for wearing two strings of beads! That's rather dear. *'Lex duri carminis.'* Who's that fellow? Robin Chief-de-Ville, hauberk-maker,—for having been passed and received as a master of the said trade? It's his entrance-fee. Hollo! two gentlemen among these varlets,— Aiglet de Soins, Hutin de Mailly. Two esquires, *Corpus Christi!* Ah, ha! they've been playing at dice. When shall I see our rector here? A hundred Paris pounds fine to the king! Barbedienne hits hard, like a deaf man as he is! I wish I may be my brother the archdeacon if this prevent me from gambling,—gambling by day, gambling by night, living a gambler, dying a gambler, and gambling away my soul when my last rag's gone! Holy Virgin! what a lot of girls! One after the other, my lambs! Ambroise Lécuyère! Isabeau la Paynette! Bérarde Gironin! I know them all, by heaven! Fine 'em! fine 'em! That'll teach you to wear gilt belts! Ten Paris pence, coquettes! Oh, what an old dog of a judge! deaf and imbecile! Oh, Florian, you blockhead! Oh, Barbedienne, you booby! See him sit at table! He gobbles the suitor, he gobbles the suit, he minces, he munches, he stuffs himself, he fills himself full. Fines, estrays, taxes, expenses, legal costs, wages, damages, torture, prison and jail and stocks, are Christmas cakes and Saint John's marchpane to him! Just look at him, the pig! Now, then, good! Still another amorous dame! Thibaud-la-Thibaude, and no one else,—for leaving the Rue Glatigny! Who is that fellow? Gieffroy Mabonne, bowman of the guard. He swore by the Holy Name, did he?—A fine, Thibaude! a fine, Gieffroy! Fine 'em both! Deaf old fool! he must have mixed the two charges up! Ten to one, he'll fine the woman for swearing, and the bowman for making love! Attention, Robin Poussepain! Whom are they bringing in now? What a lot of serjeants! By Jupiter! all the hounds in the pack are here. This must be the best head of game they've got,—a wild boar. It *is* one, Robin, it is indeed,—and a fine one too! By Hercules! it's our yesterday's prince, our Lord of Misrule, our bell-ringer, our one-eyed, humpbacked pet, our wryface! It's Quasimodo!"

It was no less a personage, indeed.

It was Quasimodo, bound, corded, tied, garotted, and well guarded. The squad of men who had him in charge were assisted by the captain of the watch in person, wearing the arms of France embroidered on his breast, and the city arms on his back. There was nothing, however, about Quasimodo, except his deformity, which could justify this display of halberds and arquebuses; he was sombre, silent, and quiet. His solitary eye merely cast an occasional crafty, angry glance at the bonds which held him.

He gazed around him with the same expression, but so dull and sleepy was it that the women only pointed him out to each other to mock at him.

But Master Florian, the auditor, was attentively turning over the brief containing the charge against Quasimodo, which the clerk had just handed him, and having examined the papers, seemed to be meditating for a moment. Thanks to this precaution, which he was always careful to take just before proceeding to an examination, he knew in advance the name, condition, and crimes of the prisoner, had his answer ready for replies which he expected, and succeeded in extricating himself from all intricacies of the examination without making his deafness too apparent. The brief therefore was to him like the blind man's dog. If he chanced to betray his infirmity by an occasional incoherent remark or an unintelligible question, it passed with some for profundity, and with others for imbecility. In either case, the honour of the magistracy was unimpeached; for it is much better that a judge should be considered stupid or profound than deaf. He accordingly took great pains to hide his deafness from all, and usually succeeded so well that he had actually come to deceive himself,—a thing, moreover, which is easier than you would think. All hunchbacks carry their heads high, all stammerers are fond of speechifying, all deaf people speak in low tones. As for him, at most he thought himself a little hard of hearing. This was the sole concession which he was willing to make to the public opinion upon this point, in his moments of perfect frankness and self-examination.

Having therefore considered Quasimodo's case, he threw back his head and half closed his eyes, in order to look more majestic and impartial, so that for the time being he was both deaf and blind,—a twofold condition, without which there can be no perfect judge. In this magisterial attitude he began his cross-examination.

"Your name?"

Now, here was a case which had not been "provided for by the law,"—that of one deaf man questioning another.

Quasimodo, quite unconscious of the question, continued to gaze fixedly at the judge, and made no answer. The judge, deaf, and wholly unaware of the prisoner's deafness, supposed that he had answered, as all prisoners were wont to do, and went on, with his mechanical and stupid assurance,—

"Good! Your age?"

Quasimodo made no answer. The judge was satisfied, and continued,—

"Now, your business?"

Still the same silence. The audience began to whisper and look at each other.

"That will do," resumed the imperturbable auditor, when he supposed that the prisoner had ended his third answer. "You are accused, before us: *primo,* of making a nocturnal disturbance; *secundo,* of an indecent assault upon the person of a light woman, *in præjudicium meretricis; tertio,* of rebellion and disloyalty towards the archers of the guard of our lord the king. What have you to say for yourself on all these points? Clerks, have you written down all that the prisoner has said thus far?"

At this unfortunate question a shout of laughter burst from both clerk and audience, so violent, so hearty, so contagious, so universal, that even the two deaf men could not fail to notice it. Quasimodo turned away, shrugging his hump in disdain; while Master Florian, equally surprised, and supposing the laughter of the spectators to be provoked by some irreverent reply from the prisoner, made apparent to him by that shrug, addressed him most indignantly,—

"Such an answer as that, you rascal, deserves a halter! Do you know to whom you speak?"

This sally was scarcely adapted to silence the outburst of merriment. It seemed to all so absurd and ridiculous that the contagious laughter spread to the very serjeants from the Commonalty Hall, the kind of men-at-arms whose stupidity is their uniform. Quasimodo alone preserved his gravity, for the very good reason that he understood nothing of what was going on around him. The judge, more and more indignant, felt obliged to proceed in the same strain, hoping in this way to strike the prisoner with a terror which would react upon the audience and restore them to a due sense of respect for him.

"So then, perverse and thievish knave, you venture to insult the auditor of the Châtelet, the chief magistrate of the police courts of Paris, appointed to inquire into all crimes, offences, and misdemeanours; to control all trades and prevent monopoly; to keep the pavements in repair; to put down hucksters of poultry, fowl, and wild game; to superintend the measuring of logs and firewood; to cleanse the city of mud and the air of contagious diseases,—in a word, to watch continually over the public welfare, without wages or hope of salary! Do you know that my name is Florian Barbedienne, and that I am the lord provost's own deputy, and, moreover, commissary, comptroller, and examiner with equal power in provosty, bailiwick, court of registration, and presidial court?"

There is no reason why a deaf man talking to a deaf man should ever cease. Heaven knows when Master Florian, thus launched on the full flood of his own eloquence, would have paused, if the low door at the back of the room had not suddenly opened and admitted the provost himself.

At his entrance Master Florian did not stop short, but turning half round on his heel and abruptly addressing to the provost the harangue with which but a moment before he was overwhelming Quasimodo, he said: "My lord, I demand such sentence as it may please you to inflict upon the prisoner here present, for his grave and heinous contempt of court."

And he sat down again quite out of breath, wiping away the big beads of moisture which ran down his face like tears, wetting the papers spread out before him. Master Robert d'Estouteville frowned, and commanded Quasimodo's attention by a sign so imperious and significant that even the deaf man understood something of his meaning.

The provost addressed him severely: "What brings you here, scoundrel?"

The poor wretch, supposing that the provost asked his name, broke his wonted silence, and answered in a hoarse and guttural voice, "Quasimodo."

The answer had so little to do with the question than an irresistible laugh again ran round the room, and Master Robert cried out, red with rage,—

"Would you mock me too, you arrant knave?"

"Bell-ringer of Notre-Dame," replied Quasimodo, fancying himself called upon to explain to the judge who he was.

"Bell-ringer, indeed!" responded the provost, who, as we have already said, had waked in an ill enough humour that morning not to require any fanning of the flames of his fury by such strange answers. "Bell-ringer! I'll have a peal of switches rung upon your back through all the streets of Paris! Do you hear me, rascal?"

"If you want to know my age," said Quasimodo, "I believe I shall be twenty on Saint Martin's Day."

This was too much; the provost could bear it no longer.

"Oh, you defy the provost's office, do you, wretch! Vergers, take this scamp to the pillory in the Grève; beat him well, and then turn him for an hour. He shall pay me for this, odzooks! And I order this sentence to be proclaimed, by the aid of four sworn trumpeters, throughout the seven castellanies of the viscounty of Paris."

The clerk at once wrote down the sentence.

"A wise sentence, by God!" exclaimed the little student, Jehan Frollo du Moulin, from his corner.

The provost turned, and again fixed his flashing eyes upon Quasimodo: "I believe the scamp said 'By God!' Clerk, add a fine of twelve Paris pence for swearing, and let half of it go to the Church of Saint Eustache; I am particularly fond of Saint Eustache."

In a few moments the sentence was drawn up. It was simple and brief in tenor. The common law of the provosty and viscounty of Paris had not yet been elaborated by the president, Thibaut Baillet, and by Roger Barmue, the king's advocate; it was not then obscured by that mass of quirks and quibbles which these two lawyers intro duced at the beginning of the sixteenth century. Everything about it was clear, expeditious, and explicit. It went straight to the mark, and at the end of every path, unconcealed by brambles or briers, the wheel, the gallows, or the pillory were plainly to be seen from the very outset. At least, you knew what was coming.

The clerk handed the sentence to the provost, who affixed his seal to it, and left the room to continue his round of the courts, in a state of mind which must have added largely that day to the population of the jails of Paris. Jehan Frollo and Robin Poussepain laughed in their sleeves. Quasimodo looked on with indifference and surprise.

But the clerk, just as Master Florian Barbedienne was reading the sentence in his turn before signing it, felt a twinge of pity for the poor devil of a prisoner, and in the hope of gaining some diminution of his punishment, leaned as close as he could to the auditor's ear, and said, pointing to Quasimodo, "That fellow is deaf."

He hoped that their common infirmity might rouse Master Florian's interest in the prisoner's favour. But, in the first place, we have already observed that Master Florian did not care to have his deafness noticed. In the next place, he was so hard of hearing that he caught not one word of what the clerk said to him; and yet, he wanted to have it appear that he heard, and therefore answered, "Oho! that's a different matter; I did not know that. Give him another hour in the pillory, in that case."

And he signed the sentence with this modification.

"Well done!" said Robin Poussepain, who bore Quasimodo a grudge; "that will teach him to maltreat folks."

CHAPTER II

THE RAT-HOLE

WITH the reader's permission, we will return to the Grève which we left yesterday with Gringoire, to follow Esmeralda.

It is ten o'clock in the morning; everything smacks of the day after a holiday. The pavement is covered with fragments,—ribbons, scraps, feathers from the plumes, drops of wax from torches, crumbs from the public feast. A number of citizens are lounging here and there, occasionally stirring the dying embers of the bonfire with their feet, going into ecstasies over the Pillar House, as they recall the fine hangings of the previous day, and staring at the nails which held them, the last remnant of their pleasure. The venders of cider and beer roll their barrels through the various groups. A few busy passers come and go. The shop-keepers chat and gossip with one another at the door of their shops. The festival, the ambassadors, Coppenole, the Lord of Misrule, are on every tongue, each vying with the other in the severity of his criticisms and the loudness of his laughter. And yet four mounted police, who have just stationed themselves at the four corners of the pillory, have already collected about them a goodly portion of the populace scattered about the square, and willing to stand stupidly still for any length of time, in the hope of witnessing some petty punishment.

If now the reader, having looked upon this lively and noisy scene enacting in every part of the square, will turn his gaze towards that ancient half-Gothic, half-Roman structure known as Tour-Roland, which forms the western angle of the quay, he may perceive at the corner of its façade a large public breviary, richly illuminated, protected from the rain by a small pent-house, and from thieves by a grating, which, however, allows the passer-by to turn over its leaves. Beside this breviary is a narrow arched window, guarded by two iron bars placed crosswise, and looking out upon the square,—the only opening through which a little air and light reach a tiny cell without a door, built on the ground-floor, in the thickness of the wall of the old house, and filled with a peace made more profound, a silence made more melancholy, by the fact that a public square, the noisiest and most thickly peopled place in all Paris, swarms and shrieks just outside.

This cell has been celebrated throughout Paris for almost three centuries; since Madame Rolande, of the Tour-Roland, being in mourning for her father, who died while on a Crusade, had it hewed out of the wall of her own house and shut herself up in it forever, keeping no part of her palace but this one lodging, the door of which was walled up and the window open, in winter as in summer, giving all the rest of her property to God and the poor. The desolate dame did indeed await death for twenty years within this premature tomb, praying night and day for her father's soul, sleeping upon a bed of ashes, without even a stone for a pillow, clad in black sack-cloth, and living on such portions of bread and water as the pity of the passers-by placed on her window-sill; thus accepting charity after having bestowed it. At her death, as she was about to pass to another tomb, she bequeathed this one in perpetuity to all afflicted women, mothers, widows, or daughters, who had great need to pray for others or themselves, and who wished to bury themselves alive in token of their great grief or great penitence. The poor of her time paid her the best of funeral rites in their tears and blessings; but, to their great regret, the pious dame could not be canonized a saint, for lack of patronage. Those of them who were inclined to be impious hoped that the matter might be more readily arranged in paradise than at Rome, and quite simply prayed to God instead of to the Pope, for the deceased. Most of them were satisfied with holding her memory sacred and making relics of her rags. The city, for its part, founded for the lady's sake a public breviary, which was fastened to the wall near the window of the cell, so that those who passed might occasionally stop, if only to pray, that so the prayer might lead them to think of alms, and that the poor recluses, the heirs of Madame Rolande's cell, might not die of hunger and neglect.

Nor was this sort of tomb a great rarity in the cities of the Middle Ages. There might frequently be found, in the most crowded street, in the most motley and clamorous market-place, in the very midst of the confusion, under the horses' feet, under the cart-wheels, as it were, a cellar, a well, a walled and grated cell, within which some human being prayed night and day, voluntarily vowed to everlasting lamentation, to some extra-ordinary expiation. And all the reflections which would be roused to-day by so singular a sight,—that horrid cell, a sort of connecting link between the house and the tomb, the cemetery and the city; that living creature cut off from human companionship and thenceforth reckoned with the dead; that lamp consuming its last drop of oil in darkness; that remnant of life flickering in a grave; that breath, that voice, that perpetual prayer, in a coffin of stone; that face forever turned towards the other world; that eye already illumined by another sun; that ear glued to the wall of the tomb; that soul imprisoned in that body; that body imprisoned in that dungeon; and beneath that double casing of flesh and stone the murmur of that suffering soul,—nothing of all this was noted by the crowd.

The unreasoning and far from subtile piety of that day could not conceive of so many sides to an act of religion. It viewed the thing as a whole, and honoured, venerated, sanctified the sacrifice if need be, but did not analyze the suffering, and pitied it but slightly. It occasionally bestowed some pittance on the wretched penitent, looked through the hole to see if he were still alive, knew not his name, hardly knew how many years it was since he began to die, and to the stranger who asked about the living skeleton rotting in that cellar, the neighbours simply answered, "That is the recluse."

People saw things in this way then,—without metaphysics, without exaggeration, without magnifying-glass, with the naked eye. The microscope had not yet been invented, either for material or for spiritual things.

Besides, although people marvelled so little at them, instances of this kind of claustration in the heart of a town were really very frequent, as we just now observed. Paris contained a goodly number of these cells for praying to God and doing penance; they were almost all occupied. It is true that the clergy did not care to leave them empty, as that would imply luke-warmness among the faithful; and they therefore put lepers into them when they had no penitents. Besides the cell in the Grève, there was one at Montfaucon, one at the charnel-house of the Cemetery of the Innocents, another,—I've forgotten just where,—at Clichon House, I believe; others again in many other places, traces of which may yet be found in popular tradition, for lack of monuments. The University also had cells of its own. On St. Geneviève's Mount a kind of mediæval Job for thirty years sang the seven penitential psalms upon a dunghill, at the bottom of a cistern, beginning again whenever he reached the end, chanting louder by night,—*magna voce per umbras*; and even now the antiquary fancies that he hears his voice when he enters the street known as Rue Puits-qui-parle ("Talking Well").

But to keep to the cell of the Tour-Roland, we should mention that it had never wanted for recluses. Since Madame Rolande's death, it had seldom been vacant for more than a year. Many women had gone thither to weep, until death, for parents, lovers, or sins. Parisian malice, which interferes with everything, even those things which concern it least, asserted that very few widows had ever been seen within its walls.

As was the fashion of that period, a Latin inscription on the wall informed the learned passers-by of the pious purpose of this cell. The custom was retained until the middle of the sixteenth century, of explaining the purpose of a building in a brief device inscribed above the door. Thus we still read in France, over the gate of the prison belonging to the manor of the Lord of Tourville: *"Sileto et spera;"* in Ireland, under the escutcheon over the great door of Fortescue Castle: *"Forte scutum, salus ducum;"* and in England, over the main entrance to the hospitable manor of Earl Cowper: *"Tuum est."* In those days every edifice embodied a thought.

As there was no door to the walled cell in the Tour-Roland, some one had carved in Roman capitals over the window these two words:—

"TU, ORA."

Hence the people, whose mind never grasps such nice distinctions, and who are quite ready to translate *Ludovico Magno* into the Porte Saint-Denis, gave this dark, damp, gloomy cavern the name of the *"Trou-aux-Rats,"* or the Rat-Hole,—an explanation possibly less sublime, but certainly more picturesque than the other.

CHAPTER III

THE STORY OF A WHEATEN CAKE

AT the time of which this story treats, the cell in the Tour-Roland was occupied. If the reader wish to know by whom, he has but to listen to the conversation of three worthy gossips, who, at the moment when we drew his attention to the Rat-Hole, were walking directly that way, going from the Châtelet towards the Grève, along the water's edge.

Two of these women were dressed like good citizens of Paris. Their fine white gorgets; their petticoats of striped linsey-woolsey, red and blue; their white knitted stockings, with coloured clocks, pulled well up over the leg; their square-toed shoes of tan-coloured leather with black soles; and above all their head-dress,—a sort of tinsel horn overloaded with ribbons and lace, still worn by the women of Champagne and by the grenadiers of the Russian Imperial Guard,—proclaiming that they belonged to that class of rich tradesfolk occupying the middle ground between what servants call "a woman" and what they call "a lady." They wore neither rings nor gold crosses; and it was easy to see that this was not from poverty, but quite simply from fear of a fine. Their companion was attired in much the same style; but there was something in her appearance and manner which bespoke the country notary's wife. It was evident by the way in which her girdle was arranged high above her hips, that she had not been in Paris long; add to this a pleated gorget, knots of ribbon on her shoes, the fact that the stripes of her petticoat ran breadthwise, and a thousand other enormities revolting to good taste.

The first two walked with the gait peculiar to Parisian women showing Paris to their country friends. The country-woman held by the hand a big boy, who grasped in his hand a large cake. We regret that we must add that, owing to the severity of the season, his tongue did duty as a pocket-handkerchief.

The child loitered ("*non passibus æquis*," as Virgil has it), and stumbled constantly, for which his mother scolded him well. True, he paid far more attention to the cake than to the pavement. Undoubtedly he had some grave reason for not biting it (the cake), for he contented himself with gazing affectionately at it. But his mother should have taken charge of the cake. It was cruel to make a Tantalus of the chubby child.

But the three damsels (for the term "dame" was then reserved for noble ladies) were all talking at once.

"Make haste, Damoiselle Mahiette," said the youngest of the three, who was also the biggest, to the country-woman. "I am mightily afraid we shall be too late; they told us at the Châtelet that he was to be taken directly to the pillory."

"Nonsense! What do you mean, Damoiselle Oudarde Musnier?" replied the other Parisian. "He is to spend two hours in the pillory. We have plenty of time. Did you ever see any one pilloried, my dear Mahiette?"

"Yes," said the country-woman, "at Rheims."

"Pooh! What's your pillory at Rheims? A miserable cage, where they turn nothing but peasants! A fine sight, truly!"

"Nothing but peasants!" said Mahiette, "in the Cloth-market! at Rheims! We've seen some very fine criminals there,—people who had killed both father and mother! Peasants, indeed! What do you take us for, Gervaise?"

The country-lady was certainly on the eve of losing her temper in defence of her pillory. Fortunately the discreet Damoiselle Oudarde Musnier changed the subject in time:—

"By-the-bye, Damoiselle Mahiette, what do you say to our Flemish ambassadors? Have you any as fine at Rheims?"

"I confess," answered Mahiette, "that there is no place like Paris for seeing such Flemings as those."

"Did you see among the embassy that great ambassador who is a hosier?" asked Oudarde.

"Yes," responded Mahiette. "He looks like a regular Saturn."

"And that fat one with the smooth face?" added Gervaise. "And that little fellow with small eyes and red lids, as ragged and hairy as a head of thistle?"

"Their horses were the finest sight," said Oudarde, "dressed out in the fashion of their country."

"Oh, my dear," interrupted the rustic Mahiette, assuming an air of superiority in her turn, "what would you say if you had seen, in 1461, at the coronation at Rheims, now eighteen years ago, the horses of the princes and of the king's escort? Housings and trappings of every description: some of damask cloth, of fine gold, trimmed with sable; others, of velvet, trimmed with ermines' tails; others, loaded down with goldsmiths' work and great gold and silver bells! And the money that it must have cost! And the lovely page-boys that rode on them!"

"That does not alter the fact," drily responded Damoiselle Oudarde, "that the

Flemings have very fine horses, and that they had a splendid supper last night given them by the mayor at the City Hall, where they were treated to sugarplums, hippocras, spices, and other rarities."

"What are you talking about, neighbour!" cried Gervaise. "It was at the Petit-Bourbon, with the Cardinal, that the Flemings supped."

"Not at all. At the City Hall."

"Yes, indeed. At the Petit-Bourbon!"

"So surely was it at the City Hall," returned Oudarde, sharply, "that Doctor Scourable made them a speech in Latin with which they seemed mightily pleased. It was my husband, who is one of the licensed copyists, who told me so."

"So surely was it at the Petit-Bourbon," replied Gervaise, with no whit less of animation, "that I can give you a list of what the Cardinal's attorney treated them to: Twelve double quarts of hippocras, white, yellow, and red; twenty-four boxes of double gilt Lyons marchpane; as many wax torches of two pounds each, and six half-casks of Beaune wine, red and white, the best to be found. I hope that's decisive." I have it from my husband, who is captain of fifty men in the Commonalty Hall, and who was only this morning comparing the Flemish ambassadors with those sent by Prester John and the Emperor of Trebizond, who came from Mesopotamia to Paris during the reign of the last king, and who had rings in their ears."

"It is true that they supped at the City Hall," replied Oudarde, but little moved by this display of eloquence, "that no one ever saw such an exhibition of meats and sugar-plums before."

"But I tell you that they were served by Le Sec, one of the city guard, at the Petit-Bourbon, and that's what misled you."

"At the City Hall, I say!"

"At the Petit-Bourbon, my dear! For didn't they illuminate the word 'Hope,' which is written over the great entrance, with magical glasses?"

"At the City Hall! at the City Hall! Don't I tell you that Husson-le-Voir played the flute?"

"I tell you, no!"

"I tell you, yes!"

"And I tell you, no!"

The good fat Oudarde was making ready to reply, and the quarrel might have come to blows, if Mahiette had not suddenly exclaimed, "Only see those people crowding together at the end of the bridge! There's something in the midst of them, at which they're all looking."

"Truly," said Gervaise, "I do hear the sound of a tambourine. I verily believe it's that little Smeralda playing her tricks with her goat. Come quick, Mahiette! Make haste and pull your boy along faster. You came here to see all the sights of Paris. Yesterday you saw the Flemings; to-day you must see the gipsy girl."

"The gipsy," said Mahiette, turning back abruptly, and grasping her son's arm more firmly. "Heaven preserve us! She might steal my child!—Come, Eustache!"

And she set out running along the quay towards the Grève, until she had left the bridge far behind her. But the child, whom she dragged after her, stumbled, and fell upon his knees; she stopped, out of breath. Oudarde and Gervaise rejoined her.

"That gipsy girl steal your child!" said Gervaise. "What a strange idea!"

Mahiette shook her head with a pensive air.

"The queer part of it is," observed Oudarde, "that the nun has the same opinion of the gipsies."

"What do you mean by the nun?" said Mahiette.

"Why!" said Oudarde, "Sister Gudule."

"And who," returned Mahiette, "is Sister Gudule?"

"You must indeed be from Rheims, not to know that!" replied Oudarde. "She is the recluse of the Rat-Hole."

"What!" asked Mahiette, "the poor woman to whom we are carrying this cake?"

Oudarde nodded.

"Exactly so. You will see her presently at her window on the Grève. She feels just as you do about those gipsy vagabonds who go about drumming on the tambourine and telling people's fortunes. No one knows what gave her such a horror of gipsies. But you, Mahiette,—why should you take to your heels in such haste at the mere sight of them?"

"Oh," said Mahiette, clasping her child to her bosom, "I could not bear to have the same thing happen to me that happened to Paquette la Chantefleurie."

"Oh, do tell us the story, my dear Mahiette," said Gervaise, taking her arm.

"Gladly," answered Mahiette; "but you must indeed be from Paris, not to know that! You must know, then,—

but we need not stand here to tell the tale,—that Paquette la Chantefleurie was a pretty girl of eighteen when I was one too; that is to say, some eighteen years ago, and it is her own fault if she is not now, like me, a happy, hale, and hearty mother of six-and-thirty, with a husband and a son. However, from the time she was fourteen, it was too late! She was the daughter of Guybertaut, minstrel to the boats at Rheims, the same who played before King Charles VII., at his coronation, when he sailed down the river Vesle from Sillery to Muison, and, more by token, the Maid of Orleans was in the boat with him. Her old father died when Paquette was still a mere child; then she had no one but her mother, a sister to Pradon, the master brazier and coppersmith at Paris, in the Rue Parin-Garlin, who died last year. You see that she came of an honest family. The mother was a good, simple woman, unfortunately, and taught Paquette nothing but a little fringe-making and toy-making, which did not keep the child from growing very tall and remaining very poor. The two lived at Rheims, on the water's edge, in the Rue Folle-Peine. Note this. I think this was what brought ill-luck to Paquette. In '61, the year of the coronation of our King Louis XI.,—may Heaven preserve him!—Paquette was so merry and so pretty that every one knew her as Chantefleurie. Poor girl! She had lovely teeth, and she liked to laugh, so that she might show them. Now, a girl who likes to laugh is on the high-road to weep; fine teeth spoil fine eyes. Such was Chantefleurie. She and her mother had hard work to earn a living;

they were greatly reduced after the minstrel's death; their fringe-making did not bring them in more than six farthings a week, which doesn't make quite two pence. Where was the time when Father Guybertaut earned twelve Paris pence at a single coronation for a single song? One winter (it was that same year of '61), when the two women had not a stick of firewood and it was bitterly cold, the cold gave Chantefleurie such a fine colour that the men called her Paquette,—some called her Pâquerette,—and she went to the bad. —Eustache! don't you let me see you nibble that cake!—We soon saw that she was ruined, when she came to church one fine Sunday with a gold cross on her neck. At fourteen years of age! Think of that! First it was the young Vicomte de Cormontreuil, whose castle is about three quarters of a league away from Rheims; then M. Henri de Triancourt, the king's equerry; then something lower, Chiart de Beaulin, serjeant-at-arms; then, still lower, Guery Aubergeon, the king's carver; then, Macé de Frépus, the dauphin's barber; then, Thévenin-le-Moine, the king's cook; then, still descending to older and meaner men, she fell into the hands of Guillaume Racine, viol-player, and of Thierry-de-Mer, the lantern-maker. Then—poor Chantefleurie!— she became common property; she had come to the last copper of her gold piece. How shall I tell you, ladies? At the time of the coronation, in that same year '61, it was she who made the king of ribalds' bed,—that selfsame year!"

Mahiette sighed, and wiped a tear from her cheek.

"No very uncommon story," said Gervaise; "and I don't see that it has anything to do with gipsies, or with children."

"Patience!" replied Mahiette: "we shall soon come to the child. In '66, sixteen years ago this very month, on Saint Paula's Day, Paquette gave birth to a little girl. Poor thing! Great was her joy; she had long wished for a child. Her mother, good woman, who never knew how to do anything but shut her eyes to her daughter's faults,—her mother was dead. Paquette had no one left to love, no one to love her. Five years had passed since her fall, and Chantefleurie was but a miserable creature. She was alone, alone in the world, pointed at, hooted after in the street, beaten by the police, mocked by little ragged boys. And then, she was now twenty years old; and twenty is old age to such women. Vice had ceased to bring her in much more than her fringe-making used to do; every fresh wrinkle took away another coin. Winter was once more a hard season for her; wood was again scarce upon her hearth, and bread in her cupboard. She could no longer work; for when she took to a life of pleasure she learned to be lazy, and she suffered far more than before, because in learning to be lazy she became accustomed to pleasure,—at least, that's the way the priest of Saint-Remy explains it to us that such women feel cold and hunger more than other poor folks do when they are old."

"Yes," remarked Gervaise; "but the gipsies?"

"One moment, Gervaise!" said Oudarde, whose attention was less impatient. "What would there be left for the end, if everything came at the beginning? Go on, Mahiette, please. Poor Chantefleurie!"

Mahiette continued:—

"So she was very wretched, very unhappy, and her tears wore deep furrows in her cheeks. But in her shame, her disgrace, and her misery, it seemed to her that she should feel less ashamed, less disgraced, and less miserable, if she had something to love or some one to love her. It must be a child; for only a child could be innocent enough for that. She recognized this after trying to love a thief,—the only man who would have anything to say to her; but after a little she saw that even the thief despised her. Women of that sort must have a lover or a child to fill up their hearts, otherwise they are very unhappy. As she could not have a lover, she gave herself up to longing for a child; and as she had never given over being pious, she prayed night and day that the good God would give her one. The good God had pity on her, and gave her a little girl. I cannot describe to you her delight; she covered it with a perfect rain of tears, kisses, and caresses. She nursed her child herself, made swaddling-clothes for it of her own coverlet,—the only one she had on her bed,—and no longer felt cold or hungry. She grew handsome again. An old maid makes a young mother. She took to her former courses; her old friends came back to see her, and she readily found customers for her wares, and with the price of all these iniquities she bought baby linen, caps, and bibs, lace gowns and little satin bonnets, without ever thinking of buying herself another coverlet. — Master Eustache

didn't I tell you not to eat that cake?— It is certain that little Agnès,—that was the child's name, her given name; for as to a surname, Chantefleurie had long since ceased to have one,—it is certain that the little thing was more tricked out with ribbons and embroidery than a dauphiness from Dauphiny! Among other things, she had a pair of tiny shoes, the like of which even King Louis XI. himself surely never had! Her mother sewed and embroidered them herself; she put all the dainty arts of her fringe-making into them, and as many intricate stitches as would make a gown for the Holy Virgin. They were the two sweetest little pink shoes imaginable. They were no longer than my thumb, and you must have seen the child's tiny feet slip out of them, or you would never have believed they could have gone in. To be sure, those little feet were so small, so pink, and so pretty!—pinker than the satin of the shoes! When you have children of your own, Oudarde, you will know that there is nothing prettier than those little feet and hands!"

"I ask nothing better," said Oudarde, sighing; "but I must wait the good pleasure of Master Andry Musnier."

"Besides," resumed Mahiette, "Paquette's child had not merely pretty feet. I saw her when she was only four months old; she was a perfect love! Her eyes were bigger than her mouth, and she had the finest black hair, which curled already! She would have made a splendid brunette if she had lived to be sixteen. Her mother became more and more crazy about her every day. She fondled her, kissed her, tickled her, washed her, decked her out, almost ate her up! She lost her head over her; she thanked God for her. Her pretty little pink feet particularly were an endless wonder, the cause of a perfect delirium of joy! Her lips were forever pressed to them; she could never cease admiring their smallness. She would put them into the tiny shoes, take them out again, admire them, wonder at them, hold them up to the light, pity them when they tried to walk upon the bed, and would gladly have spent her life on her knees, putting the shoes on and off those feet, as if they had been those of an infant Jesus."

"A very pretty story," said Gervaise in a low voice; "but what has all this to do with the gipsies?"

"This," replied Mahiette. "There came one day to Rheims some very queer-looking men on horseback. They were beggars and vagrants roaming about the country, under the lead of their duke and their counts. They were swarthy, all had curly hair, and silver rings in their ears. The women were even uglier than the men. Their faces were blacker, and always uncovered; they wore shabby blouses, with an old bit of cloth woven of cords tied over their shoulders, and their hair hung down like a horse's tail. The children wallowing under their feet would have frightened a monkey. A band of outlaws! They all came in a direct line from Lower Egypt to Rheims by way of Poland. People said that the Pope had confessed them, and ordered them, by way of penance, to travel through the world for seven years in succession, without ever sleeping in beds. So they called themselves penitents, and smelt horribly. It seems that they were once Saracens, so they must have believed in Jupiter; and they demanded ten Tours pounds from every crosiered and mitred archbishop, bishop, and abbot. It was a papal bull that gave them this right. They came to Rheims to tell fortunes in the name of the King of Algiers and the Emperor of Germany. You may imagine that this was quite enough reason for forbidding them to enter the town. So the whole band encamped near the Porte de Braine with a good grace, on that hill where there is a mill, close by the old chalk-pits; and every one in Rheims made haste to visit them. They looked into your hand and told you marvellous things; they were quite capable of predicting to Judas that he should be pope! And yet there were evil reports of their having stolen children, cut purses, and eaten human flesh. Wise folks said to the simple, 'Keep away from them!' and then went themselves in secret. It was a perfect rage. The fact is, they said things that would have amazed a cardinal. Mothers boasted loudly of their children, after the gipsies had read all sorts of miracles written in their hands in Turkish and in heathen tongues. One had an emperor for her son, another a pope, and another a captain. Poor Chantefleurie was seized with curiosity; she longed to know what her child would be, and whether her pretty little Agnès would not one day be Empress of Armenia, or something of that sort. So she carried her to the gipsies; and the gipsies admired the child, caressed her, and kissed her with their black mouths, and wondered at her little hand, alas! to the great delight of her mother. They were particularly charmed with her pretty feet and her pretty shoes. The child was not a year old then. She already lisped a few words, laughed at her mother like a little madcap, was round and fat, and had a thousand enchanting little tricks like those of the angels in paradise. She was sorely afraid of the gipsy women, and cried. But her mother kissed her the harder, and went away charmed with the good luck which the fortune-tellers had promised her Agnès. She was to be beautiful, virtuous, and a queen. She therefore returned to her garret in the Rue Folle-Peine, quite proud of carrying a queen in her arms. Next day she took advantage of a moment while the child was asleep on her bed (for she always had it sleep in her own bed), softly left the door ajar, and ran out to tell a neighbour in the Rue de la Séchesserie that her daughter Agnès would one day have the King of England and the Duke of Ethiopia to wait upon her at table, and a hundred other surprising things. On her return, hearing no sound as she climbed the stairs, she said to herself, 'Good! baby is still asleep.' She found the door much wider open than she had left it; but she went in, poor mother! and ran to the bed. The child was gone; the place was empty. There was nothing left of the child but one of her pretty little shoes. She rushed from the room, flew down the stairs, and began to beat the walls with her head, crying, 'My child! my child! Where is my child? Who has taken away my child?' The street was deserted, the house stood alone; no one could give her any information. She went through the town, searched every street, ran up and down all day long, mad, distracted,

terrible, staring in at doors and windows, like a wild beast that has lost its young. She was breathless, dishevelled, fearful to look upon, and there was a fire in her eyes which dried her tears. She stopped the passers-by, and cried, 'My daughter! my daughter! my pretty little daughter! If any one will give me back my daughter, I will be his servant, the servant of his dog, and he shall devour my heart if he will.' She met the priest of Saint-Remy, and said to him: 'I will dig the ground with my nails, only give me back my child!' It was heartrending, Oudarde; and I saw a very hard-hearted man, Master Ponce Lacabre, the attorney, weep. Ah, poor mother! When night came, she went home. During her absence a neighbour had seen two gipsy women go slyly upstairs with a bundle in their arms, then shut the door again and hurry away. After they had gone, a child's cries were heard, coming from Paquette's room. The mother laughed wildly, flew over the stairs as if she had wings, burst open her door, and went in. A frightful thing had happened, Oudarde! Instead of her lovely little Agnès, so rosy and so fresh, who was a gift from the good God, there lay a hideous little monster, blind, lame, deformed, squalling, and crawling about the brick floor. She hid her eyes in horror. 'Oh!' she exclaimed, 'can the witches have changed my daughter into this horrible beast?' The little club-foot was hastily removed; he would have driven her mad. He was the monstrous offspring of some gipsy woman given over to the devil. He seemed to be about four years old, and spoke a language which was no human tongue; such words were quite impossible. Chantefleurie flung herself upon the little shoe,—all that was left her of all that she had loved. She lay there so long, motionless, silent, apparently not breathing, that the neighbours thought she must be dead. Suddenly she trembled from head to foot, covered her precious relic with frantic kisses, and burst into sobs as if her heart were broken. I assure you that we all wept with her. She said: 'Oh, my little girl! my pretty little girl! where are you?' And that would have wrung your hearts. I cry now when I think of it. Our children, you see, are the very marrow of our bones.—My poor Eustache! you are so handsome! If you only knew what a darling he is! Yesterday he said to me, 'I mean to be one of the city guard, I do.' Oh, my Eustache! if I were to lose you!—Chantefleurie got up all at once and began to run about Rheims, shouting, 'To the gipsy camp! to the gipsy camp! Guard, burn the witches!' The gipsies were gone. It was night. No one could follow them. Next day, two leagues away from Rheims, on a heath between Gueux and Tilloy, were found the remains of a great fire, some ribbons which had belonged to Paquette's child, drops of blood, and some goats' dung. The night just passed happened to be a Saturday night. No one doubted any longer that the gipsies had kept their Sabbath on that heath, and that they had devoured the child in company with Beelzebub, as the Mahometans do. When Chantefleurie heard these horrible things, she did not shed a tear; she moved her lips as if to speak, but could not. Next day her hair was grey. On the following day she had disappeared."

"A terrible story indeed," said Oudarde, "and one that would make a Burgundian weep!"

"I am no longer surprised," added Gervaise, "that the fear of the gipsies haunts you so."

"And you had all the more reason," continued Oudarde, "to run away with your Eustache just now, because these are also Polish gipsies."

"Not at all," said Gervaise; "they say they came from Spain and Catalonia."

"Catalonia? That may be," replied Oudarde; "Polonia, Catalonia, Valonia, —those places are all one to me; I always mix them up. There's one thing sure; they are gipsies."

"And their teeth are certainly long enough to eat little children. And I should not be a bit surprised if Smeralda ate a little too, for all her dainty airs. Her white goat plays too many clever tricks to be all right."

Mahiette walked on in silence. She was absorbed in that sort of reverie which seems to be the continuation of a painful story, and which does not cease until it has imparted its own emotion, throb by throb, to the innermost fibres of the heart. Gervaise, however, addressed her: "And did no one ever know what became of Chantefleurie?" Mahiette made no answer. Gervaise repeated the question, shaking her arm and calling her by name as she did so. Mahiette seemed to wake from her dream.

"What became of Chantefleurie?" she said, mechanically repeating the words whose sound was still fresh in her ear; then, making an effort to fix her attention upon the meaning of the words, she said quickly, "Oh, no one ever knew."

She added, after a pause:—

"Some said they saw her leave Rheims at dusk by the Porte Fléchembault; others, at daybreak, by the old Porte Basée. A poor man found her gold cross hanging to the stone cross in the fair-grounds. It was that trinket which caused her ruin in '61. It was a gift from the handsome Vicomte de Cormontreuil, her first lover. Paquette never would part with it, however poor she might be. She clung to it like her own life. So when this cross was found, we all thought that she was dead. Still, there were people at Cabaret-les-Vautes who said they saw her pass by on the road to Paris, walking barefoot over the stones. But in that case she must have left town by the Porte de Vesle, and all these stories don't agree; or, rather, I believe she did actually leave by the Porte de Vesle, but that she left this world."

"I don't understand you," said Gervaise.

"The Vesle," replied Mahiette, with a melancholy smile, "is the river."

"Poor Chantefleurie!" said Oudarde, with a shudder; "drowned!"

"Drowned!" returned Mahiette; "and who could have told good father Guybertaut, when he floated down the river beneath the Pont de Tinquex, singing in his boat, that his dear little Paquette would one day pass under that same bridge, but without boat or song?"

"And the little shoe?" asked Gervaise.

"It disappeared with the mother," replied Mahiette.

"Poor little shoe!" said Oudarde.

Oudarde, a fat and tender-hearted woman, would have been quite content to sigh in company with Mahiette; but Gervaise, who was more curious, had not come to the end of her questions.

"And the monster?" she suddenly said to Mahiette.

"What monster?" asked the latter.

"The little gipsy monster left by the witches in Chantefleurie's room in exchange for her daughter. What did you do with it? I really hope you drowned it, too."

"Not a bit of it," replied Mahiette.

"What! You burned it then? After all, that was better. A sorcerer's child!"

"Nor that either, Gervaise. My lord the archbishop took an interest in the gipsy child; he exorcised it, blessed it, carefully took the devil out of the boy's body, and sent him to Paris to be exposed upon the wooden bed at Notre-Dame, as a foundling."

"These bishops," grumbled Gervaise, "never do anything like other people, just because they are so learned. Just think, Oudarde, of putting the devil among the foundlings! For that little monster is sure to have been the devil. Well, Mahiette, what did they do with him in Paris! I'm sure no charitable person would take him."

"I don't know," replied the native of Rheims; "it was just at that very time that my husband bought the tabellion's office at Beru, two leagues away from town, and we thought no more about the matter; particularly as near Beru there are the two hills of Cernay, which quite hide the spires of the Rheims cathedral."

While talking thus, the three worthy women had reached the Grève. In their preoccupation, they had passed the public breviary of the Tour-Roland without stopping, and were proceeding mechanically towards the pillory, around which the crowd increased momentarily. Probably the sight which at this instant attracted every eye would have made them completely forget the Rat-Hole, and the visit which they meant to pay, if the sturdy six-year-old Eustache, whom Mahiette led by the hand, had not suddenly reminded them of it by saying, as if some instinct warned him that the Rat-Hole lay behind him, "Mother, may I eat the cake now?"

Had Eustache been more crafty, that is to say less greedy, he would have waited still longer, and would not have risked the timid question, "Mother, may I eat the cake now?" until they were safe at home again, at Master Andry Musnier's house, in the University, in the Rue Madame-la-Valence, when both branches of the Seine and the five bridges of the City would have been betwixt the Rat-Hole and the cake.

This same question, a very rash one at the time that Eustache asked it, roused Mahiette's attention.

"By the way," she exclaimed, "we are forgetting the recluse! Show me your Rat-Hole, that I may carry her my cake."

"Directly," said Oudarde. "It's a true charity."

This was not at all to Eustache's liking.

"Oh, my cake! my cake!" he whined, hunching up first one shoulder and then the other,—always a sign of extreme displeasure in such cases.

The three women retraced their steps, and as they approached the Tour-Roland, Oudarde said to the other two:—

"It will never do for all three of us to peep in at the hole at once, lest we should frighten the nun. You two must pretend to be reading the Lord's Prayer in the breviary while I put my nose in at the window; the nun knows me slightly. I'll tell you when to come."

She went to the window alone. As soon as she looked in, profound pity was expressed in every feature, and her bright frank face changed colour as quickly as if it had passed from sunlight into moonlight; her eyes grew moist, her mouth quivered as if she were about to weep. A moment later, she put her finger to her lips and backoned to Mahiette.

Mahiette silently joined her, on tip-toe as if by the bedside of a dying person.

It was indeed a sad sight which lay before the two women, as they gazed without moving or breathing through the grated window of the Rat-Hole.

The cell was small, wider than it was long, with a vaulted roof, and seen from within looked like the inside of an exaggerated bishop's mitre. Upon the bare stone floor, in a corner, sat, or rather crouched a woman. Her chin rested on her knees, which her crossed arms pressed closely against her breast. Bent double in this manner, clad in brown sackcloth, which covered her loosely from head to foot, her long grey locks drawn forward and falling over her face, down her legs to her feet, she seemed at first sight some strange shape outlined against the dark background of the cell, a sort of blackish triangle, which the ray of light entering at the window divided into two distinct bands of light and shadow. She looked like one of those spectres, half darkness and half light, which we see in dreams, and in the extraordinary work of Goya,—pale, motionless, forbidding, cowering upon a tomb or clinging to the grating of a dungeon. It was neither man, nor woman, nor living being, nor any definite form; it was a figure; a sort of vision in which the real and the imaginary were blended like twilight and daylight. Beneath her dishevelled hair, which fell to the ground, the outlines of a stern and emaciated profile were barely visible; the tip of one bare foot just peeped from the hem of her garment, seeming to be curled up on the hard, cold floor. The little of human form which could be dimly seen beneath that mourning garb made the beholder shudder.

This figure, which seemed rooted to the ground, appeared to have neither motion, thought, nor breath. In that thin sackcloth, in January, lying half naked on a granite floor, without fire, in the darkness of a dungeon, whose slanting window never admitted the sun, only the icy blast, she did not seem to suffer, or even to feel.

She seemed to have been turned to stone like her cell, to ice like the season. Her hands were clasped, her eyes were fixed. At the first glance, she seemed a spectre, at the second, a statue.

And yet at intervals her blue lips were parted by a breath, and trembled; but they seemed as dead and as destitute of will as leaves blowing in the wind.

Yet her dull eyes gazed with an ineffable expression, a deep, mournful, serious, perpetually fixed expression, on a corner of the cell hidden from those outside; her look seemed to connect all the sombre thoughts of her distressed soul with some mysterious object.

Such was the creature who was called "the recluse" from her habitation, and "the nun" from her dress.

The three women—for Gervaise had joined Mahiette and Oudarde—peered through the window. Their heads cut off the faint light which entered the dungeon; but the wretched inmate seemed unconscious of her loss, and paid no attention to them. "Don't disturb her," said Oudarde in low tones; "she is in one of her ecstatic fits; she is praying."

But Mahiette still gazed with ever-increasing anxiety at the wan, wrinkled face, and those dishevelled locks, and Her eyes filled with tears. "How strange that would be!" she muttered.

She put her head through the iron bars, and at last contrived to get a glimpse of the corner upon which the unhappy woman's eyes were forever riveted.

When she withdrew her head from the window, her face was bathed in tears.

"What is that woman's name?" she asked Oudarde.

Oudarde answered,—

"We call her Sister Gudule."

"And I," returned Mahiette,—"I call her Paquette Chantefleurie."

Then, putting her finger to her lip, she signed to the amazed Oudarde to put her head through the aperture and look.

Oudarde looked, and saw, in the corner upon which the recluse's eye was fixed in such sad ecstasy, a tiny pink satin shoe, embroidered with gold and silver spangles.

Gervaise looked in after Oudarde, and then the three women began to weep at the sight of that miserable mother.

However, neither their looks nor their tears disturbed the recluse. Her hands were still clasped, her lips dumb, her eyes set; and to those who knew her story it was heartrending to see her sit and gaze at that little shoe.

The three had not yet breathed a word; they dared not speak, even in a whisper. This profound silence, this great grief, this entire oblivion of all but one thing, affected them like the high altar at Easter or at Christmas-tide. They were silent, absorbed, ready to fall upon their knees. They felt as if they had just gone into church on Holy Saturday and heard the *Tenebræ*.

At last Gervaise, the most curious, and consequently the least sensitive of the three, made an attempt to draw the recluse into conversation: "Sister! Sister Gudule!"

She repeated the call three times, raising her voice each time. The recluse did not stir; there was not a word, not a look, not a sign of life.

Oudarde, in her turn, in a gentler and more affectionate tone, said, "Sister! holy Sister Gudule!"

The same silence, the same absolute repose as before.

"What a strange woman!" cried Gervaise; "I don't believe she would mind a cannonade!"

"Perhaps she's deaf," said Oudarde.

"Maybe blind," added Gervaise.

"Perhaps dead," said Mahiette.

Certainly, if the soul had not already quitted that inert, torpid, lethargic body, it had at least withdrawn into it and concealed itself in depths to which the perceptions of the external organs did not penetrate.

"We shall have to leave the cake on the window-sill," said Oudarde; "but then some boy will steal it. How can we rouse her?"

Eustache, who had thus far been absorbed in a little wagon drawn by a big dog, which was just passing, suddenly noticed that his three companions were looking at something through the window, and, seized by curiosity in his turn, he scrambled upon a post, stood on tiptoe, and put his fat, rosy face to the opening, shouting,

"Mother, let me see, too!"

At the sound of this childish voice, clear, fresh, and ringing, the recluse trembled. She turned her head with the abrupt, quick, motion of a steel spring, her long, thin hands brushed the hair from her face, and she fixed her astonished, unhappy, despairing eyes upon the child. The look was like a flash of lightning.

"Oh, my God!" she instantly exclaimed, hiding her head upon her knees, and it seemed as if her hoarse voice tore her chest, "at least do not show me those of others!"

"Good-morning, madame," said the child, gravely.

But the shock had, as it were, aroused the recluse. A long shudder ran through her entire frame from head to foot; her teeth chattered; she half raised her head, and said, as she pressed her elbows to her sides and took her feet in her hands as if to warm them,—

"Oh, how bitterly cold!"

"Poor woman!" said Oudarde, pitifully; "would you like a little fire?"

She shook her head in token of refusal.

"Well," added Oudarde, offering her a bottle, "here is some hippocras, which will warm you; drink."

She again shook her head, looked steadily at Oudarde, and answered, "Water."

Oudarde insisted. "No, sister, water is no fit drink for January. You must drink a little hippocras, and eat this wheaten cake, which we have made for you."

She put aside the cake which Mahiette offered her, and said, "Some black bread."

"Come," said Gervaise feeling a charitable impulse in her turn, and unfastening her wollen mantle, "here is a covering somewhat warmer than yours. Throw this over your shoulders."

She refused the mantle as she had the bottle and the cake, and answered, "A cloth."

"But," resumed the kind-hearted Oudarde, "you must have seen that yesterday was a holiday."

"I knew it," said the recluse; "for two days I have had no water in my jug."

She added after a pause: "On a holiday, every one forgets me. They do well. Why should people remember me, who never think of them? When the fire goes out, the ashes are soon cold."

And as if wearied by so many words, she let her head fall upon her knees once more. The simple and charitable Oudarde, who interpreted her last words as another complaint of the cold, answered innocently, "Then wouldn't you like a little fire?"

"Fire!" said the recluse in a singular tone; "and will you give me a little for the poor baby too,—the baby who has been under ground these fifteen years?"

She trembled in every limb, her voice quivered, her eyes flashed; she had risen to her knees; she suddenly stretched her thin white hand towards the child, who was looking at her in surprise.

"Take away that child!" she cried. "The gipsy woman will soon pass by."

Then she fell face downwards, and her forehead struck the floor, with the sound of one stone upon another. The three women thought her dead. But a moment later she stirred, and they saw her drag herself upon her hands and knees to the corner where the little shoe lay. They dared not look longer; they turned away their eyes; but they heard a thousand kisses and a thousand sighs, mingled with agonizing cries and dull blows like those of a head dashed against a wall; then after one of these blows, so violent that they all three started, they heard nothing more.

"Has she killed herself?" said Gervaise, venturing to put her head through the bars. "Sister! Sister Gudule!"

"Sister Gudule!" repeated Oudarde.

"Oh, heavens! She does not move!" exclaimed Gervaise. "Can she indeed be dead? Gudule! Gudule!"

Mahiette, until now so choked by emotion that she could not speak, made an effort. "Wait a minute," she said; then going to the window, she cried, "Paquette! Paquette Chantefleurie!"

A child who innocently blows on an ill-lighted firecracker and makes it explode in his face, is no more alarmed than was Mahiette at the effect of the name so suddenly flung into Sister Gudule's cell.

The recluse trembled from head to foot, sprang to her bare feet, and rushed to the window with such flaming eyes that Mahiette, Oudarde, the other woman and the child retreated to the farthest edge of the quay.

But still the forbidding face of the recluse remained pressed against the window-bars. "Oh! oh!" she screamed with a terrible laugh, "the gipsy woman calls me!"

At this instant the scene which was passing at the pillory caught her wild eye. Her brow wrinkled with horror; she stretched her skeleton arms from her cell and cried in a voice which sounded like a death rattle. "Have you come again, you daughter of Egypt? Is it you who call me, you child-stealer? Well! may you be accursed! accursed! accursed! accursed!"

CHAPTER IV

A TEAR FOR A DROP OF WATER

THESE words were, so to speak, the connecting link between two scenes which up to this instant had gone on simultaneously, each upon its own particular stage: one, of which we have just read, at the Rat-Hole; the other, of which we shall now read, at the pillory. The former was witnessed only by the three women whose acquaintance the reader has just made; the spectators of the latter consisted of the crowd of people whom we saw some time since gathering in the Grève, about the gibbet and the pillory.

This crowd, whom the sight of the four officers posted at the four corners of the pillory ever since nine in the

morning led to expect an execution of some sort, perhaps not a hanging, but a whipping, cropping of ears, or something of the sort,—this crowd had grown so rapidly that the four officers, too closely hemmed in, were more than once obliged to drive the people back by a free use of their whips and their horses' heels.

The populace, well accustomed to wait for public executions, betrayed no great impatience. They amused themselves by looking at the pillory,—a very simple structure, consisting of a cube of masonry some ten feet high, and hollow within. A very steep flight of stairs of unhewn stone, called the ladder, led to the upper platform, upon which was a horizontal wheel made of oak. The victim was bound to this wheel in a kneeling posture, with his hands behind him. A wooden shaft, set in motion by a capstan concealed inside the machine, made the wheel revolve horizontally, thus presenting the prisoner's face to each side of the square in turn. This was called "turning" a criminal.

It is evident that the pillory of the Grève was far from possessing all the attractions of the pillory of the Markets. There was nothing architectural or monumental about it. It had no roof with an iron cross, no octagonal lantern, no slender columns expanding at the edge of the roof into capitals composed of acanthus-leaves and flowers, no huge fantastic gutter-spouts, no carved woodwork, no delicate sculpture cut deep into the stone.

Here the spectator must needs be content with the four rough walls, two stone facings, and a shabby stone gibbet, plain and bare.

The treat would have been a sorry one for lovers of Gothic architecture. It is true that no one was ever less interested in monuments than your good cockney of the Middle Ages, who paid very little heed to the beauty of a pillory.

The victim appeared at last, tied to the tail of a cart; and when he had been hoisted to the top of the platform, where he could be seen from all parts of the square bound to the wheel of the pillory with straps and ropes, a prodigious hooting, mingled with shouts and laughter, burst from the spectators. They had recognized Quasimodo.

It was indeed he. It was a strange reverse. He was now pilloried on the same place where he was the day before hailed, acclaimed, and proclaimed Pope and Prince of Fools, Lord of Misrule, and attended by the Duke of Egypt, the King of Tunis, the Emperor of Galilee! One thing is certain; there was not a soul in the crowd, not even himself, in turn triumphant and a victim, who could distinctly draw a mental comparison between these two situations. Gringoire and his philosophy were wanting to the spectacle.

Soon Michel Noiret, sworn trumpeter to our lord the king, imposed silence on all beholders, and proclaimed the sentence, according to the provost's order and command. He then retired behind the cart, with his men in livery coats.

Quasimodo, utterly impassive, never winked. All resistance on his part was rendered impossible by what was then called, in the language of criminal law, "the vehemence and firmness of the bonds;" which means that the chains and thongs probably cut into his flesh. This, by-the-bye, is a tradition of the jail and the convict prison which is not yet lost, and which the handcuffs still preserve as a precious relic among us, civilized, mild, and humane as we are (not to mention the guillotine and the galleys).

He allowed himself to be led, pushed, carried, lifted, tied, and re-tied. His face revealed nothing more than the surprise of a savage or an idiot. He was known to be deaf; he seemed to be blind.

He was placed upon his knees on the circular plank; he made no resistance. He was stripped of shirt and doublet to the waist; he submitted. He was bound with a fresh system of straps and buckles; he suffered himself to be buckled and bound. Only from time to time he breathed heavily, like a calf whose head hangs dangling from the back of the butcher's cart.

"The booby!" said Jehan Frollo du Moulin to his friend Robin Poussepain (for the two students had followed the victim, as a matter of course); "he understands no more about it than a cockchafer shut up in a box!"

A shout of laughter ran through the crowd when Quasimodo's hump, his camel breast, his horny, hairy shoulders, were bared to view. During this burst of merriment, a man in the city livery, short of stature, and strong, mounted the platform and took his place by the prisoner's side. His name was soon circulated among the spectators. It was Master Pierrat Torterue, sworn torturer of the Châtelet.

He began by placing on one corner

of the pillory a black hour-glass, the upper part of which was full of red sand, which dropped slowly into the lower half; then he took off his party-coloured coat, and there was seen hanging from his right hand a slim, slender whip with long white thongs, shining, knotted, braided, armed with metal tips. With his left hand he carelessly rolled his right shirt-sleeve up to his armpit.

Meanwhile Jehan Frollo shouted, lifting his fair curly head high above the crowd (he had climbed Robin Poussepain's shoulders for the express purpose), "Come and see, gentlemen and ladies! They are going straightway to flog Master Quasimodo, the bell-ringer of my brother the archdeacon of Josas, a strange specimen of Oriental architecture, with a dome for his back and twisted columns for legs."

All the people laughed, especially the children and the young girls.

At last the executioner stamped his foot. The wheel began to turn. Quasimodo reeled in spite of his bonds. The astonishment suddenly depicted upon his misshapen face redoubled the bursts of laughter around him.

Suddenly, just as the wheel in its revolution presented to Master Pierrat Quasimodo's mountainous back, Master Pierrat raised his arm; the thin lashes hissed through the air like a brood of vipers, and fell furiously upon the wretched man's shoulders.

Quasimodo started as if roused abruptly from a dream. He began to understand. He writhed in his bonds; surprise and pain distorted the muscles of his face, but he did not heave a sigh. He merely bent his head back, to the right, then to the left, shaking it like a bull stung in the flank by a gad-fly.

A second blow followed the first, then a third, and another, and another, and so on and on. The wheel did not cease from turning, or the blows from raining down.

Soon the blood spurted; it streamed in countless rivulets over the hunchback's shoulders; and the slender thongs, as they rent the air, sprinkled it in drops among the crowd.

Quasimodo had resumed, apparently at least, his former impassivity. He had tried at first, secretly and without great visible effort, to burst his bonds. His eye kindled, his muscles stiffened, his limbs gathered all their force, and the straps and chains stretched. The struggle was mighty, prodigious, desperate; but the tried and tested fetters of the provosty held firm. They cracked; and that was all. Quasimodo fell back exhausted. Surprise gave way, upon his features, to a look of bitter and profound dejection. He closed his single eye, dropped his head upon his breast, and feigned death.

Thenceforth he did not budge. Nothing could wring a movement from him, —neither his blood, which still flowed, nor the blows, which increased in fury, nor the rage of the executioner, who became excited and intoxicated by his work, nor the noise of the horrid lashes, keener and sharper than the sting of wasps.

At last an usher from the Châtelet, dressed in black, mounted on a black horse, who had been posted beside the ladder from the beginning of the execution of the sentence, extended his ebony wand towards the hour-glass. The executioner paused. The wheel stopped. Quasimodo's eye reopened slowly.

The flagellation was ended. Two attendants of the execution washed the victim's bleeding shoulders, rubbed them with some salve which at once closed all the wounds, and threw over his back a piece of yellow cloth cut after the pattern of a priest's cope. Meanwhile Pierrat Torterue let his red lashes soaked with blood drip upon the pavement.

But all was not over for Quasimodo. He had still to spend in the pillory that hour so judiciously added by Master Florian Barbedienne to the sentence of Master Robert d'Estouteville, —all to the greater glory of Jean de Cumène's old physicological and psychological pun: "*Surdus absurdus.*"

The hour-glass was therefore turned, and the hunchback was left bound to the plank as before, in order that justice might be executed to the utmost.

The people, particularly in the Middle Ages, were to society what the child is to a family. So long as they remain in their primitive condition of ignorance, of moral and intellectual nonage, it may be said of that as of a child,—

"That age is without pity."

We have already shown that Quasimodo was the object of universal hatred, —for more than one good reason, it is true. There was hardly a single spectator in the crowd who had not—or did not think he had—grounds for complaint against the malicious hunchback of Notre-Dame. Every one was delighted to see him in the pillory; and the severe punishment which he had just received, and the piteous state in which it had left him, far from softening the hearts of the populace, had made their hatred keener by adding to it a spice of merriment.

Thus, "public vengeance," as the legal jargon still styles it, once satisfied, a thousand private spites took their turn at revenge. Here, as in the Great Hall, the women made themselves especially conspicuous. All bore him a grudge,— some for his mischief, others for his ugliness. The latter were the more furious.

"Oh, you image of Antichrist!" said one.

"Broomstick-rider!" cried another.

"What a fine tragic face!" yelled a third. "It would surely make you Lord of Misrule, if to-day were only yesterday."

"That's right," added an old woman. "This is the pillory face. When shall we have the gallows face?"

"When shall we see you buried a hundred feet below ground, with your big bell upon your head, you cursed bell-ringer?"

"And to think that it's this demon that rings the Angelus!"

"Oh, you deaf man! you blind man! you hunchback! you monster!"

And the two students, Jehan du Moulin and Robin Poussepain, sang at the top of their voices the old popular refrain:—

"A halter for the gallows-bird!

A fagot for the ugly ape!"

Countless other insults rained upon him, mingled with hoots, curses, laughter, and occasional stones.

Quasimodo was deaf, but his sight was capital, and the fury of the mob was no less forcibly painted on their faces than in their words. Besides, the stones which struck him explained the peals of laughter.

He bore it for a time; but little by little his patience, which had resisted the torturer's whip, gave way, and rebelled against all these insect stings. The Asturian bull, which pays but little heed to the attacks of the picador, is maddened by the dogs and the banderillos.

At first he glanced slowly and threateningly around the crowd; but, bound fast as he was, his glance was impotent to drive away those flies which galled his wounds. Then he struggled in his fetters, and his frantic efforts made the old pillory wheel creak upon its timbers. All this only increased the shouts and derision of the crowd.

Then the wretched man, unable to break the collar which held him chained like a wild beast, became quiet again; only at intervals a sigh of rage heaved his breast. His face showed no trace of mortification or shame. He was too far removed from the existing state of society, and too nearly allied to a state of nature, to know what shame was. Besides, it is doubtful if infamy be a thing which can be felt by one afflicted with that degree of deformity. But rage, hate, despair, slowly veiled the hideous face with a cloud which grew darker and darker, more and more heavily charged with an electricity revealed by countless flashes from the eye of the Cyclop.

However, this cloud was lightened for a moment as a mule passed through the crowd, bearing a priest on his back. As soon as he saw that mule and that priest, the poor sufferer's face softened. The fury which convulsed it gave way to a strange smile, full of ineffable sweetness, affection, and tenderness. As the priest approached, this smile became more pronounced, more distinct, more radiant. It was as if the unhappy man hailed the coming of a Saviour. Yet, when the mule was near enough to the pillory for his rider to recognize the prisoner, the priest cast down his eyes, turned back abruptly, spurred his animal on either side as if in haste to avoid humiliating appeals, and very far from anxious to be greeted and recognized by a poor devil in such a plight.

The priest was the archdeacon Don Claude Frollo.

The cloud grew darker than ever upon the face of Quasimodo. The smile lingered for some time, although it became bitter, dejected, profoundly sad.

Time passed. He had been there at least an hour and a half, wounded, illtreated, incessantly mocked, and almost stoned to death.

Suddenly he again struggled in his chains with renewed despair, which made all the timbers that held him quiver; and breaking the silence which he had hitherto obstinately kept, he cried in a hoarse and furious voice more like the bark of a dog than a human cry, and which drowned the sound of the hooting, "Water!"

This exclamation of distress, far from exciting compassion, only increased the amusement of the good Parisian populace who surrounded the ladder, and who, it must be confessed, taken in the mass and as a multitude, were at this time scarcely less cruel and brutish than that horrible tribe of Vagrant Vagabonds to whom we have already introduced the reader, and who were simply the lowest stratum of the people. Not a voice was raised around the wretched sufferer, except to mock at his thirst.

Certainly he was at this moment more grotesque and repulsive than he was pitiable, with his livid and streaming face, his wild eye, his mouth foaming with rage and suffering, and his tongue protruding. It must also be acknowledged, that, even had there been in the throng any charitable soul tempted to give a cup of cold water to the miserable creature in his agony, so strong an idea of shame and ignominy was attached to the infamous steps of the pillory, that this alone would have sufficed to repel the Good Samaritan.

In a few minutes Quasimodo cast a despairing look upon the crowd, and repeated in a still more heart-rending voice, "Water!"

Every one laughed.

"Drink that!" shouted Robin Poussepain, flinging in his face a sponge which had been dragged through the gutter. "There, you deaf monster! I owe you something."

A woman aimed a stone at his head:—

"That will teach you to wake us at night with your cursed chimes!"

"Well, my boy!" howled a cripple, striving to reach him with his crutch, "will you cast spells on us again from the top of the towers of Notre-Dame?"

"Here's a porringer to drink out of!" added a man, letting fly a broken jug at his breast. "'Twas you who made my wife give birth to a double-headed child, just by walking past her."

"And my cat have a kitten with six feet!" shrieked an old woman, hurling a tile at him.

"Water!" repeated the gasping Quasimodo for the third time.

At this moment he saw the crowd separate. A young girl, oddly dressed, stepped from their midst. She was accompanied by a little white goat with gilded horns, and held a tambourine in her hand.

Quasimodo's eye gleamed. It was the gipsy girl whom he had tried to carry off the night before,—a freak for which he dimly felt that he was even now being punished; which was not in the least true, since he was only punished for the misfortune of being deaf, and having been tried by a deaf judge. He did not doubt that she too came to be avenged, and to take her turn at him with the rest.

He watched her nimbly climb the ladder. Rage and spite choked him. He longed to destroy the pillory; and had the lightning of his eye had power to blast, the gipsy girl would have been reduced to ashes long before she reached the platform.

Without a word she approached the sufferer, who vainly writhed and twisted to avoid her, and loosening a gourd from her girdle, she raised it gently to the parched lips of the miserable wretch.

Then from that eye, hitherto so dry and burning, a great tear trickled, and rolled slowly down the misshapen face, so long convulsed with despair. It was perhaps the first that the unfortunate man had ever shed.

But he forgot to drink. The gipsy girl made her customary little grimace of impatience, and smilingly pressed the neck of the gourd to Quasimodo's jagged mouth.

He drank long draughts; his thirst was ardent.

When he had done, the poor wretch put out his black lips, doubtless to kiss the fair hand which had helped him. But the girl, perhaps not quite free from distrust, and mindful of the violent attempt of the previous night, withdrew her hand with the terrified gesture of a child who fears being bitten by a wild animal.

Then the poor deaf man fixed upon her a look of reproach and unutterable sorrow.

It would anywhere have been a touching sight, to see this lovely girl, fresh, pure, charming, and yet so weak, thus devoutly hastening to the help of so much misery, deformity, and malice. Upon a pillory, the sight was sublime.

The people themselves were affected by it, and began to clap their hands and shout,—

"Noël! Noël!"

It was at this instant that the recluse saw, from the window of her cell, the gipsy girl upon the pillory, and hurled her ominous curse at her head:—

"May you be accursed, daughter of Egypt! accursed! accursed!"

CHAPTER V

END OF THE STORY OF THE CAKE

ESMERALDA turned pale, and descended from the pillory with faltering steps. The voice of the recluse still pursued her:—

"Come down! come down, you gipsy thief! You will go up again!"

"The nun has one of her ill turns to-day," muttered the people, and they said no more; for women of this sort were held in much awe, which made them sacred. No one liked to attack those who prayed night and day.

The hour had come to release Quasimodo. He was unbound, and the mob dispersed.

Near the great bridge, Mahiette, who was returning home with her two companions, stopped suddenly:—

"By the way, Eustache, what have you done with the cake?"

"Mother," said the child, "while you were talking to the woman in that hole, there came a big dog and bit a piece out of my cake; so then I took a bite too."

"What, sir!" she continued, "did you eat it all?"

"Mother, it was the dog. I told him not to eat it, but he wouldn't mind me. So then I took a bite too; that's all!"

"What a bad boy you are!" said his mother, smiling and scolding at once. "Only think, Oudarde! he ate every cherry on the tree in our orchard at Charlerange; so his grandfather says that he is sure to be a soldier. Let me catch you at it again, Master Eustache! Get along, you greedy boy!"

BOOK VII

THE INSCRIPTION

CHAPTER I

ON THP DANGER OF CONFIDING A SECRET TO A GOAT

SEVERAL weeks had passed. It was early in March. The sun, which Dubartas, that classic father of periphrase, had not yet dubbed "the grand duke of candles," was none the less bright and gay. It was one of those spring days which are so full of sweetness and beauty that all Paris, flocking into the squares and parks, keeps holiday as if it were a Sunday. On such clear, warm, peaceful days, there is one particular hour when the porch of Notre-Dame is especially worthy of admiration. It is the moment when the sun, already sinking towards the west, almost exactly faces the cathedral. Its rays, becoming more and more level, withdraw slowly from the pavement of the square, and climb the perpendicular face of the church, the shadows setting off the countless figures in high relief, while the great central rose-window flames like the eye of a Cyclop lighted up by reflections from his forge.

It was just that hour.

Opposite the lofty cathedral, reddened by the setting sun, upon the stone balcony built over the porch of a handsome Gothic house at the corner of the square and the Rue du Parvis, a group of lovely young girls were laughing and chatting gracefully and playfully. By the length of the veil which hung from the peak of their pointed coif, twined with

pearls, down to their heels, by the fineness of the embroidered tucker which covered their shoulders, but still revealed, in the pleasing fashion of the day, the swell of their fair virgin bosoms, by the richness of their under petticoats, even costlier than their upper garments (wonderful refinement!), by the gauze, the silk, the velvet in which they were arrayed, and especially by the whiteness of their hands, which proved that they led a life of idle ease, it was easy to guess that these were rich heiresses. They were in fact Damoiselle Fleur-de-Lys de Gondelaurier and her companions, Diane de Christeuil, Amelotte de Montmichel, Colombe de Gaillefontaine, and the little De Champchevrier, all daughters of noble houses, just now visiting the widowed Madame de Gondelaurier, on account of Monseigneur de Beaujeu and his wife, who were coming to Paris in April to choose maids of honour to meet the Dauphiness Marguerite in Picardy and receive her from the hands of the Flemings. Now, all the country squires for thirty miles around aspired to win this favour for their daughters, and many of them had already been brought or sent to Paris. The damsels in question were intrusted by their parents to the discreet and reverend care of Madame Aloïse de Gondelaurier, the widow of a former officer of the king's crossbowmen, living in retirement, with her only daughter, in her house on the square in front of Notre-Dame.

The balcony upon which the young

girls sat opened from a room richly hung with fawn-coloured Flemish leather stamped with golden foliage. The transverse beams on the ceiling, diverted the eye by countless grotesque carvings, painted and gilded. Splendid enamels glittered here and there upon sculptured presses. A boar's head made of earthenware crowned a superb sideboard, the two steps of which showed that the mistress of the house was the wife or widow of a knight banneret. At the end of the room, beside a tall chimney-piece covered with armorial bearings and escutcheons, sat, in a rich red velvet arm-chair, Madame de Gondelaurier, whose fifty-five years were as plainly written in her garments as on her face. Near her stood a young man of aristocratic though somewhat arrogant and swaggering mien,—one of those fine fellows about whom all women agree, although serious men and physiognomists shrug their shoulders at them. This youthful cavalier wore the brilliant uniform of a captain of the archers of the household troops, which is too much like the dress of Jupiter, described in the first part of this story, for us to inflict a second description of it upon the reader.

The damsels were seated, some in the room, some upon the balcony, the former upon squares of Utrecht velvet with golden corner-pieces, the latter on oaken stools carved with flowers and figures. Each held upon her knees a portion of a large piece of tapestry, at which they were all working together, and a long end of which trailed over the matting that covered the floor.

They talked together in the undertone and with the suppressed laughter common to a group of young girls when there is a young man among them. The young man whose presence sufficed to call forth all these feminine wiles seemed, for his part, to pay but little heed to them; and while these lovely girls vied with one another in trying to attract his attention, he seemed chiefly occupied in rubbing up his belt-buckle with his buckskin glove.

From time to time the elderly lady addressed some remark to him in a very low voice, and he replied as best he could, with awkward and forced courtesy. By Madame Aloïse's smiles and little significant signs, as well as by the glances which she cast at her daughter Fleur-de-Lys while she whispered to the captain, it was easy to see that she was talking of the recent betrothal, and of the marriage, doubtless to come off soon, between the young man and Fleur-de-Lys; and by the officer's coldness and embarrassment, it was plain that on his side at least there was no question of love. His whole manner expressed a weariness and constraint such as the young officers of our day would aptly translate by saying that he was "deucedly bored!"

The good lady, utterly infatuated with her daughter, like the silly mother that she was, did not perceive the officer's lack of enthusiasm, and did her best to point out to him in a whisper the infinite perfection with which Fleur-de-Lys plied her needle or wound her skeins of silk.

"There, cousin," she said, plucking him by the sleeve that she might speak in his ear, "just look at her now! See how gracefully she stoops!"

"To be sure," replied the young man;

and he relapsed into his cold and careless silence.

A moment after, he was forced to bend anew, and Dame Aloïse said,—

"Did you ever see a merrier or more attractive face than that of your betrothed? Could any one have a fairer, whiter skin? Aren't those clever hands; and isn't her neck a perfect match in grace for a swan's? How I envy you at times! and how lucky it is for you that you are a man, wicked scamp that you are! Isn't my Fleur-de-Lys adorably lovely, and aren't you dead in love with her?"

"Of course," he replied, with his mind upon other things.

"But why don't you talk to her?" suddenly observed Madame Aloïse, giving him a push. "Say something to her; you are wonderfully shy all of a sudden."

We can assure our readers that shyness was neither one of the captain's failings nor good points; but he tried to do what was required of him.

"Fair cousin," said he, approaching Fleur-de-Lys, "what is the subject of your tapestry-work?"

"Fair cousin," answered Fleur-de-Lys in an injured tone, "I have told you three times already: it is Neptune's grotto."

It was plain that Fleur-de-Lys was far more clear-sighted than her mother in regard to the captain's cold and careless manners. He felt that he must needs make a little conversation.

"And what is all this Neptune-work for?" he asked.

"For the Abbey of Saint-Antoine des Champs," said Fleur-de-Lys, without raising her eyes.

The captain picked up a corner of the tapestry.

"And who, my fair cousin, is that fat fellow with puffy cheeks, blowing his trumpet so vigorously?"

"That is Triton," she answered.

There was still a somewhat offended tone about Fleur-de-Lys' brief words. The captain saw that he must absolutely whisper something in her ear,—a compliment, a bit of nonsense, never mind what. He bent towards her accordingly, but his imagination suggested nothing tenderer or more familiar than this: "Why does your mother always wear a petticoat wrought with coats-of-arms, such as our grandmothers wore in the time of Charles VII.? Do tell her, fair cousin, that it is no longer the fashion, and that her laurel-tree and her hinges emblazoned all over her gown make her look like a walking mantelpiece. Really, nobody sits upon their banner in that way now, I swear they don't."

Fleur-de-Lys raised her lovely eyes full of reproach.

"Is that all you have to swear to me?" she said in a low voice.

Meantime good Dame Aloïse, enchanted to see them chatting thus confidently, said, as she played with the clasps of her prayer-book,—

"What a touching picture of love!"

The captain, more and more embarrassed, fell back on the tapestry. "That really is a beautiful piece of work!" he exclaimed.

Upon this remark, Colombe de Gaillefontaine, another charming, fair-haired, white-skinned girl, in a high-necked blue damask gown, timidly ventured to address Fleur-de-Lys, in the hope that the handsome captain would reply: "My dear Gondelaurier, have you seen the tapestries at the Roche-Guyon house?"

"Isn't that the house with the garden, which belongs to the linen-dealer of the Louvre?" asked Diane de Christeuil with a laugh; for she had fine teeth, and consequently laughed on every occasion.

"And where there is that big old tower belonging to the ancient wall of Paris," added Amelotte de Montmichel, a pretty, curly-haired, rosy-cheeked brunette, who was as much given to sighing as the other was to laughing, without knowing ..1y.

"My dear Colombe," put in Dame Aloïse, "are you talking of the house which belonged to M. de Bacqueville in the reign of King Charles VI.? It does indeed contain some superb high-warp tapestries."

"Charles VI.! Charles VI.!" muttered the young captain, twirling his moustache. "Heavens! What a memory the good lady has for by-gone things!"

Madame de Gondelaurier went on: "Beautiful tapestries, indeed. Such magnificent work that it is thought to be unique!"

At this instant Bérangère de Champchevrier, a slender little girl of seven, who was gazing into the square through the trefoils of the balcony railing, cried out,—

"Oh, look, pretty godmamma Fleur-de-Lys, see that dear dancing-girl dancing down there on the pavement, and playing on the tambourine among those common clowns!"

The shrill jingle of a tambourine was in fact heard by all.

"Some gipsy girl," said Fleur-de-Lys, turning nonchalantly towards the square.

"Let us see! let us see!" exclaimed her lively companions; and they all ran to the edge of the balcony, while Fleur-de-Lys, musing over her lover's coldness, followed them slowly, and her lover, relieved by this incident, which cut short an embarrassing conversation, returned to the farther end of the room with the satisfied air of a soldier released from duty. Yet it was a delightful and an easy duty to wait upon the fair Fleur-de-Lys, and so it had once seemed to him; but the captain had gradually wearied of it; the prospect of a speedy marriage grew less and less attractive day by day. Besides, he was of an inconstant humour, and—must we own it? —his taste was somewhat vulgar. Although of very noble birth, he had contracted while in harness more than one of the habits of the common soldier. He loved the tavern and all its accompaniments. He was never at his ease except among coarse witticisms, military gallantries, easy-going beauties, and facile conquests. He had received some education and some polish from his family; but he had roamed the country too young, joined the garrison too young, and every day the veneer of the gentleman was worn away a little more by the hard friction of his military baldric. Although he still visited her occasionally, from a lingering spark of common respect, he felt doubly embarrassed in Fleur-de-Lys' presence: first, because by dint of distributing his love in all sorts of places he had very little left for her; and next, because amid so many stately, starched, and modest dames he trembled continually lest his lips, accustomed to oaths, should suddenly lose all restraint and break out into the language of the tavern. Fancy what the effect would be!

However, with all this were mingled great pretensions to elegance in dress and to a fine appearance. Let those who can reconcile these things. I am only the historian.

He had been standing for some moments, thinking or not thinking, leaning silently against the carved chimney-piece, when Fleur-de-Lys, turning suddenly, spoke to him. After, all, the poor girl only looked black at him in self-defence.

"Fair cousin, didn't you tell us of a little gipsy girl whom you rescued from a dozen robbers some two months since, while you were on the night patrol?"

"I think I did, fair cousin," said the captain.

"Well," she continued, "it may be that same gipsy girl who is dancing in the square below. Come and see if you recognize her, fair Cousin Phœbus!"

He perceived a secret desire for reconciliation in this gentle invitation to return to her side, and in the pains she took to call him by his Christian name. Captain Phœbus de Châteaupers (for it is he whom the reader has had before him from the beginning of this chapter) slowly approached the balcony. "There," said Fleur-de-Lys, tenderly, laying her hand upon Phœbus's arm, "look at that little thing dancing in the ring. Is that your gipsy girl?"

Phœbus looked, and said,—

"Yes; I know her by her goat."

"Oh, yes! what a pretty little goat!" said Amelotte, clasping her hands in admiration.

"Are its horns really, truly gold?" asked Bérangère.

Without moving from her easy-chair, Dame Aloïse took up the word: "Isn't it one of those gipsies who came here last year through the Porte Gibard?"

"Mother," said Fleur-de-Lys, gently, "that gate is now called Porte d'Enfer."

Mademoiselle de Gondelaurier knew how much her mother's superannuated modes of speech shocked the captain. In fact, he began to sneer, and muttered between his teeth: "Porte Gibard! Porte Gibard! That's to admit King Charles VI."

"Godmamma," cried Bérangère, whose restless eyes were suddenly raised to the top of the towers of Notre-Dame, "what is that black man doing up there?"

All the girls looked up. A man was indeed leaning on his elbows on the topmost balustrade of the northern tower, overlooking the Grève. He was a priest. His dress was distinctly visible, and his face rested on his hands. He was as motionless as a statue. His eye was fixed intently on the square.

There was something in his immobility like a kite which has just discovered a nest of sparrows, and gazes at it.

"It is the archdeacon of Josas," said Fleur-de-Lys.

"You have good eyes if you can recognize him from this distance!" remarked Mademoiselle Gaillefontaine.

"How he watches the little dancer," added Diane de Christeuil.

"The gipsy girl had better beware," said Fleur-de-Lys, "for he is not fond of gipsies."

" 'Tis a great pity the man should stare at her so," added Amelotte de Montmichel, "for she dances ravishingly."

"Fair Cousin Phœbus," suddenly said Fleur-de-Lys, "as you know this little gipsy girl, pray beckon to her to come up. It will amuse us."

"Oh, yes!" cried all the girls, clapping their hands.

"What nonsense!" replied Phœbus. "She has doubtless forgotten me, and I don't even know her name. Still, if you wish it, ladies, I will make an attempt;" and leaning over the balcony-rail, he called, "Little one!"

The dancer was not playing her tambourine at the moment. She turned her head towards the point whence this call came, her sparkling eye fell on Phœbus, and she stopped short.

"Little one!" repeated the captain; and he signed to her to come.

The young girl looked at him again; then she blushed as if her cheeks were on fire, and putting her tambourine under her arm, she moved through the astonished spectators towards the door of the house to which Phœbus called her, with slow, hesitating steps, and the troubled gaze of a bird yielding to the fascination of a snake.

A moment later, the tapestry hanging before the door was lifted, and the gipsy appeared on the threshold of the room, red, abashed, breathless, her large eyes cast down, and not daring to advance another step.

Bérangère clapped her hands.

But the dancer stood motionless at the door. Her appearance produced a strange effect upon the group of young girls. It is certain that a vague and indistinct desire to please the handsome officer animated them all alike; that his splendid uniform was the aim of all their coquetries; and that so long as he was present there was a certain secret lurking rivalry among them, which they hardly confessed to themselves, but which none the less appeared every instant in their gestures and words. Still, as they were possessed of an almost equal share of beauty, the contest was a fair one, and each might well hope for victory. The gipsy's arrival abruptly destroyed this equilibrium. Her beauty was so remarkable that when she appeared on the threshold of the room she seemed to diffuse a sort of light peculiar to herself. Shut into this room, in this dark frame of hangings and wainscotting, she was incomparably more beautiful and more radiant than in the public square. She was like a torch brought from broad daylight into darkness. The noble maidens were dazzled in spite of themselves. Each of them felt her beauty in some sort impaired. Therefore their battle-front (if we may be pardoned the expression) changed at once, without exchanging a word. Still, they understood one another to perfection. The instincts of women read and reply to one another more rapidly than the understandings of men. An enemy had arrived; all felt it, all rallied for mutual support. A drop of wine is enough to redden a whole glass of water; the entrance of a prettier woman than themselves is enough to tinge a whole party of pretty women with a certain amount of ill-humour,—especially when there is but one man present.

Thus their reception of the gipsy girl was marvellously cold. They examined her from head to foot, then looked at one another, and that was enough: they understood one another. But the young girl waited for them to speak, so much agitated that she dared not raise her eyes.

The captain was the first to break the silence.

"On my word," he said in his tone of bold assurance, "a charming creature! What do you think of her, fair cousin?"

The observation, which a more delicate admirer would at least have uttered in an undertone, was not adapted to soothe the feminine jealousies arrayed against the gipsy girl.

Fleur-de-Lys answered the captain with a sweet affectation of disdain: "She's not bad-looking."

The others whispered together.

At last Madame Aloïse, who was not the least jealous of the party since she was jealous for her daughter, addressed the dancer. "Come in, little one."

"Come in, little one!" repeated, with comic dignity, Bérangère, who would have reached about to the gipsy's waist.

Esmeralda approached the noble lady.

"My pretty child," said Phœbus with emphasis, taking a few steps towards her, "I don't know whether I have the supreme happiness of being recognized by you—"

She interrupted him with a smile and a glance of infinite sweetness,—

"Oh, yes!"

"She has a good memory," observed Fleur-de-Lys.

"Now, then," continued Phœbus, "you escaped very nimbly the other night. Did I frighten you?"

"Oh, no!" said the gipsy.

There was an indefinite something in the tone in which this "Oh, no!" was uttered directly after the "Oh, yes!" which wounded Fleur-de-Lys.

"You left me in your place, my beauty," resumed the captain, whose tongue was loosened when he talked to a girl from the streets, "a very surly knave, blind of one eye, and a hunchback, the bishop's bell-ringer, I believe. They tell me he's the archdeacon's son, and a devil. He has a droll name; they call him Ember Days, Palm Sunday, Shrove Tuesday, or something of the sort! He's named for some high holiday or other! He took the liberty of carrying you off; as if you were a mate for such as he! That was coming it rather strong. What the devil did that screech-owl want with you, eh? Tell me!"

"I don't know," answered she.

"Did any one ever hear of such insolence,—a bell-ringer to carry off a girl as if he were a viscount! a common fellow to poach the game of gentlemen! A pretty state of things, indeed! However, he paid dearly for it. Master Pierrat Torterue is the roughest groom that ever combed and curried a knave; and I can tell you, if it will please you, that he gave your bell-ringer's hide a most thorough dressing."

"Poor man!" said the gipsy, reminded by these words of the scene at the pillory.

The captain burst out laughing. "By the great horn-spoon! your pity is as much out of place as a feather on a pig's tail. May I be as fat as a pope, if—"

He stopped short. "Excuse me, ladies! I was just about to utter a folly."

"Fie, sir!" said Gaillefontaine.

"He speaks to that creature in her own tongue!" added Fleur-de-Lys in a low voice, her anger growing every instant. Nor was this wrath diminished when she saw the captain, charmed with the gipsy and above all with himself, turn on his heel, repeating with the coarse and frank gallantry of a soldier,—

"A lovely girl, upon my soul!"

"Very badly dressed," said Diane de Christeuil, smiling to show her fine teeth.

This remark was a ray of light to the others. It showed them the gipsy's vulnerable point: unable to carp at her beauty, they attacked her dress.

"Why, that's true, little one," said Montmichel; "where did you learn to run about the streets in this way, without a wimple or a neckerchief?"

"Your skirt is so short it fairly makes me shiver," added Gaillefontaine.

"My dear," continued Fleur-de-Lys, somewhat sharply, "you will be taken up one of these days, by the serjeants of the dozen, for your gilded belt."

"Little one, little one," resumed Christeuil with a pitiless smile, "if you wore a decent pair of sleeves upon your arms, they would be less sunburnt."

It was indeed a scene worthy of a more intelligent spectator than Phœbus, to see how these beautiful girls, with their angry, venomous tongues, glided and twisted and twined about the street dancer; they were cruel and yet gracious; they maliciously searched and scanned her shabby, fantastic garb of rags and tinsel. Their laughter, their mockery, and their sneers were endless. Sarcasms rained upon the gipsy, with wicked glances and a haughty pretence of benevolence. They were like those young Roman damsels who amused themselves by plunging golden pins into the bosom of a beautiful slave girl. They were like elegant greyhounds, hanging, with distended nostrils and fiery eyes, about a poor wood-deer which

their master's eye forbids them to devour.

After all, what was a miserable street dancer to these daughters of noble houses? They seemed to pay no heed to her presence, and spoke of her, before her, to her, in loud tones as of something rather dirty, rather low, but still rather pretty.

The gipsy was not insensible to these pin-pricks. Now and then a flush of shame, a flash of anger, kindled in her eyes or on her cheeks; a scornful word seemed trembling on her lips; she made that little grimace with which the reader is familiar, in token of her contempt, but she stood motionless; she fixed a sad, sweet look of resignation upon Phœbus.

This look was also full of happiness and affection. She seemed to be restraining herself, for fear she should be turned out.

Phœbus also laughed, and took the gipsy's part with a mixture of impertinence and pity.

"Let them talk, little one," he repeated, jingling his golden spurs; "no doubt your dress is somewhat extravagant and peculiar; but what does that matter to such a charming girl as you are?"

"Good gracious!" exclaimed the fair-haired Gaillefontaine, straightening her swan-like neck with a bitter smile, "I see that the officers of the king's guard easily take fire at the bright eyes of a gipsy."

"Why not?" said Phœbus.

At this answer, carelessly uttered by the captain, like a stone cast at random, which falls unnoted, Colombe began to laugh, as did Diane and Amelotte and

Fleur-de-Lys, into whose eyes tears started at the same time.

The gipsy, whose eyes had drooped at the words of Colombe de Gaillefontaine, now raised them beaming with pride and pleasure, and fixed them again upon Phœbus. She was beautiful indeed at this moment.

The old lady, who was watching this scene, felt offended, though she did not know why.

"Holy Virgin!" she suddenly exclaimed, "what is this thing poking about under my feet? Oh, the ugly beast!"

It was the goat, which had entered in search of its mistress, and which, in its haste to reach her, had caught its horns in the mass of folds which the noble dame's draperies formed about her feet when she was seated.

This caused a diversion. The gipsy girl, without speaking, released her pet.

"Oh, there's the little goat with the golden feet!" cried Bérangère, jumping with joy.

The gipsy girl crouched upon her knees and pressed her cheek against the goat's fond head. She seemed to be begging its pardon for having thus deserted it.

But Diane whispered in Colombe's ear,—

"Gracious! why didn't I think of it before? It's the gipsy girl with the goat, of whom I have so often heard. They say she is a witch, and that her goat performs very marvellous tricks."

"Very well," said Colombe, "the goat must now amuse us, in its turn, by performing some miracle."

Diane and Colombe addressed the gipsy eagerly.—

"Little one, make your goat perform some miracle."

"I don't know what you mean," replied the dancer.

"A miracle, a piece of magic, some witchcraft."

"I don't understand;" and she began to fondle the pretty creature, repeating, "Djali! Djali!"

At this instant Fleur-de-Lys noticed an embroidered leather bag hanging from the goat's neck.

"What is that?" she asked.

The gipsy raised her large eyes to the girl's face and replied gravely, "That is my secret."

"I should very much like to know what your secret is," thought Fleur-de-Lys.

Meanwhile the good lady rose angrily, saying,—

"Come, gipsy, if neither you nor your goat can dance for us, why do you loiter here?"

The gipsy, without answering, moved slowly towards the door; but the nearer she came to it, the slower grew her steps. An irresistible magnet seemed to hold her back. All at once she turned her eyes wet with tears upon Phœbus, and paused.

"Zounds!" cried the captain; "you mustn't go in that way. Come back, and dance something for us. By the way, my beauty, what is your name?"

"Esmeralda," said the dancer, without taking her eyes from his face.

At this strange name the young girls burst into a fit of laughter.

"A terrible name for a girl," said Diane.

"You see now," added Amelotte, "that she is an enchantress."

"My dear," solemnly exclaimed Dame Aloïse, "your parents never fished out that name for you from the baptismal font."

Some moments previous, however, Bérangère, unheeded by the rest, had lured the goat into one corner of the room by a bit of marchpane. In an instant they were good friends. The curious child had removed the bag from the goat's neck, had opened it, and emptied its contents upon the matting; they consisted of an alphabet, each letter being written upon a separate square of boxwood. No sooner were these playthings scattered over the floor, than the child was amazed to see the goat, one of whose "miracles" this undoubtedly was, select certain letters with her golden hoof and arrange them, by a series of gentle pushes, in a particular order. In a moment a word was spelled out which the goat seemed to have been trained to write, so little did she hesitate in the task; and Bérangère exclaimed suddenly, clasping her hands in admiration,—

"Godmamma Fleur-de-Lys, do see what the goat has just done!"

Fleur-de-Lys looked, and shuddered. The letters arranged upon the floor spelled this word:—

"PHŒBUS."

"Did the goat do that?" she asked in an altered tone.

"Yes, godmamma," answered Bérangère.

It was impossible to doubt her, for the child could not spell.

"This is her secret!" thought Fleur-de-Lys.

Meantime, at the child's shout, the whole party hastened to her side,—the mother, the girls, the gipsy, and the officer.

The gipsy saw the folly which her goat had committed. She turned first red, then pale, and trembled like a criminal before the captain, who regarded her with a smile of mingled satisfaction and surprise.

"Phœbus," whispered the astonished girls. "Why, that's the captain's name!"

"You have a marvellous memory!" said Fleur-de-Lys to the stupefied gipsy. Then bursting into sobs, she stammered out in an agony, hiding her face in her lovely hands, "Oh, she is a witch!" and she heard a voice more bitter yet, which said to her inmost heart, "She is your rival!"

She fell fainting to the floor.

"My daughter! my daughter!" screamed the terrified mother. "Begone, you devilish gipsy!"

Esmeralda picked up the unlucky letters in the twinkling of an eye, made a sign to Djali, and went out at one door as Fleur-de-Lys was borne away by another.

Captain Phœbus, left alone, hesitated a moment between the two doors; then he followed the gipsy.

CHAPTER II

SHOWING THAT A PRIEST AND A PHILOSOPHER ARE TWO VERY DIFFERENT PERSONS

THE priest whom the girls had noticed on the top of the north tower, leaning over to look into the square and watching the gipsy's dance so closely, was no other than Claude Frollo.

Our readers have not forgotten the

mysterious cell which the archdeacon reserved to himself in that tower. (I do not know, let me observe by the way, whether or not this be the same cell, the interior of which may still be seen through a tiny grated loop-hole, opening to the eastward, at about the height of a man from the floor, upon the platform from which the towers spring; a mere hole, now bare, empty, and dilapidated, the ill-plastered walls "adorned" here and there, at the present time, with a few wretched yellow engravings, representing various cathedral fronts. I presume that this hole is conjointly inhabited by bats and spiders, and that consequently a double war of extermination is waged against flies.)

Every day, an hour before sunset, the archdeacon climbed the tower stairs and shut himself up in this cell, where he often passed whole nights. On this especial day, just as, having reached the low door of his retreat, he was fitting into the lock the complicated little key, which he always carried about with him in the purse hanging at his side, the sound of tambourine and castanets struck upon his ear. The sound came from the square in front of the cathedral. The cell, as we have already said, had but one window looking upon the roof of the church. Claude Frollo hastily withdrew the key, and an instant later he was upon the top of the tower, in the gloomy and meditative attitude in which the ladies had seen him.

There he was, serious and motionless, absorbed in one sight, one thought. All Paris lay beneath his feet, with its countless spires and its circular horizon of gently sloping hills, with its river winding beneath its bridges, and its

people flowing through its streets, with its cloud of smoke and its mountainous chain of roofs crowding Notre-Dame close with their double rings of tiles; but of this whole city the archdeacon saw only one corner,—the square in front of the cathedral; only one figure in all that crowd,—the gipsy.

It would have been hard to explain the nature of his gaze, and the source of the fire which flashed from his eyes. It was a fixed gaze, and yet it was full of agitation and trouble. And from the perfect repose of his whole body, scarcely shaken by an occasional involuntary shiver, like a tree stirred by the wind; from the stiffness of his elbows, more stony than the railing upon which they rested; from the rigid smile which contracted his face, you would have said that there was nothing living about Claude Frollo but his eyes.

The gipsy danced; she twirled her tambourine upon the tip of her finger, and tossed it into the air as she danced her Provençal sarabands: light, alert, and gay, quite unconscious of the weight of that terrible gaze which fell perpendicularly upon her head.

The crowd swarmed about her. Now and then a man accoutred in a loose red and yellow coat waved the people back into a circle, then sat down again in a chair a few paces away from the dancer, and let the goat lay its head upon his knees. This man seemed to be the gipsy's comrade. From the lofty point where he stood, Claude Frollo could not distinguish his features.

From the moment that the archdeacon observed this stranger, his attention seemed to be divided between him and the dancer, and his face grew blacker and blacker. Suddenly he straightened himself up, and trembled from head to foot. "Who is that man?" he muttered between his teeth. "I have always seen her alone till now!"

Then he plunged down the winding stairs once more. As he passed the half-open belfry door, he saw something which struck him: he saw Quasimodo, who, leaning from an opening in one of those slate pent-houses which look like huge Venetian blinds, was also gazing steadily out into the square. He was so absorbed in looking that he paid no heed to his foster father's presence. His savage eye had a strange expression; it looked both charmed and gentle. "How strange!" murmured Claude. "Can he be looking at the gipsy?" He continued his descent. In a few moments the anxious archdeacon came out into the square through the door at the foot of the tower.

"What has become of the gipsy girl?" he said, joining the group of spectators called together by the sound of the tambourine.

"I don't know," answered one of his neighbours. "She has just vanished. I think she has gone to dance some sort of a fandango in the house over opposite, where they called her in."

In the gipsy's place, upon the same carpet whose pattern had but just now seemed to vanish beneath the capricious figures of her dance, the archdeacon saw no one but the red-and-yellow man, who, hoping to gain a few coppers in his turn, was walking round the ring, his elbows on his hips, his head thrown back, his face scarlet, his neck stretched to its utmost extent, and a chair between his teeth. Upon this chair was fastened a

cat, lent by a neighbouring woman, which spit and squalled in desperate alarm.

"By'r Lady!" cried the archdeacon, as the mountebank, dripping with perspiration, passed him with his pyramid of chair and cat, "what is Master Pierre Gringoire doing here?"

The archdeacon's stern voice so agitated the poor wretch that he lost his balance, and his entire structure, chair, cat, and all, fell pell-mell upon the heads of the spectators, amid a storm of inextinguishable shouts and laughter.

Master Pierre Gringoire (for it was indeed he) would probably have had a serious account to settle with the mistress of the cat, and the owners of all the bruised and scratched faces around him, if he had not hastily availed himself of the confusion to take refuge in the church, where Claude Frollo had beckoned him to follow.

The cathedral was dark and deserted; the side aisles were full of shadows, and the lamps in the chapels began to twinkle like stars, so black had the arched roofs grown. Only the great rose-window in the front, whose myriad hues were still bathed in a ray from the setting sun, gleamed through the darkness like a mass of diamonds, and threw a dazzling reflection to the farther end of the nave.

When they had gone a few paces, Don Claude leaned his back against a pillar and looked steadily at Gringoire. It was not such a look as Gringoire had dreaded, in his shame at being caught by a grave and learned person in this merryandrew attire. The priest's glance had nothing mocking or ironical about it; it was serious, calm, and piercing.

The archdeacon was first to break the silence.

"Come hither, Master Pierre. You have may matters to explain to me. And, first of all, how comes it that I have not seen you for these two months past, and that I now find you in the streets, in a pretty plight indeed,—half red and half yellow, like a Caudebec apple?"

"Sir," said Gringoire, in piteous tones, "it is in sooth a monstrous garb, and I feel as much abashed as a cat with a calabash on her head. 'Tis very ill done, I feel, to expose the gentlemen of the watch to the risk of cudgelling the shoulders of a Pythagorean philosopher under this loose coat. But what else could I do, my reverend master? The blame belongs entirely to my old doublet, which basely deserted me at the very beginning of winter, on the plea that it was falling to pieces, and must needs take a little rest in some ragpicker's basket. What could I do? Civilization has not yet reached the point where a man may go naked, as Diogenes of old desired. Besides, the wind blew very cold, and the month of January is not a good time to introduce such a new measure to mankind with any hope of success. This coat offered itself; I accepted it, and left behind my old black frock, which, for a Hermetic like myself, was far from being hermetically closed. So here I am in the dress of a mountebank, like Saint Genest. How can I help it? It is an eclipse; but even Apollo kept the swine of Admetus."

"A fine trade you have there," replied the archdeacon.

"I confess, master, that it is far better to philosophize and poetize, to blow the flame in the furnace, or to receive it from heaven, than to carry cats upon your shield; so, when you addressed me, I felt as silly as any donkey before a turnspit. But what was I to do, sir? A man must live; and the finest Alexandrine verses are not such good eating as a bit of Brie cheese. Now, I wrote that famous epithalamium for Margaret of Flanders, which you know all about, and the city has never paid me, under the pretext that it was not very good; as if one could furnish such tragedies as those of Sophocles for four crowns! I almost starved to death. Luckily, I discovered that I had rather a strong jaw. I said to this jaw of mine, 'Perform some feats of strength and balancing; feed yourself,' —*Ale te ipsam*. A lot of tatterdemalions, with whom I have made friends, taught me some score of Herculean tricks, and now I give my teeth every night the bread which I have earned through the day by the sweat of my brow. After all (*concedo*), I confess that it is a sad waste of my intellectual faculties, and that man was never made to spend his life in drumming on the tambourine and biting into chairs. But, reverend master, it is not enough to spend one's life; one must earn his living."

Don Claude listened in silence. All at once his sunken eyes assumed so sagacious and penetrating an expression that Gringoire felt that the look searched his inmost soul.

"Very good, Master Pierre; but how comes it that you are now keeping company with that gipsy dancing-girl?"

"I' faith" said Gringoire, "because she is my wife and I am her husband."

The priest's gloomy eyes blazed with wrath.

"Have you done this, miserable fellow?" cried he, furiously seizing Gringoire by the arm! "can you have been so forsaken of God as to have laid your hands upon that girl?"

"By my hopes of paradise, my lord," replied Gringoire, trembling in every limb, "I swear to you that I have never laid a finger upon her, if that is what disturbs you."

"Then, what do you mean by talking about husband and wife?" said the priest.

Gringoire hastily gave him as brief an account as possible of his adventure in the Court of Miracles, and his marriage with the broken jug, all of which the reader already knows. It seemed, moreover, that this marriage had as yet had no result, the gipsy always contriving to slip away and leave him as she had done on their wedding night. "It is very mortifying," said he in conclusion, "but that's the consequence of my being so unlucky as to marry a maid."

"What do you mean?" asked the archdeacon, who had gradually grown calmer as he listened to this tale.

"That's not easy to explain," replied the poet. "It's a superstition. My wife, according to an old prig whom we call the Duke of Egypt, is a foundling or a lost child, which comes to the same thing in the end. She wears about her neck an amulet which they say will some day restore her to her parents, but which will lose its virtue should the young girl lose hers. Hence it follows that we are both leading the most virtuous of lives."

"Then," continued Claude, whose brow had cleared more and more, "you think, Master Pierre, that this creature has never been approached by any man?"

"What chance, Don Claude, could any man have against a superstition? She has a mania upon this point. I certainly consider it a great rarity to find such nun-like prudery fiercely maintained in the midst of those gipsy girls, who are so easily tamed. But she has three safeguards,—the Duke of Egypt, who has taken her under his protection, perhaps intending to sell her to some gentleman priest; her whole tribe, who hold her in singular veneration, as if she were another Virgin Mary; and a certain dainty little dagger, which the hussy always carries somewhere about her, in spite of the provost's orders against wearing concealed weapons, and which always springs into her hand if you do but clasp her waist. She's a regular wasp, I can tell you!"

The archdeacon pressed Gringoire with questions.

In Gringoire's opinion Esmeralda was a charming, harmless creature, pretty, if it were not for a grimace which she was always making; a simple, affectionate girl, ignorant of all evil, and enthusiastic about everything; particularly fond of dancing, of noise, of the open air; a sort of woman bee, with invisible wings to her feet, and living in a whirl. She owed this nature to the wandering life which she had always led. Gringoire had managed to find out that while still a child she had travelled through Spain and Catalonia, to Sicily; he even fancied that she was taken, by the caravan of gipsies to which she belonged, to the kingdom of Algiers, a country situated in Achaia, which Achaia, on one side borders Albania and Greece, on the other the Sicilian sea, which is the road to Constantinople. The gipsies, said Gringoire, are vassals of the King of Algiers, in his capacity of chief of the nation of white Moors. One thing is certain, that Esmeralda came to France when very young, by way of Hungary. From all these countries the girl had gathered scraps of strange tongues, queer songs and notions, which made her conversation as motley a piece of patchwork as her dress, half Parisian and half African. Moreover, the people of those quarters of the town which she frequented, loved her for her gaiety, her gracefulness, her lively ways, her dances, and her songs. She knew but two persons in the whole city who disliked her, of whom she often spoke with terror,—the nun of the Tour-Roland, a dreadful recluse who had some special spite against all gipsies, and cursed the poor dancer every time she passed her window; and a priest, who never met her without looking at her and speaking to her in a way that frightened her. This latter circumstance greatly troubled the archdeacon, although Gringoire paid but little heed to his agitation; so completely had two months sufficed to blot from the careless poet's mind the singular details of that evening upon which he first met the gipsy, and the archdeacon's presence on that occasion. Except for this, the little dancer feared nothing; she never told fortunes, which prevented all danger of a trial for witchcraft, such as was frequently brought against the other gipsy women. And then, Gringoire took the place of a brother, if not of a husband to her. After all, the philosopher bore this kind of Platonic marriage very patiently. At any rate, it ensured him food and lodging. Every morning he set forth from the vagrant's headquarters, generally in Esmeralda's company; he helped her to reap her harvest of coin along the streets; every night he shared the same roof with her, allowing her to bolt herself into her tiny cell, and slept the sleep of the just. A very pleasant life, take it all in all, he thought, and very conducive to reverie. And then, in his innermost soul the philosopher was not so absolutely sure that he was desperately in love with the girl. He loved her goat almost as well. It was a charming animal, gentle, intelligent, quick,—a learned goat. Nothing was more common in the Middle Ages than these learned animals, at which men marvelled vastly, and which often conducted their instructors to the stake. And yet, the sorceries of the goat with the golden hoofs were very innocent tricks. Gringoire explained them to the archdeacon, whom these particulars seemed to interest greatly. All that was necessary, in most cases, was to hold the tambourine out to the goat in such or such a fashion, to make the creature perform the desired trick. It had been trained to do all this by the gipsy girl, who had such rare skill as an instructor that it took her only two months to teach the goat to write the word "Phœbus" with movable letters.

"Phœbus," said the priest; "and why 'Phœbus?'"

"I don't know," answered Gringoire. "It may be a word which she thinks has some secret magic virtue. She often repeats it in an undertone when she thinks she is alone."

"Are you sure," returned Claude, with his penetrating glance, "that it is a word, and not a name?"

"Whose name?" said the poet.

"How do I know?" said the priest.

"This is what I believe, sir. These gipsies are a kind of fire-worshippers, and worship the sun. Hence, 'Phœbus.'"

"That is not so clear to me as to you, Master Pierre."

"Never mind; it doesn't concern me. Let her mumble her 'Phœbus' as much as she likes. I'm sure of one thing; and that is, that Djali is almost as fond of me as of her."

"Who is Djali?"

"That's the goat."

The archdeacon rested his chin on his hand, and seemed for a moment lost in thought. Suddenly he turned abruptly to Gringoire.

"And you swear that you have never touched her?"

"Who?" said Gringoire,—"the goat?"

"No, that woman."

"My wife? I swear I never have."

"And you are often alone with her?"

"A good hour every evening."

Don Claude frowned.

"Oh! oh! *Solus c....t sola non cogitabuntur orare Pater noster.*"

"By my soul! I might repeat the *Pater,* and the *Ave Maria,* and the *Credo in Deum patrem omnipotentem,* without her taking any more notice of me than a hen would of a church."

"Swear to me by your mother's soul," repeated the archdeacon, vehemently, "that you have never laid the tip of your finger upon the girl."

"I will swear it by my father's head

as well, if you like. But, my reverend master, let me ask one question in my turn."

"Speak, sir."

"What difference does it make to you?"

The archdeacon's pale face turned red as a girl's cheek. For a moment he made no answer; then, with evident embarrassment, he said,—

"Hark ye, Master Pierre Gringoire. You are not yet damned, so far as I know. I am interested in you, and wish you well. Now, the slightest contact with that devilish gipsy girl would make you the slave of Satan. You know that it is always the body which destroys the soul. Woe betide you if you approach that woman. That is all."

"I tried it once," said Gringoire, scratching his ear. "That was the first day; but I got stung."

"Had you the effrontery, Master Pierre?"

And the priest's face clouded.

"Another time," said the poet, smiling, "I peeped through her keyhole before I went to bed, and I saw, in her shift, as delicious a damsel as ever made a bed creak beneath her naked foot."

"Go to the devil!" cried the priest, with a terrible look; and pushing away the amazed Gringoire by the shoulders, he was soon lost to sight beneath the gloomiest arches of the cathedral.

CHAPTER III

THE BELLS

EVER since the morning when he was pilloried, the people living in the neighbourhood of Notre-Dame fancied that

Quasimodo's zeal for bell-ringing had grown very cold. Up to that time he had pulled the bells upon every occasion and no occasion at all; their music sounded from prime to complines; the belfry rang a peal for high mass, or the bells sounded a merry chime for a wedding or a christening, mingling and blending in the air like a rich embroidery of all sorts of melodious sounds. The old church, resonant and re-echoing, was forever sounding its joy-bells. There seemed to be an ever-present spirit of noise and caprice, which shouted and sang through those brazen tongues. Now that spirit seemed to have vanished; the cathedral seemed sombre, and given over to silence; for festivals and funerals there was still the simple tolling dry and bare, such as the ritual required, and nothing more; of the double noise which a church sends forth, from its organ within and its bells without, only the organ remained. It seemed as if there were no musician left in the belfry towers. And yet, Quasimodo was still there. What had happened to him? Did the shame and despair felt upon the pillory still rankle within him; did the executioner's lashes still tingle in his soul; and had the agony caused by such treatment killed all emotion within him, even his passion for the bells? Or had big Marie a rival in the heart of the ringer of Notre-Dame, and were the big bell and her fourteen sisters neglected for a fairer and more attractive object?

It happened that in this year of grace 1482 the Feast of the Annunciation fell upon Tuesday, the 25th of March. On that day the air was so pure and so clear that Quasimodo felt some slight return of his love for the bells. He therefore climbed up into the north tower, while below, the beadle threw wide open the church doors, which were then made of huge panels of hard wood covered with leather, edged with gilded iron nails, and framed in carvings "very cunningly wrought."

The high belfry cage reached, Quasimodo gazed at the six bells for some time with a sad shake of the head, as if mourning over the strange thing which had come between his heart and them. But when he had set them swinging; when he felt that cluster of bells vibrating beneath his touch; when he saw —for he could not hear—the quivering octave run up and down that sonorous scale as a bird hops from twig to twig; when the demon of music, that demon which shakes a dazzling sheaf of runs, trills, and arpeggios, had taken possession of the poor deaf fellow,—then he was happy again; he forgot everything; and as his heart swelled with bliss his face grew radiant.

He came and went, he clapped his hands, he ran from one rope to another, he encouraged the six singers with voice and gesture, as the leader of an orchestra spurs on intelligent performers.

"Go on," he cried; "go on, Gabrielle! Pour all your music into the public square; this is a high holiday. Thibauld, no laziness! your pace is slackening; go on, go on, I say! Are you growing rusty, sluggard? That's good! quick! quick! don't let me see the clapper. Make them all as deaf as I am. That's it, Thibauld! bravely done! Guillaume! Guillaume! you are the biggest of them all, and Pasquier is the smallest, and yet Pasquier rings the best. I'll wager that they who can hear, hear him better than

they do you. Good! good! my Gabrielle! louder! louder! Hollo! what are
you two doing up there, you Sparrows?
I don't see you make the very least
noise. What are those brazen beaks about
yonder, that they seem to yawn when
they should be singing? There, work
away! 'Tis the Feast of the Annunciation. The sun shines bright; we want
a fine peal of bells. Poor Guillaume!
you're quite out of breath, my fat lad."

He was wholly absorbed in urging on
his bells, all six of which bounded to
and fro as best they could, and shook
their shining sides, like a noisy team of
Spanish mules goaded by the sharp voice
of their driver.

All at once, as his gaze fell between
the broad slate scales which covered
the steep belfry wall up to a certain
height, he saw in the square below a
young girl quaintly attired, who paused,
spread a carpet on the ground, upon
which a little goat took its place, and
a group of spectators formed about
them. This sight suddenly changed the
course of his ideas, and chilled his musical enthusiasm as a blast of wind chills
melted resin. He stopped, turned his
back on the chime of bells, and crouched
behind the slated eaves, fixing on the
dancing-girl that dreamy, tender, gentle
look which had once before astonished
the archdeacon. The neglected bells
ceased suddenly and all at once, to the
great disappointment of the lovers of
chimes, who were eagerly listening to
the peal from the Pont au Change, and
who now went away as much amazed
as a dog that has been shown a bone
and then receives a stone.

CHAPTER IV

'ANA'ΓKH

IT happened that on a fine morning in
that same month of March,—I believe it
was Saturday, the 29th,—Saint Eustache's Day, our young friend the student, Jehan Frollo du Moulin, noticed
while dressing that his breeches, which
contained his purse, gave forth no clink
of metal. "Poor purse!" said he, pulling
it from his pocket; "what! not the
smallest coin! How cruelly have the
dice, Venus, and mugs of beer gutted
thee! How empty, wrinkled, and flat
you are! You look like the breast of
a Fury! I just ask you, Master Cicero
and Master Seneca, whose dog's-eared
works I see scattered over the floor,
what does it avail me to know, better
than any governor of the Mint or any
Jew from the Pont au Change, that one
golden crown-piece is worth thirty-five
unzains at twenty-five pence and eight
Paris farthings each, and that another
is worth thirty-six unzains at twenty-
six pence and six Tours farthings each,
if I have not a paltry copper to stake
upon the double-six? Oh, Consul Cicero! that is not a calamity to be overcome by periphrases,—by *quemadmo-
dum* and *verum enim vero.*"

He dressed himself sadly. A thought
struck him as he laced his shoes, but he
at first rejected it; however, it recurred
to him, and he put on his waistcoat
wrong side out,—an evident sign of some
violent mental conflict. At last he
dashed down his cap, exclaimed, "So
much the worse! Come what will, I
will go to my brother. I shall catch a
lecture, but I shall also catch a crown."

Then he hastily put on his cassock with furred shoulder-pads, picked up his cap, and dashed out of the room.

He went down the Rue de la Harpe towards the City. As he passed the Rue de la Huchette, the smell of those wonderful spits perpetually revolving there tickled his olfactories, and he cast an affectionate glance at the gigantic cookshop which once drew from the Franciscan friar Calatagirone the pathetic exclamation, — *"Veramente, queste rotisserie sono cosa stupenda!"* But Jehan had no money to pay for breakfast; and with a deep sigh he entered the door of the Petit-Châtelet,— that huge double trefoil of massive towers which guarded the entrance to the City.

He did not even take time to throw a stone as he passed, as was customary, at the wretched statue of that Périnet Leclerc who deliverd over the Paris of Charles VI. to the English,—a crime which his effigy, its surface defaced by stones and covered with mud, has expiated for three centuries, at the corner of the Rues de la Harpe and de Buci, as in a perpetual pillory.

Crossing the Petit-Pont, and striding down the Rue Neuve-Sainte Geneviève, Jehan de Molendino found himself face to face with Notre-Dame. Then his former indecision overcame him, and he walked around the statue of Monsieur Legris for several moments, repeating in agony, "The lecture is a certainty; the crown-piece is doubtful!"

He stopped a beadle as he came from the cloister.

"Where is the archdeacon of Josas?"

"I think that he is in his cell in the tower," said the beadle; "and I don't advise you to disturb him, unless you come from some such person as the pope or the king."

Jehan clapped his hands.

"The devil! what a splendid opportunity to see the famous abode of sorceries!"

Strengthened by this thought, he boldly entered the little black door, and began to climb the winding staircase of Saint-Gilles, which leads to the upper stories of the tower. "We'll see!" said he as he climbed. "By the Holy Virgin's shoestrings! it must be something very queer which my reverend brother keeps so closely hidden. They say that he lights the fires of hell up there, and cooks the philosopher's stone over the blaze. My word! I care no more for the philosopher's stone than for any common pebble; and I should rather find a good omelet of Easter eggs over his fire than the biggest philosopher's stone in the world!"

Reaching the gallery of little columns, he stopped a moment to take breath, and to swear at the interminable staircase by I know not how many millions of cartloads of devils; then he resumed his ascent by the little door of the north tower, now closed to the public. A few moments later, after passing the belfry cage, he reached a small landing-place built in a lateral recess, and under the arch, a low pointed door,—an opening cut through the circular wall of the staircase enabling him to see its enormous lock and strong iron framework. Persons desirous of visiting this door at the present time may recognize it by the inscription in white letters on the black wall, "I adore Coralie. 1823.

Signed, Eugène." The word "signed" is in the original.

"Oho!" said the student; "this must be the place."

The key was in the lock. The door was ajar; he pushed it gently, and put his head through the opening.

The reader has doubtless seen the admirable works of Rembrandt, that Shakspeare of painting. Among many marvellous engravings, there is one especial etching which is supposed to represent Doctor Faustus, and at which it is impossible to look without being dazzled. It represents a dark cell; in the foreground is a table covered with hideous objects,—skulls, globes, alembics, compasses, hieroglyphic parchments. The Doctor is at this table, dressed in his coarse great-coat, a furred bonnet pulled down to his eyebrows. He is painted at half-length. He has half risen from his vast arm-chair, his clinched fists rest on the table, and he stares with curiosity and terror at a large luminous circle, composed of magical letters, which gleams on the opposite wall like the solar spectrum in the camera obscura. The cabalistic sun seems to shimmer as we look, and fills the gloomy cell with its mysterious radiance. It is horrible, and the same time beautiful.

Something very similar to Faust's cell appeared to Jehan when he ventured to put his head in at the half-open door. This, too, was a dark and dimly lighted dwelling. There, too, were the large chair and large table, the compasses and alembics, skeletons of animals hanging from the roof, a globe rolling over the floor, hippocamps pell-mell with glass jars in which quivered leaf gold, death's-heads lying on vellum scrawled over with figures and letters, thick manuscripts, open, and piled one upon another, without regard to the fragile corners of the parchment,—in short, all the rubbish of science, and over all this litter, dust and cobwebs; but there was no circle of luminous letters, no rapt doctor gazing at the flaming vision as the eagle looks upon the sun.

And yet the cell was not deserted. A man sat in the arm-chair, leaning over the table. Jehan, to whom his back was turned, could see only his shoulders and the back of his skull; but he found no difficulty in recognizing the bald head, which Nature had endowed with an enduring tonsure, as if wishing to mark by this outward symbol the archdeacon's irresistible clerical vocation.

Jehan recognized his brother; but the door had opened so softly that nothing warned Don Claude of his presence. The curious student took advantage of this fact to examine the cell at his leisure. A large stove, which he had not at first observed, stood to the left of the arm-chair, under the dormer-window. The rays of light which penetrated that aperture passed through a round cobweb covering the pointed arch of the window with its delicate tracery, in the centre of which the insect architect lay motionless, like the nave of this wheel of lacework. Upon the stove were heaped in confusion all sorts of vessels,—earthen flasks, glass retorts, and charcoal matrasses. Jehan noticed, with a sigh, that there was not a single saucepan.

"The kitchen utensils are cold!" thought he.

Moreover, there was no fire in the stove, and it even seemed as if none had been lighted for a long time. A glass mask, which Jehan noted among the alchemist's tools, and doubtless used to protect the archdeacon's face when handling any dangerous substance, lay in one corner, covered with dust, and apparently forgotten. Beside it lay an equally dusty pair of bellows, upon the upper surface of which was the motto, inlaid in copper, *"Spira, spera."*

Other mottoes were written on the walls, after the manner of the Hermetics, in great number,—some in ink, others engraved with a metal point. Moreover, Gothic letters, Hebrew letters, Greek letters, and Roman letters were used indiscriminately,—the inscriptions overlapping each other at haphazard, the newest effacing the oldest, and all entangled together, like the branches in a thicket, like the pikes in an affray. There was a confused medley of all human philosophy, thought, and knowledge. Here and there one shone out among the rest like a flag among the spear-heads. They were for the most part brief Greek or Latin devices, such as the Middle Ages expressed so well: *"Unde? inde?" "Homo homini monstrum." "Astra, castra, nomen, numen."* *"Μέγα βιβλίον, μέγα κακόν." "Sapere aude." "Flat ubi vult."* etc. Sometimes a single word without any apparent meaning, *"'Αναγκοφαγία,"* which possibly hid a bitter allusion to the monastic system; sometimes a simple maxim of clerical discipline in the form of a regular hexameter, *"Cælestem dominum, terrestrem dicito domnum."* There were also Hebrew hieroglyphics, of which Jehan, who did not even know much Greek, could make nothing; and the whole was crisscrossed in every direction with stars, figures of men and animals, and intersecting triangles, which contributed not a little to make the blotted wall of the cell look like a sheet of paper which a monkey had bedaubed with an inky pen.

The entire abode, moreover, had a look of general desertion and decay, and the bad condition of the implements led to the conjecture that their owner had for some time been distracted from his labours by other cares.

This owner, however, bending over a huge manuscript adorned with quaint paintings, seemed tormented by a thought which mingled constantly with his meditations,—at least, so Jehan judged from hearing him exclaim, with the pensive pauses of a man in a brown study thinking aloud:—

"Yes, Manu said it, and Zoroaster taught it,—the sun is the offspring of fire, the moon of the sun; fire is the central soul of the great whole; its elementary atoms perpetually overflow, and flood the world in boundless currents! At the points where these currents cross in the heavens, they produce light; at their points of intersection on the earth, they produce gold. Light, gold; the same thing! From fire to the concrete state. The difference between the visible and palpable, between the fluid and solid of the same substance, between steam and ice,—nothing more. These are not mere dreams,—it is the general law of Nature. But how are we to wrest from science the secret of this general law? Why, this light which irradiates my hand is gold! these selfsame atoms, expanded in harmony with a certain law, only require to be condensed in accordance with another law.

And how? Some have fancied it was by burying a sunbeam. Averroës,—yes, it was Averroës,—Averroës interred one under the first column to the left in the sanctuary of the Koran, in the great mosque of Cordova; but the vault may not be opened to see if the operation be successful, until eight thousand years have passed."

"The deuce!" said Jehan aside, "that's a long time to wait for a crown."

"Others have thought," continued the musing archdeacon, "that it was better to work with a ray from Sirius. But it is not easy to get such a ray pure, on account of the simultaneous presence of other stars which blend with it. Flamel! What a name for one of the elect, *Flamma!*—Yes, fire. That is all: the diamond lurks in the coal; gold is to be found in fire. But how to extract it? Magistri declares that there are certain feminine names possessing so sweet and mysterious a spell that it is enough to pronounce them during the operation. Let us read what Manu says under this head: 'Where women are reverenced, the divinities rejoice; where they are scorned, it is vain to pray to God. A woman's mouth is ever pure; it is like running water, it is like a sunbeam. A woman's name should be agreeable, soft, fantastic; it should end with long vowels, and sound like words of blessing.' Yes, the sage is right,—indeed, Maria, Sophia, Esmeral— Damnation! again that thought!"

And he closed the book violently.

He passed his hand across his brow, as if to drive away the idea which possessed him; then he took from the table a nail and a small hammer, the handle of which was curiously painted with cabalistic letters.

"For some time," said he with a bitter smile, "I have failed in all my experiments; a fixed idea possesses me, and is burned into my brain as with a red-hot iron. I have not even succeeded in discovering the lost secret of Cassiodorus, whose lamp burned without wick or oil. And yet it is a simple matter!"

"A plague upon him!" muttered Jehan.

"A single wretched thought, then," continued the priest, "is enough to make a man weak and mad! Oh, how Claude Pernelle would laugh me to scorn,—she who could not for an instant turn Nicholas Flamel from his pursuit of the great work! Why, I hold in my hand the magic hammer of Ezekiel! At every blow which the terrible rabbi, in the seclusion of his cell, struck on this nail with his hammer, that one of his foes whom he had condemned, were he two thousand leagues away, sank an arm's-length into the earth, which swallowed him up. The King of France himself, having one night knocked heedlessly at the magician's door, sank knee-deep into the pavement of his own city of Paris. Well, I have the hammer and the nail, and they are no more powerful tools in my hand than a cooper's tiny mallet would be to a smith; and yet I only need to recover the magic word uttered by Ezekiel as he struck his nail."

"Nonsense!" thought Jehan.

"Let me see, let me try," resumed the archdeacon, eagerly. "If I succeed, I shall see a blue spark flash from the head of the nail. '*Emen-Hétan! Emen-Hétan!*' That's not it. '*Sigéani! Sigéani!*' May this nail open the gates of the tomb for every one who bears the name of Phœbus! A curse upon it! Always, always and forever the same idea!"

And he threw the hammer from him angrily. Then he sank so far forward over the table that Jehan lost sight of him behind the huge back of the chair. For some moments he saw nothing but his fist convulsively clinched upon a book. All at once Don Claude rose, took up a pair of compasses, and silently engraved upon the wall, in capital letters, this Greek word:—

'ANA'TKH

"My brother is mad," said Jehan to himself; "it would have been much simpler to write *Fatum*; every one is not obliged to understand Greek."

The archdeacon resumed his seat in his arm-chair, and bowed his head on his hands, like a sick man whose brow is heavy and burning.

The student watched his brother in surprise. He, who wore his heart on his sleeve, who followed no law in the world but the good law of Nature, who gave free rein to his passions, and in whom the fountain of strong feeling was always dry, so clever was he at draining it daily,—he could not guess the fury with which the sea of human passions bubbles and boils when it is denied all outlet; how it gathers and grows, how it swells, how it overflows, how it wears away the heart, how it breaks forth in repressed sobs and stifled convulsions, until it has rent its dikes and burst its bed. Claude Frollo's stern and icy exterior, that cold surface of rugged and inaccessible virtue, had always misled Jehan. The jovial student had never

dreamed of the boiling lava which lies deep and fiery beneath the snowy front of Ætna.

We know not if he was suddenly made aware of these things; but, feather-brain though he was, he understood that he had seen what he was never meant to see, that he had surprised his elder brother's soul in one of its most secret moments, and that he must not let Claude discover it. Noting that the archdeacon had relapsed into his former immobility, he drew his head back very softly, and made a slight noise behind the door, as if he had just arrived, and wished to warn his brother of his approach.

"Come in!" cried the archdeacon from within the cell; "I expected you. I left the door on the latch purposely; come in, Master Jacques."

The student entered boldly. The archdeacon, much annoyed by such a visit in such a place, started in his chair. "What! is it you, Jehan?"

"It is a J, at any rate," said the student, with his merry, rosy, impudent face.

Don Claude's features resumed their usual severe expression.

"Why are you here?"

"Brother," replied the student, trying to put on a modest, unassuming, melancholy look, and twisting his cap with an innocent air, "I came to ask you—"

"What?"

"For a little moral lecture, which I sorely need." Jehan dared not add aloud, "And a little money, which I need still more sorely." The last part of his sentence was left unspoken.

"Sir," said the archdeacon in icy

tones, "I am greatly displeased with you."

"Alas!" sighed the student.

Don Claude turned his chair slightly, and looked steadily at Jehan.

"I am very glad to see you."

This was a terrible beginning. Jehan prepared for a severe attack.

"Jehan, I hear complaints of you every day. How about that beating with which you bruised a certain little Viscount Albert de Ramonchamp?"

"Oh!" said Jehan, "that was nothing, —a mischievous page, who amused himself with spattering the students by riding his horse through the mud at full speed!"

"How about that Mahiet Fargel," continued the archdeacon, "whose gown you tore? *'Tunicam dechiraverunt,'* the complaint says."

"Oh, pooh! a miserable Montaigu cape,—that's all!"

"The complaint says *'tunicam,'* and not *'cappettam.'* Do you know Latin?"

Jehan made no answer.

"Yes," resumed the priest, shaking his head, "this is what study and learning have come to now. The Latin language is hardly understood, Syriac is an unknown tongue, Greek is held in such odium that it is not considered ignorance for the wisest to skip a Greek word without reading it, and to say, *'Græcum est, non legitur.'* "

The student boldly raised his eyes: "Brother, would you like me to explain in good every-day French that Greek word written yonder on the wall?"

"Which word?"

'ANA'TKH

A slight flush overspread the archdeacon's dappled cheeks, like the puff of smoke which proclaims to the world the secret commotion of a volcano. The student scarcely noticed it.

"Well, Jehan!" stammered the elder brother with an effort, "what does the word mean?"

"FATE."

Don Claude turned pale again, and the student went on carelessly,—

"And that word below it, written by the same hand 'Αναγνεία, means 'impurity.' You see I know my Greek."

The archdeacon was still silent. This Greek lesson had given him food for thought.

Little Jehan, who had all the cunning of a spoiled child, thought this a favourable opportunity to prefer his request. He therefore assumed a very sweet tone, and began:—

"My good brother, have you taken such an aversion to me that you pull a long face for a few paltry cuffs and thumps distributed in fair fight to no one knows what boys and monkeys (*quibusdam marmosetis*)? You see, dear brother Claude, that I know my Latin."

But all this affectionate hypocrisy failed of its usual effect on the stern elder brother. Cerberus did not snap at the sop. The archdeacon's brow did not lose a single wrinkle.

"What are you driving at?" said he, drily.

"Well, then, to the point! This is it," bravely responded Jehan; "I want money."

At this bold declaration the archdeacon's face assumed quite a paternal and pedagogic expression.

"You know, Master Jehan, that our Tirechappe estate only brings us in, reckoning the taxes and rents of the twenty-one houses, thirty-nine pounds eleven pence and six Paris farthings. It is half as much again as in the time of the Paclet brothers, but it is not much."

"I want money," stoically repeated Jehan.

"You know that it has been officially decided that our twenty-one houses were held in full fee of the bishopric, and that we can only buy ourselves off from this homage by paying two silver gilt marks of the value of six Paris pounds to the right reverend bishop. Now, I have not yet been able to save up those two marks. You know this."

"I know that I want money," repeated Jehan for the third time.

"And what would you do with it?"

This question made the light of hope shine in Jehan's eyes. He resumed his demure, caressing manner.

"See here, dear brother Claude; I do not come to you with any evil intention. I don't want to cut a dash at the tavern with your money, or to walk the streets of Paris in garments of gold brocade with my lackey, *cum meo laquasio*. No, brother; I want the money for a charity."

"What charity?" asked Claude with some surprise.

"There are two of my friends who want to buy an outfit for the child of a poor widow in the Haudry almshouse. It is a real charity. It will cost three florins; I want to give my share."

"Who are your two friends?"

"Pierre l'Assommeur and Baptiste Croque-Oison."

"Hum!" said the archdeacon; "those names are as fit for charity as a bombard for the high altar."

Certainly Jehan had chosen very suspicious names for his two friends, as he felt when it was too late.

"And then," added the sagacious Claude, "what kind of an outfit could you buy for three florins, and for the child of one of the women in the Haudry almshouse, too? How long have those widows had babies in swaddling-clothes?"

Jehan broke the ice once more:—

"Well, then, if I must tell you, I want the money to go to see Isabeau la Thierrye tonight, at the Val-d'Amour."

"Impure scamp!" cried the priest.

"'Αναγνεία," said Jehan.

This quotation, borrowed, perhaps maliciously, by the student from the wall of the cell, produced a strange effect upon the priest. He bit his lip, and his rage was extinguished in a blush.

"Begone!" said he to Jehan. "I am expecting someone."

The student made another effort,—

"Brother Claude, at least give me a few farthings for food."

"How far have you got in Gratian's decretals?" asked Don Claude.

"I've lost my copy-books."

"Where are you in the Latin humanities?"

"Somebody has stolen my copy of Horace."

"Where are you in Aristotle?"

"My faith, brother! what Father of the Church says that the errors of heretics have in all ages taken refuge in the brambles of Aristotle's metaphysics? Plague take Aristotle! I will not destroy my religion with his metaphysics."

"Young man," resumed the archdeacon, "at the king's last entry there was a gentleman called Philippe de

Comines, who had embroidered on his horse's housings this motto, which I advise you to consider: *'Qui non laborat non manducet.'* "

The student was silent for a moment, his finger to his ear, his eye fixed upon the ground, and an angry air.

Suddenly he turned to Claude with the lively quickness of a water wagtail,—

"So, good brother, you refuse to give me a penny to buy a crust from a baker?"

" *'Qui non laborat non manducet.'* "

At this reply from the inflexible archdeacon, Jehan hid his face in his hands like a woman sobbing, and exclaimed in accents of despair, "'Οτοτοτοτοτοῖ!"

"What do you mean by that, sir?" asked Claude, amazed at this outburst.

"Why," said the student,—and he looked up at Claude with impudent eyes into which he had just rubbed his fists to make them look red with crying,— "it is Greek! It is an anapæst of Æschylus which expresses grief perfectly."

And here he burst into laughter so absurd and so violent that it made the archdeacon smile. It was really Claude's fault; why had he so spoiled the child?

"Oh, good brother Claude," added Jehan, emboldened by this smile, "just see my broken buskins! Was there ever more tragic cothurnus on earth than boots with flapping soles?"

The archdeacon had promptly resumed his former severity.

"I will send you new boots, but no money."

"Only a paltry penny, brother," continued the suppliant Jehan. "I will learn Gratian by heart. I will believe heart-ily in God. I will be a regular Pythagoras of learning and virtue. But give me a penny, for pity's sake! Would you have me devoured by famine, which gapes before me with its jaws blacker, more noisome, deeper than Tartarus or a monk's nose?"

Don Claude shook his wrinkled brow: " *'Qui non laborat,—'* "

Jehan did not let him finish.

"Well, then," he cried, "to the devil! Hurrah for fun! I'll go to the tavern, I'll fight, I'll drink, and I'll go to see the girls!"

And upon this, he flung up his cap and cracked his fingers like castanets.

The archdeacon looked at him with a gloomy air.

"Jehan, you have no soul!"

"In that case, according to Epicurus, I lack an unknown quantity composed of unknown qualities."

"Jehan, you must think seriously of reform."

"Oh, come!" cried the student, gazing alternately at his brother and at the alembics on the stove; "is everything crooked here,—ideas as well as bottles?"

"Jehan, you are on a very slippery road. Do you know where you are going?"

"To the tavern," said Jehan.

"The tavern leads to the pillory."

"It's as good a lantern as any other, and perhaps it was the one with which Diogenes found his man."

"The pillory leads to the gallows."

"The gallows is a balance, with a man in one scale and the whole world in the other. It is a fine thing to be the man."

"The gallows leads to hell."

"That's a glorious fire."

"Jehan, Jehan, you will come to a bad end!"

"I shall have had a good beginning."

At this moment the sound of footsteps was heard on the stairs.

"Silence!" said the archdeacon, putting his finger to his lip: "here comes Master Jacques. Listen, Jehan," he added in a low voice; "take care you never mention what you may see and hear here. Hide yourself quickly under that stove, and don't dare to breathe."

The student crawled under the stove; there, a capital idea occurred to him.

"By the way, brother Claude, I want a florin for holding my breath."

"Silence! you shall have it."

"Then give it to me."

"Take it!" said the archdeacon, angrily, flinging him his purse.

Jehan crept farther under the stove, and the door opened.

CHAPTER V

THE TWO MEN DRESSED IN BLACK

The person who entered wore a black gown and a gloomy air. Our friend Jehan (who, as may readily be supposed, had so disposed himself in his corner that he could see and hear everything at his good pleasure) was struck, at the first glance, by the extreme melancholy of the new-comer's face and attire. Yet a certain amiability pervaded the countenance, albeit it was the amiability of a cat or a judge,—a sickly amiability. The man was very grey, wrinkled, bordering on sixty years; had white eyebrows, hanging lip, and big hands. When Jehan saw that he was a mere no-body,—that is, probably a doctor or a magistrate, and that his nose was very far away from his mouth, a sure sign of stupidity,—he curled himself up in his hiding-place, in despair at having to pass an indefinite length of time in so uncomfortable a position and in such poor company.

Meantime, the archdeacon did not even rise from his chair to greet this person. He signed to him to be seated on a stool near the door, and after a few moments' silence, which seemed the continuation of a previous meditation, he said in a somewhat patronizing tone, "Good-morning, Master Jacques."

"Your servant, master," replied the man in black.

In the two ways of pronouncing,—on the one hand that "Master Jacques," and on the other that distinctive "master,"—there was the difference that there is between *domine* and *domne*. It bespoke the greeting of teacher and pupil.

"Well," resumed the archdeacon after a fresh pause, which Master Jacques took care not to break, "have you succeeded?"

"Alas! master," said the other, with a sad smile, "I am still blowing away. As many ashes as I choose; but not a particle of gold."

Don Claude made an impatient gesture. "I'm not talking about that, Master Jacques Charmolue, but about the trial of your sorcerer, Marc Cenaine,—wasn't that what you called him?—the butler to the Court of Accounts. Does he confess his magic? Was the rack successful?"

"Alas! no," replied Master Jacques, still with the same sad smile, "we have not that consolation. The man is as hard as flint; we might boil him at the Pig-market before he would say a word. And yet, we have spared nothing to get at the truth; all his bones are out of joint already; we have left no stone unturned. As the old comic author, Plautus, says:—

'Advorsum stimulos, laminas, crucesque,
        compedesque,
Nervos, catenas, carceres, numellas,
        pedicas, boias.'
All in vain; the man is terrible indeed. I can't make him out!"

"You've not found anything new at his house?"

"Yes, indeed," said Master Jacques, fumbling in his purse; "this parchment. There are words written on it which we cannot comprehend. And yet the criminal lawyer, Philippe Lheulier, knows a little Hebrew, which he picked up in that affair of the Jews in the Rue Kantersten at Brussels."

So saying, Master Jacques unrolled a parchment.

"Give it to me," said the archdeacon. And casting his eyes over the writing, he exclaimed, "Clear magic, Master Jacques! *'Emen-Hétan!'* that is the cry of the vampires as they appear at their Sabbath. *'Per ipsum, et cum ipso, et in ipso!'*—that is the word of command which rechains the devil in hell. *'Hax, pax, max!'* this belongs to medicine: a prescription against the bite of mad dogs. Master Jacques, you are the king's proxy to the Ecclesiastical Court. This parchment is an abomination."

"We will return the man to the rack. Here again," added Master Jacques, rummaging in his wallet once more, "is

something else which we found in Marc Cenaine's house."

It was a vessel similar to those which covered Don Claude's stove.

"Ah!" said the archdeacon, "an alchemist's crucible."

"I must confess," replied Master Jacques, with his shy, awkward smile, "that I tried it on my furnace, but I succeeded no better than with my own."

The archdeacon began to examine the vessel.

"What has he inscribed upon his crucible? *'Och! Och!'*—the word which drives away fleas! This Marc Cenaine is a dolt! I can easily believe that you will never make gold with this. Put it in your alcove in summer, for that's all it's fit for."

"Talking of mistakes," said the king's proxy, "I have just been studying the porch below before I came upstairs; is your reverence very sure that it is the opening of the book of physics which is represented there on the side towards the Hospital; and that, of the seven nude figures at the feet of the Virgin, the one with wings at his heels is meant for Mercury?"

"Yes," replied the priest; "it is so written by Augustin Nypho, that Italian doctor who had a bearded familiar spirit, which taught him everything. However, we will go down, and I will explain all this to you on the spot."

"Thanks, master," said Charmolue, bowing to the ground. "By the way, I forgot! When will it please you to have the little witch arrested?"

"What witch?"

"That gipsy girl whom you know well, who comes every day and dances in the square before the cathedral. despite the official prohibition. She has a goat which is possessed, and which has the devil's own horns; which reads and writes, and is as good a mathematician as Picatrix, and would be quite enough to hang an entire tribe of gipsies. The papers are ready; the case will be a short one, I warrant! A pretty creature, by my soul,—that dancing-girl! The finest black eyes! Two carbuncles! When shall we begin?"

The archdeacon was extremely pale.

"I will let you know," he stammered in a voice which was scarcely articulate; then he added, with an effort, "Devote yourself to Marc Cenaine."

"Never fear," said Charmolue, smiling; "I'll have him re-strapped to the leather bed when I go back. But he's a devil of a fellow; he would tire out Pierrat Torterue himself, and his hands are bigger than mine. As the worthy Plautus says:—

'*Nudus vinctus, centum pondo, es quando pendes per pedes.*'

The torture of the wheel! That's the best thing we have. He shall take a turn at that."

Don Claude seemed absorbed in gloomy reverie. He turned to Charmolue with the words,—

"Master Pierrat,—Master Jacques, I mean,—devote yourself to Marc Cenaine."

"Yes, yes, Don Claude. Poor man! he must have suffered like Mummol. But then, what an idea, to go to the Witches' Sabbath,—a butler of the Court of Accounts, who must know Charlemagne's text, '*Stryga vel masca!*' As for that little girl,—Smelarda, as they call her,—I will await your orders. Ah! and as we pass through the porch you will also explain to me the meaning of the gardener painted in relief at the entrance to the church. The Sower, isn't it? Eh! master, what are you thinking about?"

Don Claude, lost in his own thoughts, did not hear him. Charmolue, following the direction of his gaze saw that it was fixed mechanically upon the large cobweb which covered the window. At this instant a rash fly, in search of the March sun, plunged headlong into the trap and was caught in it. At the vibration of its web the huge spider made a sudden sally from its central cell, and with one bound fell upon the fly, which it doubled up with its front antennæ, while its hideous proboscis dug out the head. "Poor fly!" said the king's proxy to the Ecclesiastical Court; and he raised his hand to save it. The archdeacon, with a start, held back his arm with convulsive force.

"Master Jacques," he cried, "do not interfere with the work of Fate!"

The attorney turned in alarm; he felt as if iron pincers had seized his arm. The priest's eye was fixed, wild, and flaming, and was still fastened upon the horrible little group of the spider and the fly.

"Oh, yes," added the priest in a voice which seemed to come from his very entrails, "this is a universal symbol. The insect flies about, is happy, is young; it seeks the spring sun, the fresh air, freedom; oh, yes, but it runs against the fatal web; the spider appears,—the hideous spider! Poor dancing-girl! poor predestined fly! Master Jacques, do not interfere! it is the hand of Fate! Alas! Claude, you are the spider. Claude, you are the fly as well! You flew abroad in search of learning, light, and sun; your only desire was to gain the pure air, the broad light of eternal truth; but in your haste to reach the dazzling window which opens into the other world,—the world of intellect, light, and learning,—blind fly! senseless doctor! you failed to see that subtle spider's web woven by Fate between the light and you; you plunged headlong into it, wretched fool! and now you struggle in its meshes, with bruised head and broken wings, in the iron grasp of destiny. Master Jacques, Master Jacques, let the spider do its work!"

"I assure you," said Charmolue, looking at him uncomprehendingly, "I will not touch it. But for mercy's sake, master, let go my arm! Your hand is like a pair of pincers."

The archdeacon did not hear him. "Oh, madman!" he resumed, without taking his eyes from the window. "And if you could have broken this dreadful web with your frail wings, do you think you could have reached the light? Alas! how could you have passed that pane of glass beyond it,—that transparent obstacle, that crystal wall harder than iron, which separates all philosophy from truth? Oh, vanity of science! How many sages have flown from afar to bruise their heads against it! How many contending systems have rushed pell-mell against that everlasting pane of glass!"

He ceased speaking. These last ideas, which had insensibly diverted his thoughts from himself to science, seemed to have calmed him. Jacques Charmolue completely restored him to a sense of reality by asking him this question: "Come, master, when are you going to help me to make gold? I long for success."

The archdeacon shook his head with a bitter smile:

"Master Jacques, read Michel Psellus, *'Dialogues de Energia et Operatione Dæmonum.'* Our work is not altogether innocent."

"Not so loud, master! I fear you are right," said Charmolue. "But I must needs dabble a little in hermetics, being only the king's proxy to the Ecclesiastical Court, at a salary of thirty Tours crowns a year. But speak lower."

At this moment the sound of champing and chewing proceeding from under the stove, attracted Charmolue's anxious ear.

"What was that?" he asked.

It was the student, who, greatly cramped and much bored in his hiding-place, had contrived to find an old crust of bread and a bit of mouldy cheese, and had set to work to devour them without more ado, by the way of consolation and of breakfast. As he was ravenously hungry, he made a great deal of noise, and smacked his lips loudly over every mouthful as to give the alarm to the lawyer.

"It is my cat," said the archdeacon, hastily, "feasting under there upon some mouse."

This explanation satisfied Charmolue.

"Indeed, master," he replied with a respectful smile, "every philosopher has had his familiar animal. You know what Servius says: *'Nullus enim locus sine genio est.'*"

But Don Claude, who feared some fresh outbreak from Jehan, reminded his worthy disciple that they had certain figures on the porch to study together;

and the two left the cell, to the great relief of the student, who began seriously to fear that his knees would leave their permanent mark upon his chin.

CHAPTER VI

THE EFFECT PRODUCED BY SEVEN OATHS IN THE OPEN AIR

"TE DEUM Laudamus!" cried Master Jehan, as he stepped from his hiding-place; "the two screech-owls have gone. *Och! och! Hax! pax! max!* the fleas! the mad dogs! the devil! I've had enough of their talk! My head rings like a belfry. Mouldy cheese into the bargain! Now, then! let us be off; let us take our big brother's purse, and convert all these coins into bottles!"

He cast a look of tenderness and admiration into the interior of the precious purse, adjusted his dress, wiped his boots, dusted his poor shoulder-pads all grey with ashes, whistled a tune, frisked about, looked to see if there was nothing left in the cell which he might carry off, scraped up a few glass charms and trinkets from the top of the stove, thinking he might pass them off upon Isabeau la Thierrye for jewels, then gave a push to the door, which his brother had left ajar as a final favour, and which he left open in his turn as a final piece of mischief, and hopped down the winding stairs as nimbly as a bird.

In the midst of the shadows of the spiral staircase he elbowed something which moved aside with a growl; he took it for granted that it was Quasimodo, and this struck him as so droll that he held his sides with laughter all the rest

of the way down. As he came out into the public square, he was still laughing.

He stamped his foot when he found himself on solid ground once more. "Oh," said he, "good and honourable pavement of Paris! Cursed stairs, which would put all the angels of Jacob's ladder out of breath! What was I thinking of when I poked myself into that stone gimlet which pierces the sky; and all to eat musty cheese, and to see the steeples of Paris through a garret window!"

He walked on a few paces, and saw the two screech-owls—that is to say, Don Claude and Master Jacques Charmolue—lost in contemplation of a bit of carving on the porch. He approached them on tiptoe, and heard the archdeacon say in a very low voice to Charmolue, "It was Guillaume de Paris who had a Job graven on that lapis-lazuli coloured stone, gilded at the edges. Job represents the philosopher's stone, which must also be tried and tortured before it can become perfect, as Raymond Lulle says: *'Sub conservatione formæ specificæ salva anima.'*"

"That's all one to me," said Jehan. "'Tis I who hold the purse."

At this instant he heard a loud ringing voice pronounce a terrible string of oaths just behind him.

"Zounds! Odds bodikins! By the Rood! By Cock and pye! Damme! 'Sdeath! Thunder and Mars!"

"By my soul," exclaimed Jehan, "that can be no other than my friend Captain Phœbus!"

The name of Phœbus reached the archdeacon's ears, just as he was explaining to the king's proxy the dragon hiding his tail in a bath from which rise smoke and a king's head. Don Claude shuddered, stopped short, to the great surprise of Charmolue, turned, and saw his brother Jehan talking to a tall officer at the door of the Gondelaurier house.

It was indeed Captain Phœbus de Châteaupers. He was leaning against the corner of his lady-love's house, and swearing like a pirate.

"My word! Captain Phœbus," said Jehan, taking him by the hand, "you swear with admirable spirit!"

"Thunder and Mars!" replied the captain.

"Thunder and Mars, yourself!" responded the student. "Now, then, my fine captain, what has caused such an outburst of elegant epithets?"

"Your pardon, good comrade Jehan," cried Phœbus, shaking him by the hand; "but a horse running at full speed cannot stop short. Now, I was swearing at full gallop. I have just come from those prudes; and when I leave them, I always have my mouth full of oaths; I must needs spit them out, or I should choke. Thunder and guns!"

"Will you take a drink?" asked the student. This proposition calmed the captain.

"With pleasure; but I've no money."

"But I have!"

"Pshaw! let me see!"

Jehan displayed the purse to the captain's eyes, with dignity and simplicity. Meanwhile the archdeacon, having left the amazed Charmolue, had approached them, and stood some paces distant, watching them both unobserved by them, so absorbed were they in looking at the purse.

Phœbus exclaimed, "A purse in your pocket, Jehan! That's like the moon in a pail of water. I see it, but it is not really there. It's only a shadow. By Heaven! I wager there's nothing but pebbles in it!"

Jehan answered coldly, "I'll show you the kind of pebbles that I pave my pocket with."

And without another word he emptied the purse upon a neighbouring post, with the air of a Roman saving his country.

"Good God!" muttered Phœbus; "gold pieces, big silver pieces, little silver pieces, crowns, shillings, and pence! It is dazzling!"

Jehan remained dignified and unmoved. A few pennies had rolled into the mud; the captain, in his enthusiasm, stooped to pick them up. Jehan restrained him, saying,—

"Fie, Captain Phœbus de Châteaupers!"

Phœbus counted the money, and turning solemnly to Jehan, asked, "Do you know, Jehan, that you have here twenty-three crowns? Whom did you rob last night in the Rue Coupe-Gueule?"

Jehan threw back his fair curly head, and said, half closing his eyes in scorn,—

"I have a brother who is an archdeacon and a fool."

"Confound it!" cried Phœbus; "so you have, the worthy fellow!"

"Let us take a drink," said Jehan.

"Where shall we go?" said Phœbus; "to the Pomme d'Eve!"

"No, Captain; let us go to the Vieille Science. An old woman who handles a saw to saw a handle,—that's a rebus; and I love that sort of thing."

"A plague on rebuses, Jehan! The wine is better at the Pomme d'Eve; and besides, at the door is a vine in the sun, which cheers me as I drink."

"So be it," said the student; and taking Phœbus by the arm, the two friends set out for that tavern. It is needless to say that they first picked up the money, and that the archdeacon followed them.

The archdeacon followed them, sad and worn. Was this the Phœbus whose accursed name, since his interview with Gringoire, had mingled with all his thoughts? He knew not; but at any rate it was a Phœbus, and that magic name was enough to make the archdeacon follow the two heedless comrades with stealthy tread, listening to their every word and noting their least gesture with eager attention. Moreover, nothing was easier than to hear everything they said; for they spoke very loud, utterly regardless of the fact that they were taking the passers-by into their confidence. They talked of duels, women, drinking, and riots.

At the corner of a street the sound of a tambourine was heard from a neighbouring cross-way. Don Claude overheard the officer say to the student,—

"Thunder! We must hasten."

"Why, Phœbus?"

"I'm afraid the gipsy girl will see me."

"What gipsy girl?"

"That little thing with the goat."

"Smeralda?"

"Just so, Jehan. I alway forget her devil of a name. Make haste; she would be sure to recognize me. I don't wish to have that girl accost me in the street."

"Do you know her, Phœbus?"

Here the archdeacon saw Phœbus chuckle, put his mouth to Jehan's ear, and whisper a few words to him; then he burst out laughing, and shook his head with a triumphant air.

"Really?" said Jehan.

"Upon my soul!" said Phœbus.

"To-night?"

"To-night."

"Are you sure she will come?"

"Are you mad, Jehan? How can there be any doubt in such matters?"

"Captain Phœbus, you are a lucky soldier!"

The archdeacon heard every word of this conversation. His teeth chattered; he shook from head to foot. He stood still a moment, leaned against a post like a drunken man, then followed in the track of the two jolly scamps.

When he rejoined them they had changed the subject. He heard them singing at the top of their voices the old refrain:—

"The lads of Petty-Tiles, they say,
Like calves are butchered every day."

CHAPTER VII

THE SPECTRE MONK

THE famous tavern known as the Pomme d'Eve was situated in the University, at the corner of the Rue de la Rondelle and the Rue du Bâtonnier. It was a large, low room on the ground-floor, with an arched roof, the central spring of which rested on a huge wooden pillar painted yellow; there were tables in every direction, shining pewter jugs hung on the wall; there were always plenty of topers, lots of girls, a window looking on the street, a vine at the door, and over the door a creaking piece of sheet iron, on which were painted a woman and an apple, rusted by the rain and swinging in the wind on an iron rod. This kind of weathercock, which overlooked the pavement, was the sign. Night was falling; the streets were dark. The tavern, full of candles, flared from a distance like a forge in the gloom; a noise of glasses, of feasting, of oaths, and of quarrels escaped from the broken window-panes. Through the mist with which the heat of the room covered the glazed casement in front of the inn swarmed a myriad of confused figures, and from time to time a ringing burst of laughter was heard. People passing, intent on their own affairs, hastened by that noisy window without a glance; but now and then some little ragged boy would raise himself on tiptoe to the window-sill, and scream into the tavern the old mocking cry with which drunkards were often greeted at this period:—

"Back to your glasses,
Ye drunken, drunken asses."

One man, however, marched imperturbably up and down in front of the noisy tavern, looking continually, and never stirring farther away from it than a pikeman from his sentry-box. His cloak was pulled up to his very nose. This cloak he had just bought from the old-clothes man who lived hard by the Pomme d'Eve, doubtless to shield himself from the chill of the March evening, perhaps to hide his dress. From time to time he paused before the dim panes set in lead, listened, looked, and stamped his feet impatiently.

At last the tavern door opened. This seemed to be what he was waiting for. Two tipplers came out. The ray of light which escaped through the door, for a moment reddened their jovial faces. The man with the cloak took up his position under a porch on the other side of the street.

"Thunder and guns!" said one of the two drinkers. "It will strike seven directly. It is the hour for my appointment."

"I tell you," resumed his companion, with a thick utterance, "that I do not live in the Rue des Mauvaises-Paroles, *indignus qui inter mala verba habitat.* My lodgings are in the Rue Jean-Pain-Mollet, *in vico Johannis-Pain-Mollet.* You are more unreasonable than a unicorn, if you say to the contrary. Everybody knows that he who has once climbed upon a bear's back is never afraid; but you've a fine nose for scenting out dainty bits like Saint-Jacques de l'Hôpital."

"Jehan, my friend, you are drunk," said the other.

He replied, staggering, "So it pleases you to say, Phœbus; but it is well proven that Plato had the profile of a hunting-dog."

The reader has undoubtedly recognized our two worthy friends, the captain and the student. It seems that the man lurking in the shadow had also recognized them; for he followed with slow steps all the zig-zags which the student forced the captain to describe, the latter, a more hardened drinker, having preserved entire self-possession. By listening carefully, the man with the cloak was able to catch the whole of the following interesting conversation:—

"Body of Bacchus! do try to walk straight, Master Bachelor. You know that I shall have to leave you. Here it is seven o'clock. I have an appointment with a woman."

"Leave me then, do. I see fiery stars and spears. You are like the Château-de-Dampmartin, which burst with laughter."

"By my grandmother's warts, Jehan! your nonsense is rather too desperate. By-the-bye, Jehan, haven't you any money left?"

"Mr. Rector, there's no mistake: the little butcher's shop, *parva boucheria.*"

"Jehan, friend Jehan! you know that I made an appointment to meet that little girl at the end of the Pont Saint-Michel; that I can't take her anywhere but to Mother Falourdel,—the old hag on the bridge; and that I must pay for the room; the white-whiskered old jade gives no credit. Jehan, for pity's sake, have we drunk up the priest's whole purse? Haven't you a penny left?"

"The consciousness that you have spent the rest of your time well is a good and savoury table-sauce."

"Thunder and blazes! A truce to your nonsense! Tell me, Jehan, you devil! have you any money left? Give it to me, by Heaven! or I will rob you, were you as leprous as Job and as mangy as Cæsar!"

"Sir, the Rue Galiache is a street which runs from the Rue de la Verrerie to the Rue de la Tixeranderie."

"Yes, yes, good friend Jehan, my poor comrade, the Rue Galiache,—that's all right, quite right, but in Heaven's name, come to your senses! I want only a few pence, and my appointment is for seven o'clock."

"Silence all around, and pay attention to my song:

'When the rats have eaten every case,
The king shall be lord of Arras race.
When the sea, so deep and wide,
Is frozen o'er at Saint John's tide,
Across the ice we then shall see
The Arras men their city flee.' "

"There, then, scholar of Antichrist, the foul fiend fly away with you!" cried Phœbus; and he gave the tipsy student a violent push, which sent him reeling against the wall, whence he fell gently to the pavement of Philip Augustus. With a remnant of that brotherly compassion which never quite forsakes the heart of a toper, Phœbus rolled Jehan with his foot over upon one of those pillows which the poor which Providence keeps in readiness at every street corner in Paris, and which the rich scornfully stigmatize as dunghills. The captain arranged Jehan's head on an inclined plane of cabbage-stalks, and the student instantly began to snore in a magnificent bass. However, all rancour was not yet dead in the captain's heart. "So much the worse for you if the devil's cart picks you up as it passes!" said he to the poor sleeping scholar; and he went his way.

The man in the cloak, who had not ceased following him, paused for a moment beside the prostrate student, as if uncertain; then, heaving a deep sigh, he also departed in the captain's wake.

Like them, we will leave Jehan to sleep under the friendly watch of the bright stars, and we too will follow them, if it so please the reader.

As he emerged into the Rue Saint-André-des-Arcs, Captain Phœbus discovered that some one was following him. As he accidentally glanced behind him, he saw a kind of shadow creeping behind him along the walls. He stopped, it stopped; he walked on again, the shadow also walked on. This troubled him but very little. "Pooh!" said he to himself, "I have not a penny about me."

In front of the Collège d'Autun, he came to a halt. It was at this college that he had passed through what he was pleased to call his studies, and from a habit learned in his student days he never passed the statue of Cardinal Pierre Bertrand without stopping to mock at it. He therefore paused before the statue as usual. The street was deserted, save for the shadow approaching slowly,—so slowly that he had ample time to observe that it wore a cloak and a hat. Coming close up to him, it stopped, and stood more motionless than the statue of Cardinal Bertrand itself; but it fastened upon Phœbus a pair of eyes full of that vague light seen at night in the pupil of a cat's eye.

The captain was brave, and would not have cared a farthing for a thief with a bludgeon in his hand; but this walking statue, this petrified man, froze his very blood. At that time there were current in society strange stories of the spectral monk, who prowled the streets of Paris by night. These tales now came confusedly to his mind, and for some moments he stood stupefied; at last he broke the silence with a forced laugh, saying,—

"Sir, if you are a robber, as I hope, you remind me of a heron attacking a nutshell; I am the son of a ruined family, my dear fellow. You've come to the wrong shop; you'd better go next door. In the chapel of that college there is a piece of the true cross set in silver."

The hand of the shadow was stretched from under the cloak, and swooped down upon Phœbus's arm with the grip of an eagle's talons. At the same time the shadow spoke:—

"Captain Phœbus de Châteaupers!"

"What! the devil!" said Phœbus; "do you know my name?"

"I not only know your name," replied the man in the cloak, with his sepulchral voice, "but I know that you have an appointment this evening?"

"Yes," answered the astonished Phœbus.

"At seven o'clock."

"In fifteen minutes."

"At Mother Falourdel's."

"Exactly so."

"The old hag of the Pont Saint-Michel."

"Saint Michel the archangel, as the Pater Noster says."

"Impious wretch!" muttered the spectre. "With a woman?"

"Confiteor."

"Whose name is—"

"Esmeralda," said Phœbus, cheerfully. He had gradually recovered all his unconcern.

At this name the shadow's claws shook the captain's arm furiously.

"Captain Phœbus de Châteaupers, you lie!"

Any one who could at this moment have seen the captain's flaming face, his backward bound, so violent that it released him from the vice-like grasp that held him, the haughty air with which he clapped his hand to his sword-hilt, and the gloomy immobility of the man in the cloak in the presence of this rage,

—any one who saw all this would have trembled with fear. It was something like the fight between Don Juan and the statue.

"Christ and Satan!" cried the captain; "that is a word which seldom greets the ears of a Châteaupers! You dare not repeat it!"

"You lie!" said the shadow, coldly.

The captain gnashed his teeth. Spectre monk, phantom, superstitions, all were forgotten at this instant. He saw nothing but a man and an insult.

"Ha! it is well!" he stammered in a voice stifled by rage. He drew his sword; then, stuttering,—for anger makes a man tremble as well as fear, "Here! on the spot! Now then! swords! swords! Blood upon these stones!"

But the other never stirred. When he saw his adversary on his guard, and ready to burst with wrath, he said,—

"Captain Phœbus,"—and his voice quivered with bitterness,—"you forget your appointment."

The fits of passion of such men as Phœbus are like boiling milk,—a drop of cold water is enough to check their fury. At these simple words the sword which glittered in the captain's hand was lowered.

"Captain," continued the man, "to-morrow, the day after to-morrow, in a month, in ten years, you will find me ready to cut your throat; but keep your appointment first."

"Indeed," said Phœbus, as if trying to compound with his conscience, "a sword and a girl are both charming things to encounter by appointment; but I do not see why I should miss one for the sake of the other, when I might have both."

He replaced his sword in his scabbard.

"Go to your appointment," replied the stranger.

"Sir," answered Phœbus with some embarrassment, "many thanks for your courtesy. You are right in saying that to-morrow will be time enough for us to cut slashes and buttonholes in Father Adam's doublet. I am obliged to you for allowing me to pass another agreeable quarter of an hour. I did indeed hope to put you to bed in the gutter, and yet be in time for my fair one,— the more so that it is genteel to keep the women waiting a little in such cases. But you look to me like a determined dog, and it is safer to put the party off until to-morrow. I will therefore go to my appointment; it is for seven o'clock, as you know." Here Phœbus scratched his ear. "Ah, by my halidom! I forgot; I have not a penny to pay the toll for the use of the garret, and the old hag must be paid in advance. She won't trust me."

"Here is money to pay her."

Phœbus felt the stranger's cold hand slip a large piece of money into his. He could not help taking the money and squeezing the hand.

"By God!" he exclaimed, "you're a good fellow!"

"One condition," said the man. "Prove to me that I was wrong, and that you spoke the truth. Hide me in some corner where I can see whether this woman be really she whose name you mentioned."

"Oh," answered Phœbus, "with all my heart! We will take Saint Martha's room; you can look in very easily from the kennel beside it."

"Come on, then!" said the shadow.

"At your service," replied the captain. "I don't know whether or no you are Master Diabolus in *propria persona*: but let us be good friends for to-night; to-morrow I will pay you all my debts, of purse and sword."

They set forth at a rapid pace. In a few moments the sound of the river warned them that they stood on Pont Saint-Michel, then covered with houses.

"I will first introduce you," said Phœbus to his companion; "then I will go and fetch my charmer, who was to wait for me near the Petit-Châtelet."

His comrade made no answer; since they had walked side by side he had not said a word. Phœbus stopped before a low door and knocked loudly; a light appeared through the chinks of the door.

"Who is there?" cried a mumbling voice.

"By Saint Luke's face! By God's passion! By the Rood!" answered the captain.

The door opened instantly, and revealed to the new-comers an old woman and an old lamp, both in a very shaky state. The old woman was bent double, dressed in rags; her head shook; she had very small eyes, wore a dish-clout on her head, and her hands, face, and neck were covered with wrinkles; her lips retreated under her gums, and she had tufts of white hair all around her mouth, which gave her the demure look of a cat.

The interior of the hovel was as dilapidated as its mistress; there were whitewashed walls, black beams running across the ceiling, a dismantled fireplace, cobwebs in every corner; in the middle of the room stood a rickety collection of tables and chairs; a dirty child played in the ashes; and in the background a staircase, or rather a wooden ladder, led to a trap-door in the ceiling.

On entering this den Phœbus's mysterious companion pulled his cloak up to his eyes. But the captain, swearing all the time like a Turk, hastened "to make the sun flash from a crown-piece," as our all-accomplished Régnier says.

"Saint Martha's room," said he.

The old woman treated him like a lord, and put the coin away in a drawer. It was the money which the man in the black cloak had given Phœbus. While her back was turned, the ragged, dishevelled little boy, who was playing in the ashes, went adroitly to the drawer, took out the crown-piece, and put in its place a dried leaf which he had pulled from a fagot.

The old woman beckoned to the two gentlemen, as she called them, to follow her, and climbed the ladder before them. On reaching the upper floor, she placed her lamp upon a chest; and Phœbus, as one familiar with the house, opened a door leading to a dark hole. "Go in there, my dear boy," said he to his comrade. The man in the cloak obeyed without a word; the door closed behind him; he heard Phœbus bolt it, and a moment after go downstairs again with the old woman. The light had disappeared.

CHAPTER VIII

THE ADVANTAGE OF WINDOWS OVERLOOKING THE RIVER

CLAUDE FROLLO (for we presume that the reader, more clever than Phœbus, has discovered that this spectral monk was no other than the archdeacon), Claude Frollo groped about for some time in the gloomy hole into which the captain had bolted him. It was one of those nooks such as architects sometimes leave at the junction of the roof and outer wall. The vertical section of this kennel—as Phœbus had so aptly called it—would have formed a triangle. Moreover, there was neither window nor loop-hole, and the pitch of the roof was so steep that it was impossible to stand upright. Claude therefore squatted in the dust and mortar which crumbled beneath him. His head was burning; as he felt about him with his hands, he found upon the ground a bit of broken glass, which he pressed to his forehead, its coolness somewhat refreshing him.

What went on at this moment in the archdeacon's dark soul? God and himself alone knew.

According to what fatal order did he dispose in his thoughts Esmeralda, Phœbus, Jacques Charmolue, his young brother, so greatly loved, deserted by him in the mud, his archdeacon's gown, perhaps his reputation, dragged through the mire of Mother Falourdel's abode,—all these images, all these adventures? I cannot say; but it is certain that the ideas formed a horrible group in his mind.

He waited a quarter of an hour; he felt as if a century had been added to his age. All at once he heard the boards of the wooden staircase creak; some one was coming up. The trap-door opened; a light appeared. There was a considerable crack in the worm-eaten door of his prison: to this he glued his face. Thus he could see everything that happened in the next room. The cat-faced old woman first rose from the trap-door, lamp in hand; then came Phœbus, twirling his moustache; then a third person,—that lovely, graceful creature, Esmeralda. The priest saw her rise from below like a dazzling apparition. He trembled; a cloud came before his eyes; his veins swelled to bursting; everything swam before him; he saw and heard nothing more.

When he recovered his senses, Phœbus and Esmeralda were alone, seated on the wooden chest beside the lamp, whose light revealed to the archdeacon's eyes their two youthful figures, and a miserable pallet at the back of the garret.

Beside the pallet there was a window, through whose panes, shattered like a cobweb upon which rain has fallen, were seen a patch of sky, and the moon in the distance resting on a bed of soft clouds.

The young girl was blushing and trembling, and confused. Her long, drooping lashes shaded her flushed cheeks. The officer, to whose face she dared not raise her eyes, was radiant. Mechanically, and with a charming awkwardness, she drew meaningless lines on the bench with her finger-tips, and then looked at her finger. Her feet were hidden, for the little goat was lying upon them.

The captain was very gallantly arrayed; at his wrists and neck he wore embroidery, then considered very elegant.

Don Claude could scarcely hear what they said, for the throbbing of his temples.

Lovers' talk is very commonplace. It

is a perpetual "I love you." A very bare and very insipid phrase to an indifferent ear, unless adorned with a few grace-notes; but Claude was not an indifferent listener.

"Oh," said the girl, without raising her eyes, "do not despise me, my lord Phœbus! I feel that I am doing very wrong."

"Despise you, pretty child!" replied the officer with an air of extreme gallantry,—"despise you! By God's passion! and why?"

"For coming here with you."

"On that point, my beauty, we are not agreed. I should not despise you, but hate you."

The young girl gazed at him in affright. "Hate me! What have I done?"

"For requiring so much urging."

"Alas!" said she, "that is because I am breaking a sacred vow. I shall never find my parents! The amulet will lose its virtue; but what does that matter? Why should I need father or mother now?"

So saying, she fixed upon the captain her large dark eyes, moist with love and joy.

"Deuce take me if I understand you!" exclaimed Phœbus.

Esmeralda was silent for a moment, then a tear fell from her eyes, a sigh from her lips, and she said, "Oh, my lord, I love you!"

There was such an odour of chastity, such a charm of virtue about the young girl, that Phœbus did not feel wholly at his ease with her. But this speech emboldened him. "You love me!" said he, with transport; and he threw his arm around the gipsy's waist. He had only waited for such an opportunity.

The priest saw him, and tested with the tip of his finger the point of a dagger hidden in his bosom.

"Phœbus," continued the gipsy girl, gently removing the captain's stubborn hands from her girdle, "you are good, you are generous, you are kind; you saved me,—me, who am but a poor gipsy foundling. I have long dreamed of an officer who should save my life. It was of you I dreamed before I ever knew you, my Phœbus; the image of my dreams had a gorgeous uniform like yours, a grand air, a sword. Your name is Phœbus; it is a beautiful name. I love your name; I love your sword. Draw your sword, Phœbus, and let me see it."

"Child!" said the captain; and he unsheathed his rapier with a smile.

The gipsy girl studied the handle, the blade, examined the letters on the hilt with adorable curiosity, and kissed the sword, as she said,—

"You are a brave man's sword. I love my captain."

Phœbus again took advantage of the situation to imprint on her lovely bent neck a kiss which made the girl start up as red as a cherry. The priest ground his teeth in the darkness at the sight.

"Phœbus," resumed the gipsy, "let me talk to you. Walk about a little, so that I may have a good look at you, and hear your spurs jingle. How handsome you are!"

The captain rose to gratify her, while he scolded her with a smile of satisfaction:—

"What a child you are! By the way,

my charmer, did you ever see me in my full dress uniform?"

"Alas, no!" she replied.

"Well, that is really fine!"

Phœbus came back and sat down beside her, but much nearer than before.

"Look here, my dear—"

The gipsy gave him a few little taps on the lips with her pretty hand, with a childish playfulness full of gaiety and grace.

"No, no, I will not listen. Do you love me? I want you to tell me if you love me."

"Do I love you, angel of my life!" cried the captain, half kneeling before her. "My body, my soul, my blood, are yours. I am all yours,—all yours. I love you, and never loved any one but you."

The captain had so often repeated this phrase on many a similar occasion, that he uttered it in a breath, without making a single mistake. At this passionate declaration the gipsy turned towards the dirty ceiling, which took the place of heaven, a look of angelic happiness. "Oh," she murmured, "at such a moment one might well wish to die!"

Phœbus thought "the moment" a good one to steal another kiss, which inflicted fresh torment on the wretched archdeacon in his lair.

"To die!" exclaimed the amorous captain. "What are you talking about, my lovely angel? It is just the time to live, or Jupiter is but a paltry knave! Die at the beginning of such a pleasant thing! By Saint Luke's face, what a joke! that would never do! Listen, my dear Similar—Esmenarda—— Forgive me! but you have such a vastly outlandish name that I can never get it

straight. I'm forever getting entangled in it."

"Good Heavens!" said the poor girl, "and I thought the name pretty just for its oddness! But if you don't like it, I am quite ready to change it for anything you please."

"Ah, do not cry for such a trifle, my dearest! It's a name to which one has to get used, that's all. Once I have learned it by heart, it will be all right. Now listen, my dear Similar; I adore you passionately. I love you to such a degree that it is really marvellous. I know a little girl who is bursting with rage about it—"

The jealous damsel cut him short: "Who is she?"

"What difference does that make to us?" said Phœbus; "do you love me?"

"Oh!" said she.

"Well, then, that is all that is necessary. You shall see how I love you, too. May the great devil Neptune bestride me if I do not make you the happiest creature in the world. We will have a pretty little room somewhere! I will review my archers under your windows. They are all mounted, and make nothing of Captain Mignon's men. There are spearmen, cross-bowmen, and culverin men. I will take you to see the great Paris musters at the Grange de Rully. It's a very fine sight, —eighty thousand helmeted heads; thirty thousand bright harnesses, coats of mail, or brigandines; sixty-seven banners of the various guilds; the standards of the Parliament, the Chamber of Accounts, the Treasury, the Assistants in the Mint; in fact, the devil's own train! I will take you to see the lions at the king's palace, which are wild beasts; all the women like that."

For some moments the young girl, wrapped in her own delightful thoughts, had been dreaming to the sound of his voice, without heeding the meaning of his words.

"Oh, how happy you will be!" continued the captain; and at the same time he gently unclasped the gipsy's belt.

"What are you doing?" said she, quickly. This act of violence startled her from her reverie.

"Nothing," answered Phœbus; "I was merely saying that you must give up this ridiculous mountebank dress when you come to live with me."

"When I live with you, my Phœbus!" said the young girl, tenderly.

She again became pensive and silent.

The captain, made bold by her gentleness, took her by the waist without any resistance on her part, then began noiselessly to unlace the poor child's bodice, and so disarranged her neckerchief that the panting priest saw the gipsy's lovely shoulder issue from the gauze, plump and brown, like the moon rising through the mists on the horizon.

The young girl let Phœbus have his way. She did not seem conscious of what he was doing. The bold captain's eyes sparkled.

All at once she turned towards him.

"Phœbus," she said, with a look of infinite love, "instruct me in your religion."

"My religion!" cried the captain, bursting into laughter. "I instruct you in my religion! Thunder and guns! What do you want with my religion?"

"To be married to you," she answered.

The captain's face assumed an expression of mingled surprise, scorn, recklessness, and evil passion.

"Nonsense!" said he. "Why should we marry?"

The gipsy turned pale, and let her head sink sadly on her breast.

"My pretty love," tenderly added Phœbus, "what are all these foolish ideas? Marriage is nothing! Is any one less loving for not having spouted a little Latin in some priest's shop?"

So saying in his sweetest voice, he approached extremely near the gipsy girl; his caressing hands had resumed their place around the lithe, slender waist, and his eyes kindled more and more, and everything showed that Master Phœbus was about to enjoy one of those moments in which Jupiter himself commits so many follies that the good Homer is obliged to call in a cloud to help him.

But Don Claude saw all. The door was made of decayed puncheon staves, which left ample room between them for the passage of his hawk-like glance. The brown-skinned broad-shouldered priest, hitherto comdemned to the austere rule of the convent, shuddered and burned at this scene of love, darkness, and passion.

The young and lovely girl, her garments in disorder, abandoning herself to this ardent young man, made his veins run molten lead. An extraordinary agitation shook him; his eye sought, with lustful desire, to penetrate beneath all these unfastened pins. Any one who had at this moment seen the the face of the unhappy man glued to the worm-eaten bars, might have thought he saw a tiger glaring from his cage at some jackal devouring a gazelle. His pupils glowed like a candle through the cracks of the door.

Suddenly, with a rapid motion, Phœbus removed the gipsy's neckerchief. The poor child, who still sat pale and dreamy, sprang up with a start; she retreated hastily from the enterprising officer, and, glancing at her bare throat and shoulders, red, confused, and dumb with shame, she crossed her lovely arms over her bosom to cover it. But for the flame which mantled her cheeks, any one seeing her thus silent and motionless, might have thought her a statue of Modesty. Her eyes were downcast.

Meantime the captain's action had exposed the mysterious amulet which she wore about her neck.

"What's this?" said he, seizing this pretext to draw nearer to the beautiful creature whom he had alarmed.

"Do not touch it!" replied she, quickly "it is my protector. It will help me to find my family, if I am still worthy of it. Oh, leave me, Mr. Captain! My mother! my poor mother! Mother, where are you? Help me now! For Heaven's sake, Mr. Phœbus, give me back my neckerchief!"

Phœbus drew back, and said in a cold tone,—

"Oh, young lady! I see very plainly that you do not love me!"

"I do not love him!" exclaimed the unhappy creature, and at the same time she hung upon the captain, whom she drew to a seat by her side. "I not love you, my Phœbus? How can you say so, you wicked man, to break my heart? Oh, come! take me, take every-thing! Do with me what you will; I am yours. What do I care for the amulet! What is my mother to me now! You are my mother, for I love you! Phœbus, my adored Phœbus, do you see me? It is I, look at me; it is that little girl whom you cannot repulse, who comes,—who comes herself in search of you. My soul, my life, my person, are yours; I am all yours, my captain. No, then, we will not marry; it would trouble you; and what am I? A miserable child of the gutter; while you, my Phœbus, are a gentleman. A fine thing, truly,—a dancing-girl to marry an officer! I was mad. No, Phœbus, no; I will be your mistress, your amusement, your pleasure, when you will; always yours. I am only made for that,—to be soiled, despised, dishonoured; but what matter? I shall be loved. I shall be the proudest and happiest of women. And when I grow old or ugly, Phœbus, when I am no longer fit to love you, my lord, you will still suffer me to serve you. Others may embroider your scarves; but I, your servant, will take care of them. You will let me polish your spurs, brush your coat, dust your riding-boots. You will have this much pity for me, my Phœbus, will you not? Meantime, take me! There, Phœbus, all this belongs to you, only love me. We gipsy girls need nothing else,— nothing but air and love."

As she said this, she flung her arms around the officer's neck; she gazed up into his face imploringly, and with a lovely smile through her tears. Her delicate throat rubbed against his cloth doublet with its rough embroideries. She threw herself across his lap, her

beautiful body half revealed. The en-
raptured captain pressed his burning
lips to those beautiful brown shoulders.
The young girl, her eyes fixed on the
ceiling, her head thrown back, shuddered and trembled at his kiss.

All at once above the head of Phœbus she saw another head,—a livid,
green, convulsed face, with the look of
a soul in torment; beside this face
there was a hand which held a dagger.
It was the face and the hand of the
priest; he had broken open the door,
and he was there. Phœbus could not
see him. The girl was motionless,
frozen, mute, at the frightful apparition, like a dove which chances to raise
its head at the instant when the sea-
eagle glares into its nest with fiery
eyes.

She could not even utter a cry. She
saw the dagger descend upon Phœbus
and rise again reeking.

"Malediction!" said the captain; and
he fell.

She fainted.

As her eyes closed, as all consciousness left her, she fancied she felt a
fiery touch upon her lips, a kiss more
burning than the torturer's red-hot iron.

When she recovered her senses she
was surrounded by the soldiers of the
watch, some of whom were just carrying off the captain bathed in his own
blood; the priest had vanished; the
window at the back of the room, which
opened upon the river, was wide open;
some one picked up a cloak which he
supposed belonged to the officer, and she
heard the soldiers say,—

"She is a sorceress who has stabbed
a captain."

BOOK VIII

HEARTS

CHAPTER I

THE CROWN CHANGED TO A DRY LEAF

GRINGOIRE and the entire Court of
Miracles were in a terrible state of
anxiety. Esmeralda had not been heard
from for a whole long month, which
greatly grieved the Duke of Egypt and
his friends the Vagrants; nor did any
one know what had become of her
goat, which redoubled Gringoire's grief.
One night the gipsy girl had disappeared, and since then had given no
sign of life. All search for her was
vain. Some malicious dummy chuckers
told Gringoire that they had met her
that same evening near the Pont Saint-
Michel, walking with an officer; but
this husband, after the fashion of
Bohemia, was an incredulous philosopher,
and besides, he knew better than any
one else how chaste his wife was. He
had been able to judge what invincible
modesty resulted from the two combined virtues of the amulet and the
gipsy, and he had made a mathematical
calculation of the resistance of that
chastity multiplied into itself. He was
therefore quite easy on this point.

But he could not explain her disappearance. It was a great grief to him, and he would have grown thin from fretting had such a thing been possible. He had forgotten everything else,—even his literary tastes, even his great work, *"De figuris regularibus et irregularibus,"* which he intended to have printed with the first money which he might have (for he raved about printing ever since he had seen the *"Didascalon"* of Hugues de Saint-Victor printed with the celebrated types of Vindelin de Spire).

One day, as he was walking sadly by the Tournelle, he noticed a crowd before one of the doors of the Palace of Justice.

"What's the matter?" he asked a young man who was just coming out.

"I don't know, sir," replied the young man. "I hear that they are trying a woman who murdered a man-at-arms. As it seems that there was witchcraft about it, the bishop and the judge of the Bishop's Court have interfered in the matter; and my brother, who is archdeacon of Josas, spends his entire time here. Now, I wanted to speak to him; but I could not get at him on account of the crowd, which annoys me mightily, for I am in need of money."

"Alas! sir," said Gringoire, "I wish I could lend you some; but if my breeches are full of holes, it is not from the weight of coins."

He dared not tell the young man that he knew his brother the archdeacon, whom he had not revisited since the scene in the church,—a neglect which embarrassed him.

The student went his way, and Gringoire followed the crowd, going up the stairs to the Great Hall. He considered that there was nothing like the sight of a criminal trial to dispel melancholy, the judges being generally most delightfully stupid. The people with whom he had mingled walked on and elbowed one another in silence. After a slow and tiresome progress through a long dark passage which wound through the Palace like the intestinal canal of the ancient edifice, he reached a low door opening into a hall, which his tall figure enabled him to examine over the moving heads of the mob.

The hall was huge and ill-lighted, which made it seem still larger. Evening was coming on; the long-pointed windows admitted but a faint ray of daylight, which faded before it reached the vaulted ceiling,—an enormous lattice-work of carved beams, whose countless figures seemed to move confusedly in the shadow. There were already several lighted candles here and there on the tables, and shining upon the heads of clerks bending over musty papers. The front of the hall was occupied by the crowd; to the right and left there were lawyers in their robes, and tables; in the background, upon a daïs, a number of judges, the last rows of whom were lost in the darkness; their faces were forbidding and unmoved. The walls were plentifully sprinkled with *fleurs-de-lis.* A huge crucifix was dimly visible over the heads of the judges, and everywhere there were pikes and halberds tipped with fire by the light of the candles.

"Sir," asked Gringoire of one of his neighbours, "who are all those people drawn up in line yonder, like prelates in council?"

"Sir," said the neighbour, "those are the councillors of the High Chamber on the right, and the councillors of inquiry on the left,—the referendaries in black gowns, and the masters in scarlet ones."

"Yonder, above them," added Gringoire, "who is that big red-faced fellow in such a perspiration?"

"That is the president."

"And those sheep behind him?" continued Gringoire, who, as we have already said, did not love the magistracy. This was perhaps partly due to the grudge which he had borne the Palace of Justice ever since his dramatic misadventure.

"Those are the masters of requests of the king's household."

"And that boar in front of them?"

"That is the clerk to the Court of Parliament."

"And that crocodile on the right?"

"Master Philippe Lheulier, advocate extraordinary to the king."

"And that big black cat on the left?"

"Master Jacques Charmolue, king's proxy to the Ecclesiastical Court, with the officials."

"Now, then, sir," said Gringoire, "what are all these worthy men doing here?"

"They are trying a case."

"Whom are they trying? I do not see the prisoner."

"It's a woman, sir. You cannot see her. She has her back to us, and is hidden from us by the crowd. Stay; there she is, where you see that group of halberds."

"Who is the woman?" asked Gringoire. "Do you know her name?"

"No, sir; I have only just got here. I merely suppose that there is sorcery in the case, because the judge of the Bishop's Court is present at the trial."

"Well," said our philosopher, "we will see all these men of the gown devour human flesh. It is as good a sight as any other."

"Sir," remarked his neighbour, "doesn't it strike you that Master Jacques Charmolue has a very amiable air?"

"Hum!" replied Gringoire. "I always suspect an amiability with pinched nostrils and thin lips."

Here their neighbours demanded silence from the two chatterers; an important piece of evidence was being heard.

"Gentlemen," said an old woman in the middle of the hall, whose face was so lost in the abundance of her garments that she looked like a walking rag-bag,—"gentlemen, the thing is as true as it is true that my name is Falourdel, and that I have lived for forty years on the Pont Saint-Michel, paying my rent, lord's dues, and quit-rents punctually; and the door is just opposite the house of Tassin-Caillart the dyer, which is on the side looking up stream; a poor old woman now, a pretty girl once, gentlemen. Some one said to me only a few days ago, 'Mother Falourdel, don't sit at your wheel and spin too much of an evening; the devil loves to comb old women's distaffs with his horn. It is very certain that the spectre monk who roamed about the Temple last year now haunts the City. Mother Falourdel, beware lest he knock at your door.' One evening I was spinning at my wheel; there was a knock at the door. I asked who was there. Some one swore roundly. I opened. Two men came in,—one in black, with a handsome officer. I could only see the eyes of the one in black,— two burning coals; all the rest was hat and cloak. This is what they said to me: 'The Saint Martha room.' That is my upstairs room, gentlemen,—my nicest one. They gave me a crown. I put the crown in my drawer, and I said, 'That shall be to buy tripe to-morrow at the Glorictte shambles.' We went up. When we got to the upper room, while my back was turned the black man disappeared. This startled me a little. The officer, who was as handsome as any great lord, went downstairs again with me. He left the house. By the time I had spun a quarter of a skein he was back with a lovely young girl,—a puppet who would have shone like the sun if her hair had been well dressed. She had with her a goat,—a big goat. I have forgotten now whether it was black or white. That bothered me. As for the girl, she was none of my business; but the goat! I don't like those animals; they have a beard and horns. They look like men. And then, they savour of sorcery. However, I said nothing. I had the crown-piece. That was right, my lord judge, wasn't it? I took the captain and the girl to the upper room, and I left them alone,— that is, with the goat. I went down and began to spin again. You must know that my house has a ground-floor and a floor above; it overlooks the river at the back, like all the rest of the houses on the bridge, and the window on the ground-floor and the one above both open upon the water. As I say,

I was spinning. I don't know how I fell to thinking of the goblin monk, of whom the goat had reminded me; and then, that pretty girl was so queerly rigged out. All at once I heard a scream upstairs, and something fell on the floor, and the window opened. I ran to my window, which is just under it, and I saw a dark mass fall past me into the water. It was a phantom dressed like a priest. It was bright moonlight. I saw as plainly as possible. He swam away towards the City. Then, all in a tremble, I called the watch. Those gentlemen entered, and being somewhat merry, and not knowing what the matter was, they fell to beating me. But I soon explained things to them. We went upstairs, and what did we find? My poor room all stained with blood, the captain stretched out at full length with a dagger in his throat, the girl pretending to be dead, and the goat in a terrible fright. 'Well done!' said I; 'it will take me more than a fortnight to scrub up these boards. I shall have to scrape them; it will be a dreadful piece of work!' They carried off the officer,—poor young man!—and the girl, all dishevelled and in disorder. But stay; the worst of all is that next day, when I went to get the crown to buy my tripe, I found a withered leaf in its place."

The old woman paused. A murmur of horror ran round the room.

"The phantom, the goat, and all that, savour of sorcery," said one of Gringoire's neighbours.

"So does that withered leaf!" added another.

"No doubt," continued a third, "the girl was a witch, who was in league with the goblin monk to plunder officers."

Gringoire himself was inclined to consider the whole story both terrible and probable.

"Woman Falourdel," said the president, majestically, "have you nothing more to tell the court?"

"No, my lord," replied the old woman, "except that in the report my house was called a dirty, rickety hut, which is an outrageous way to talk. The houses on the bridge are not much to look at, because there are so many people there; but all the same even butchers don't scorn to live there, and some of them are rich folks, and married to very neat, handsome women."

The magistrate who had reminded Gringoire of a crocodile now rose.

"Silence!" said he. "I beg you, gentlemen, not to lose sight of the fact that a dagger was found upon the prisoner. Woman Falourdel, did you bring that leaf into which the crownpiece which the evil spirit gave you was changed?"

"Yes, my lord," replied she; "I found it. Here it is."

An usher handed the dead leaf to the crocodile, who shook his head mournfully, and passed it to the president, who sent it on to the king's proxy to the Ecclesiastical Court; and in this way it went the round of the room.

"It is a birch-leaf," said Master Jacques Charmolue. This was a fresh proof of magic.

A councillor next took up the word.

"Witness, two men went upstairs together in your house. The black man,—whom you first saw disappear, and afterwards swim the Seine in a

priest's gown,—and the officer. Which of the two gave you the money?"

The old woman thought for a moment, and said, "It was the officer."

A confused clamour ran through the crowd.

"Ah!" thought Gringoire, "that shakes my conviction."

However, Master Philippe Lheulier, advocate extraordinary to the king, interfered afresh.

"I must remind you, gentlemen, that in his deposition, written at his bedside, the murdered officer, while he declares that he had a vague idea at the instant the man in black accosted him that it might easily be the goblin monk, added that the phantom had urged him to keep his appointment with the prisoner; and upon his remarking that he had no money, gave him the crown, which the said officer paid away to Mother Falourdel. Therefore, the crown was a coin from hell."

This conclusive observation seemed to dispel all the doubts of Gringoire and the other sceptics in the audience.

"Gentlemen, you have the brief," added the king's advocate, sitting down; "you can consult the statement of Phœbus de Châteaupers."

At the sound of this name the prisoner rose; her head appeared above the crowd. The terrified Gringoire recognized Esmeralda.

She was pale; her hair, once so gracefully braided and spangled with sequins, fell about her in disorder; her lips were livid; her hollow eyes were horrible. Alas!

"Phœbus!" said she, wildly, "where is he? Oh, gentlemen, before you kill me, in pity tell me if he still lives!"

"Be silent, woman!" replied the president; "that does not concern us."

"Oh, have mercy! Tell me if he is alive!" she repeated, clasping her beautiful but emaciated hands; and her chains rattled as she moved.

"Well," said the king's advocate, drily, "he is dying! Are you satisfied?"

The wretched girl fell back upon her seat, voiceless, tearless, white as a waxen image.

The president leaned towards a man standing at his feet, with a golden cap and a black gown, a chain about his neck, and a wand in his hand.

"Usher, bring in the other prisoner."

All eyes were turned upon a small door which opened, and to Gringoire's great dismay a pretty goat, with gilded horns and hoofs, appeared. The dainty creature paused a moment on the threshold, stretching her neck as if, perched on the point of a rock, she had a vast horizon before her. All at once she saw the gipsy girl, and leaping over the table and the head of a clerk with two bounds, she was at her knees; then she curled herself gracefully at the feet of her mistress, imploring a word or a caress; but the prisoner remained motionless, and even poor Djali could not win a look from her.

"Why, but— That is the ugly beast I told you about," said old Falourdel; " and I recognize the pair of them well enough!"

Jacques Charmolue interrupted her.

"If it please you, gentlemen, we will proceed to examine the goat."

Such was indeed the other prisoner. Nothing was simpler at that time than to bring a suit for witchcraft against an animal. Among other details, we find in the provost's accounts for 1466 a curious item of the costs of the trial of Gillet-Soulart and his sow, "executed for their demerits," at Corbeil. Everything is set down,—the cost of the pen in which the sow was imprisoned, the five hundred bundles of short fagots brought from the port of Morsant, the three pints of wine and the bread ·for the victim's last repast, fraternally shared by the executioner; even the eleven days' feeding and keep of the sow, at eight Paris pence each. Sometimes they went even beyond animals. The capitularies of Charlemagne and Louis the Debonair inflict severe penalties upon those fiery phantoms who take the liberty of appearing in mid-air.

Meantime the king's proxy to the Ecclesiastical Court cried aloud, "If the devil possessing this goat, and which has resisted every exorcism, persist in his evil deeds, if he terrify the court with them, we warn him that we shall be compelled to send him to the gibbet or the stake."

Gringoire was in a cold perspiration. Charmolue took from a table the gipsy girl's tambourine, and presenting it to the goat in a particular way, he asked the creature:

"What time is it?"

The goat looked at him with an intelligent eye, lifted her gilded hoof, and struck seven blows. It was indeed seven o'clock. A movement of terror ran through the crowd.

Gringoire could not restrain himself.

"She is lost!" he cried aloud; "you see that she doesn't know what she is doing."

"Silence among the people at the end of the hall!" said the usher, sharply.

Jacques Charmolue, by the aid of the same manœuvres with the tambourine, made the goat perform various other tricks as to the day of the month, the month of the year, etc., which the reader has already witnessed. And, by an optical illusion common to judicial debates, those same spectators who had perhaps more than once applauded the innocent pranks of Djali in the public streets, were terrified by them within the walls of the Palace of Justice. The goat was clearly the devil.

It was still worse when, the king's proxy having emptied out upon the floor a certain leather bag full of movable letters, which Djali wore about her neck, the goat selected with her foot the separate letters spelling out the fatal name "Phœbus." The spells to which the captain had fallen a victim seemed to be irresistibly demonstrated; and, in all eyes, the gipsy girl—that enchanting dancer who had so often dazzled the passers-by with her grace— was nothing but a horrible witch.

Moreover, she gave no sign of life; neither the pretty pranks of Djali, nor the threats of the magistrates, nor the muttered curses of the audience seemed to reach her ear.

In order to rouse her, an officer was forced to shake her most unmercifully, the president raising his voice solemnly as he said:—

"Girl, you are of the gipsy race, addicted to sorceries. You, with your accomplice, the bewitched goat involved in the charge, did, upon the night of the 29th of March last, murder and stab, in league with the powers of darkness, by the aid of charms and spells, a captain of the king's troops, one Phœ-bus de Châteaupers. Do you persist in denying this?"

"Horrible!" cried the young girl, hiding her face in her hands. "My Phœbus! oh, this is indeed hell!"

"Do you persist in your denial?" coldly asked the president.

"Certainly I deny it!" said she, in terrible accents; and she rose to her full height, her eyes flashing.

The president continued bluntly:— "Then how do you explain the facts alleged against you?"

She answered in a broken voice,— "I have told you already. I do not know. It was a priest,—a priest whom I do not know; an infernal priest who has long pursued me!"

"There it is," said the judge; "the goblin monk."

"Oh, my lords, have pity! I am only a poor girl."

"A gipsy," said the judge.

Master Jacques Charmolue said gently,—

"In view of the prisoner's painful obstinacy, I demand that she be put to the rack."

"Agreed," said the president.

The wretched girl shuddered. Still, she rose at the order of the halberdiers, and walked with quite firm step, preceded by Charmolue and the priests of the Bishop's Court, between two rows of halberds, towards a low door, which suddenly opened and closed behind her, making the unhappy Gringoire feel as if she had been devoured by some awful monster.

As she disappeared, a plaintive bleat was heard. It was the little goat mourning for her.

The hearing was over. A councillor

remarked that the gentlemen were tired, and that it would be a long time for them to wait until the torture was over; and the president replied that a magistrate should be ever ready to sacrifice himself to his duty.

"What a disagreeable, tiresome jade," said an old judge, "to force us to send her to the rack when we have not supped!"

CHAPTER II

SEQUEL TO THE CROWN CHANGED TO A DRY LEAF

AFTER going up a few steps and down a few steps in corridors so dark that they were lighted with lamps at midday, Esmeralda, still surrounded by her dismal escort, was pushed by the serjeants of the Palace into a room of forbidding appearance. This room, round in form, occupied the ground-floor of one of these great towers which still rise above the layer of modern structures with which the new Paris has covered the old city. There were no windows in this vault, nor was there any opening save the low entrance closed by a huge iron door. Still, there was no lack of light; a furnace was built in the thickness of the wall; a vast fire had been kindled in it, which filled the vault with its red glow, and robbed a paltry candle, placed in a corner, of all its radiance. The iron grating which served to close the furnace was just now raised, only showing, at the mouth of the flaming chasm against the dark wall, the lower edge of its bars, like a row of sharp black teeth set at regular intervals, which

made the furnace look like the mouth of one of those legendary dragons that spit forth fire. By the light which it cast, the prisoner saw, all around the room, terrible instruments whose use she did not understand. In the middle of the room was a leather mattress laid almost flat upon the ground, over which hung a strap with a buckle, attached to a copper ring held by a flat-nosed monster carved on the keystone of the vaulted ceiling. Pincers, nippers, and broad ploughshares filled the interior of the furnace, and glowed in a confused white-hot heap upon the living coals. The blood-red light of the furnace illuminated in the entire room nothing but a mass of horrible objects.

This Tartarus was known as "the torture-chamber."

Upon the bed sat carelessly Pierrat Torterue, the sworn torturer. His assistants, two square-faced gnomes with leather aprons and linen breeches, were stirring the iron instruments upon the coals.

In vain the poor girl strove to summon all her courage; as she entered the room a feeling of terror overcame her.

The serjeants of the Bailiff of the Palace ranged themselves on one side, the priests of the Bishop's Court on the other. A clerk, pen, ink, and paper, and a table were in one corner.

Master Jacques Charmolue approached the girl with a very sweet smile, saying,—

"Do you still persist in your denial, my dear child?"

"Yes," replied she in a faint voice.

"In that case," resumed Charmolue, "it will be our very painful duty to question you more urgently than we could wish. Be kind enough to take your seat on that bed. Master Pierrat, make room for the young lady, and close the door."

Pierrat rose with a grunt.

"If I close the door," he muttered, "my fire will go out."

"Very well, my dear fellow," replied Charmolue; "then leave it open."

But Esmeralda still stood. That leather bed, upon which so many wretches had writhed in torment, alarmed her. Terror froze the marrow in her bones; she stood there, stupefied and bewildered. At a sign from Charmolue, the two assistants took hold of her and seated her upon the bed. They did not hurt her; but when they touched her, when the leather touched her, she felt all the blood in her body flow back to her heart. She cast a desperate look around the room. She seemed to see all those monstrous tools of torture, which were to the instruments of every sort which she had hitherto seen, what bats, spiders, and wood-lice are to birds and insects, moving and advancing towards her from every direction, to crawl over her and bite her and pinch her.

"Where is the doctor?" asked Charmolue.

"Here," replied a black gown which she had not noticed before.

She shivered.

"Young lady," resumed the caressing voice of the king's proxy to the Ecclesiastical Court, "for the third time, do you persist in denying those things of which you are accused?"

This time she could only nod her head. Her voice failed her.

"You persist?" said Jacques Char-

molue. "Then I am extremely sorry, but I must perform the duty of my office."

"Mr. Proxy," said Pierrat, abruptly, "with what shall we begin?"

Charmolue hesitated a moment, with the doubtful face of a poet in search of a rhyme.

"With the buskin," said he at last.

The unfortunate girl felt herself so wholly forsaken by God and man, that her head fell upon her breast like a lifeless thing destitute of all strength.

The torturer and the doctor approached her together. At the same time the two assistants began to rummage in their hideous arsenal.

At the clink of that frightful heap of iron, the unhappy creature trembled like a dead frog when galvanism is applied to it. "Oh," she murmured in so low a tone that no one heard it, "oh, my Phœbus!" Then she relapsed into her former immobility and marble-like silence. The sight would have rent any heart save the hearts of judges. She seemed some poor sinning soul questioned by Satan at the scarlet gates of hell. Could it be that this gentle, fair, and fragile creature, a poor grain of millet given over by human justice to be ground in the fearful mills of torture, was the miserable body upon which that frightful array of saws, wheels, and racks was to fasten,—the being whom the rough hands of executioners and pincers were to handle?

But the horny fingers of Pierrat Torterue's assistants had already brutally bared that charming leg and that tiny foot, which had so often amazed the by-standers with their grace and beauty in the streets of Paris.

" 'Tis a pity!" growled the torturer, as he looked at the dainty and delicate limb.

Had the archdeacon been present, he would certainly have recalled at this moment his symbol of the spider and the fly. Soon the wretched victim saw, through a cloud which spread before her eyes, the buskin approach; soon she saw her foot, locked between the iron-bound boards, hidden by the hideous machine. Then terror restored her strength.

"Take it off!" she cried frantically; and starting up all dishevelled, "Mercy!"

She sprang from the bed to fling herself at the feet of the king's proxy; but her leg was held by the heavy mass of wood and iron, and she sank down upon the buskin, more helpless than a bee with a leaden weight upon its wing.

At a sign from Charmolue she was replaced upon the bed, and two coarse hands bound about her slender waist the strap which hung from the ceiling.

"For the last time, do you confess the facts in the case?" asked Charmolue with his unshaken benevolence.

"I am innocent."

"Then, young lady, how do you explain the circumstances brought against you?"

"Alas! sir, I do not know!"

"Then you deny everything?"

"Everything!"

"Proceed," said Charmolue to Pierrat.

Pierrat turned the handle of the screw-jack, the buskin contracted, and the wretched girl uttered one of those terrible shrieks which defy all orthography in any human language.

"Stop!" said Charmolue to Pierrat. "Do you confess?" said he to the gipsy.

"Everything!" cried the miserable girl. "I confess, I confess! Mercy!"

She had not calculated her strength when she braved the torture. Poor child! her life thus far had been so joyous, so sweet, so smooth, the first pang vanquished her.

"Humanity compels me to tell you," remarked the king's proxy, "that if you confess, you can look for nothing but death."

"I hope so, indeed!" said she. And she fell back upon the leather bed, almost fainting, bent double, suspended by the strap buckled around her waist.

"There, my beauty, hold up a little," said Master Pierrat, lifting her. "You look like the golden sheep which hangs on my Lord of Burgundy's neck."

Jacques Charmolue raised his voice,—

"Clerk, write. Young gipsy girl, you confess your complicity in the love-feasts, revels, and evil practices of hell, with wizards, demons, and witches? Answer!"

"Yes," said she, in so low a voice that it was scarcely more than a whisper.

"You confess that you have seen the ram which Beelzebub reveals in the clouds to summon his followers to the Witches' Sabbath, and which is only seen by sorcerers?

"Yes."

"You confess that you have worshipped the heads of Bophomet, those abominable idols of the Templars?"

"Yes."

"That you have held constant intercourse with the devil in the shape of a tame goat, included in the trial?"

"Yes."

"And, finally, you acknowledge and confess that, with the help of the foul fiend and the phantom commonly called the goblin monk, on the night of the 29th of March last you did murder and assassinate a certain captain named Phœbus de Châteaupers?"

She raised her large steady eyes to the magistrate's face, and answered as if mechanically, without any effort or convulsion,—

"Yes."

It was plain that she was utterly broken.

"Write, clerk," said Charmolue; and addressing the torturers: "Release the prisoner, and lead her back to the court-room."

When the prisoner was "unshod," the king's proxy examined her foot, still numb with pain.

"Come!" said he; "there is no great harm done. You screamed in time. You can dance yet, my beauty."

Then he turned to his companions from the Bishop's Court—

"So justice is enlightened at last! That's a comfort, gentlemen! The young lady will bear witness that we have acted with the utmost gentleness."

CHAPTER III

END OF THE CROWN CHANGED TO A DRY LEAF

WHEN she returned to the audience-chamber, pale and limping, she was greeted with a general buzz of pleasure. On the part of the audience, it was caused by that feeling of satisfied im-patience which is felt at the theatre, at the end of the final intermission, when the curtain rises and the last act begins. On the part of the judges, it came from a prospect of supping ere long. The little goat also bleated with joy. She tried to run to meet her mistress, but she was tied to the bench.

Night had now fallen. The candles, whose number had not been increased, cast so little light that the walls of the court-room could not be seen. Shadows wrapped everything in a sort of mist. The apathetic faces of some of the judges could just be distinguished in the gloom. Opposite them, at the extreme end of the long hall, they could make out a vague white patch against the dark background. It was the prisoner.

She had dragged herself painfully to her place. When Charmolue had magisterially installed himself in his, he sat down, then rose, and said, without too great a show of vanity at his success, "The prisoner has confessed everything."

"Gipsy girl," began the president, "have you confessed all your crimes of sorcery, prostitution, and murder committed upon Phœbus Châteaupers?"

Her heart sank within her, and she sobbed aloud in the darkness.

"Whatever you please," she replied feebly; "but kill me quickly!"

"Sir Proxy to the Ecclesiastical Court," said the president, "the court is ready to hear your requisitions."

Master Charmolue drew forth a tremendous bundle of papers, and began to read, with many gestures, and the exaggerated emphasis common to lawyers, a Latin speech, in which all the evidence produced during the trial was set forth in Ciceronian periphrases, flanked by quotations from Plautus, his favourite comic author. We regret that we cannot present our readers with this remarkable piece of oratory. The speaker delivered it with wonderful effect. Long before he had ended the exordium, the perspiration poured down his face, and his eyes seemed starting from his head.

All at once, in the very middle of a period, he paused, and his glance, usually mild enough and even stupid, became withering·

"Gentlemen," he exclaimed (but in French, for this was not set down in his manuscript), "Satan plays so large a part in this affair, that yonder he stands, listening to our discussions and making a mock of their majesty. Behold!"

As he spoke, he pointed to the little goat, which, seeing Charmolue gesticulate, sincerely thought that it was but right for her to do the same, and sitting up on her haunches, was imitating to the best of her ability, with her forefeet and her bearded head, the pathetic pantomime of the king's proxy. This was, it may be remembered, one of her best tricks. This incident—this final proof—produced a great effect. The goat's feet were tied together, and the king's proxy resumed the thread of his eloquence.

His speech was very long, but the peroration was admirable. We give the concluding phrase; the reader may imagine Master Charmolue's hoarse voice and frantic gestures:—

"*Ideo, Domni, coram stryga demonstrata, crimine patente, intentione crim-*

inis existente, in nomine sanctæ ecclesiæ Nostræ-Dominæ Parisiensis, quæ est in saisina habendi omnimodam altam et bassam justitiam in illa hac intemerata Civitatis insula, tenore præsentium declaramus nos requirere, primo, aliquandam pecuniariam indemnitatem; secundo, amendationem honorabilem ante portalium maximum Nostræ-Dominæ, ecclesiæ cathedralis; tertio, sententiam in virtute cujus ista stryga cum sua capella, seu in trivio vulgariter dicto the Grève, *seu in insula exeunte in fluvio se canæ, juxta pointam jardini regalis, executatæ sint!*"

He put on his cap and sat down.

"*Eheu!*" said the agonized Gringoire; "*bassa latinitas!*"

Another man in a black gown, near the prisoner, rose. This was her lawyer. The judges, being hungry, began to murmur.

"Be brief, Sir Lawyer," said the president.

"Mr. President," replied the lawyer, "the defendant having confessed her crime, I have but a few words to say to the bench. It is laid down in the Salic law that 'If a witch have devoured a man, and she be convicted of the crime, she shall pay a fine of eight thousand farthings, which make two hundred pence in gold.' May it please the court to sentence my client to pay this fine."

"That law is obsolete," said the king's proxy·

"*Nego,*" replied the lawyer.

"Put it to the vote!" said a councillor; "the crime is clear and it is late."

The question was put to the vote without leaving the hall. The judges nodded assent; they were in haste.

Their hooded heads were uncovered one after the other in the darkness, in response to the fatal question put to them in a low tone by the president. The poor prisoner seemed to be looking at them, but her dim eyes saw nothing.

The clerk began to write; then he handed the president a lengthy parchment.

The unhappy girl heard a stir among the people, the pikes clashed, and an icy voice said:—

"Gipsy girl, upon such day as it shall please the lord our king, at the hour of noon, you shall be taken in a trumbel, in your shift, barefoot, a rope around your neck, to the square before the great door of Notre-Dame, and shall there do proper penace, with a wax candle of the weight of two pounds in your hand; and thence you shall be taken to the Grève, where you shall be hanged and strangled on the city gibbet; and likewise this your goat; and you shall pay to the judges of the Bishop's Court three golden lions, in atonement for the crimes by you committed and by you confessed, of sorcery, magic, incontinence, and murder, upon the person of Lord Phœbus de Châteaupers! And may God have mercy on your soul!"

"Oh, it is a dream!" she murmured; and she felt rude hands bear her away.

CHAPTER IV

LASCIATE OGNI SPERANZA

IN the Middle Ages, when a building was finished, there was almost as much of it below as above ground. Unless built upon piles, like Notre-Dame, a palace, a fortress, a church, had always a double foundation. In the case of cathedrals, it was almost like another and subterranean cathedral, low, dark, mysterious, blind and mute, beneath the upper nave, which blazed with light and echoed with the sound of organ and bells day and night; sometimes it was a sepulchre. In palaces and fortresses it was a prison; sometimes, too, a tomb, sometimes a combination of both. These mighty structures, whose mode of formation and slow growth we have explained elsewhere, had not merely foundations, but as it were roots which extended under the earth, branching out into rooms, galleries, staircases, in imitation of the building above. Thus churches, palaces, and fortresses were buried midway in the earth. The cellars of an edifice formed another edifice, into which one descended instead of ascending, and whose subterranean stories were evolved below the pile of upper stories of the monument, like those forests and mountains seen reversed in the mirroring water of a lake beneath the forests and mountains on its shore.

In the Bastille Saint-Antoine, the Palace of Justice at Paris, and the Louvre, these underground structures were prisons. The various stories of these prisons as they sank deeper into the ground became darker and more contracted. They formed so many zones presenting various degrees of horror. Dante could have found no better image of his hell. These tunnel-like dungeons usually ended in a deep hole like a tub, such as Dante chose for the abode of Satan, and where society placed those condemned to death. When once any poor wretch was buried there, he bade farewell to light, air, life, all hope; he never left it save for the gallows or the stake. Sometimes he lay there and rotted. Human justice styled this "forgetting." Between mankind and himself the prisoner felt that a mountain of stones and jailers weighed him down; and the entire prison, the massive fortress, became but a huge complicated lock which shut him off from the living world.

It was in a dungeon-hole of this kind, in one of the oubliettes dug by Saint Louis, the *in pace* of the Tournelle, that Esmeralda was placed when condemned to the gallows, doubtless lest she would try to escape, with the colossal Palace of Justice above her head. Poor fly, which could not have stirred the smallest one of the unhewn stones!

Certainly Providence and mankind were equally unjust. Such a lavish display of misery and torment was needless to crush so frail a creature.

There she lay, lost in the darkness, buried, entombed, immured. Whoever had seen her in that state, after having seen her laugh and dance in the sunshine, must have shivered. Cold as night, cold as death, not a breath of air to flutter her hair, not a human sound in her ear, not a ray of daylight in her eyes, bent double, crushed beneath her chains, crouching beside a jug and a loaf of bread, upon a little straw, in the pool of water formed beneath her by the damp oozing of her cell, motionless, nearly breathless, she was almost beyond all sense of suffering. Phœbus, the sun, high noon, the fresh air, the streets of Paris, her dancing always hailed with

applause, the sweet prattle of love with the officer; then the priest, the old hag, the dagger, the blood, the torture, and the gallows,—all these things had hovered before her, now like a gay and golden vision, now like a monstrous nightmare; but they were now naught but a vague and horrible struggle lost in the darkness, or like distant music played above, on the earth, and no longer heard in the depths to which the wretched girl had fallen.

Since she had been there she had neither waked nor slept. In her misery, in her dungeon, she could no more distinguish waking from sleeping, a dream from reality, than she could day from night. All was mingled, broken, vague, floating confusedly before her mind. She felt nothing, knew nothing, thought nothing; at best, she only dreamed. Never did living creature pierce so far into the realm of nothingness.

Thus benumbed, frozen, petrified, she had scarcely noted the sound of a trap-door which was twice or thrice opened somewhere above her without even admitting a ray of light, and through which a hand had thrown a crust of black bread. And yet this was her only remaining means of communication with men,—the periodical visit of the jailer.

One thing only still mechanically caught her ear: over her head the dampness filtered through the mouldy stones of the roof, and at regular intervals a drop of water fell. She listened stupidly to the noise made by this drop of water as it dripped into the pool beside her.

This drop of water falling into the pool was the only movement still stirring around her, the only clock which marked the time, the only sound of all the noises made upon the surface of the earth which reached her.

To be exact, she did also feel from time to time, in this sink of mire and gloom, something cold crawling hither and thither over her foot or her arm, and she suddered.

How long had she been there? She did not know. She remembered a death sentence pronounced somewhere, against some one; then she was borne away, and she waked icy cold, in the midst of night and silence. She had dragged herself about on her hands and knees; then iron rings had cut her ankle, and chains had clanked. She discovered that there was a wall all about her, that there was a tiled floor under her, covered with water, and a bundle of straw; but neither lamp nor ventilator. There she seated herself upon the straw, and occasionally, for a change of position, on the last step of some stone stairs in her cell.

At one time she tried to count the dark moments measured for her by the drop of water; but soon this sad task of a diseased brain ceased of its own accord, and left her in a stupor.

At last, one day, or one night,—for midnight and noon wore the same hue in this tomb,—she heard above her a noise louder than that usually made by the turnkey when he brought her bread and water. She raised her head, and saw a reddish ray coming through the cracks in the sort of trap-door made in the room of the *"in pace."*

At the same time the heavy iron creaked, the trap-door grated on its rusty hinges, turned, and she saw a lan-tern, a hand, and the lower part of the bodies of two men, the door being too low for her to see their heads. The light hurt her so cruelly that she shut her eyes.

When she reopened them, the door was again closed, the lantern was placed on a step of the staircase, a man alone stood before her. A black gown fell to his feet; a cowl of the same colour hid his face. Nothing of his person was visible, neither his face nor his hands. He looked like a long black winding-sheet standing bolt upright, under which something seemed to move. She gazed fixedly for some moments at this spectre. Still, neither she nor he spoke. They seemed two statues confronting each other. Two things only seemed to live in the cave,—the wick of the lantern, which crackled from the dampness of the atmosphere, and the drop of water from the ceiling, which interrupted this irregular crackle with its monotonous plash, and made the light of the lantern quiver in concentric rings upon the oily water of the pool.

At last the prisoner broke the silence,—

"Who are you?"

"A priest."

The word, the accent, the sound of his voice, made her tremble.

The priest added in a hollow tone,—

"Are you prepared?"

"For what?"

"To die."

"Oh," said she, "will it be soon?"

"To-morrow."

Her head, which she had lifted with joy, again sank upon her breast·

"That is a very long time yet!" she

murmured; "why did they not make it to-day?"

"Then you are very unhappy?" asked the priest, after a pause.

"I am very cold," replied she.

She took her feet in her hands,—a common gesture with those wretched people who suffer from cold, and which we have already observed in the recluse of the Tour-Roland,—and her teeth chattered.

The priest seemed to cast his eyes about the cell, from beneath his hood.

"No light! no fire! in the water! It is horrible!"

"Yes," she answered, with the look of surprise which misfortune had imprinted on her face. "Daylight is for every one. Why is it that they give me nothing but night?"

"Do you know," resumed the priest, after a fresh pause, "why you are here?"

"I think I did know once," said she, passing her thin fingers over her brow as if to help her memory, "but I don't know now."

All at once she began to cry like a little child.

"I want to get out, sir. I am cold, I am frightened, and there are creatures which crawl all over me."

"Well, follow me."

So saying, the priest took her by the arm. The unfortunate creature was frozen to the marrow; but still that hand gave her a sensation of cold.

"Oh," she murmured, "it is the icy hand of death. Who are you?"

The priest threw back his hood; she looked. It was that evil face which had so long haunted her; that demon head which had appeared to her at the house of old Falourdel above the adored head of her Phœbus; that eye which she had last seen sparkle beside a dagger.

This apparition, always so fatal to her, and which had thus urged her on from misfortune to misfortune and even to torture, roused her from her torpor. The veil which had clouded her memory seemed rent in twain. Every detail of her mournful adventure, from the night scene at the house of Falourdel down to her condemnation at the Tournelle, rushed upon her mind at once, not vague and confused as heretofore, but clear, distinct, vivid, living, terrible. The sombre figure before her recalled those half-effaced memories almost blotted out by excess of suffering, as the heat of the fire brings back in all their freshness invisible letters traced on white paper with sympathetic ink. She felt as if every wound in her heart were torn open and bled together.

"Ha!" she cried, pressing her hands to her eyes with a convulsive shudder, "it is the priest!"

Then her arms fell listlessly at her side, and she sat with downcast head and eyes, mute and trembling.

The priest gazed at her with the eye of a kite which has long hovered high in the heavens above a poor meadow-lark crouching in the wheat, gradually and silently descending in ever lessening circles, and, suddenly swooping upon his prey like a flash of lightning, grasps it panting in his clutch.

She murmured feebly,—

"Do your work! do your work! strike the last blow!" and her head sank between her shoulders in terror, like that of a lamb awaiting the butcher's axe.

"You look upon, me with horror, then?" he asked at length.

She made no answer.

"Do you look on me with horror?" he repeated.

Her lips moved as if she smiled.

"Yes," said she, "the executioner jests with the prisoner. For months he has pursued me, threatened me, terrified me! But for him, my God, how happy I should have been! It is he who hurled me into this gulf of woe! Oh, heavens! it is he who killed,— it is he who killed *him*, my Phœbus!"

Here, bursting into sobs and raising her eyes to the priest, she cried,—

"Oh, wretch! who are you? What have I done to you? Do you hate me so much? Alas! what have you against me?"

"I love you!" exclaimed the priest.

Her tears ceased suddenly; she stared vacantly at him. He had fallen upon his knees, and devoured her face with eyes of flame.

"Do you hear? I love you!" he again exclaimed.

"What love!" said the miserable girl shuddering.

He replied,—

"The love of a damned man."

Both were silent for some moments, oppressed by the intensity of their emotions,—he mad, she stunned.

"Listen," said the priest at last, and a strange calm seemed to have taken possession of him. "You shall know all. I will tell you that which as yet I have hardly ventured to confess myself, when I secretly questioned my own soul in those dead hours of the night when the darkness is so profound that it seems as if even God could no longer see us. Listen. Before I met you, girl, I was happy."

"And I!" she faintly sighed.

"Do not interrupt me! Yes, I was happy,—at least I thought so. I was pure; my soul was filled with limpid light. No head was held higher or happier than mine. Priests consulted me on chastity, doctors on doctrines. Yes, science was all in all to me; it was a sister,—and a sister was all I asked. Not but that, as I grew older, other ideas came to me. More than once my flesh thrilled as a woman's form passed by. That force of sex and passion which, although in the pride of youth, I had imagined I had stifled forever, more than once has rebelled against the chain of the iron vows which bind me, —wretch that I am!—to the cold stones of the altar. But fasting, prayer, study, and monastic mortifications again made my spirit ruler of my body. And then I shunned women. I had only to open a book, and all the impure vapours of my brain were banished by the glorious sunbeams of science. In a few moments I felt the gross things of earth fly far away, and I was once more calm and serene, bathed in the tranquil light of eternal truth. So long as the demon sent only vague shadows to attack me, passing singly before me, in church, in the streets, or in the fields, and scarcely recurring in my dreams, I conquered him easily. Alas! if the victory be not still mine, God is to blame, who failed to make man and the devil of equal strength. Listen! One day—"

Here the priest paused, and the prisoner heard him utter agonizing sighs.

He continued:—

"One day I was leaning from the window of my cell. What book was I reading? Oh, all that is confused and vague to me now. I had been reading. The window looked upon a public square. I heard the sound of tambourine and music. Vexed at being thus disturbed in my reverie, I looked out. What I saw was seen by many others as well, and yet it was not a spectacle for mere mortal eyes. There, in the middle of the pavement,—it was noon, the sun shone brightly,—a creature was dancing,—a creature so beautiful that God would have preferred her to the Virgin, and chosen her to be his mother, and would have wished to be born of her, had she existed when he was made man! Her eyes were black and lustrous; amidst her black hair certain locks shone in the sun like threads of gold. Her feet moved so swiftly that they faded from sight like the spokes of a wheel revolving rapidly. About her head, in her black braids, there were metallic plates which glittered in the sun and made a crown of stars above her brow. Her gown, sprinkled with spangles, scintillated, blue, and sown with a thousand sparks like a summer night. Her pliant brown arms waved and twined about her waist like two scarves. Her figure was of surpassing beauty. Oh, how resplendent was that form which stood out like something luminous even in the very light of the sun itself! Alas! girl, it was you. Surprised, intoxicated, charmed, I suffered myself to gaze. I gazed so long that, all at once, I shuddered with terror. I felt that Fate had overtaken me."

The priest, oppressed, again paused a moment. Then he resumed:—

"Already half fascinated I tried to lay hold of something and to stay myself from falling. I recalled the traps which Satan had already laid for me. The creature before me possessed that superhuman beauty which could only proceed from heaven or from hell. That was no mere girl made of common clay, and dimly illumined within by the flickering rays of a woman's soul. It was an angel,—but of darkness, of flame, and not of light!

"Just as I was thinking thus, I saw close beside you a goat, a devilish beast, which looked at me and laughed. The midday sun made its horns seemed tipped with fire. Then I recognized the snare of the demon, and no longer doubted that you came from hell, and that you came for my perdition. I believed it."

Here the priest looked in the prisoner's face, and added coldly:—

"I believe so still. However, the charm worked little by little. Your dance went round and round in my brain; I felt the mysterious spell acting within me. All which should have waked slumbered in my soul, and, like men perishing in the snow, I found pleasure in the approach of this slumber. All at once you began to sing. What could I do, miserable man? Your singing was even more enchanting than your dancing. I strove to escape. Impossible. I was nailed, I was rooted to the spot. It seemed as if the marble of the floor had risen to my knees. I was forced to stay to the end. My feet were ice, my head burned. At last,—perhaps you pitied me,—you ceased to sing; you disappeared. The reflection of the dazzling vision, the echo of the enchanting music gradually faded from my eyes and ears. Then I sank into the corner of the window, stiffer and more helpless than a fallen statue. The vesper bell aroused me. I rose to my feet; I fled; but, alas! something within me had fallen which could never be raised up; something had overtaken me which I could not escape."

He paused once more, and then went on:—

"Yes, from that day forth there was another man within me, whom I did not know. I strove to apply all my remedies,—the cloister, the altar, work, books. Follies, all! Oh, how empty science seems when we beat against it in despair a head filled with frantic passion! Girl, do you know what I always saw between my book and me? You, your shadow, the image of the bright vision which had once passed before me. But that image was no longer of the same colour; it was gloomy, funereal, sombre as the black circle which long haunts the sight of the imprudent man who looks steadily at the sun.

"Unable to rid myself of it, forever hearing your song ring in my ears, forever seeing your feet dance over my breviary, forever feeling at night, in dreams, your form against mine, I longed to see you once more, to touch you, to know who you were, to see if you were indeed like the ideal image which I had formed of you,—to destroy perhaps my dream by confronting it with the reality. In any case, I hoped that a fresh impression might dispel the first, and the first had become unendurable. I sought you out; I saw you again. Misery! Having seen you twice, I longed to see you a

thousand times,—I longed to see you forever. Then,—how may a man stop short upon that steep descent to hell? —then I ceased to be my own master. The other end of the cord which the demon had fastened to my wings was tied to his own foot. I became a wanderer and a vagrant like you. I waited for you beneath porches, I lurked at street corners, I watched you from the top of my tower. Every night I found myself more charmed, more desperate, more bewitched, nearer perdition!

"I had learned who you were,—a gipsy. How could I doubt your magic powers? I hoped that a criminal suit would set me free from your spell. A sorceress once enchanted Bruno d'Ast; he had her burned alive, and was cured. I knew it. I decided to try this remedy. I at first attempted to have you forbidden all access to the square in front of Notre-Dame, hoping that I might forget you if you no longer came thither. You paid no heed to the prohibition; you returned. Then I thought of carrying you off. One night, I tried to do so. There were two of us. We already had you in our grasp, when that miserable officer appeared. He rescued you. He thus began your misfortune, mine, and his own. Finally, not knowing what to do or what would become of me, I denounced you to the judges.

"I thought that I should be cured, like Bruno d'Ast. I also vaguely thought that a criminal trial would make you mine; that in a prison I should have you, should be able to hold you mine; that there you could not escape me; that you had possessed me so long that I might well possess you in my turn. When a man does wrong, he should do all the wrong he can; it is madness to stop half-way in crime! The extremity of guilt has its raptures of joy. A priest and a witch can mingle in delight upon the scanty straw of a cell!

"Accordingly I denounced you. It was then that I terrified you when we met. The plot which I was contriving against you, the storm which I was about to bring upon your head, burst from me in threats and in lightning flashes. And yet I still hesitated. My scheme had terrible sides which made me shrink.

"Perhaps I might have given it up; perhaps my odious thought might have withered in my brain, without bearing fruit. I thought that it would always be in my power to continue or to stay the prosecution; but every evil thought is inexorable, and insists upon becoming a deed. Where I supposed myself all-powerful, Fate was mightier than I. Alas, alas! it is she which captured you and delivered you over to the terrible wheels of the machine which I secretly constructed! Listen. I am near the end.

"One day—again the sun shone bright and warm—I saw a man pass who pronounced your name and laughed, and whose eyes were full of passion. Damnation! I followed him. You know the rest."

He ceased.

The young girl could only utter the words,—

"Oh, my Phœbus!"

"Not that name!" said the priest, seizing her angrily by the arm. "Do not utter that name! Oh, unhappy wretches that we are! it was that name which ruined us! or rather we have ruined each other by the inexplicable caprice of Fate! You suffer, do you not? You are cold, the darkness blinds you, the dungeon wraps you round; but perhaps you have still some ray of light in your innermost soul, were it but your childish love for that empty man who played with your heart, while I have a dungeon within me; within me all is winter, ice, despair; my soul is full of darkness.

"Do you know all that I have suffered? I was present at your trial. I sat upon the bench with the judges. Yes, beneath one of those priests' cowls were the contortions of the damned. When you were brought in, I was there; when you were cross-questioned, I was there. The den of wolves! It was my crime, it was my gibbet which I saw slowly rise above your head. At each witness, each proof, each plea, I was there; I counted your every step on the road of agony; I was there again when that savage beast— Oh, I did not foresee the torture! Listen. I followed you to the torture-chamber. I saw you stripped, and handled half naked by the infamous hands of the executioner. I saw your foot,—that foot upon which I would have given an empire to press a single kiss and die; that foot by which I would with rapture have been crushed,—I saw it enclosed in the horrid buskin which converts the limbs of a living creature into bleeding pulp. Oh, wretched me! As I saw these things, I grasped beneath my sackcloth a dagger, with which I slashed my breast. At the shriek which you uttered, I plunged it deep into my flesh; had you shrieked again, it would have pierced my heart. Look. I think it still bleeds."

He opened his cassock. His breast was indeed torn as if by a tiger's claw, and upon his side was a large, open wound.

The prisoner shrank from him in horror.

"Oh," said the priest, "have pity on me, girl! You think yourself unhappy. Alas! alas! You do not know the meaning of misery. Oh, to love a woman! to be a priest! to be abhorred! to love her with all the strength of your soul; to feel that you would give your blood, your life, your reputation, your salvation, immortality and eternity, this life and the next, for the least of her smiles; to regret that you are not a king, a genius, an emperor, an archangel, a god, to place at her feet a grander slave; to clasp her in your arms night and day, in your dreams and in your thoughts; and then to see her enamoured of a soldier's uniform, and to have nothing to offer her but a priest's dirty gown, which would terrify and disgust her; to be present with your jealousy and your rage while she lavishes upon a miserable idiotic braggart the treasures of her love and beauty! To see that body whose form inflames you, that bosom which has so much sweetness, that flesh tremble and blush under the kisses of another! Oh, Heaven! to love her foot, her arm, her shoulder; to think of her blue veins, of her brown skin, until one has writhed whole nights on the floor of one's cell, and to see all the caresses which you have dreamed of bestowing upon her end on the rack; to have succeeded only in stretching her upon the leather bed,—oh, these are indeed tongs heated red-hot in the fires of hell! Oh,

happy is he who is sawn asunder between two planks, or torn in quarters by four horses! Do you know what agony he feels through long nights, whose arteries boil, whose heart seems bursting, whose head seems splitting, whose teeth tear his hands,—remorseless tormentors which turn him incessantly, as on a fiery gridiron, over a thought of love, jealousy, and despair! Mercy, girl! One moment's truce! Cast a handful of ashes upon the coals! Wipe away, I conjure you, the big drops of sweat that trickle from my brow! Child, torture me with one hand, but caress me with the other! Have pity, maiden,—have pity upon me!"

The priest wallowed in the water which lay on the floor, and beat his head against the edge of the stone stairs. The girl listened to him, looked at him.

When he ceased speaking, panting and exhausted, she repeated in a low tone,—

"Oh, my Phœbus!"

The priest dragged himself towards her on his knees.

"I entreat you," he cried; "if you have any feeling, do not repulse me! Oh, I love you! I am a miserable wretch! When you utter that name, unhappy girl, it is as if you ground the very fibres of my heart between your teeth! Have mercy! If you come from hell, I will go there with you.

"I have done everything to that end. The hell where you are will be paradise to me; the sight of you is more blissful than that of God! Oh, speak! Will you not accept me? I should have thought that on the day when a woman could repel such love the very mountains themselves would move! Oh, if you would but consent! Oh, how happy we might be! We would fly,—I would help you to escape.

"We would go somewhere; we would seek out that spot of earth where there was most sunshine, most trees, most blue sky. We would love each other; we would pour our two souls one into the other, and we would thirst inextinguishably each for the other, quenching our thirst forever and together at the inexhaustible cup of love."

She interrupted him with a loud burst of terrible laughter.

"Only look, father! There is blood upon your nails!"

The priest for some moments stood petrified, his eyes fixed on his hands.

"Ah, yes!" he replied at length, with strange gentleness; "insult me, mock me, overwhelm me! But come, come. We must hasten. To-morrow is the day, I tell you. The gallows in the Grève, you know! It is ever ready. It is horrible,—to see you borne in that tumbrel! Oh, have mercy! I never felt before how much I loved you. Oh, follow me! You shall take your time to love me after I have saved you. You shall hate me, too, as long as you will. But come. To-morrow! to-morrow! the gallows! your execution! Oh, save yourself! spare me!"

He seized her by the arm; he was frantic; he strove to drag her away.

She fixed her eyes steadily upon him.

"What has become of my Phœbus?"

"Ah!" said the priest, releasing her arm, "you are pitiless!"

"What has become of Phœbus?" she repeated coldly.

"He is dead!" cried the priest.

"Dead!" said she, still motionless and icy; "then why do you talk to me of living?"

He did not listen to her.

"Oh, yes," said he, as if speaking to himself, "he must indeed be dead. The blade entered very deeply. I think I touched his heart with the point. Oh, my very life hung upon that dagger!"

The young girl threw herself upon him like an angry tigress, and pushed him towards the stairs with supernatural strength.

"Begone, monster! begone, assassin! Leave me to die! May the blood of both of us forever stain your brow; Be yours, priest? Never! never! Nothing shall ever unite us,—not even hell! Go, accursed man! never!"

The priest had stumbled to the stairs. He silently freed his feet from the folds of his cassock, took up his lantern, and slowly ascended the steps leading to the door. He reopened the door and went out.

All at once the young girl saw his head reappear; his face wore a frightful expression, and he cried to her with a gasp of rage and despair,—

"I tell you he is dead!"

She fell face downwards on the ground, and no sound was heard in the dungeon save the sighing of the drop of water which rippled the water in the darkness.

CHAPTER V

THE MOTHER

I DO not think that there is anything in the world more delightful than the ideas aroused in a mother's heart by the sight of her child's little shoe, especially if it be a best shoe, a Sunday shoe, a christening shoe, a shoe embroidered down to the very sole, a shoe in which the child has never yet taken a step. That shoe is so dainty, so tiny, it is so impossible for it to walk, that it is to the mother as if she saw her child itself. She smiles at it, kisses it, talks to it; she asks it if there can really be so small a foot; and if the child be absent, the pretty shoe is quite enough to bring the sweet and fragile creature before her eyes. She fancies she sees it; she does see it, from head to foot full of life and laughter, with its delicate hands, its round head, its pure lips, its clear eyes, whose very white is blue. If it be winter, it is there; it crawls over the carpet; it laboriously climbs upon a stool, and the mother trembles lest it go too near the fire. If it be summer, it creeps about the courtyard or the garden, pulls up the grass which grows between the paving-stones, gazes innocently and fearlessly at the big dogs and horses, plays with shells and flowers, and makes the gardener scold when he finds sand on his borders and dirt in his paths. All is bright and gay; all is mirth around it like itself, even to the breeze and the sunbeam, which vie with each other in sporting among the light curls of its hair. The shoe shows the mother all this, and makes her heart melt within her like wax before the fire.

But if she has lost her child, these thousand images of bliss, delight, and love which hover around the little shoe become so many horrid visions. The pretty embroidered shoe ceases to be aught but an instrument of torture, forever rending the mother's heart. The same fibre still vibrates,—the deepest and most sensitive fibre; but instead of being caressed by an angel, it is wrenched by a demon.

One morning, as the May sun was rising in a deep-blue sky, such as Garofolo loved to use for the background of his "Descents from the Cross," the recluse of the Tour-Roland heard the noise of wheels, horses' hoofs, and the clink of iron in the Grève. She paid but little heed to it, pulled her hair over her ears to drown it, and again fell to gazing, on her knees, at the inanimate object which she had thus adored for fifteen years. This little shoe, as we have already said, was the entire universe to her. Her every thought was bound up in it, never to be parted until death. The gloomy cavern of the Tour-Roland alone knew how many bitter curses, how many touching lamentations, prayers, and sobs, she had addressed to Heaven on behalf of that dainty pink satin toy. Never was greater despair lavished on a prettier, more graceful object.

On this particular morning it seemed as if her grief burst forth with even greater violence than usual; and those who passed by outside heard her wailing in a loud monotonous tone which pierced their very hearts.

"Oh, my daughter," she moaned, "my daughter! My poor, dear little child, I shall never see you again, then! It is all over! It always seems to me as if it were but yesterday that it happened! My God, my God, it would have been better never to give her to me, if you meant to snatch her from me so soon! Perhaps you did not know that our children are a part of ourselves, and that a mother who loses her child can no longer believe in God! Ah, wretch that I was, to go out that day! Lord! Lord! to take her from me thus, you could never have seen me with her when I warmed her, all rapture, at my fire; when she laughed at my breast; when I helped her little feet to climb up my bosom to my lips! Oh, if you had seen all this, my God, you would have had pity on my joy; you would not have robbed me of the only love left in my heart! Was I, then, so miserable a creature, Lord, that you could not look upon me before you condemned me? Alas! alas! here is the shoe, but where is the foot; where is the rest; where is the child? My daughter, my daughter! what have they done with you? Lord, restore her to me! My knees have been bruised for fifteen years in praying to you, my God! Will that not suffice? Restore her to me for a day, an hour, a single instant,—one instant only, Lord!—and then cast me to the devil for all eternity! Oh, if I did but know where to find the skirts of your garment, I would cling to them with both hands until you gave me back my child! Have you no mercy, when you see her pretty little shoe, Lord? Can you condemn a poor mother to fifteen years of torment? Kind Virgin, gracious Lady of Heaven! they have taken away my child-Jesus; they have stolen her; they devoured her

flesh upon the heath, they drank her blood, they gnawed her bones! Gracious Virgin, have pity upon me! My daughter! I must have my daughter! What do I care if she is in paradise? I don't want an angel; I want my child. I am a lioness, roaring for my whelp. Oh, I will writhe upon the ground, I will beat my forehead against the stones, and I will be forever damned, and I will curse you, Lord, if you keep my child from me! You see that my arms are all bitten and torn, Lord! Has the good God no compassion? Oh, give me nothing but salt and black bread, but give me back my daughter, and she will warm me like the sun! Alas! God, my Lord, I am but a vile sinner; but my daughter made me pious. I was full of religion from love of her; and I saw you through her smile as through an opening in the heavens. Oh, if I could only once, once more, just once more, put this shoe on her pretty little rosy foot, I would die, kind Virgin, blessing you! Ah! 'twas fifteen years ago. She would be almost a woman now! Unhappy child! What! then it is indeed true I shall never see her again, not even in heaven, for I shall never go there! Oh, what misery! to think that there is her shoe, and that is all I have left!"

The unhappy woman had flung herself upon the shoe, for so many years her consolation and her despair, and she burst into heartrending sobs as if it were the very day it happened; for to a mother who has lost her child, her loss is ever present. Such grief as that never grows old. The garments of mourning may rust and wear out; the heart remains forever darkened.

At this instant the fresh, gay voices of a band of children were heard outside, passing the cell. Every time that a child met her eye or ear, the poor mother rushed into the blackest corner of her tomb, and seemed trying to bury her head in the stone walls, that she might not hear or see them. But to-day, on the contrary, she sprang up hastily, and listened eagerly. One of the little boys said,—

"They are going to hang a gipsy girl to-day."

With the sudden leap of that spider which we saw rush upon a fly when her web quivered, she ran to her window, which looked, as the reader knows, upon the Grève. A ladder was indeed erected close to the permanent gallows, and the hangman's assistant was arranging the chains rusted by the rain. A number of people stood about watching him.

The laughing group of children had already vanished. The nun looked about for some passer-by, whom she might question. She noticed, close by her cell, a priest, who feigned to be reading the public breviary, but who was far less occupied with the "letters latticed with iron" than with the gibbet, towards which he cast repeated wild and gloomy glances. She recognized him as the archdeacon of Josas, a holy man.

"Father," she asked, "who is to be hanged yonder?"

The priest stared at her, and made no answer; she repeated her question. Then he said,—

"I do not know."

"The children said that it was a gipsy girl," continued the recluse.

"I believe it is," said the priest.

Then Paquette la Chantefleurie burst into a hyena-like laugh.

"Sister," said the archdeacon, "do you hate the gipsies so intensely?"

"Do I hate them!" cried the recluse; "they are witches, child-stealers! They devoured my little girl, my child, my only child! I have no heart now; they ate it!"

She was frightful to look upon. The priest gazed coldly at her.

"There is one whom I hate particularly, and whom I have cursed," she added; "she is young,—about the age that my daughter would have been if her mother had not eaten my girl. Every time that young viper passes my cell, my blood boils!"

"Well, then, sister, rejoice," said the priest, as cold as the statue on a monument; "it is the same girl whose death you are about to witness."

His head fell upon his breast and he moved slowly away.

The recluse wrung her hands with joy.

"I told her she would mount those steps! Thanks, Sir Priest!" she cried.

And she began to stride up and down behind her barred window, with dishevelled hair and flaming eyes, striking her shoulder against the wall as she moved, with the savage air of a caged wolf which has long gone hungry, and knows that feeding-time is at hand.

Chapter VI

THREE MEN'S HEARTS, DIFFERENTLY CONSTITUTED

Phœbus, however, was not dead. Men of his kind are hard to kill. When Master Philippe Lheulier, advocate extraordinary to the king, said to poor Esmeralda, "He is dying," he was either mistaken or joking. When the arch-deacon, in pronouncing her sentence, re-peated, "He is dead," the fact was that he knew nothing whatever about it, but that he supposed so, he reckoned upon it, had no doubt of it, sincerely hoped it was so. It would have been too much to expect of him, that he should carry good news of his rival to the woman he loved. Any man would have done the same in his place.

Not that Phœbus's wound was not severe, but it was less so than the arch-deacon flattered himself. The surgeon, to whose house the soldiers of the watch had at once carried him, had for a week feared for his life, and even told him so in Latin. However, youth tri-umphed; and, as frequently happens, prognosis and diagnosis to the contrary, Nature amused herself by saving the patient in spite of the doctor. It was while he still lay upon the surgeon's truckle-bed that he underwent the first examination from Philippe Lheulier and the board of inquiry from the Bishop's Court, which annoyed him exceedingly. Accordingly, one fine morning, feeling better, he left his golden spurs in pay-ment of the doctor, and slipped away. This circumstance, moreover, did not at all disturb the legal proceedings. Jus-tice in those days cared little for pre-cision and accuracy in a criminal suit. Provided the prisoner were hanged, that was all that was necessary. Now, the judges had proof enough against Es-meralda. They believed Phœbus to be dead, and that was the end of the matter.

Phœbus, for his part, had not gone far. He simply rejoined his company, then in garrison at Queue-en-Brie, in the Ile-de-France, a few relays away from Paris.

After all, he had no desire to appear at the trial in person. He had a vague feeling that he should play a ridiculous part in it. In fact, he did not quite know what to think about the matter. Irreligious and superstitious, like most soldiers who are nothing but soldiers, when he questioned himself concerning the affair, he felt somewhat uneasy about the goat, about the strange fashion in which he first met Esmeralda, the no less strange fashion in which she had allowed him to guess her love for him, the fact of her gipsy blood, and lastly the goblin monk. He had a dim idea that there was far more magic than love in the story, that there was prob-ably a witch, perhaps the devil, mixed up in it; it was a very disagreeable farce, or, to use the language of the day, a mystery, in which he played a most awkward part,—that of the butt for cuffs and laughter. He felt quite sheepish about it; he experienced that kind of shame which La Fontaine so admirably defines:—

"Shamefaced as a fox by timid
    chicken caught."

However, he hoped that the affair would not be noised abroad, and that he being absent, his name would scarcely be mentioned, and in any case would not be known outside the court-room. In this he was not mistaken; for there was no Police Gazette then; and as a week seldom passed but there was some coiner boiled, or witch hanged, or here-tic burned, by one of the innumerable justices of Paris, people were so much accustomed to seeing the old feudal Themis at every street corner, with her sleeves tucked up and her arms bare, doing her work at the gibbet, the whipping-post, or the pillory, that they hardly noticed her. The aristocracy of that day scarcely knew the name of the victim who passed them on the street, and at most it was only the mob that regaled itself with this coarse meat. An execution was a common incident in the highways, like a baker's kneading-trough, or the butcher's shambles. The hangman was but a kind of butcher a shade more skilful than the other.

Phœbus accordingly soon set his mind at rest in regard to the enchantress Esmeralda, or Similar, as he called her; to the stab inflicted by the gipsy or the goblin monk (to him it mattered little which); and to the issue of the trial. But no sooner was his heart vacant on that score, than the image of Fleur-de-Lys re-entered it. The heart of Captain Phœbus, like the physics of that time, abhorred a vacuum.

Besides, Queue-en-Brie was a very tedious abode,—a village of farriers, and dairymaids with chapped hands; a long string of huts and hovels bordering the high-road on either side for half a league.

Fleur-de-Lys was his last passion but one,—a pretty girl with a delightful dowry; therefore, one fine morning, completely cured of his wound, and feeling sure that after a lapse of two months the gipsy matter must be past and forgotten, the amorous knight appeared in state at the door of the Gondelaurier house.

He paid no heed to a somewhat numerous crowd which had gathered in the square in front of Notre-Dame; he recollected that it was the month of May; he supposed there was some procession, that it was Pentecost or some other holiday, fastened his horse to the ring at the porch, and went joyously upstairs to see his fair betrothed.

She was alone with her mother.

Fleur-de-Lys ever had upon her mind the scene with the sorceress, her goat, her accursed alphabet, and Phœbus's long absence. Still, when her captain entered, he looked so handsome with his spick-and-span new uniform, his glittering baldric, and his impassioned air, that she blushed for pleasure.

The noble damsel herself was more lovely than ever. Her superb light hair was braided in the most ravishing manner; she was dressed from head to foot in that sky-blue which is so becoming to fair skins,—a piece of coquetry which Colombe had taught her; and her eyes swam in that languor of love which is still more becoming.

Phœbus, who had seen no beauties of any sort since he left the rustic wenches of Queue-en-Brie, was carried away by Fleur-de-Lys, and this lent such cordiality and gallantry to his manner that his peace was soon made. Madame de Gondelaurier herself, still seated maternally in her great arm-chair, had not the courage to scold him. As for the reproaches of Fleur-de-Lys, they died away in tender cooings.

The young girl sat by the window, still working away at her Neptune's cave. The captain leaned against the back of her chair, and she addressed her affectionate complaints to him in an undertone.

"Where have you been for these two months, you naughty fellow?"

"I swear," replied Phœbus, somewhat embarrassed by the question, "that you are handsome enough to disturb the dreams of an archbishop."

She could not help smiling.

"There, there, sir! Leave my beauty out of the question, and answer me. Fine beauty, indeed!"

"Well, dear cousin, I was sent back to garrison."

"And where, pray? And why didn't you come and take leave of me?"

"At Queue-en-Brie."

Phœbus was enchanted that the first question helped him to evade the second.

"But that is close by, sir. Why did you never come to see us?"

Here Phœbus was seriously embarrassed.

"Why — my duties — And then, fair cousin, I have been ill."

"Ill!" she repeated in alarm.

"Yes,—wounded."

"Wounded!"

The poor child was quite overcome.

"Oh, don't be frightened about that!" said Phœbus, indifferently; "it was nothing. A quarrel, a sword-thrust; why should that trouble you?"

"Why should that trouble me?" cried Fleur-de-Lys, raising her lovely eyes bathed in tears. "Oh, you do not really mean what you say! What was this sword-thrust? I insist upon knowing everything."

"Well, then, my dear, I had a row with Mahé Fédy,—you know whom I mean,—the lieutenant from Saint-Germain-en-Laye; and each of us ripped up a few inches of the other's skin. That's all there is about it."

The lying captain was well aware that an affair of honour always exalts a man in a woman's eyes. In fact, Fleur-de-Lys looked him in the face, quivering with terror, delight, and admiration. Still, she was not completely reassured.

"If you are sure that you are quite cured, dear Phœbus!" said she. "I don't know your Mahé Fédy, but he is a bad man. And what did you quarrel about?"

Here Phœbus, whose imagination was only tolerably active, began to wonder how he was to get out of the scrape.

"Oh, I don't know,—a trifle, a horse, a bit of gossip! Fair cousin," cried he, in order to change the conversation, "what can that noise be in the square?"

He stepped to the window.

"Heavens! fair cousin, what a crowd there is in the square!"

"I don't know," said Fleur-de-Lys, "but I heard that a witch was to do public penance this morning before the church, and to be hanged afterwards."

The captain felt so sure that Esmeralda's affair was well over, that he took very little interest in Fleur-de-Lys' words. Still he asked her one or two questions.

"What is this witch's name?"

"I do not know," replied she.

"And what do they claim that she has done?"

She again shrugged her white shoulders.

"I don't know."

"Oh, my sweet Saviour!" said the mother, "there are so many sorcerers nowadays that they burn them, I verily believe, without knowing their names. You might as well try to find out the name of every cloud in the sky. After all, we may rest easy. The good God keeps his list." Here the venerable lady rose, and came to the window. "Good Lord!" said she, "you're right, Phœbus. What a rabble! Bless me! if they haven't climbed upon the house-tops! Do you know, Phœbus, it reminds me of my young days. When King Charles VII. entered Paris, there was exactly such a crowd. I've forgotten, now, just what year that was. When I talk to you of such matters, it seems to you like ancient history, doesn't it, while to me it seems quite recent. Oh, that was a much finer-looking crowd than this is! They even hung upon the battlements of the Porte Saint-Antoine. The king had the queen on the crupper behind him, and after their Highnesses came all the ladies riding on the cruppers of all the lords. I remember people laughed well because beside Amanyon de Garlande, who was very short of stature, was my lord Matefelon, a knight of gigantic size, who had killed heaps of Englishmen. It was a splendid sight. A procession of all the gentlemen in France, with their oriflammes blazing in our very eyes. Some bore pennons and some bore banners. How can I tell you who they all were? There was the Lord of Calan, with his pennon; Jean de Châteaumorant with his banner; the Lord of Coucy, with his banner, and a showier one it was, too, than any of the others except that of the Duc de Bourbon. Alas! how sad it is to think that all that has been, and that nothing of it remains!"

The two lovers did not listen to the worthy dowager. Phœbus again leaned on the back of his sweetheart's chair, —a charming position, whence his impu-dent gaze pierced every opening in Fleur-de-Lys' neckerchief. This neck-erchief gaped so opportunely, and per-mitted him to note so many exquisite things, and to divine so many others, that, dazzled by her skin with its satiny gloss, he said to himself, "How can anybody ever fall in love with any but a fair-skinned woman?"

Both were silent. The young girl oc-casionally looked up at him with rap-ture and affection, and their hair mingled in a spring sunbeam.

"Phœbus," suddenly said Fleur-de-Lys in a low voice, "we are to marry in three months; swear to me that you have never loved any other woman but me."

"I swear it, lovely angel!" replied Phœbus, and his passionate gaze com-bined with the truthful accent of his voice to convince Fleur-de-Lys. Per-haps he even believed it himself at that instant.

Meanwhile the good mother, charmed to see the lovers on such excellent terms, had left the room to attend to some domestic detail. Phœbus perceived this, and solitude so emboldened the adven-turous captain that his brain soon filled with very strange ideas. Fleur-de-Lys loved him; he was her betrothed; she was alone with him; his former fancy for her revived, not in all its freshness, but in all its ardour. After all, it is no great crime to eat some of your fruit before it is harvested. I know not whether all these thoughts passed through his mind, but certain it is that Fleur-de-Lys was suddenly frightened by the expression of his eyes. She looked about her, and saw that her mother had gone.

"Heavens!" said she, blushing and confused, "how warm I feel!"

"Indeed, I think," said Phœbus, "that it must be almost noon. The sun is very annoying; I had better close the curtains."

"No, no," cried the poor girl; "on the contrary, I want air."

And like a deer which feels the hot breath of the pack, she rose, ran to the window, opened it, and rushed out upon the balcony.

Phœbus, vexed enough, followed her.

The square before the cathedral of Notre-Dame, upon which, as we know, the balcony looked, at this moment offered a strange and painful spectacle, which quickly changed the nature of the timid Fleur-de-Lys' fright.

A vast throng, which overflowed into all the adjacent streets, completely blocked the square. The little wall, breast-high, which surrounded the central part, known as the Parvis, would not have sufficed to keep it clear if it had not been reinforced by a thick hedge of serjeants of the Onze-Vingts, and hackbuteers, culverin in hand. Thanks to this thicket of pikes and arquebuses, it remained empty. The entrance was guarded by a body of halberdiers bearing the bishop's arms. The wide church-doors were closed, in odd contrast to the countless windows overlooking the square, which, open up to the very gables, revealed thousands of heads heaped one upon the other almost like the piles of cannon-balls in an artillery park.

The surface of this mob was grey, dirty and foul. The spectacle which it was awaiting was evidently one of those which have the privilege of extracting and collecting all that is most unclean in the population. Nothing could be more hideous than the noise which arose from that swarm of soiled caps and filthy headgear. In that crowd there was more laughter than shouting; there were more women than men.

Now and then some sharp, shrill voice pierced the general uproar.

. . . .

"Hollo! Mahiet Baliffre. Will she be hung yonder?"

"Fool! that is where she's to do penance in her shift. The priest will spit a little Latin at her. It's always done here at noon. If you are looking for the gallows, you must go to the Grève."

"I'll go afterwards."

. . . .

"I say, Boucanbry, is it true that she has refused a confessor?"

"So it seems, Bechaigne."

"Look at that, the heathen!"

. . . .

"Sir, it is the custom. The Palace bailiff is bound to deliver over the malefactor, sentence having been pronounced, for execution, if it be one of the laity, to the provost of Paris; if it be a scholar, to the judges of the Bishop's Court."

"I thank you, sir."

. . . .

"Oh, Heavens!" said Fleur-de-Lys, "the poor creature!"

The thought of the unfortunate victim filled with sadness the glance which she cast upon the crowd. The captain, far more absorbed in her than in that collection of rabble, amorously fingered her girdle from behind. She turned with the smiling entreaty,—

"For pity's sake, let me alone, Phœbus! If my mother returned, she would see your hand!"

At this instant the clock of Notre-Dame slowly struck twelve. A murmur of satisfaction burst from the crowd. The last vibration of the twelfth stroke had scarcely died away, when the sea of heads tossed like the waves on a windy day, and a vast shout rose from the street, the windows, and the roofs:—

"There she is!"

Fleur-de-Lys covered her eyes with her hands that she might not see.

"My charmer," said Phœbus, "will you go in?"

"No," replied she; and those eyes which she had closed from fear she opened again from curiosity.

A tumbrel, drawn by a strong Norman cart-horse, and entirely surrounded by cavalry in violet livery with white crosses, had just entered the square from the Rue Saint-Pierre aux Bœufs. The officers of the watch made a passage for it through the people with lusty blows of their whips. Beside the tumbrel rode a number of officers of justice and of police who might be known by their black dress and their awkward seat in the saddle. Master Jacques Charmolue paraded at their head. In the fatal wagon sat a young girl, her arms bound behind her, and no priest at her side. She was in her shift; her long black locks (it was the fashion then not to cut them until the foot of the gibbet was reached) fell upon her breast and over her half-naked shoulders.

Through this floating hair, glossier than the raven's wing, a rough grey cord was twisted and knotted, chafing her delicate skin, and winding about the poor girl's graceful neck like an earthworm around a flower. Beneath this rope glittered a tiny amulet ornamented with green glass beads, which she had doubtless been allowed to keep, because nothing is refused to those about to die. The spectators posted at the windows could see at the bottom of the tumbrel her bare legs, which she tried to hide under her, as if by a last feminine instinct. At her feet was a little goat, also bound. The prisoner held in her teeth her shift, which was not securely fastened.

Even in her misery she seemed to suffer at being thus exposed almost naked to the public gaze. Alas! it is not for such tremors that modesty is made.

"Only see, fair cousin," said Fleur-de-Lys quickly to the captain, "it is that wicked gipsy girl with the goat."

So saying, she turned to Phœbus. His eyes were fixed upon the tumbrel. He was very pale.

"What gipsy girl with the goat?" he stammered.

"Why, Phœbus!" rejoined Fleur-de-Lys; "don't you remember—"

Phœbus interrupted her:—

"I don't know what you mean."

He took a step to re-enter; but Fleur-de-Lys, whose jealousy, already so deeply stirred by this same gipsy, was again revived, cast a suspicious and penetrating look at him. She now vaguely recalled having heard that there was a captain concerned in the trial of this sorceress.

"What ails you?" said she to Phœbus, "one would think that this woman had disturbed you."

Phœbus tried to sneer.

"Me! Not the least in the world! Me, indeed!"

"Then, stay," returned she, imperiously; "let us see it out."

The luckless captain was forced to remain. He was somewhat reassured when he found that the prisoner did not raise her eyes from the bottom of her tumbrel. It was but too truly Esmeralda. Upon this last round of the ladder of opprobrium and misfortune she was still beautiful; her large black eyes looked larger than ever from the thinness of her cheeks; her livid profile was pure and sublime. She resembled her former self as one of Masaccio's Virgins resembles a Virgin by Raphael,—feebler, thinner, weaker.

Moreover, her whole being was tossed hither and thither, and save for her sense of modesty, she had abandoned everything, so utterly was she crushed by stupor and despair. Her body rebounded with every jolt of the cart, like some shattered, lifeless thing. A tear still lingered in her eye, but it was motionless, and, as it were, frozen.

Meantime the mournful cavalcade had traversed the crowd amid shouts of joy and curious stares. Still, we must confess, as faithful historians, that many, even the hardest hearted, were moved to pity at the sight of so much beauty and so much misery.

The tumbrel had entered the Parvis.

Before the central door it stopped. The escort was drawn up in line on either side. The mob was hushed, and amidst this solemn, anxious silence the two leaves of the great door moved, as if spontaneously, upon their creaking hinges. Then the entire length of the deep, dark church was seen, hung with black, faintly lighted by a few glimmering tapers upon the high altar, and opening like the jaws of some cavern in the middle of the square, dazzling with light. At the very end, in the shadows of the chancel, a huge silver cross was dimly visible, standing out in relief against a black cloth which hung from the roof to the floor. The whole nave was empty; but heads of priests were seen moving confusedly among the distant choir-stalls, and, at the moment that the great door was thrown open, a loud, solemn, and monotonous chant proceeded from the church, casting fragments of dismal psalms, like gusts of wind, upon the pristoner's head:—

"Non timebo millia populi circumdantis me: exsurge, Domine; salvum me fac, Deus!

"Salvum me fac, Deus, quoniam intraverunt aquæ usque ad animam meam.

"Infixus sum in limo profundi; et non est substantia."

At the same time another voice, apart from the choir, intoned from the steps of the high altar this mournful offertory:—

"Qui verbum meum audit, et credit ei qui misit me, habet vitam, æternam et in judicium non venit; sed transit a morte in vitam."

This chant, sung afar off by a few old men lost in the darkness, over that beautiful being full of life and youth, caressed by the warm air of spring, bathed in sunshine, was a part of the mass for the dead.

The people listened quietly.

The wretched victim, in her terror, seemed to lose all power of sight and thought in the dark interior of the church. Her pale lips moved as if in prayer, and when the hangman's assistant approached to help her down from the cart, he heard her murmur in an undertone the word "Phœbus."

Her hands were untied, and she alighted, accompanied by her goat, which was also unbound, and which bleated with delight at regaining its freedom; and she was then led barefooted over the hard pavement to the foot of the steps leading to the porch. The cord about her neck trailed behind her, like a serpent pursuing her.

Then the chanting in the church ceased. A great gold cross and a file of tapers began to move in the gloom; the halberds of the beadles in their motley dress clashed against the floor; and a few moments later a long procession of priests in chasubles and deacons in dalmatics marched solemnly towards the prisoner, singing psalms as they came. But her eyes were fixed upon him who walked at their head, immediately after the cross-bearer.

"Oh," she whispered shudderingly, "there he is again! the priest!"

It was indeed the archdeacon. On his left was the assistant precentor, and on his right the precentor himself, armed with the wand of his office. He advanced, with head thrown back, eyes fixed and opened wide, chanting in a loud voice:—

"De ventre inferi clamavi, et exaudisti vocem meam.

"Et projecisti me in profundum in corde maris, et flumen circumdedit me."

When he appeared in full daylight under the lofty pointed arch of the portal, wrapped in a vast cope of cloth of silver embroidered with a black cross, he was so pale that more than one of the crowd thought that he must be one of those marble bishops kneeling upon the monuments in the choir, who had risen and come forth to receive on the threshold of the tomb her who was about to die.

She, no less pale and no less rigid, hardly noticed that a heavy lighted taper of yellow wax had been placed in her hand; she did not hear the shrill voice of the clerk reading the fatal lines of the penance; when she was told to answer "Amen," she answered "Amen." Nor was she restored to any slight sense of life and strength until she saw the priest sign to her jailers to retire, and himself advance alone towards her.

Then the blood boiled in her veins, and a lingering spark of indignation was rekindled in that already numb, cold soul.

The archdeacon approached her slowly; even in this extremity she saw him gaze upon her nakedness with eyes glittering with passion, jealousy, and desire. Then he said to her aloud, "Young girl, have you asked God to pardon your faults and failings?"

He bent to her ear and added (the spectators supposed that he was receiving her last confession). "Will you be mine? I can save you even yet!"

She gazed steadily at him: "Begone, demon! or I will denounce you!"

He smiled a horrible smile. "No one will believe you; you would only add a scandal to a crime. Answer quickly! Will you be mine?"

"What have you done with my Phœbus?"

"He is dead!" said the priest.

At this moment the miserable archdeacon raised his head mechanically, and saw at the opposite end of the square, upon the balcony of the Gondelaurier house, the captain standing beside Fleur-de-Lys. He staggered, passed his hand over his eyes, looked again, murmured a curse, and all his features were violently convulsed.

"So be it! die yourself!" he muttered. "No one else shall possess you."

Then, raising his hand above the gipsy girl's head, he exclaimed in funereal tones, *"I nunc, anima anceps, et sit tibi Deus misericors!"*

This was the awful formula with which these sombre ceremonies were wont to close. It was the signal agreed upon between the priest and the executioner.

The people knelt.

"Kyrie, eleison," said the priests beneath the arch of the portal.

"Kyrie, eleison," repeated the multitude with a noise which rose above their heads like the roar of a tempestuous sea.

"Amen," said the archdeacon.

He turned his back upon the prisoner, his head again fell upon his breast, his hands were crossed, he rejoined his train of priests, and a moment later he disappeared, with cross, candles, and copes, beneath the dim arches of the cathedral, and his sonorous voice faded slowly down the choir, chanting these words of despair:—

"Omnes gurgites tui et fluctus tui super me transierunt!"

At the same time the intermittent echo of the iron-bound shaft of the beadles' halberds, dying away by degrees

between the columns of the nave, seemed like the hammer of a clock sounding the prisoner's final hour.

Meantime the doors of Notre-Dame remained open, revealing the church, empty, desolate, clad in mourning, silent and unlighted.

The prisoner stood motionless in her place, awaiting her doom. One of the vergers was obliged to warn Master Charmolue, who during this scene had been studying the bas-relief upon the great porch, which represents, according to some, the Sacrifice of Abraham; according to others, the great Alchemical Operation, the sun being typified by the angel, the fire by the fagot, and the operator by Abraham.

He was with some difficulty withdrawn from this contemplation; but at last he turned, and at a sign from him, two men clad in yellow, the executioner's aids, approached the gipsy girl to refasten her hands.

The unhappy creature, as she was about to remount the fatal tumbrel and advance on her last journey, was perhaps seized by some poignant regret for the life she was so soon to lose. She raised her dry and fevered eyes to heaven, to the sun, to the silvery clouds here and there intersected by squares and triangles of azure; then she cast them down around her, upon the ground, the crowd, the houses. All at once, while the men in yellow were binding her elbows, she uttered a terrible shriek,—a shriek of joy. Upon yonder balcony, there, at the corner of the square, she had just seen him, her lover, her lord, Phœbus, the other apparition of her life.

The judge had lied! the priest had lied! It was indeed he, she could not doubt it; he was there, handsome, living, clad in his splendid uniform, the plume upon his head, his sword at his side!

"Phœbus!" she cried; "my Phœbus!"

And she strove to stretch out her arms quivering with love and rapture; but they were bound.

Then she saw the captain frown, a lovely young girl who leaned upon him look at him with scornful lip and angry eyes; then Phœbus uttered a few words which did not reach her, and both vanished hastily through the window of the balcony, which was closed behind them.

"Phœbus," she cried in despair, "do you believe this thing?"

A monstrous idea had dawned upon her. She remembered that she had been condemned for the murder of Captain Phœbus de Châteaupers.

She had borne everything until now. But this last blow was too severe. She fell senseless upon the pavement.

"Come," said Charmolue, "lift her into the tumbrel, and let us make an end of it!"

No one had observed, in the gallery of statues of the kings carved just above the pointed arches of the porch, a strange spectator who had until now watched all that happened with such impassivity, with so outstretched a neck, so deformed a visage, that, had it not been for his party-coloured red and violet garb, he might have passed for one of those stone monsters through whose jaws the long cathedral gutters have for six centuries past disgorged themselves. This spectator had lost nothing that had passed since noon before the doors of Notre-Dame. And at the very beginning, unseen by any one, he had firmly attached to one of the small columns of the gallery a strong knotted rope, the end of which trailed upon the ground below. This done, he began to look about him quietly, and to whistle from time to time when a blackbird flew by him.

All at once, just as the hangman's assistants were preparing to execute Charmolue's phlegmatic order, he bestrode the balustrade of the gallery, seized the rope with his feet, knees, and hands; then he slid down the façade as a drop of rain glides down a window-pane, rushed towards the two executioners with the rapidity of a cat falling from a roof, flung them to the ground with his two huge fists, seized the gipsy girl in one hand, as a child might a doll, and with one bound was in the church, holding her above his head, and shouting in a tremendous voice,—

"Sanctuary!"

All this was done with such speed that had it been night, one flash of lightning would have sufficed to see it all.

"Sanctuary! sanctuary!" repeated the mob; and the clapping of ten thousand hands made Quasimodo's single eye flash with pride and pleasure.

This shock restored the prisoner to her senses. She raised her eyelids, looked at Quasimodo, then closed them suddenly, as if alarmed by her saviour.

Charmolue stood stupefied, and the hangman and all the escort did the same. In fact, within the precincts of Notre-Dame the prisoner was secure:

the cathedral was a sure place of refuge; all human justice died upon its threshold.

Quasimodo had paused beneath the great portal, his broad feet seeming as firmly rooted to the pavement of the church as the heavy Roman pillars. His big bushy head was buried between his shoulders like the head of a lion which also has a mane and no neck. He held the young girl, trembling from head to foot, suspended in his horny hands like a white drapery; but he carried her as carefully as if he feared he should break or injure her. He seemed to feel that she was a delicate, exquisite, precious thing, made for other hands than his. At times he looked as if he dared not touch her, even with his breath. Then, all at once, he pressed her close in his arms, upon his angular bosom, as his treasure, his only wealth, as her mother might have done. His gnome-like eye, resting upon her, flooded her with tenderness, grief, and pity, and was suddenly lifted, flashing fire. Then the women laughed and wept, the mob stamped with enthusiasm, for at that instant Quasimodo was truly beautiful. He was beautiful,—he, that orphan, that foundling, that outcast; he felt himself to be august and strong; he confronted that society from which he was banished, and with whose decrees he had so powerfully interfered, that human justice from which he had wrested its prey, all those tigers with empty jaws, those myrmidons, those judges, those executioners, all that royal will which he had crushed, he,—

the lowliest of creatures, with the strength of God.

Then, too, how touching was the protection extended by so deformed a creature to one so unfortunate as the girl condemned to die, and saved by Quasimodo! It was the two extreme miseries of Nature and society meeting and mutually aiding each other.

However, after a few moments of triumph, Quasimodo plunged abruptly into the church with his burden. The people, lovers of all prowess, followed him with their eyes, regretting that he had so soon withdrawn from their plaudits. All at once he reappeared at one end of the gallery of the kings of France; he ran along it like a madman, holding his conquest aloft, and shouting, "Sanctuary!" The crowd broke into fresh applause. The gallery traversed, he again rushed into the interior of the church. A moment after, he reappeared upon the upper platform, the gipsy still in his arms, still running frantically, still shouting, "Sanctuary!" and the mob applauded. At last he appeared for the third time upon the summit of the tower of the big bell; from thence he seemed with pride to show the whole city her whom he had saved, and his thundering voice—that voice so rarely heard by any one, and never by himself —repeated thrice, with frenzy that pierced the very clouds: "Sanctuary! Sanctuary! Sanctuary!"

"Noël! Noël!" cried the people in their turn; and that vast shout was heard with amazement by the throng in the Grève on the other bank of the river, and by the recluse, who still waited, her eyes riveted to the gallows.

The Hunchback of Notre-Dame

BOOK IX

ACCUMULATED AFFLICTIONS

CHAPTER I

DELIRIUM

CLAUDE FROLLO was no longer in Notre-Dame when his adopted son so abruptly cut the fatal knot in which the wretched archdeacon had caught the gipsy and was himself caught. Returning to the sacristy, he had snatched off his alb, cope, and stole, flung them all into the hands of the amazed sacristan, fled through the private door of the cloisters, ordered a boatman of the Terrain to set him over to the left bank of the Seine, and plunged in among the hilly streets of the University, not knowing whither he went, meeting at every turn bands of men and women hastening gaily towards the Pont Saint-Michel in the hope that they might yet be in time to see the witch hanged,—pale, haggard, more bewildered, blinder, and fiercer than a night-bird let loose in broad daylight and pursued by a troop of boys. He no longer knew where he was, what he did, whether he was dreaming or awake. He went on, he walked, he ran, taking any street at haphazard, but still urged forward by the Grève, the horrible Grève, which he vaguely felt behind him.

In this way he passed St. Geneviève's Mount, and finally left the town by the Porte Saint-Victor. He continued to flee as long as he could see, on turning, the ring of towers around the University, and the scattered houses of the suburb; but when at last a ridge completely hid that odious Paris, when he could imagine himself a hundred leagues away in the fields, in a desert, he paused, and it seemed as if he breathed again.

Then frightful thoughts crowded upon him. Once more he saw into his soul as clear as day, and he shuddered at the sight. He thought of the unhappy girl who had destroyed him, and whom he had destroyed. He cast a despairing glance at the doubly-crooked path along which Fate had led their destinies, up to the meeting-point where it had pitilessly dashed them against each other. He thought of the folly of eternal vows, of the vanity of chastity, science, religion, virtue, and the uselessness of God. He indulged in evil thoughts to his heart's content, and as he yielded to them he felt himself giving way to Satanic laughter.

And as he thus searched his soul, when he saw how large a space Nature had reserved therein for the passions, he sneered more bitterly still. He stirred up all the hatred and malice from the very depths of his heart; and he recognized, with the cold gaze of a physician studying his patient, that this malice was nothing but love perverted; that love, the source of all virtue in man, turned to horrible things in the heart of a priest, and that a man formed like him, when he became a priest became a demon. Then he laughed fearfully, and all at once he again turned pale, as he considered the most forbidding side of his fatal passion,—of that corrosive, venomous, malignant, implacable love which led but to the gallows for one, to hell for the other: she condemned, he damned.

And then he laughed anew as he reflected that Phœbus was alive; that after all the captain lived, was lighthearted and content, had finer uniforms than ever, a new sweetheart whom he brought to see the old one hanged. His sneers were redoubled when he reflected that, of all the living beings whose death he had desired, the gipsy girl, the only creature whom he did not hate, was the only one who had not escaped him.

Then from the captain his mind wandered to the mob, and he was overcome with jealousy of an unheard-of kind. He thought that the mob, too, the entire mob, had had before their eyes the woman whom he loved, in her shift, almost naked. He writhed as he thought that this woman, whose form, half seen by him alone in darkness would have afforded him supreme delight, had been exposed in broad daylight at high noon to an entire multitude clad as for a night of pleasure. He wept with rage over all those mysteries of love profaned, soiled, exposed, withered forever. He wept with rage, picturing to himself the foul eyes which had revelled in that scanty covering; and that that lovely girl, that virgin lily, that cup of modesty and delight, to which he dared not place his lips without trembling, had been made common property, a vessel from which the vilest rabble of Paris, thieves, beggars, and lackeys, had come to quaff together a shameless, impure, and depraved pleasure.

And when he strove to picture the bliss which he might have found upon earth if she had not been a gipsy and he had not been a priest, if Phœbus had never lived, and if she had loved him; when he imagined the life of peace and love which might have been possible for him also; when he thought that there were even at that very instant here and there on the earth happy couples lost in long talks beneath orange-trees, on the border of streams, beneath a setting sun or a starry heaven; and that, had God so willed, he might have formed with her one of those blest couples, his heart melted within him in tenderness and despair.

Oh, she! it is she! She,—the one idea which returned ever and again, torturing him, turning his brain, gnawing his vitals. He regretted nothing, repented nothing; all that he had done he was ready to do again; he preferred to see her in the hangman's hands rather than in the captain's arms. But he suffered; he suffered so intensely that at times he tore out his hair by handfuls, to see if it had not turned white with anguish.

There was one moment among the rest when it occurred to him that this was possibly the minute when the hideous chain which he had seen that morning was drawing its iron noose closer and ever closer around that slender, graceful neck. This idea made the perspiration start from every pore.

There was another moment when, while laughing devilishly at himself, he pictured at one and the same time Esmeralda as he had first seen her,—alert, heedless, happy, gaily dressed, dancing, winged, and harmonious,—and Esmeralda as he had last seen her, in her shift, with the rope about her neck, slowly approaching with her bare feet the cruel gallows; and this double picture was so vivid that he uttered a terrible cry.

While this whirlwind of despair overwhelmed, crushed, broke, bent, and uprooted everything in his soul, he considered the scene around him. At his feet some hens were pecking and scratching among the bushes, enamelled beetles crawled in the sun; above his head, groups of dappled grey clouds sailed over the blue sky; in the horizon, the spire of the Abbey of Saint-Victor cut the curve of the hill with its slated obelisk; and the miller of the Buttes Copeau whistled as he watched the busy wheels of his mill go round. All this active, industrious, tranquil life, reproduced around him in a thousand forms, hurt him. He again tried to escape.

Thus he ran through the fields until nightfall. This flight from Nature, life, himself, man, God, everything, lasted the entire day. Sometimes he threw himself face downwards upon the earth, and tore up the young corn with his nails: sometimes he paused in some deserted village street; and his thoughts were so unendurable that he seized his head in both hands and tried to snatch it from his shoulders that he might dash it to pieces upon the ground.

Towards sunset he examined himself anew, and found that he was almost mad. The tempest which had been raging within him from the instant that he lost all hope and will to save the gipsy girl had not left a single sane idea, a single sound thought, in his brain. His reason was laid low by it, was almost wholly destroyed by it. His mind retained but two distinct images, —Esmeralda and the scaffold; all else was black. Those two closely connected images presented a frightful group; and the more he fixed upon them such power of attention and intellect as he still retained, the more they seemd to grow, by a fantastic progression,—the one in grace, charm, beauty, light, the other in horror; so that at last Esmeralda appeared to him as a star, the gibbet as an enormous fleshless arm.

It was a remarkable thing that in spite of all this torment he never seriously thought of suicide. The wretch was so constituted. He clung to life. Perhaps he really saw hell lurking in the background.

Meantime, the day continued to decline. That spark of life which still burned within him dreamed dimly of returning home. He fancied himself remote from Paris; but on examination he discovered that he had merely made the circuit of the University. The spire of Saint-Sulpice and the three lofty pinnacles of Saint-Germain des Prés rose above the horizon on his right.

He proceeded in that direction. When he heard the challenge of the abbot's men-at-arms around the battlemented walls of Saint-Germain he turned aside, took a footpath which he saw between the abbey mill and the lazaretto of the suburb, and in a few moments found himself at the edge of the Pré-aux-Clercs. This meadow was famous for the riots going on there continually, day and night; it was the "hydra-headed monster" of the poor monks of Saint-Germain: *"Quod monachis Sancti-Germani pratensis hydra fuit, clericis nova semper dissidiorum capita suscitantibus."* The archdeacon dreaded meeting some one there; he was afraid of any human face; he had shunned the University and the village of Saint-Germain; he was determined not to enter the city streets any earlier than he could help.

He skirted the Pré-aux-Clercs, took the deserted path dividing it from the Dieu-Neuf, and at last reached the bank of the river. There he found a boatman, who for a few farthings rowed him up the Seine as far as the City, where he landed him on that strip of waste land where the reader has already seen Gringoire indulging in a reverie, and which extended beyond the king's gardens, parallel with the island of the Passeur aux Vaches.

The monotonous rocking of the boat and the ripple of the water had somewhat stupefied the unhappy Claude. When the boatman had gone, he stood upon the shore in a dazed condition, staring straight forward, and seeing everything in a sort of luminous mist which seemed to dance before his eyes.

The fatigue of great grief often produces this effect upon the brain.

The sun had set behind the tall Tour de Nesle. It was twilight. The sky was silvery, the water in the river was silvery too. Between these two silver whites, the left bank of the Seine, upon which his eyes were riveted, stretched its sombre length, and, tapering in the distance, faded away at last among the hazes of the horizon in the shape of a black spire. It was covered with houses, whose dark outlines only were visible, cast in strong relief against the bright background of cloud and water. Here and there windows began to glow like live embers. The vast black obelisk thus detached between the two white masses of sky and river, the latter very broad just here, produced a strange effect on Don Claude,—such as might be felt by a man lying flat on his back at the foot of the Strasburg cathedral, and gazing up at the huge spire piercing the twilight shadows over his head. Only here, Claude was standing and the obelisk lying low; but as the river, by reflecting the sky, prolonged the abyss beneath, the vast promontory seemed to shoot into space as boldly as any cathedral spire; and the impression produced was the same. The impression was made even stronger and more singular by the fact that it was indeed the Strasburg steeple, but the Strasburg steeple two leagues high,—something unheard-of, gigantic, immeasurable; a structure such as no human eye ever beheld; a Tower of Babel. The chimneys of the houses, the battlements of the wall, the carved gables of the roofs, the spire of the Augustine monastery, the Tour de Nesle, all these projections which marred the outline of the colossal obelisk, added to the illusion by grotesquely counterfeiting to the eye the indentations of some rich and fantastic carving.

Claude, in the state of hallucination in which he then was, believed that he saw—saw with his bodily eyes—the pinnacles of hell; the countless lights scattered from end to end of the awful tower appeared to him like so many doors leading to the vast furnace within; the voices and the sounds which arose from it, like so many shrieks and groans. Then he was terrified; he clapped his hands to his ears that he might not hear them, turned his back that he might not see, and hastened away from the fearful vision.

But the vision was within him.

When he once more entered the city streets, the passing people elbowing each other in the light of the shop windows affected him like the never-ending coming and going of spectres. There were strange noises in his ears; extraordinary images troubled his senses. He saw neither houses, nor pavement, nor chariots, nor men and women, but a chaos of indeterminate objects which melted into one another. At the corner of the Rue de la Barillerie there was a grocer's shop, the sloping roof of which was, according to immemorial custom, hung with tin hoops, from each of which was suspended a circle of wooden candles, which clattered and clashed in the wind like castanets. He fancied he heard the heap of skeletons at Montfaucon knocking their bones against one another in the darkness.

"Oh," he muttered, "the night wind dashes them together, and mingles the sound of their chains with the rattle of their bones! Perhaps she too is there among them!"

Bewildered and distracted, he knew not where he went. After walking a few steps, he found himself upon the Pont Saint-Michel. There was a light at the window of a room on the ground-floor; he went up to it. Through a cracked pane he saw a dirty room, which roused a vague memory in his brain. In this room, dimly lighted by a small lamp, there was a fresh, fair-haired, merry-faced youth, who with loud bursts of laughter kissed a gaudily-dressed girl; and near the lamp sat an old woman spinning and singing in a cracked voice. As the young man occasionally ceased laughing, fragments of the old woman's song reached the priest; it was something unintelligible and frightful:—

"Bark, Grève, growl, Grève!
Spin, spin, my spindle brave,
For the hangman spin a cord,
As he whistles in the prison yard,
Bark, Grève, growl, Grève!

"The lovely hempen cord forevermore!
Sow from Issy e'en to Vanvre's shore
Hemp, and never of corn a grain.
No thief will ever steal for gain
The lovely hempen cord.

"Growl, Grève, bark, Grève!
To see the wanton and the knave
Hanging on the gallows high,
Every window is an eye.
Growl, Grève, bark, Grève!"

Hereupon the young man laughed, and caressed the girl. The old woman was Mother Falourdel; the girl was a woman of the town; the young man was his brother Jehan.

He continued to gaze. As well this sight as another.

He saw Jehan go to a window at the back of the room, open it, cast a glance at the quay, where countless lighted windows gleamed in the distance, and he heard him say, as he closed the window,—

"By my soul! it is night already. The citizens have lighted their candles, and the good God his stars."

Then Jehan went back to the girl and broke a bottle which stood on the table, exclaiming,—

"Empty already, by Jove! and I have no more money! Isabeau, my love, I shall never feel content with Jupiter until he turns your two white breasts into two black bottles, whence I may suck Beaune wine night and day."

This witticism made the girl laugh, and Jehan sallied forth.

Don Claude had barely time to throw himself on the ground, lest he should be encountered, looked in the face, and recognized by his brother. Luckily, the street was dark, and the student was drunk. However, he noticed the archdeacon lying on the pavement in the mire.

"Ho! ho!" said he; "here's a fellow who has led a jolly life to-day."

With his foot he stirred Don Claude, who held his breath.

"Dead drunk," continued Jehan. "Well, he is full,—a regular leech dropped from a cask because he can suck no more. He is bald," he added, stooping; "he is an old man! *Fortunate senex!*"

Then Don Claude heard him move off, saying,—

"All the same, reason is a fine thing, and my brother the archdeacon is very lucky to be both wise and rich."

The archdeacon then rose, and ran at full speed in the direction of Notre-Dame, whose enormous towers rose before him in the darkness above the surrounding houses.

When, quite breathless, he reached the square in front of the cathedral, he shrank back, and dared not raise his eyes to the fatal building.

"Oh," said he in a low tone, "is it indeed true that such a thing can have occurred here to-day,—this very morning?"

Still he ventured to look at the church. The front was dark; the sky behind it glittered with stars. The crescent moon, which had just risen above the horizon, had that instant paused at the summit of the right-hand tower, and seemed to have perched, like a luminous bird, on the edge of the railing, which was cut into black trefoils.

The cloister door was closed, but the archdeacon always carried about him the key to the tower in which was his laboratory. He now used it to let himself into the church.

Inside, all was gloomy and silent as the tomb. By the heavy shadows falling on all sides in broad masses, he knew that the hangings put up for the morning's ceremonies had not yet been removed. The great silver cross gleamed through the darkness, dotted with sparkling points of light, like the milky way of this sepulchral night. The long choir windows showed the tops of their pointed arches above the black drapery, the panes, traversed by a moonbeam, wearing only the doubtful colours of the night,—a sort of violet, white, and blue, in tints which are found nowhere else save on the face of the dead. The archdeacon, seeing these pale points of arches all around the choir, fancied that he beheld the mitres of bishops who had been damned. He shut his eyes, and when he reopened them, he imagined that there was a circle of ashen faces gazing at him.

He fled across the church. Then it seemed to him that the church, too, moved, stirred, breathed, and lived; that each big column became a monstrous leg, which pawed the ground with its broad stone hoof; and that the vast cathedral was only a sort of prodigious elephant, which panted and trampled, with pillars for feet, its two towers for tusks, and the immense black draperies for caparison.

Thus his fever, or mania, had attained such a degree of intensity that the external world had ceased to be to the unfortunate man anything more than a sort of Apocalypse, visible, tangible, terrifying.

For one moment he was comforted. As he entered the aisles, he perceived, behind a group of pillars, a reddish light, towards which he hastened as towards a star. It was the poor lamp which burned day and night above the public breviary of Notre-Dame, under its iron grating. He fell eagerly to reading the sacred book, in the hope of finding some consolation or some encouragement. The volume was open at this passage from Job, over which his fixed eye ran:—

"Then a spirit passed before my face; the hair of my flesh stood up."

On reading this melancholy passage, he felt as a blind man feels who is pricked by the staff which he has picked up. His knees gave way beneath him, and he sank to the ground, thinking of her who had that day perished. Such awful fumes rose up and penetrated his brain that it seemed to him as if his head had become one of the mouths of hell.

He remained some time in this position, incapable of thought, crushed and powerless in the hand of the demon that possessed him. At last, some measure of strength returned to him; it occurred to him to take refuge in the tower with his faithful Quasimodo. He rose, and as he was frightened, he took, to light his steps, the lamp from the breviary. This was a sacrilege, but he had ceased to heed such trifles.

He slowly climbed the tower stairs, full of secret terror, which must have been shared by the few passers-by outside in the square, who saw the mysterious light of his lamp moving at that late hour from loop-hole to loop-hole, to the top of the tower.

All at once he felt a freshness upon his face, and found himself under the door of the uppermost gallery. The air was cold; the sky was overcast with clouds, whose large white masses encroached one upon the other, rounding the sharp corners, and looking like the breaking-up of the ice in a river in winter. The crescent moon, stranded in the midst of the clouds, seemed a celestial ship caught fast among these icebergs of the air.

He cast down his eyes, and looked for a moment between the iron rails of the small columns which connect the two towers, far away, through a mist of fog and smoke, at the silent throng of the roofs of Paris,—steep, numberless, crowded close together, and small as the waves of a calm sea on a summer's night.

The moon shed a faint light, which lent an ashen tint to both heaven and earth.

At this moment the clock raised its shrill, cracked voice; it struck midnight. The priest's thoughts reverted to noon-day; it was again twelve o'clock. "Oh," he whispered, "she must be cold by this time!"

Suddenly a blast of wind extinguished his lamp, and almost at the same instant he saw, at the opposite corner of the tower, a shadow, something white, a figure, a woman. He trembled. By this woman's side was a little goat, which mingled its bleat with the final bleat of the bell.

He had the courage to look at her. It was she.

She was pale; she was sad. Her hair fell loosely over her shoulders, as in the morning, but there was no rope about her neck; her hands were no longer bound. She was free; she was dead.

She was dressed in white, and had a white veil over her head.

She came towards him slowly, looking up to heaven. The supernatural goat followed her. He felt as if turned to stone, and too heavy to escape. At each step that she advanced, he took one backwards, and that was all. In this way he retreated beneath the dark arch

of the staircase. He was frozen with fear at the idea that she might perhaps follow him thither; had she done so, he would have died of terror.

She did indeed approach the stair-case door, pause there for a few moments, look steadily into the dark-ness, but without appearing to see the priest, and pass on. She seemed to him taller than in life; he saw the moon through her white robes; he heard her breathe.

When she had passed him, he began to descend the stairs with the same slow motion as the spectre, imagining that he too was a spectre,—haggard, his hair erect, his extinguished lamp still in his hand; and as he went down the spiral stairs, he distinctly heard in his ear a mocking voice, which repeated the words,—

"A spirit passed before my face; the hair of my flesh stood up."

CHAPTER II

DEFORMED, BLIND, LAME

EVERY city in the Middle Ages—and up to the time of Louis XII. every city in France—had its places of refuge, its sanctuaries. These places of refuge, amidst the deluge of penal laws and barbarous jurisdictions which flooded the city of Paris, were like so many islands rising above the level of human justice. Every criminal who landed there was saved. In each district there were almost as many places of refuge as gallows. The abuse of a privilege went side by side with the abuse of punishment,—two bad things, each striving to correct the other. Royal palaces, princely mansions, and above all churches, had the right of sanctuary; sometimes an entire town which stood in need of repopulation was given the temporary right. Louis XI. made Paris a sanctuary in 1467.

Having once set foot within the sanctuary, the criminal was sacred; but let him beware how he ventured forth: one step outside his shelter plunged him again in the billows. The wheel, the gibbet, and the strappado kept close guard around the place of refuge, and watched their prey unceasingly, like sharks in a vessel's wake. Thus men have been known to grow grey in a convent, on a palace staircase, in abbey fields, under a church porch; so that the sanctuary became a prison in all save name. It sometimes happened that a solemn decree from Parliament violated the sanctuary, and gave up the criminal to justice; but this occurrence was rare. The Parliaments stood in some awe of the bishops; and when cowl and gown came into collision, the priest usually got the best of it. Sometimes, however, as in the matter of the assassins of Petit-Jean, the Paris hangman, and in that of Emery Rousseau, Jean Valleret's murderer, Justice overrode the Church, and proceeded to carry out her sentences; but, without an order from Parliament, woe to him who violated any sanctuary by armed force! We know what fate befell Robert de Clermont, Marshal of France, and Jean de Châlons, Marshal of Champagne; and yet the case in question was merely that of one Perrin Marc, a money-changer's man, a miserable assassin. But the two marshals broke open the

doors of Saint-Méry; therein lay the crime.

Such was the veneration felt for these refuges that, as tradition goes, it occasionally extended even to animals. Aymoin relates that a stag chased by Dagobert, having taken refuge near the tomb of Saint Denis, the pack stopped short, barking loudly.

Churches had usually a cell prepared to receive suppliants. In 1407 Nicolas Flamel had built for them upon the arches of Saint-Jacques de la Boucherie, a chamber which cost him four pounds six pence sixteen Paris farthings.

At Notre-Dame it was a cell built over the aisles under the flying buttresses, on the very spot where the wife of the present keeper of the towers has made a garden, which compares with the hanging gardens of Babylon as a lettuce with a palm-tree, or a porter's wife with Semiramis.

It was here that Quasimodo had deposited Esmeralda after his frantic and triumphal race through the towers and galleries. While that race lasted, the young girl did not recover her senses,—half dozing, half waking, conscious only of being borne upward through the air, whether floating or flying, or lifted above the earth by some unknown power. From time to time she heard the noisy laughter, the harsh voice of Quasimodo in her ear. She half opened her eyes; then beneath her she saw dimly all Paris dotted with countless roofs of slate and tiles, like a red and blue mosaic; above her head the fearful, grinning face of Quasimodo. Her eyelids fell; she thought that all was over, that she had been hanged during her swoon. and that the misshapen spirit which ruled her destiny had again taken possession of her and carried her away. She dared not look at him, but yielded to his sway.

But when the breathless and dishevelled bell-ringer laid her down in the cell of refuge, when she felt his great hands gently untie the rope which bruised her arms, she experienced that sort of shock which wakens with a start the passengers on a ship that runs aground in the middle of a dark night. Her ideas woke too, and returned to her one by one. She saw that she was still in Notre-Dame; she remembered being torn from the hangman's hands; that Phœbus lived, that Phœbus had ceased to love her; and these two ideas, one of which lent such bitterness to the other, presenting themselves simultaneously to the poor victim, she turned to Quasimodo, who stood before her and who terrified her, saying,—

"Why did you save me?"

He looked anxiously at her, as if striving to guess what she said. She repeated her question. He gazed at her with profound sadness, and fled.

She was amazed.

A few moments later he returned, brining a packet which he threw at her feet. It contained clothes left at the door of the church for her by charitable women.

Then she looked down at herself, saw that she was almost naked, and blushed. Life had returned.

Quasimodo appeared to feel something of her shame. He covered his eye with his broad hand, and again departed, but with lingering steps.

She hastily dressed herself. The garments given her consisted of a white gown and veil,—the dress of a novice at the Hôtel-Dieu, the great hospital managed by nuns.

She had scarcely finished when Quasimodo returned. He carried a basket under one arm and a mattress under the other. In the basket were a bottle, a loaf of bread, and a few other provisions. He set the basket down, and said, "Eat!" He spread the mattress on the floor, and said, "Sleep!"

It was his own food, his own bed, which the bell-ringer had brought.

The gipsy lifted her eyes to his face to thank him, but she could not utter a word. The poor devil was hideous indeed. She hung her head with a shudder of fright.

Then he said,—

"I alarm you. I am very ugly, am I not? Do not look at me; only listen to me. During the day, you must stay here; by night, you can walk anywhere about the church; but do not leave the church by day or night. You would be lost. They would kill you, and I should die."

Moved by his words, she raised her head to reply. He had vanished. Alone once more, she pondered the strange words of this almost monstrous being, struck by the sound of his voice, which was so hoarse and yet so gentle.

Then she examined her cell. It was a room of some six feet square, with a little dormer-window and a door opening on the slightly sloping roof of flat stones. Various gutter-spouts in the form of animals seemed bending over her and stretching their necks to look at her through the window. Beyond the roof she saw the tops of a thousand chimneys, from which issued the smoke of all the fires of Paris. A sad spectacle for the poor gipsy girl,—a foundling condemned to death, an unhappy creature, without a country, without a family, without a hearth.

Just as the thought of her forlorn condition struck her more painfully than ever, she felt a hairy, bearded head rub against her hands and knees. She trembled (everything frightened her now) and looked down. It was the poor goat, the nimble Djali, who had escaped with her when Quasimodo scattered Charmolue's men, and who had been lavishing caresses on her feet for nearly an hour without winning a glance. The gipsy girl covered her with kisses.

"Oh, Djali," said she, "how could I forget you! But you never forget me! Oh, you at least are not ungrateful!"

At the same time, as if an invisible hand had lifted the weight which had so long held back her tears, she began to weep; and as her tears flowed, she felt the sharpest and bitterest of her grief going from her with them.

When evening came, she thought the night so beautiful, the moon so soft, that she took a turn in the raised gallery which surrounds the church. She felt somewhat refreshed by it, the earth seemed to her so peaceful, viewed from that height.

CHAPTER III

DEAF

NEXT morning she found on waking that she had slept. This strange fact amazed her; it was so long since she had slept! A bright beam from the rising sun came in at her window and shone in her face. With the sun, she saw at the same window an object that alarmed her,—the unhappy face of Quasimodo. Involuntarily she reclosed her eyes, but in vain; she still seemed to see through her rosy lids that one-eyed, gap-toothed, gnome-like face. Then, still keeping her eyes shut, she heard a rough voice say very kindly,—

"Don't be frightened. I am your friend. I came to see if you were asleep. It does you no harm, does it, if I look at you when you are asleep? What does it matter to you if I am here when your eyes are shut? Now I will go. There, I have hidden myself behind the wall. You can open your eyes again."

The tone in which they were uttered was even more plaintive than the words themselves. The gipsy girl, touched by it, opened her eyes. He was no longer at the window. She went to it, and saw the poor hunchback crouched in a corner of the wall, in a painful and submissive posture. She made an effort to overcome the aversion with which he inspired her. "Come here," said she, gently. From the motion of her lips, Quasimodo thought she was ordering him away; he therefore rose and retired, limping slowly, with hanging head, not daring to raise his despairing eye to the young girl's face. "Do come!" she cried. But he still withdrew. Then she ran out of her cell, hurried after him, and took his arm. When he felt her touch, Quasimodo trembled in every limb. He raised his beseeching eye, and finding that she drew him towards her, his whole face beamed with tenderness and delight.

She tried to make him enter her cell; but he persisted in remaining on the threshold. "No, no," said he; "the owl must not enter the lark's nest."

Then she threw herself gracefully upon her bed, with the sleeping goat at her feet. For some moments both were motionless, silently contemplating, he so much grace, she so much ugliness.

Every moment she discovered some additional deformity in Quasimodo. Her gaze roved from his knock knees to his humped back, from his humped back to his single eye. She could not understand why a being so imperfectly planned should continue to exist. But withal there was so much melancholy and so much gentleness about him that she began to be reconciled to it.

He was the first to break the silence: "Did you tell me to come back?"

She nodded her head, as she said, "Yes."

He understood her nod. "Alas!" said he, as if loath to go on, "I am— I am deaf."

"Poor fellow!" cried the gipsy, with a look of kindly pity.

He smiled sadly.

"You think that I only lacked that, don't you? Yes, I am deaf. That's the way I was made. It is horrible, isn't it? And you,—you are so beautiful!"

There was so profound a sense of his misery in the poor wretch's tone, that she had not the strength to say a word. Besides, he would not have heard her. He added:—

"I never realized my ugliness till now. When I compare myself with you, I pity myself indeed, poor unhappy monster that I am! I must seem to you like some awful beast, eh? You,— you are a sunbeam, a drop of dew, a bird's song! As for me, I am something frightful, neither man nor beast,— a nondescript object, more hard, shapeless, and more trodden under foot than a pebble!"

Then he began to laugh, and that laugh was the most heartrending thing on earth. He continued:—

"Yes, I am deaf; but you can speak to me by gestures, by signs. I have a master who talks with me in that way. And then I shall soon know your wishes from the motion of your lips, and your expression."

"Well," she replied, smiling, "tell me why you saved me."

He watched her attentively as she spoke.

"I understand," he answered. "You ask me why I saved you. You have forgotten a villain who tried to carry you off one night,—a villain to whom the very next day you brought succour upon their infamous pillory. A drop of water and a little pity are more than my whole life can ever repay. You have forgotten that villain; but he remembers."

She listened with deep emotion. A tear sparkled in the bell-ringer's eye, but it did not fall. He seemed to make it a point of honour to repress it.

"Listen," he resumed, when he no longer feared lest that tear should flow; "we have very tall towers here; a man who fell from them would be dead long before he touched the pavement; whenever it would please you to have me fall, you need not even say a single word; one glance will be enough."

Then he rose. This peculiar being, unhappy though the gipsy was, yet roused a feeling of compassion in her heart. She signed him to stay. "No, no," said he. "I must not stay too long. I am not at my ease. It is out of pity that you do not turn away your eyes. I will go where I can see you without your seeing me. That will be better."

He drew from his pocket a small metal whistle.

"There," said he, "when you need me, when you wish me to come to you, when I do not horrify you too much, whistle with this. I hear that sound."

He laid the whistle on the ground, and fled.

CHAPTER IV

EARTHENWARE AND CRYSTAL

ONE day followed another.

Calm gradually returned to Esmeralda's soul. Excess of grief, like excess of joy, is a violent thing, and of brief duration. The heart of man cannot long remain at any extreme. The gipsy had suffered so much that surprise was the only emotion of which she was now capable. With security, hope had returned. She was far away from society, far from life, but she vaguely felt that it might not perhaps be impossible to return to them. She was like one dead, yet holding in reserve the key to her tomb.

She felt the terrible images which had so long possessed her fading gradually away. All the hideous phantoms, Pierrat Torterue, Jacques Charmolue,

had vanished from her mind,—all, even the priest himself.

And then, too, Phœbus lived; she was sure of it; she had seen him. To her, the life of Phœbus was all in all. After the series of fatal shocks which had laid waste her soul, but one thing was left standing, but one sentiment,—her love for the captain. Love is like a tree; it grows spontaneously, strikes its roots deep into our whole being, and often continues to flourish over a heart in ruins.

And the inexplicable part of it is, that the blinder this passion, the more tenacious it is. It is never stronger than when it is utterly unreasonable.

Undoubtedly Esmeralda's thoughts of the captain were tinged with bitterness. Undoubtedly it was frightful that he too should have been deceived, he who should have deemed such a thing impossible,—that he should have believed the stab to come from her, who would have given a thousand lives for him. But, after all, she must not blame him too severely; had she not confessed her crime? Had she not, weak woman that she was, yielded to torture? The fault was wholly hers. She should have let them tear out every nail rather than wrest a single word from her. Well, could she but see Phœbus once more, for one moment only, it would need but a word, a look, to undeceive him, to bring him back. She had no doubts in the matter. She also strove to account to herself for various strange facts,—for the accident of Phœbus's presence on the day of her doing penance, and for the young girl with whom he was. Probably she was his sister. An improbable explanation, but one with which she contented herself, because she must needs believe Phœbus still loved her, and loved her alone. Had he not sworn it to her? What more did she want, simple, credulous girl that she was? And then, in this business, were not appearances much more against her than against him? She therefore waited; she hoped.

Let us add that the church, that vast church which surrounded her on every side, which guarded her, which preserved her, was itself a sovereign anodyne. The solemn lines of its architecture, the religious attitude of every object about the young girl, the calm and pious thoughts which were emitted, as it were, from every pore of its stones, unconsciously acted upon her. Moreover, the building had sounds of such majesty and blessing that they soothed her sick soul. The monotonous chant of the officiating priests, the people's response to them, sometimes inarticulate, sometimes thunderous, the harmonious quiver of the stained-glass windows, the organ loud as the blast of a hundred trumpets, the three belfries, buzzing and humming like hives of great bees,—all this orchestra, with its gigantic gamut perpetually rising and falling, from the crowd to the belfry, lulled her memory, her imagination, her grief. The bells, particularly, soothed her. Those vast machines poured over her broad waves of mighty magnetism.

Thus, each day's rising sun found her more composed, breathing better, less pale. As her inward wounds were healed, her grace and beauty bloomed again, although she was more reserved and quiet. Her former disposition also returned,— something even of her gaiety, her pretty pout, her love for her goat, her passion for singing, and her modesty. She was careful to dress herself every morning in the corner of her cell, lest the inmate of some neighbouring garret should spy her through the window.

When the thoughts of Phœbus gave her time, the gipsy sometimes thought of Quasimodo. He was the only tie, the only bond, the only means of communication left to her with mankind, with the living. Unhappy girl! She was even more completely cut off from the world than Quasimodo. She could not understand the strange friend whom chance had given her. She often reproached herself for not feeling sufficient gratitude to blind her eyes; but, decidedly, she could not accustom herself to the poor ringer. He was too ugly.

She had left the whistle which he gave her on the floor. This did not prevent Quasimodo from appearing now and then during the first few days. She did her best not to turn away with too much aversion when he brought her the basket of food or the jug of water; but he always noticed the slightest movement of the kind, and would then go sadly away.

Once he came up just as she was fondling Djali. He stood for a few moments considering the pretty group of the girl and the goat; at last he said, shaking his heavy, clumsy head,—

"My misfortune is that I am still too much like a human being. I wish I were wholly an animal like that goat."

She looked at him in surprise.

He answered her look:—

"Oh, I very well know why." And he withdrew.

On another occasion he appeared at the door of the cell (which he never entered) as Esmeralda was singing an old Spanish ballad, the words of which she did not understand, but which had lingered in her memory because the gipsies had rocked her to sleep with it when a child. At the sight of his ugly face, coming so suddenly upon her in the midst of her song, the young girl stopped short, with an involuntary gesture of alarm. The wretched ringer fell upon his knees on the door-sill, and clasped his great misshapen hands with a beseeching air. "Oh," said he, sadly, "I pray you, go on, and do not drive me away." She was unwilling to pain him, and, trembling though she was, resumed her song. By degrees, however, her terror subsided, and she gave herself up entirely to the emotions aroused by the slow and plaintive music. He remained on his knees, his hands clasped as if in prayer, attentive, scarcely breathing, his eyes riveted upon the gipsy's sparkling orbs. He seemed to read her song in her eyes.

Another day he came to her with a timid, awkward air. "Listen to me," said he with an effort; "I have something to tell you." She signed to him that she was listening. Then he began to sigh, half opened his lips, seemed just about to speak, looked at her, shook his head, and retired slowly, pressing his hand to his head, leaving the gipsy utterly amazed.

Among the grotesque images carved upon the wall, there was one of which he was particularly fond, and with which he often seemed to exchange fraternal glances. The girl once heard him say to it, "Oh, why am not I of stone, like you!"

Finally, one morning Esmeralda ventured out to the edge of the roof, and looked into the square over the steep top of Saint-Jean le Rond. Quasimodo stood behind her. He stationed himself there to spare the girl as far as possible the annoyance of seeing him. All at once she started; a tear and a flash of joy shone together in her eyes. She knelt on the edge of the roof, and stretched out her arms in anguish towards the square, crying, "Phœbus! Come! Come! One word, only one word, for the love of Heaven! Phœbus! Phœbus!" Her voice, her face, her gesture, her whole person, wore the heartrending expression of a shipwrecked mariner making signals of distress to a ship sailing merrily by in the distance, lit up by a sunbeam on the horizon.

Quasimodo bent over the parapet, and saw that the object of this frenzied entreaty was a young man, a captain, a handsome knight, glittering with arms and ornaments, who pranced and curveted through the square on horseback, waving his plumed helmet to a lovely damsel smiling from her balcony. However, the officer did not hear the unhappy girl's appeal; he was too far away.

But the poor deaf man heard it. A deep sigh heaved his breast; he turned away; his heart swelled with suppressed tears; his clenched fists beat his brow, and when he withdrew them, each of them grasped a handful of red hair.

The gipsy paid no heed to him. He gnashed his teeth, and muttered,—

"Damnation! So that is how one should look! One only needs a handsome outside!"

Meantime, she remained on her knees, crying with great agitation,—

"Oh, now he is dismounting from his horse! He is going into that house! Phœbus! He does not hear! Phœbus! How cruel of that woman to talk to him at the same time that I do! Phœbus! Phœbus!"

The deaf man watched her. He understood her pantomime. The poor bell-ringer's eye filled with tears, but he did not let a single one flow. All at once he plucked her gently by the hem of her sleeve. She turned. He had assumed a tranquil air, and said,—

"Shall I go and fetch him?"

She uttered a cry of joy.

"Oh, go! go! run, quick! that captain! that captain! bring him to me! I will love you!"

She clasped his knees. He could not help shaking his head sadly.

"I will bring him to you," said he in a faint voice. Then he turned his head and hurried quickly down the stairs, choked with sobs.

When he reached the square, he saw nothing but the fine horse tied to the post at the door of the Gondelaurier house; the captain had already entered.

He raised his eyes to the roof of the church. Esmeralda was still in the same place, in the same position. He shook his head sorrowfully, then leaned against one of the posts before the Gondelaurier porch, determined to await the captain's coming.

Within the house, it was one of those gala days which precede a wedding. Quasimodo saw many people go in, and

none come out. From time to time he looked up at the roof; the gipsy girl was as motionless as he. A groom came, unfastened the horse, and led him into the stable.

The whole day passed thus,—Quasimodo against the pillar, Esmeralda on the roof, Phœbus, doubtless, at the feet of Fleur-de-Lys.

At last night came,—a moonless night, a dark night. In vain Quasimodo fixed his eyes upon Esmeralda; she soon ceased to be anything more than a white spot in the dusk; then she vanished. Everything faded out; all was dark.

Quasimodo saw the front windows of the Gondelaurier mansion lighted up from top to bottom; he saw the other windows on the square lighted, one by one; he also saw the lights extinguished to the very last, for he remained at his post all the evening. The officer did not come out. When the latest passers had gone home, when all the windows in the other houses were black, Quasimodo was left alone, entirely in the darkness. There were no street lamps in the Parvis then.

But the windows of the Gondelaurier house remained lighted, even after midnight. Quasimodo, motionless and alert, saw countless moving, dancing shadows pass across the many-coloured panes. If he had not been deaf, as the noise of sleeping Paris ceased, he would have heard more and more distinctly, within the house, the sounds of revelry, music and laughter.

About one o'clock in the morning the guests began to go. Quasimodo, wrapped in darkness, watched them as they passed beneath the porch bright with torches. The captain was not among them.

He was filled with sad thoughts; at times he looked up into the air, as if tired of waiting. Great, black, heavy clouds, torn and ragged, hung like masses of crape from the starry arch of night. They seemed like the cobwebs of the vaulted sky.

In one of these upward glances he suddenly saw the long window of the balcony whose stone balustrade was just over his head, mysteriously open. Two persons passed out through the glass door, closing it noiselessly behind them; they were a man and a woman. It was not without some difficulty that Quasimodo succeeded in recognizing in the man the handsome captain; in the woman, the young lady whom he had that morning seen wave a welcome to the officer from that self-same balcony. The square was perfectly dark, and a double crimson curtain, which fell again behind the door as it closed, scarcely permitted a ray of light from the room to reach the balcony.

The young man and the girl, as far as our deaf man could judge without hearing a single one of their words, seemed to give themselves up to a very tender tête-à-tête. The young girl had apparently allowed the officer to encircle her waist with his arm, and was making a feeble resistance to a kiss.

Quasimodo looked on from below at this scene, which was all the more attractive because it was not meant to be seen. He beheld that happiness and beauty with bitterness. After all, nature was not mute in the poor devil, and his spinal column, wretchedly crooked as it was, was quite as susceptible of a

thrill as that of any other man. He reflected on the miserable part which Providence had assigned him; that woman, love, pleasure, were forever to pass before him, while he could never do more than look on at the happiness of others. But what pained him most in this sight, what added indignation to his annoyance, was the thought of what the gipsy girl must suffer could she see it. True, the night was very dark; Esmeralda, if she had remained at her post (which he did not doubt), was very far away, and it was all he could do himself, to distinguish the lovers on the balcony. This comforted him.

Meantime, their conversation became more and more animated. The young lady seemed to be entreating the officer to ask no more of her. Quasimodo could only make out her fair clasped hands, her smiles blent with tears, her upward glances, and the eyes of the captain eagerly bent upon her.

Luckily,—for the young girl's struggles were growing feebler,—the balcony door was suddenly reopened, and an old lady appeared; the beauty seemed confused; the officer wore a disappointed air, and all three re-entered the house. A moment later a horse was pawing the ground at the door, and the brilliant officer, wrapped in his cloak, passed quickly by Quasimodo.

The ringer let him turn the corner of the street, then ran after him with his monkey-like agility, shouting:

"Hollo there! Captain!"

The captain stopped.

"What can that rascal want?" said he, seeing in the shadow the ungainly figure limping quickly towards him.

Meantime Quasimodo caught up with

him, and boldly seized the horse by the bridle:—

"Follow me, Captain; there is some one here who wishes to speak with you."

"The devil!" muttered Phœbus, "here's an ugly scarecrow whom I think I've seen elsewhere. Hollo, sirrah! will you let my horse's bridle go?"

"Captain," replied the deaf man, "don't you even ask who it is?"

"I tell you to let my horse go!" impatiently replied Phœbus. "What does the fellow mean by hanging to my charger's chamfron thus? Do you take my horse for a gallows?"

Quasimodo, far from loosing his hold on the bridle, was preparing to turn the horse's head in the opposite direction. Unable to understand the captain's resistance, he made haste to say,—

"Come, Captain, it is a woman who awaits you." He added with an effort: "A woman who loves you."

"Arrant knave!" said the captain; "do you think I am obliged to go to all the women who love me, or say they do? And how if by chance she looks like you, you screech-owl? Tell her who sent you that I am about to marry, and that she may go to the devil!"

"Hear me!" cried Quasimodo, supposing that with one word he could conquer his hesitation; "come, my lord! it is the gipsy girl, whom you know!"

These words did indeed make a strong impression upon Phœbus, but not of the nature which the deaf man expected. It will be remembered that our gallant officer retired with Fleur-de-Lys some moments before Quasimodo rescued the prisoner from the hands of Charmolue. Since then, during his visits to the Gondelaurier house he had carefully avoided

all mention of the woman, whose memory was painful to him; and, on her side, Fleur-de-Lys had not thought it politic to tell him that the gipsy still lived. Phœbus therefore supposed poor "Similar" to have died some two or three months before. Let us add that for some moments past the captain had been pondering on the exceeding darkness of the night, the supernatural ugliness and sepulchral tones of the strange messenger, the fact that it was long past midnight, that the street was as deserted as on the night when the goblin monk addressed him, and that his horse snorted at the sight of Quasimodo.

"The gipsy girl!" he exclaimed, almost terrified: "pray, do you come from the other world?"

And he placed his hand on the hilt of his dagger.

"Quick! quick!" said the deaf man. striving to urge on the horse; "this way!"

Phœbus dealt him a vigorous kick.

Quasimodo's eyes flashed. He made a movement to attack the captain. Then drawing himself up, he said,—

"Oh, how fortunate it is for you that there is some one who loves you!"

He emphasized the words *some one,* and releasing the horse's bridle, added,—

"Begone!"

Phœbus clapped spurs to his horse, with an oath. Quasimodo saw him plunge down the street and disappear in the darkness.

"Oh," murmured the poor deaf man, "to refuse that!"

He returned to Notre-Dame, lighted his lamp, and climbed the tower. As he had supposed, the gipsy was still in the same place.

As soon as she caught sight of him, she ran to meet him.

"Alone!" she cried mournfully, clasping her lovely hands.

"I could not find him," said Quasimodo, coldly.

"You should have waited all night," she replied indignantly.

He saw her angry gesture, and understood the reproach.

"I will watch better another time," said he, hanging his head.

"Go!" said she.

He left her. She was offended with him. He would rather be maltreated by her than distress her. He kept all the pain for himself.

From that day forth the gipsy saw him no more. He ceased to visit her cell. At most, she sometimes caught a glimpse of the ringer on the top of a tower, gazing sadly at her. But as soon as she saw him, he disappeared.

We must own that she was but little troubled by this wilful absence of the poor hunchback. In her secret heart she thanked him for it. However, Quasimodo did not lie under any delusion on this point.

She no longer saw him, but she felt the presence of a good genius around her. Her provisions were renewed by an invisible hand while she slept. One morning she found a cage of birds on her window-sill. Over her cell there was a piece of carving which alarmed her. She had more than once shown this feeling before Quasimodo. One morning (for all these things occurred at night) she no longer saw it; it was broken off. Any one who had clambered up to it must have risked his life.

Sometimes in the evening she heard a voice, hidden behind the wind-screen of the belfry, sing, as if to lull her to sleep, a weird, sad song, verses without rhyme, such as a deaf person might make:—

"Heed not the face,
    Maiden, heed the heart.
The heart of a fine young man is
    oft deformed.
There are hearts where Love finds
    no abiding-place.

"Maiden, the pine-tree is not fair,
Not fair as is the poplar-tree
But its leaves are green in winter
    bare.

"Alas! why do I tell you this?
Beauty alone has right to live;
Beauty can only beauty love,
April her back doth turn on
    January.

"Beauty is perfect,
    Beauty wins all.
Beauty alone is lord of all.

"The raven only flies by day,
The owl by night alone doth fly,
The swan by day and night alike
    may fly."

One morning, on waking, she saw at her window two vases full of flowers. One was a very beautiful and brilliant but cracked crystal vase. It had let the water with which it was filled escape, and the flowers which it held were withered. The other was an earthen jug, coarse and common; but it had retained all its water, and the flowers were fresh and rosy.

I do not know whether it was done purposely, but Esmeralda took the withered nosegay, and wore it all day in her bosom.

That day she did not hear the voice from the tower singing.

She cared but little. She passed her days in fondling Djali, in watching the door of the Gondelaurier house, in talking to herself about Phœbus, and in scattering crumbs of bread to the swallows.

She had entirely ceased to see or hear Quasimodo; the poor ringer seemed to have vanished from the church. But one night, when she could not sleep, and was thinking of her handsome captain, she heard a sigh close by her cell. Terrified, she rose, and saw by the light of the moon a shapeless mass lying outside across her door. It was Quasimodo sleeping there upon the stones.

CHAPTER V

THE KEY TO THE PORTE-ROUGE

MEANTIME, public rumour had informed the archdeacon of the miraculous manner in which the gipsy had been saved. When he learned of it, he knew not what he felt. He had accepted the fact of Esmeralda's death. In this way, he made himself perfectly easy; he had sounded the utmost depths of grief. The human heart (Don Claude had mused upon these matters) can hold but a certain quantity of despair. When the sponge is thoroughly soaked, the sea may pass over it without adding another drop to it.

Now, Esmeralda being dead, the sponge was soaked. Everything was over for Don Claude in this world. But to know that she was alive, and Phœbus too, was to endure afresh the torments, shocks, and vicissitudes of life; and Claude was weary of them all.

When he heard this piece of news, he shut himself up in his cloister cell. He did not appear at the chapter meetings or the sacred offices. He barred his door against every one, even the bishop, and remained thus immured for several weeks. He was supposed to be ill, and indeed was so.

What did he do in seclusion? With what thoughts was the unfortunate man battling? Was he waging a final conflict with his terrible passion? Was he plotting a final plan to kill her and destroy himself?

His Jehan, his adored brother, his spoiled child, came once to his door, knocked, swore, entreated, repeated his name half a score of times. Claude would not open.

He passed whole days with his face glued to his window-panes. From this window, in the cloisters as it was, he could see Esmeralda's cell. He often saw herself, with her goat,—sometimes with Quasimodo. He noticed the attentions of the ugly deaf man,—his obedience, his refined and submissive manners to the gipsy. He recalled,—for he had a good memory, and memory is the plague of the jealous,—he recalled the bell-ringer's strange look at the dancer on a certain evening. He asked himself what motive could have led Quasimodo to save her. He witnessed countless little scenes between the girl and the deaf man, when their gestures, seen from a distance and commented on by his passion, struck him as very tender. He distrusted women's whims. Then he vaguely felt awakening within him a jealousy such as he had never imagined possible,—a jealousy which made him blush with rage and shame. " 'Twas bad enough when it was the captain; but this fellow!" The idea overwhelmed him.

His nights were frightful. Since he knew the gipsy girl to be alive, the chill fancies of spectres and tombs which had for an entire day beset him, had vanished, and the flesh again rose in revolt against the spirit. He writhed upon his bed at the idea that the dark-skinned damsel was so near a neighbour.

Every night his fevered imagination pictured Esmeralda in all those attitudes which had stirred his blood most quickly. He saw her stretched across the body of the wounded captain, her eyes closed, her beautiful bare throat covered with Phœbus's blood, at that moment of rapture when he himself had pressed upon her pale lips that kiss which had burned the unhappy girl, half dead though she was, like a living coal. He again saw her disrobed by the savage hands of the executioners, exposing and enclosing in the buskin with its iron screws her tiny foot, her plump and shapely leg, and her white and supple knee.

He again saw that ivory knee alone left uncovered by Torterue's horrid machine. Finally, he figured to himself the young girl in her shift, the rope about her neck, her shoulders bare, her feet bare, almost naked, as he saw her on what was to have been her last day on earth. These voluptuous pictures made him clinch his hands, and caused a shudder to run from head to foot.

One night, especially, they so cruelly heated his virgin and priestly blood that he bit his pillow, leaped from his bed, threw a surplice over his shirt, and left his cell, lamp in hand, but half-dressed, wild and haggard, with flaming eyes.

He knew where to find the key to the Porte-Rouge, which led from the cloisters to the church, and he always carried about him, as the reader knows, a key to the tower stairs.

CHAPTER VI

THE KEY TO THE PORTE-ROUGE (cont.)

THAT night Esmeralda fell asleep in her cell, full of peace, hope, and pleasant thoughts. She had been asleep for some time, dreaming, as she always did, of Phœbus, when she fancied she heard a noise. Her sleep was light and restless,—a bird's sleep. A mere trifle roused her. She opened her eyes. The night was very dark. Still, she saw a face peering in at the window; the vision was lighted up by a lamp. When this face saw that Esmeralda was looking at it, it blew out the lamp. Still, the girl had had time to catch a glimpse of it; her eyes closed in terror.

"Oh," said she, in a feeble voice, "the priest!"

All her past misery flashed upon her with lightning speed. She sank back upon her bed, frozen with fear.

A moment after, she felt a touch which made her shudder so that she started up wide awake and furious.

The priest had glided to her side. He clasped her in his arms.

She tried to scream, but could not. "Begone, monster! Begone, assassin!" she said at last, in a low voice trembling with wrath and horror.

"Mercy! mercy!" murmured the priest, pressing his lips to her shoulders.

She seized his bald head in both hands by the hairs which remained, and strove to prevent his kisses as if they had been bites.

"Mercy!" repeated the unfortunate man. "If you knew what my love for you is! It is fire, molten lead, a thousand knives driven into my heart!"

And he held her arms with superhuman strength. She cried desperately: "Release me, or I shall spit in your face!"

He released her. "Degrade me, strike me, do your worst! do what you will! but have mercy! love me!"

Then she struck him with the impotent fury of a child. She clinched her lovely hands to bruise his face. "Demon, begone!"

"Love me! love me! have pity!" cried the poor priest, clasping her, and returning her blows with caresses.

All at once she felt him stronger than she.

"No more of this!" he exclaimed, gnashing his teeth.

She lay conquered, crushed, and quivering in his arms, at his mercy. She felt a wanton hand wandering over her. She made one last effort, and shrieked: "Help! help! a vampire! a vampire!"

No one came. Djali alone was awakened, and bleated piteously.

"Silence!" said the panting priest.

Suddenly, in her struggle, as she fought upon the floor, the gipsy's hand encountered something cold and metallic. It was Quasimodo's whistle. She seized it with a convulsion of hope, raised it to her lips, and blew with all her remaining strength. The whistle gave forth a sharp, shrill, piercing sound.

"What is that?" said the priest.

Almost as he spoke, he felt himself grasped by a vigorous arm. The cell was dark; he could not distinguish exactly who held him; but he heard teeth chattering with rage, and there was just enough light mingled with the darkness for him to see the broad blade of a cutlass gleam above his head.

He thought he recognized the figure of Quasimodo. He supposed that it could be no other. He remembered having stumbled, as he entered, over a bundle lying across the outside of the door. But as the new-comer did not utter a word, he knew not what to think. He flung himself upon the arm which held the cutlass, crying, "Quasimodo!" He forgot, in this moment of distress, that Quasimodo was deaf.

In the twinkling of an eye the priest was stretched on the floor, and felt a heavy knee pressed against his breast. By the angular imprint of that knee, he knew Quasimodo; but what was he to do? How was he also to be recognized by the hunchback? Night made the deaf man blind.

He was lost. The young girl, pitiless as an enraged tigress, did not interpose to save him. The cutlass came nearer his head; it was a critical moment. All at once his adversary appeared to hesitate.

"No blood upon her!" said he, in a dull voice.

It was indeed the voice of Quasimodo.

Then the priest felt a huge hand drag him from the cell by the heels; he was not to die within those walls. Luckily for him, the moon had risen some moments before.

When they crossed the threshold, its pale rays fell upon the priest. Quasimodo looked him in the face, trembled, relaxed his hold, and shrank back.

The gipsy, who had advanced to the door of her cell, saw with surprise that the actors had suddenly changed parts. It was now the priest who threatened, and Quasimodo who implored.

The priest, who was overwhelming the deaf man with gestures of wrath and reproach, violently signed him to withdraw.

The deaf man bowed his head, then knelt before the gipsy's door. "My lord," said he, in grave, submissive tones, "do what you will afterwards; but kill me first!"

So saying, he offered his cutlass to the priest. The priest, beside himself with rage, rushed upon him. But the young girl was quicker than he. She tore the knife from Quasimodo's hands, and uttered a frenzied laugh.

"Approach now!" she cried.

She held the blade high above her head. The priest stood irresolute. She would certainly have struck.

"You dare not touch me now, coward!" she exclaimed.

Then she added with a pitiless look, and knowing that her words would pierce the priest's heart like a thousand red-hot irons,—

"Ah, I know that Phœbus is not dead!"

The priest threw Quasimodo to the ground with a kick, and rushed down the stairs quivering with rage.

When he had gone, Quasimodo picked up the whistle which had just saved the gipsy.

"It was getting rusty," said he, returning it to her; then he left her alone.

The young girl, overcome by this violent scene, fell exhausted on her bed and burst into a flood of tears. Her horizon was again becoming overcast.

The priest, on his side, groped his way back to his cell.

That was sufficient. Don Claude was jealous of Quasimodo.

He repeated musingly the fatal words: "No one else shall have her!"

BOOK X

THE KING

CHAPTER I

GRINGOIRE HAS SEVERAL CAPITAL IDEAS IN SUCCESSION IN THE RUE DES BERNARDINS

WHEN Pierre Gringoire saw the turn which this whole matter was taking, and that a rope, hanging, and other unpleasant things must certainly be the fate of the chief actors in the play, he no longer cared to meddle with it. The Vagrants, with whom he remained, considering that after all they were the best company to be found in Paris,—the Vagrants still retained their interest in the gipsy. He thought this very natural on the part of people who, like her, had no prospect but Charmolue and Torterue to which to look forward, and who did not, like him, roam through the realms of imagination upon the wings of Pegasus. He learned from their conversation that his bride of the broken jug had taken refuge in Notre-Dame, and he was very glad of it; but he felt no temptation to visit her. He sometimes wondered what had become of the little goat, and that was all. In the daytime he performed feats of juggling for a living, and at night he wrought out an elaborate memorial against the Bishop of Paris; for he remembered being drenched by his mill-wheels, and he bore him a grudge for it. He also busied himself with comments on that fine work by Baudry-le-Rouge, Bishop of Noyon and Tournay, entitled *"De cupa petrarum,"* which had inspired him with an ardent taste for architecture,— a fancy which had replaced in his heart the passion for hermetics, of which indeed it was but a natural corollary, since there is a close connection between hermetics and masonry. Gringoire had turned from the love of an idea to love of the substance.

One day he halted near Saint-Germain-l'Auxerrois, at the corner of a building known as For-l'Evêque, which faces another known as For-le-Roi. This For-l'Evêque contained a charming fourteenth-century chapel, the chancel of which looked towards the street. Gringoire was devoutly studying the outside carvings. He was enjoying one of those moments of selfish, exclusive, supreme pleasure, during which the artist sees nothing in the world but art, and

sees the world in art. All at once he felt a hand laid heavily on his shoulder. He turned. It was his former friend, his former master, the archdeacon.

He was astounded. It was a long time since he had seen the archdeacon, and Don Claude was one of those solemn and impassioned men a meeting with whom always upsets the equilibrium of a sceptic philosopher.

The archdeacon was silent for some moments, during which Gringoire had leisure to observe him. He found Don Claude greatly changed,—pale as a winter morning, hollow-eyed, his hair almost white. The priest at last broke the silence, saying in a calm but icy tone,—

"How are you, Master Pierre?"

"As to my health?" answered Gringoire. "Well, well! I may say I am tolerably robust, upon the whole. I take everything in moderation. You know, master, the secret of good health, according to Hippocrates: *'Id est: cibi, potus, somni, venus, omnia moderata sint.'* "

"Then you have nothing to trouble you, Master Pierre?" replied the archdeacon, looking fixedly at Gringoire.

"No, by my faith!"

"And what are you doing now?"

"You see, master, I am examining the cutting of these stones, and the style in which that bas-relief is thrown out."

The priest smiled a bitter smile, which only lifted one corner of his mouth.

"And does that amuse you?"

"It is paradise!" exclaimed Gringoire. And bending over the sculptures with the ravished mien of a demonstrator of living phenomena, he added: "For instance, don't you think that metamorphosis in low-relief is carved with exceeding skill, refinement, and patience? Just look at this little column. Around what capital did you ever see foliage more graceful or more daintily chiselled? Here are three of Jean Maillevin's alto-relievos. They are not the finest works of that great genius. Still, the ingenuousness, the sweetness of the faces, the careless ease of the attitudes and draperies, and that inexplicable charm which is mingled with all their defects, make these tiny figures most delicate and delightful, perhaps almost too much so. Don't you think this is entertaining?"

"Yes, indeed!" said the priest.

"And if you could only see the inside of the chapel!" continued the poet, with his garrulous enthusiasm. "Carvings everywhere, crowded as close as the leaves in the heart of a cabbage! The chancel is fashioned most devoutly, and is so peculiar that I have never seen its like elsewhere."

Don Claude interrupted him,—

"So you are happy?"

Gringoire eagerly replied,—

"Yes, on my honour! At first I loved women, then animals; now I love stones. They are quite as amusing as animals or women, and they are less treacherous."

The priest pressed his hand to his head. It was his habitual gesture.

"Indeed?"

"Stay!" said Gringoire; "you shall see my pleasures!" He took the arm of the unresisting priest, and led him into the staircase turret of For-l'Evêque. "There's a staircase for you! Every time I see it I am happy. It is the simplest and yet the rarest in Paris. Every step is bevelled underneath. Its

beauty and simplicity consist in the treads, which, for a foot or more in width, are interlaced, mortised, dovetailed, jointed, linked together, and set into one another in a genuinely solid and goodly way."

"And you desire nothing more?"

"No."

"And you have no regrets?"

"Neither regret nor desire. I have arranged my mode of life."

"What man arranges," said Claude, "circumstances disarrange."

"I am a Pyrrhonian philosopher," replied Gringoire, "and I keep everything equally balanced."

"And how do you earn your living?"

"I still write occasional epics and tragedies; but what brings me in the most, is that trade which you have seen me follow, master,—namely, upholding pyramids of chairs in my teeth."

"That is a sorry trade for a philosopher."

"'Tis keeping up an equilibrium all the same," said Gringoire. "When one has but a single idea he finds it in everything."

"I know that!" responded the archdeacon.

After a pause he added,—

"And yet you are poor enough?"

"Poor! Yes; but not unhappy."

At this instant the sound of horses' hoofs was heard, and our two friends saw a company of archers belonging to the king's ordnance file by at the end of the street, with raised lances, and an officer at their head. The cavalcade was a brilliant one, and clattered noisily over the pavement.

"How you stare at that officer!" said Gringoire to the archdeacon.

"Because I think I have seen him before."

"What is his name?"

"I believe," said Claude, "that his name is Phœbus de Châteaupers."

"Phœb· a queer name! There is also a Pnœbus, Count de Foix. I once knew a girl who never swore save by Phœbus."

"Come with me," said the priest. "I have something to say to you."

Ever since the troops passed by, some agitation was apparent beneath the icy exterior of the archdeacon. He walked on; Gringoire followed, accustomed to obey him, like all who ever approached that man full of such ascendency. They reached the Rue des Bernardins in silence, and found it quite deserted. Here Don Claude paused.

"What have you to tell me, master?" asked Gringoire.

"Don't you think," replied the archdeacon, with a most reflective air, "that the dress of those horsemen whom we just saw is far handsomer than yours and mine?"

Gringoire shook his head.

"I' faith! I like my red and yellow jacket better than those scales of steel and iron. What pleasure can there be in making as much noise when you walk as the Quai de la Ferraille in an earthquake?"

"Then, Gringoire, you never envied those fine fellows in their warlike array?"

"Envied them what, Sir Archdeacon, —their strength, their armour, or their discipline? Philosophy and independence in rags are far preferable. I would rather be the head of a fly than the tail of a lion."

"That's strange," said the priest meditatively. "And yet a handsome uniform is a fine thing."

Gringoire, seeing that he was absorbed in thought, left him in order to admire the porch of a neighbouring house. He came back clapping his hands.

"If you were not so absorbed in the fine uniforms of those soldiers, Sir Archdeacon, I would beg you to take a look at that door. I always said that my lord Aubry's house had the most superb entrance in the world."

"Pierre Gringoire," said the archdeacon, "what have you done with the little gipsy dancer?"

"Esmeralda? What a sudden change of subject!"

"Was she not your wife?"

"Yes, by means of a broken jug. We are married for four years. By the way," added Gringoire, regarding the archdeacon with a half-bantering air, "are you still thinking of her?"

"And you,—do you think of her no longer?"

"Seldom. I have so many other things to occupy me. Heavens! how pretty that little goat of hers was!"

"Did not the girl save your life?"

"She did, indeed, by Jupiter!"

"Well, what has become of her? What have you done with her?"

"I can't say, I fancy that they hanged her."

"You really think so?"

"I'm not sure of it. When I saw that they had taken to hanging people, I withdrew from the game."

"Is that all you know about the matter?"

"Stay. I was told that she had taken refuge in Notre-Dame, and that she was in safety there, and I am delighted to hear it; and I can't find out whether the goat was saved along with her. And that's all I know about it."

"I'll tell you more," cried Don Claude; and his voice, hitherto so low, slow, and almost muffled, became as loud as thunder. "She did indeed take refuge in Notre-Dame. But within three days justice will again overtake her, and she will be hanged upon the Grève. Parliament has issued a decree."

"That's a pity!" said Gringoire.

The priest, in the twinkling of an eye, had recovered his coldness and calm.

"And who the devil," resumed the poet, "has amused himself by soliciting an order of restitution? Why couldn't he have left Parliament in peace? What harm does it do if a poor girl takes shelter under the flying buttresses of Notre-Dame, alongside of the swallows' nests?"

"There are Satans in the world," replied the archdeacon.

"That's a devilish bad job," observed Gringoire.

The archdeacon resumed, after a pause,—

"So she saved your life?"

"From my good friends the Vagrants. A little more, or a little less, and I should have been hanged. They would be very sorry for it now."

"Don't you want to do anything to help her?"

"With all my heart, Don Claude; but what if I should get myself into trouble?"

"What would that matter?"

"What! what would it matter? How kind you are, master! I have two great works but just begun."

The priest struck his forehead. In spite of his feigned calmness, an occasional violent gesture betrayed his inward struggles.

"How is she to be saved?"

Gringoire said: "Master, I might answer, 'Il padelt,' which is Turkish for, 'God is our hope.' "

"How is she to be saved?" dreamily repeated the archdeacon.

Gringoire in his turn clapped his hand to his head.

"See here, master, I have a lively imagination; I will devise various expedients. Suppose the king were asked to pardon her?"

"Louis XI.,—to pardon!"

"Why not?"

"As well try to rob a tiger of his bone!"

Gringoire set to work to find some fresh solution of the difficulty.

"Well!—stop!—Do you want me to draw up a petition to the midwives declaring the girl to be pregnant?"

This made the priest's hollow eye flash.

"Pregnant, villain! do you know anything about it?"

Gringoire was terrified by his expression. He made haste to say, "Oh, no, not I! our marriage was a true forismaritagium. I was entirely left out. But at any rate, we should gain time."

"Folly! infamy! be silent!"

"You are wrong to be so vexed," grumbled Gringoire. "We should gain time; it would do no one any harm, and the midwives, who are poor women, would earn forty Paris pence."

The priest paid no attention to him.

"And yet she must be got away!" he muttered. "The order will be executed within three days! Besides, even if there were no order, that Quasimodo! Women have very depraved tastes!" He raised his voice: "Master Pierre, I have considered it well; there's but one means of salvation for her."

"What is it? I, for my part, see none."

"Listen, Master Pierre, and remember that you owe your life to her. I will frankly tell you my idea. The church is watched night and day. No one is allowed to come out but those who are seen to go in. Therefore, you can go in. You will come, and I will take you to her. You will change clothes with her. She will put on your doublet; you will put on her gown."

"So far, so good," remarked the philosopher. "What next?"

"What next? She will walk out in your clothes; you will stay behind in hers. Perhaps they may hang you, but she will be saved."

Gringoire scratched his ear, with a very grave look.

"There!" said he; "that's an idea which would never have occurred to me."

At Don Claude's unexpected proposition, the poet's benign and open face had suddenly darkened, like a smiling Italian landscape when some fatal blast sweeps a cloud across the sun.

"Well, Gringoire, what do you say to the plan?"

"I say, master, that they would not hang me *perhaps*, but they would hang me without the slightest doubt."

"That does not concern us!"

"The deuce!" said Gringoire.

"She saved your life. You would only be paying your debt."

"There are plenty of others which I have not paid."

"Master Pierre, it absolutely must be done."

The archdeacon spoke with authority.

"Listen to me, Don Claude," replied the dismayed poet. "You cling to that idea, and you are wrong. I don't see why I should be hanged in another person's stead."

"What makes you so fond of life?"

"Oh, a thousand things!"

"What are they, if you please?"

"What? The air, the sky, morning and evening, moonlight, my good friends the Vagabonds, our larks with the girls, the architectural beauties of Paris to study, three big books to write,—one of which is directed against the bishop and his mills,—and I know not what else. Anaxagoras said that he came into the world to admire the sun; and besides, I have the pleasure of spending all my days, from morning till night, with a man of genius, to wit, myself, and that is a mighty agreeable thing."

"Rattle-pate!" muttered the archdeacon. "Well, speak; who preserved that life of yours which you find so delightful? To whom do you owe it that you still breathe this air, behold that sky, and are still able to amuse your feather-brain with trifles and nonsense? Where would you be now, but for her? Would you have her die, to whom you owe your life,—have her die, that sweet, lovely, adorable creature, necessary to the light of the world, more divine than God himself, while you, half madman and half sage, a mere sketch of something or other, a sort of vegetable growth which fancies that it walks and fancies that it thinks,—you are to go on living with the life of which you have robbed her, as useless as a candle at high noon? Come, have a little pity, Gringoire; be generous in your turn; she set you the example."

The priest was excited. At first Gringoire listened with an air of indecision; then he relented, and ended by pulling a tragic grimace, which made his pallid face look like that of a new-born baby with the colic.

"You are pathetic!" said he, wiping away a tear. "Well, I will consider it. That's an odd idea of yours. After all," he added, after a pause, "who knows? Perhaps they would not hang me. Betrothal is not always marriage. When they find me in her cell, so ridiculously arrayed, in cap and petticoats, perhaps they'll burst out laughing. And then, if they do hang me, why, the rope is like any other death; or, rather, it's not like any other death. It is a death worthy of the wise man who has wavered and swung to and fro all his life,—a death which is neither fish nor flesh, like the spirit of the genuine sceptic; a death fully impressed with Pyrrhonism and uncertainty, a happy medium between heaven and earth, which leaves one in suspense. It is the right death for a philosopher, and perhaps I was predestined to it. It is magnificent to die as one has lived."

The priest interrupted him: "Is it agreed?"

"What is death, after all?" continued Gringoire, with exaltation. "An unpleasant moment, a turnpike gate, the passage from little to nothing. Some one having asked Cercidas, of Magalopolis, if he was willing to die, 'Why not?' he answered: 'for after my death

I shall see those great men,—Pythagoras among the philosophers, Hecatæus among the historians, Homer among the poets, Olympus among the musicians.' "

The archdeacon offered him his hand. "It is settled, then? You will come to-morrow."

This gesture brought Gringoire back to reality.

"Oh, no! by my faith!" said he in the tone of a man awakening from sleep. "To be hanged! That is too absurd. I'll not do it."

"Farewell, then!" and the archdeacon added between his teeth, "I shall see you again!"

"I have no desire to see that devil of a man again," thought Gringoire; and he hurried after Don Claude. "Stay, Sir Archdeacon; no malice between old friends! You take an interest in that girl,—in my wife, I should say; it is well. You have planned a stratagem for rescuing her from Notre-Dame; but your scheme is a very disagreeable one for me, Gringoire. Suppose I have another! I warn you that a most brilliant inspiration has just occurred to me. What if I have a suitable plan for getting her out of her evil plight without compromising my own neck in the least of slip-nooses, what would you say? Wouldn't that satisfy you? Is it absolutely necessary that I should be hanged, to suit you?"

The priest impatiently wrenched the buttons from his cassock, saying, "What a flood of words! What is your scheme?"

"Yes," resumed Gringoire, talking to himself, and laying his finger to his nose in token of his absorption, "that's just it! The Vagabonds are brave fellows. The gipsy nation love her! They will rise at a single word! Nothing easier! A sudden attack; amidst the confusion she can readily be carried off. To-morrow night. They will ask nothing better."

"Your plan! speak!" said the priest, shaking him roughly.

Gringoire turned majestically towards him. "Let me alone! Don't you see that I am in the throes of composition?" He reflected for a few moments more, then clasped his hands in delight, exclaiming, "Capital! success is assured!"

"Your plan!" angrily repeated Claude.

Gringoire was radiant.

"Come close, and let me whisper it to you. It is really a jolly countermine, and one which will get us all out of difficulty. Zounds! you must confess that I am no fool."

He interrupted himself,—

"Oh, by the way! is the little goat still with the girl?"

"Yes. May the foul fiend fly away with you!"

"They were going to hang her too, were they not?"

"What is that to me?"

"Yes, they would have hanged her. They did hang a sow last month. The hangman likes that; he eats the animal afterwards. Hang my pretty Djali! Poor little lamb!"

"Curses on you!" cried Don Claude. "You are the executioner yourself. What means of saving her have you hit upon, rascal? Must I tear your idea from you with the forceps?"

"Softly, master! It is this."

Gringoire bent to the archdeacon's ear, and whispered to him, casting an anxious glance up and down the street meanwhile, although there was no one in sight. When he ended, Don Claude took his hand and said coldly, "It is well. Until to-morrow, then."

"Until to-morrow," repeated Gringoire. And as the archdeacon departed in one direction, he moved away in the other, muttering. "Here's a pretty business, Master Pierre Gringoire! Never mind! It shall not be said that because a man is little he is afraid of a great enterprise. Biton carried a full-grown bull upon his shoulders; wagtails, blackcaps, and stone-chats cross the sea."

CHAPTER II

TURN VAGABOND!

THE archdeacon, on returning to the cloisters, found his brother, Jehan du Moulin, awaiting him at the door of his cell. He had whiled away the fatigue of waiting by drawing upon the wall in charcoal his elder brother's profile, enriched with an exaggerated nose.

Don Claude scarcely looked at his brother; he had other cares. That merry roguish face, whose radiance had so often brightened the priest's gloomy countenance, was now incapable of dissipating the clouds which grew daily thicker over that corrupt, mephitic, stagnant soul.

"Brother," timidly said Jehan, "I have come to see you."

The archdeacon did not even deign to look at him.

"Well?"

"Brother," continued the hypocrite, "you are so good to me, and you give me such good advice, that I am always coming back to you."

"Well?"

"Alas! brother, how right you were when you said to me, 'Jehan! Jehan! *cessat doctorum doctrina, discipulorum, disciplina!* Jehan, be prudent; Jehan, be studious; Jehan, do not wander outside the college bounds at night without just cause and leave from your master. Do not quarrel with the Picards (*noli, Joannes, verberare Picardos*). Do not lie and moulder like an illiterate ass (*quasi asinus illiteratus*) amidst the litter of the schools. Jehan, suffer yourself to be punished at the discretion of your master. Jehan, go to chapel every evening, and sing an anthem with a collect and prayer to our Glorious Lady, the Virgin Mary.' Alas! What excellent counsels were these!"

"Well?"

"Brother, you see before you a guilty wretch, a criminal, a miserable sinner, a libertine, a monster! My dear brother, Jehan has trampled your advice beneath his feet. I am fitly punished for it, and the good God is strangely just. So long as I had money I rioted and revelled and led a jolly life. Oh, how charming is the face of Vice, but how ugly and crooked is her back! Now, I have not a single silver coin; I have sold my table-cloth, my shirt, and my towel; no more feasting for me! The wax candle has burned out, and I have nothing left but a wretched tallow dip, which reeks in my nostrils. The girls laugh at me. I drink water. I am tormented by creditors and remorse."

"What else?" said the archdeacon.

"Alas! dearest brother, I would fain lead a better life. I came to you full of contrition. I am penitent. I confess my sins. I beat my breast lustily. You were quite right to wish me to become a licentiate, and submonitor of the Collège of Torchi. I now feel that I have the strongest vocation for that office. But I have no ink, I must buy some; I have no pens, I must buy some; I have no paper, I have no books, I must buy some. I am in great want of a little money for all these things, and I come to you, brother, with a contrite heart."

"Is that all?"

"Yes," said the student. "A little money."

"I have none."

The student then said with a grave and at the same time resolute air, "Very well, brother: I am sorry to be obliged to tell you that very fine offers and propositions have been made me by another party. You will not give me the money? No? In that case, I shall turn Vagabond."

As he uttered this monstrous word, he assumed the expression of an Ajax, expecting to see the thunderbolt descend upon his head.

The archdeacon said coldly,—

"Turn Vagabond!"

Jehan bowed low and hurried down the cloister stairs, whistling as he went.

Just as he passed through the courtyard of the cloisters, under his brother's window, he heard that window open, looked up, and saw the archdeacon's stern face at the aperture.

"Go to the devil!" said Don Claude; "this is the last money which you will ever get from me!"

At the same time he flung at Jehan a purse which raised a large lump on his forehead, and with which he departed, at once angry and pleased, like a dog pelted with marrow-bones.

CHAPTER III

JOY FOREVER!

THE reader may remember that a part of the Court of Miracles was enclosed by the ancient boundary wall of the city, many of whose towers had at this time begun to fall into ruin. One of these towers had been made into a pleasure-house by the Vagabonds. There was a tavern in the lower portion, and other things above. This tower was the most lively and consequently the most horrible spot in the Vagrant community. It was a sort of monstrous bee-hive, which buzzed and hummed night and day. At night, when all the surplus beggars were asleep, when there was not a window still lighted in any of the dirty houses in the square, when no sound was longer to be heard from any of the innumerable hovels, the abode of swarms of thieves, prostitutes, and stolen children or foundlings, the jolly tower might always be known by the noise which rose from it, by the red light which, beaming alike from chimneys, windows, and cracks in the crumbling walls, escaped, as it were, at every pore.

The cellar, then, was the tavern. It was reached by a low door, and a flight of stairs as steep as a classic Alexandrine verse. Over the door, by way of sign, there was a marvellous daub portraying a number of coins fresh from the mint and fresh-killed chickens, with these punning words above: "The Ringers for the Dead."

One evening, when the curfew-bell was ringing from every belfry in Paris, the serjeants of the watch, had they chanced to enter the much-dreaded Court of Miracles, might have observed that there was even more uproar than usual in the tavern of the Vagabonds; that there was more drinking and more swearing than ordinary. Outside, in the square, numerous groups were chatting together in low tones, as if planning some great enterprise; and here and there some scamp squatted on the ground, sharpening a rusty iron blade upon a paving-stone. Within the tavern itself, however, cards and wine proved so powerful a diversion from the ideas which that evening occupied the minds of the Vagrant community that it would have been hard to guess from the remarks of the drinkers what the scheme on foot really was; they merely seemed somewhat more jovial than usual, and between the legs of every man glistened a weapon,—a pruning-hook, an axe, a big two-edged sword, or the hook of an old hackbut.

The room was circular in shape and very large; but the tables were so closely crowded and the topers so numerous that the entire contents of the tavern—men, women, benches, beer-jugs, drinkers, sleepers, gamblers, able-bodied and crippled—seemed to be heaped together pell-mell, with no more order or harmony than a pile of oyster-shells. A number of tallow dips burned on the tables; but the real luminary of the tavern, which played the same part as the chandelier in an opera-house, was the fire. This cellar was so damp that the fire on the hearth was never suffered to go out, even in midsummer.

There was a huge fireplace with carved overhanging mantel, bristling with clumsy iron andirons and kitchen utensils, and one of those tremendous fires of wood and turf mixed, which at night, in village streets, cast such red and spectral images on the opposite walls from the window of a forge. A large dog sat soberly in the ashes, and turned a spit laden with meat before the embers.

In spite of the confusion, after the first glance, three principal groups were readily to be distinguished, pressing about three personages with whom the reader is already acquainted. One of these persons, grotesquely decked with various gaudy Oriental rags, was Mathias Hungadi Spicali, Duke of Egypt and Bohemia. The rascal sat upon a table, with crossed legs and uplifted finger, loudly dispensing his store of black and white magic to the many gaping faces around him. Another mob crowded closely about our old friend, the worthy King of Tunis, or lord of blacklegs, Clopin Trouillefou. Armed to the teeth, he was very seriously, and in low tones, superintending the pillage of an enormous cask full of weapons which stood staved in before him, and from which were disgorged quantities of axes, swords, priming-pans, coats of mail, spear-heads and antique lance-heads, arrows and cross-bow bolts, like so many apples and grapes from a cornucopia. Each took from the heap what he chose,—one a helmet, one a sword-blade, and another a *misericordia*, or cross-handled dagger. The very children armed themselves, and there were even legless cripples, crawling about, barbed and cuirassed, between the legs of the topers, like big beetles.

Lastly a third audience—the noisest, jolliest, and most numerous of all—thronged the benches and tables, in whose midst held forth and swore a flute-like voice issuing from a heavy suit of armour, complete from helmet to spurs. The individual who had thus imprisoned himself in full panoply was so entirely hidden by his warlike habit that nothing was to be seen of him but an impudent, red, snub nose, a lock of light curly hair, a rosy mouth, and a pair of bold eyes. His belt was stuck full of daggers and knives, a huge sword hung at his side, a rusty cross-bow was on the other thigh, and a vast jug of wine stood before him; not to mention a plump and ragged damsel at his right hand. Every mouth in his vicinity laughed, cursed, and drank.

Add to these twenty secondary groups,—the serving men and maids running about with jugs on their heads; gamblers stooping over their marbles, their hop-scotch, dice, vachette, or exciting game of tringlet; the quarrels in one corner, the kisses in another,—and you will have some idea of the scene over which flickered the glare of a huge roaring fire, which made a myriad monstrous shadows dance upon the walls.

As for the noise, it was like the inside of a big bell ringing a full peal.

The dripping-pan, in which a shower of fat from the spit was crackling, filled up with its constant sputtering the intervals in the endless dialogues going on from one side of the hall to the other.

Amidst this uproar, a philosopher sat at the back of the room on the bench in the chimney-place, musing, with his feet in the ashes and his eyes on the burning brands; it was Pierre Gringoire.

"Come! make haste, arm yourselves! We march in an hour!" said Clopin Trouillefou to his Canters.

A girl hummed,—

> "Good-night, mamma; good-night, my sire;
> Who sits up last, rakes down the fire."

Two card-players disputed together. "Knave," cried the redder-faced of the two, shaking his fist at the other, "I will mark you with the club; then you can take the place of Pam in the king's own pack of cards."

"Ouf!" roared a Norman, readily to be recognized by his nasal twang; "we are crowded together here like so many saints at Caillouville!"

"Boys," said the Duke of Egypt to his followers, speaking in falsetto tones, "the witches of France attend their Sabbath without broomstick, or ointment, or any steed, merely by uttering a few magical words. Italian witches always keep a goat waiting for them at the door. All are obliged to go up the chimney."

The voice of the young scamp armed from head to foot rose above the uproar.

"Noël! Noël!" he shouted. "To-day I wear armour for the first time. A Vagrant! I am a Vagrant, by Christ's wounds! Give me drink! Friends, my name is Jehan Frollo du Moulin, and I am a gentleman born. It is my opinion that if God himself were a dragoon, he would turn plunderer. Brothers, we are about to go on a fine expedition. We are valiant fellows. Assault the church, break open the doors, carry off the lovely damsel in distress, save her from her judges, save her from the priests; dismantle the cloisters, burn the bishop in his palace. We'll do all this in less time than it takes a burgomaster to eat a spoonful of soup. Our cause is just; we will strip Notre-Dame, and that's the end of it. We'll hang Quasimodo. Do you know Quasimodo, ladies? Did you ever see him ring the big bell of a Whit-Sunday until he was out of breath? My word! it's a lovely sight! He looks like a devil astride of a great gaping pair of jaws. Friends, listen to me. I am a Vagrant to my heart's core; I am a Canter in my inmost soul; I was born a Cadger. I have been very rich, and I've devoured my fortune. My mother meant to make a soldier of me; my father, a sub-deacon; my aunt, a member of the Court of Inquiry; my grandmother, prothonotary to the king; my great-aunt, a paymaster in the army; but I,—I turned Vagrant. I told my father that I had made my choice, and he hurled a curse at my head; and my mother,—she, poor old lady, fell to weeping and sputtering, like that log on the fire. A short life and a merry one, say I! I am as good as a whole houseful of lunatics! Landlady, my darling, more wine! I've money enough still to pay for it. No more Surène wine for me; it frets my throat. Zounds! I'd as soon gargle myself with a swarm of bees!"

Meantime, the rabble applauded his words with shouts of laughter; and seeing that the tumult about him increased. the student exclaimed:—

"Oh, what a delightful confusion! *Populi debacchantis populosa debacchatio!*" Then he began to sing, his eyes rolling in feigned ecstasy, in the voice of a canon intoning vespers: "*Quæ cantica; quæ organa! quæ cantilenæ! quæ melodiæ hic sine fine decantantur! Sonant melliflua hymnorum organa, suavissima angelorum melodia cantica canticorum mira—*" He stopped short: "Here, you devil of a tavern-keeper, give me some supper!"

There was a moment of comparative quiet, during which the sharp voice of the Duke of Egypt was heard in its turn, instructing his followers:—

"The weasel is called Aduine, the fox Blue-foot or the Wood-ranger, the wolf Grey-foot, or Gold-foot, the bear Old Man or Grandfather. The cap of a gnome will make its possessor invisible, and enable him to see invisible things. Every toad that is baptized should be clad in black or red velvet, a bell round its neck and another at its feet. The godfather holds it by the head, the godmother by the legs."

The Vagrants continued to arm, whispering together as they did so, at the other end of the tavern.

"Poor Esmeralda!" said a gipsy; "she's our sister. We must rescue her."

"Is she still at Notre-Dame?" asked a Jewish-looking Cadger.

"Yes, in good sooth, she is!"

"Well, then, comrades," cried the Cadger, "on to Notre-Dame! So much the more, that there are two statues in the chapel of Saint Féréol and Saint Ferrution,—one of Saint John the Baptist and the other of Saint Anthony, —of solid gold, the two together weighing seven golden marks and fifteen sterlings, and the silver-gilt pedestals weigh seventeen marks and five ounces. I know all about this; I am a jeweller."

Here Jehan's supper was served. He exclaimed, as he threw himself back upon the bosom of the girl next him:—

"By Saint Voult-de-Lucques, known to the world at large as Saint Goguelu, I am perfectly happy. Before me stands a fool staring at me with as smug a face as any archduke. And at my left elbow sits another, with teeth so long that they hide his chin. And then, too, I'm like Marshal de Gié at the siege of Pontoise,—my right wing rests upon an eminence. Body of Mahomet! comrade, you look very like a dealer in tennis-balls, and yet you dare to take your seat by my side! I am a noble, my friend. Nobility and trade cannot keep company. Get you gone! Hollo there, you fellows! don't fall to fighting. What! Baptiste Croque-Oison, you who have so fine a nose, will you risk it against the heavy fists of yonder lout? Donkey! *non cuiquam datum est habere nasum.* You are indeed divine, Jacqueline Ronge-Oreille! 'Tis a pity you're so bald. Hollo! my name is Jehan Frollo, and my brother is an archdeacon. May the devil take him! Every word I say is true. When I turned vagabond, I cheerfully renounced the half of a house situated in paradise, which my brother promised me (*Dimidiam domum in paradiso*). I quote the Scriptures. I have an estate in fee in the Rue Tire-chappe, and all the women are in love with me as truly as it is true that Saint Aloysius was an excellent goldsmith, and that the five handicrafts of the good city of Paris are those of the tanners, leather-dressers, baldric-makers, purse-makers, and cordwainers, and that Saint Lawrence was broiled over egg-shells. I swear, comrades,—

'That for a year I'll drink no wine
If there be any lie in words
of mine!'

My charmer, it is moonlight; only look yonder, through that loop-hole; how the wind rumples the clouds,—as I do your tucker! Come, girls! snuff the children and the candles. Christ and Mahomet! what am I eating now, by Jupiter? Ho, there, you fagot! the hairs which are missing on the heads of your women, I find in your omelets. I say, old girl! I like my omelets bald. May the devil put your nose out of joint! A fine hostelry of Beelzebub this, where the wenches comb their heads with forks!"

So saying, he smashed his plate upon the paved floor, and fell to singing at the top of his lungs:—

"And for this self of mine,
Now by the Blood Divine!
No creed I crave,
No law to save.
I have no fire,
I have no hut;
And I require
No faith to put
In monarch high
Or Deity!"

Meantime, Clopin Trouillefou had finished his distribution of arms. He approached Gringoire, who seemed plunged in deep thought, with his feet upon an andiron.

"Friend Pierre," said the king of blacklegs, "what the deuce are you thinking about?"

Gringoire turned to him with a melancholy smile.

"I love the fire, my dear lord; not for the trivial reason that the fire warms our feet or cooks our soup, but because it throws out sparks. I sometimes spend hours in watching the sparks fly up. I discover a thousand things in these stars that sprinkle the black chimney-back. These stars are worlds as well."

"May I be struck by lightning if I understand you!" said the Vagrant. "Do you know what time it is?"

"I do not," replied Gringoire.

Clopin then went up to the Duke of Egypt:—

"Comrade Mathias, this is not a lucky moment for our scheme. They say that King Louis XI. is in Paris."

"So much the more reason for rescuing our sister from his claws," answered the old gipsy.

"You speak like a man, Mathias," said the King of Tunis. "Moreover, we will act adroitly. We need fear no resistance within the church. The canons are mere hares, and we muster strong. The officers of the Parliament will be nicely taken in to-morrow when they come to seize her! By the Pope's toe! I don't want the pretty maid hanged!"

With these words, Clopin left the tavern.

Meantime, Jehan shouted in hoarse tones,—

"I drink, I eat, I am drunk, I am Jupiter himself! Ha! Pierre l'Assommeur, if you stare at me like that, I'll dust your nose with a fillip or two!"

Gringoire, on his side, roused from his meditations, was contemplating the wild, noisy scene before him, muttering between his teeth: *"Luxuriosa res vinum et tumultuosa ebrietas.* Alas! I have good reasons for not drinking; and how aptly Saint Benedict says: *'Vinum apostatare facit etiam sapientes!'* "

At this instant Clopin returned, and cried in a voice of thunder,—

"Midnight!"

At this word, which had the effect of "Boot and saddle!" upon a regiment at rest, all the Vagrants, men, women, and children, rushed hurriedly from the tavern, with a great clatter of arms and old iron.

The moon was overcast.

The Court of Miracles was quite dark. There was not a light to be seen; and yet it was far from being empty. A crowd of men and women, talking together in low tones, had collected. There was an audible buzz of voices and a glitter of all sorts of weapons in the darkness. Clopin mounted a huge stone.

"To your ranks, Canters!" he cried. "To your ranks, Gipsies! To your ranks, Greeks!"

There was a stir in the gloom. The vast multitude seemed to be forming into line. After a brief pause the King of Tunis again raised his voice:—

"Now, silence as we pass through Paris! *'The chive in the cly'* is the password! The torches will not be lighted until we reach Notre-Dame! Forward, march!"

Ten minutes later the horsemen of the watch fled in terror before a long procession of dark, silent men descending upon the Pont au Change through the crooked streets which traverse the closely built region of the Markets in every direction.

CHAPTER IV

AN AWKWARD FRIEND

THAT same night Quasimodo did not sleep. He had just made his last round in the church. He did not notice, as he closed the doors, that the archdeacon passed, and seemed somewhat vexed at seeing him so carefully bolt and chain the immense iron bars which made the wide leaves as solid as a wall. Don Claude looked even more preoccupied than usual. Moreover, ever since his nocturnal adventure in the cell he had abused Quasimodo constantly; but though he maltreated him, nay, sometimes even beat him, nothing shook the submission, patience, and humble resignation of the faithful ringer. From the archdeacon he would bear anything and everything, — insults, threats, blows,—without murmuring a reproach, without uttering a complaint. At most he anxiously followed Don Claude with his eye, as he climbed the tower stairs; but the archdeacon had carefully abstained from appearing again in the gipsy's presence.

That night, then, Quasimodo, after giving a glance at his poor forsaken bells,—at Jacqueline, Marie, and Thibauld—had ascended to the roof of the north tower, and there, placing his well-closed dark-lantern upon the leads, gazed out over Paris. The night, as we have already said, was very dark. Paris, which at this time was but scantily lighted, presented to the eye a confused collection of black masses, intersected here and there by the silvery bend of the Seine. Quasimodo saw but a single light, and that in the window of a distant structure, the dim, dark outlines of which were distinctly visible above the roofs, in the direction of Porte Saint-Antoine. There, too, some one was watching.

While his one eye roamed over the expanse of mist and night, the ringer felt within him an inexplicable sense of alarm. For some days he had been upon his guard. He had constantly seen evil-looking men prowling about the church, and never taking their eyes from the young girl's hiding-place. He fancied that there might be some plot brewing against the unfortunate refugee. He imagined that she was a victim to popular hatred like himself, and that something might come of it soon. He therefore stationed himself upon his tower, on the alert, "dreaming in his dreamery," as Rabelais has it, his eye by turns bent upon the cell and upon Paris, keeping faithful watch, like a trusty dog, with a thousand doubts and fears.

All at once, while scrutinizing the great city with the one eye which Nature, by a sort of compensating justice, had made so piercing that it might almost supply the other organs which he lacked, it seemed to him that the outline of the Quai de la Vieille-Pelleterie looked somewhat peculiarly, that there was something moving at that point, that the line of the parapet darkly defined against the white water was not straight and steady like that of the other quays, but that it rippled, as he gazed, like the waves of a river or the heads of a moving multitude.

This struck him as singular. He redoubled his attention. The movement seemed to be towards the City. There was no light to be seen. It continued for some time, upon the quay; then it subsided gradually, as if whatever might be passing had entered the interior of the Island; then it ceased entirely, and the line of the quay became straight and motionless once more.

While Quasimodo was lost in conjectures, it seemed to him as if the movement had reappeared in the Rue du Parvis, which leads into the City directly opposite the front of Notre-Dame. At last, dense as was the darkness, he saw the head of a column emerge from that street, and in an instant fill the square with a crowd in which nothing could be distinguished in the shadows but that it was a crowd.

The spectacle had its terrors. It is probable that this strange procession, which seemed so desirous of stealing along unseen under cover of darkness, was equally careful to observe unbroken silence. And yet some noise appeared inevitable, were it only the tramp of feet. But this sound could not reach our deaf man's ear, and the vast host, so dimly seen, and wholly unheard by him, yet moving and marching onward so near him, produced upon him the effect of an army of ghosts, mute, impalpable, hidden in mists. He seemed to see a fog-bank full of men advancing upon him; to see shadows stirring amid the shades.

Then his fears revived; the idea of an attempt against the gipsy girl again presented itself to his mind. He had a confused sense that a violent scene was at hand. At this critical moment he held counsel with himself with better judgment and more promptness than could have been expected from so ill-organized a brain. Should he awaken the gipsy; help her to escape? Which way? The streets were invested; the church backed up against the river. There was no boat, no outlet! There was but one thing to be done,—to die if need be on the threshold of Notre-Dame; to resist at least until some help should come, if any there were, and not to disturb Esmeralda's sleep. The wretched girl would be wakened soon enough to die. This resolve once taken he began to scan the enemy with greater composure.

The crowd seemed to increase every moment in the square. He presumed that they must be making very little noise, as the windows in the streets and square remained closed. Suddenly a light shone out, and in an instant seven or eight blazing torches rose above the heads of the multitude, shaking out their tufts of flame in the darkness. Quasimodo then plainly saw an eddying, frightful mass of ragged men and women below him in the square, armed with scythes, pikes, bill-hooks, and halberds, whose myriad blades glistened on every hand. Here and there black pitchforks were reared horn-like above those hideous faces. He vaguely recalled this mob, and fancied he recognized the heads of those who had but a few months previous saluted him as Lord of Misrule. A man, grasping a torch in one hand and a whip in the other, climbed upon a post and seemed to be haranguing the crowd. At the same time the strange army went through a number of evolutions, as if taking up

their station about the church. Quasimodo picked up his lantern and descended to the platform between the towers, to get a nearer view and to consider means of defence.

Clopin Trouillefou, having arrived before the great door of Notre-Dame, had indeed drawn up his troops in line of battle. Although he did not expect to meet with any resistance, he desired, like a prudent general, to preserve such order as would enable him, if necessary, to confront a sudden attack from the watch. He had therefore stationed his brigade in such a way that, viewed from above and from a distance, you would have taken them for the Roman triangle of the battle of Ecnoma, the boar's head of Alexander, or the famous wedge of Gustavus Adolphus. The base of this triangle rested upon the farther end of the square, so that it blocked the Rue du Parvis; one side faced the Hôtel-Dieu, the other the Rue Saint-Pierre aux Bœufs. Clopin Trouillefou had placed himself at the head, with the Duke of Egypt, our friend Jehan, and the most daring of the dummy chuckers.

Such an attack as the vagrants were now planning to make upon Notre-Dame was no very uncommon thing in the towns of the Middle Ages. What are now known as police did not then exist. There was no central, controlling power in populous cities, or more particuarly in capitals. The feudal system constructed these large communities after a strange fashion. A city was a collection of a thousand seigniories, or manors, which divided it up into districts of all shapes and sizes. Hence arose a thousand contradictory police forces; that is, no police at all. In Paris, for instance, independently of the one hundred and forty-one nobles laying claim to manorial rights, there were twenty-five who also claimed the additional right to administer justice,—from the Bishop of Paris who owned one hundred and five streets, down to the Prior of Notre-Dame des Champs who owned but four. All these feudal justiciaries recognized the supreme power of the king only in name. All had right of way; all were on their own ground. Louis XI., that indefatigable labourer who did such good work in beginning the demolition of the feudal structure, carried on by Richelieu and Louis XIV. to the advantage of royalty, and completed by Mirabeau to the advantage of the people,—Louis XI. had indeed striven to break this network of seigniories which enveloped Paris, by hurling violently athwart it two or three police ordinances. Thus in 1465 the inhabitants were commanded to light their windows with candles at nightfall, and to shut up their dogs, under pain of the halter; during the same year an order was issued that the streets must be closed with iron chains after dark, and citizens were forbidden to wear daggers or any offensive weapons in the street at night. But all these attempts at municipal legislation soon fell into disuse. People let the wind blow out the candles in their windows, and allowed their dogs to roam; the iron chains were only put up in time of siege; the prohibition of daggers led to but little change. The old framework of feudal jurisdiction remained standing,—an immense number of bailiwicks and seigniories, crossing one another throughout the city, crowded, tangled, interlapping, and interwoven; a useless confusion of watches, sub-watches, and counter-watches, in spite of which brigandage, rapine, and sedition were carried on by main force. It was not, therefore, an unheard-of thing, in the midst of such disorder, for a part of the populace to make a bold attack upon a palace, a great mansion, or a house, in the most thickly settled quarters of the town. In the majority of cases the neighbours did not meddle with the matter, unless the pillage extended to their own houses. They turned a deaf ear to the musketry, closed their shutters, barricaded their doors, left the outbreak to be settled with or without the watch, and next day it would be reported: "Last night Etienne Barbette's house was entered." "Marshal Clermont was carried off," etc. Accordingly, not only royal habitations, the Louvre, the Palace, the Bastille, the Tournelles, but the houses of the nobility, the Petit-Bourbon, the Sens mansion, the D'Angoulême mansion, etc., had their battlemented walls and their portcullises. Churches were guarded by their sanctity. Certain of them, however, but not Notre-Dame, were fortified. The abbot of Saint-Germain des Prés was as strongly intrenched as any baron, and more brass was consumed there in bombards than in bells. His fortress was still standing in 1610. Now the church alone exists, and that in ruins.

Let us return to Notre-Dame.

When the first arrangements had been made (and we must say, to the honour of the discipline of the Vagrants, that Clopin's orders were carried out in silence and with admirable precision), the worthy leader of the band mounted the parapet of the Parvis, and raised his hoarse, surly voice, keeping his face turned towards Notre-Dame, and waving his torch, the flame of which, flickering in the wind, and now and again veiled by its own smoke, first revealed and then hid the front of the church, lit up with a reddish glow.

"To you, Louis de Beaumont, Bishop of Paris, Councillor of the Court of Parliament, I, Clopin Trouillefou, king of blacklegs, king of rogues, prince of cant, and bishop of fools, proclaim: Our sister, falsely condemned for magic, has taken refuge in your church. You owe her shelter and safeguard. Now, the Parliamentary Court desire to recover her person, and you have given your consent; so that indeed she would be hanged to-morrow on the Grève were not God and the Vagrants here to aid her. We have therefore come hither to you, O Bishop. If your church be sacred, our sister is likewise sacred; if our sister be not sacred, neither is your church. Wherefore we summon you to deliver over to us the girl if you would save your church, or we will seize upon the girl, and will plunder the church, which will be a righteous deed. In token whereof I here plant my banner; and may God have you in his guard, O Bishop of Paris!"

Unfortunately Quasimodo could not hear these words, uttered as they were with a sort of sombre, savage majesty. A Vagrant handed the banner to Clopin, who planted it solemnly between two flagstones. It was a pitchfork, from whose prongs hung a bleeding mass of carrion.

This done, the King of Tunis turned and glanced at his army,—a fierce host, whose eyes glittered almost as brightly as their pikes. After an instant's pause he cried,—

"Forward, boys! To your work, rebels!"

Thirty stout fellows, with sturdy limbs and crafty faces, stepped from the ranks with hammers, pincers, and crowbars on their shoulders. They advanced towards the main entrance of the church, mounted the steps, and were soon crouching beneath the arch, working away at the door with pincers and levers. A crowd of Vagrants followed them to help or encourage. They thronged the eleven steps leading to the porch.

Still the door refused to yield. "The devil! how tough and obstinate it is!" said one. "It is old, and its joints are stiff," said another. "Courage, comrades!" replied Clopin. "I'll wager my head against an old slipper that you'll have opened the door, captured the girl, and stripped the high-altar before a single sacristan is awake. Stay! I think the lock is giving way."

Clopin was interrupted by a tremendous din behind him. He turned. A huge beam had fallen from the sky; it had crushed a dozen of his Vagrants on the church steps and rebounded to the pavement with the crash of a cannon, breaking the legs of various tatterdemalions here and there in the crowd, which scattered with cries of terror. In the twinkling of an eye the enclosed portion of the square was cleared. The rebels, although protected by the deep arches of the porch, forsook the door, and Clopin himself retired to a respectful distance.

"I had a narrow escape!" cried Jehan. "I felt the wind of it as it passed, by Jove! but Pierre l'Assommeur is knocked down!"

It is impossible to picture the mingled consternation and affright which overcame the bandits with the fall of this beam. They stood for some moments staring into the air, more dismayed by that fragment of wood than by twenty thousand of the king's archers.

"Satan!" growled the Duke of Egypt; "that smells of sorcery!"

"It must be the moon which flung that log at us," said Andry le Rouge.

"Why," replied François Chanteprune, "they say the moon is a friend of the Virgin Mary!"

"By the Pope's head!" exclaimed Clopin; "but you are a parcel of fools!" And yet even he could not explain the fall of the plank.

Meanwhile, nothing was to be seen upon the front of the cathedral, to the top of which the light of the torches did not reach. The heavy plank lay in the middle of the square, and loud were the groans of the wretched men who had received its first shock, and who had been almost cut in two upon the sharp edges of the stone steps.

The King of Tunis, his first dismay over, at last hit upon an explanation which seemed plausible to his companions:—

"Odds bodikins! are the canons defending themselves? Then, sack! sack!"

"Sack!" repeated the rabble, with a frantic cheer. And they discharged a volley of cross-bows and hackbuts at the church.

At this sound the peaceable inhabitants of the houses round about were awakened; several windows were thrown open, and nightcaps and hands holding candles appeared at them.

"Fire at the windows!" roared Clopin. The windows were hastily closed, and the poor citizens, who had barely had time to cast a terrified glance at that scene of glare and tumult, returned to sweat with fear beside their wives, wondering if the witches were holding their revels in the square before Notre-Dame, or if the Burgundians had made another attack, as in '64. Then the husbands thought of robbery, the wives of violence, and all trembled.

"Sack!" repeated the Canters; but they dared not advance. They looked at the church; they looked at the beam. The beam did not bulge, the building retained its calm, deserted look; but something rooted the Vagrants to the spot.

"To work, I say, rebels!" shouted Trouillefou. "Force the door!!"

No one stirred.

"Body o' me!" said Clopin; "here's a pack of fellows who are afraid of a rafter."

"Captain, it's not the rafter that stops us; it's the door, which is entirely covered with iron bars. Our pincers are of no use."

"Well, what would you have to burst it in?" asked Clopin.

"Ah! we need a battering-ram."

The King of Tunis ran bravely up to the much-dreaded beam, and set his foot upon it. "Here you have one," he exclaimed; "the canons themselves have sent it to you." And with a mocking salutation in the direction of the church, he added, "Thanks, gentlemen!"

This piece of bravado proved effective; the charm of the beam was broken. The Vagrants recovered their courage; soon the heavy log, lifted like a feather by two hundred sturdy arms, was furiously hurled against the great door which they had vainly striven to shake. Seen thus, in the dim light cast by the scanty torches of the Vagrants, that long beam borne by that crowd of men, who rapidly dashed it against the church, looked like some monstrous beast with countless legs attacking the stone giantess headforemost.

At the shock of the log, the semimetallic door rang like a vast drum; it did not yield, but the whole cathedral shook and the deep vaults of the building re-echoed.

At the same moment a shower of large stones began to rain from the top of the façade upon the assailants.

"The devil!" cried Jehan; "are the towers shaking down their balustrades upon our heads?"

But the impulse had been given, the King of Tunis setting the example. The bishop was certainly defending himself; and so they only beat against the door with greater fury, despite the stones which cracked their skulls to right and left.

It is remarkable that these stones all fell singly, but they followed one another in rapid succession. The Canters always felt two at a time,—one at their legs, the other on their heads. Few of them missed their mark, and already a large heap of dead and wounded gasped and bled under the feet of the besiegers, whose ranks, they being now goaded to madness, were constantly renewed. The long beam still battered the door at regular intervals, like the clapper of a bell; the stones still rained down, and the door creaked and groaned.

The reader has doubtless guessed that the unexpected resistance which so enraged the Vagrants came from Quasimodo.

Chance had unluckily served the brave deaf man.

When he descended to the platform between the towers, his head whirled in confusion. For some moments he ran along the gallery, coming and going like a madman, looking down from above at the compact mass of Vagrants ready to rush upon the church, imporing God or the devil to save the gipsy girl. He thought of climbing the south belfry and ringing the alarm; but before he could set the bell in motion, before big Marie's voice could utter a single shriek, the church door might be forced ten times over. This was just the instant when the rebels advanced with their tools. What was to be done?

All at once he remembered that the masons had been at work all day repairing the wall, timbers, and roof of the south tower. This was a ray of light. The wall was of stone, the roof of lead, and the timbers of wood. (The timbers were so huge, and there were so many of them, that they went by the name of "the forest.")

Quasimodo flew to the tower. The lower rooms were indeed full of materials. There were piles of rough stones, sheets of lead in rolls, bundles of laths, heavy beams already shaped by the saw, heaps of plaster and rubbish,—a complete arsenal.

There was no time to be lost. The hammers and levers were at work below. With a strength increased tenfold by his sense of danger, he lifted one of the beams, the heaviest and longest that he could find; he shoved it through a dormer-window, then laying hold of it again outside the tower, he pushed it over the edge of the balustrade surrounding the platform, and launched it into the abyss. The enormous rafter, in its fall of one hundred and sixty feet, scraping the wall, smashing the carvings, turned over and over several times like one of the arms of a windmill moving through space. At last it reached the ground; an awful shriek rose upon the air, and the black beam, rebounding from the pavement, looked like a serpent darting on its prey.

Quasimodo saw the Vagrants scatter, as the log fell, like ashes before the breath of a child. He took advantage of their terror; and while they stared superstitiously at the club dropped from heaven, and put out the eyes of the stone saints over the porch with a volley of arrows and buckshot, Quasimodo silently collected plaster, stones, gravel, even the masons' bags of tools, upon the edge of that balustrade from which the beam had already been launched.

Thus, as soon as they began to batter at the door, the hail of stones began to fall, and it seemed to them as if the church were falling about their heads.

Any one who had seen Quasimodo at that moment would have been frightened. Besides the projectiles which he had piled upon the balustrade, he had collected a heap of stones on the platform itself. As soon as the missiles at the edge of the railing were exhausted, he had recourse to the heap below. He stooped and rose, stooped and rose again, with incredible activity. His great gnome-like head hung over the balustrade, then a huge stone fell, then another, and another. Now and again he followed a particularly fine stone with his eye, and if it did good execution he said, "Hum!"

Meantime the ragamuffins were not discouraged. More than twenty times already the heavy door which they were attacking had trembled beneath the weight of their oaken battering-ram, multiplied by the strength of a hundred men. The panels cracked; the carvings flew in splinters; the hinges, at every blow, shook upon their screw-rings; the boards were reduced to powder, crushed between the iron braces. Luckily for Quasimodo, there was more iron than wood.

Still, he felt that the great door was yielding. Although he could not hear, every stroke of the beam echoed at once through the vaults of the church and through his soul. He saw from above the Vagrants, full of rage and triumph, shaking their fists at the shadowy façade; and he coveted, for himself and for the gipsy girl, the wings of the owls which flew over his head in numbers.

His shower of stones did not suffice to repel the enemy.

At this moment of anguish he observed, a little below the balustrade from which he was crushing the Canters, two long stone gutters, or spouts, which emptied directly over the great door. The inner orifice of these spouts opened upon a level with the platform. An idea flashed into his mind. He ran to the hovel which he occupied as ringer, found a fagot, placed upon this fagot a quantity of bundles of laths and rolls of lead,—ammunition which he had not yet used,—and having carefully laid this pile before the mouth of the two spouts, he set fire to it with his lantern.

During this space of time, the stones having ceased to fall, the Vagrants had also ceased to look up. The bandits, panting like a pack of dogs which have hunted a wild boar to his lair, crowded tumultuously about the door, disfigured by the battering-ram, but still holding firm. They awaited, with a shudder of eagerness, the final blow which should shiver it. Each one strove to be nearest to it, that he might be first, when it opened, to rush into that wealthy cathedral, the vast magazine in which were stored all the riches of three centuries. They reminded each other, with roars of joy and greed, of the beautiful silver crosses, the gorgeous brocade copes, the superb monuments of silver-gilt, the magnificences of the choir, the dazzling holiday displays, the Christmas ceremonies glittering with torches, the Easters brilliant with sunshine,—all the splendid and solemn occasions when shrines, candlesticks, pyxes, tabernacles, and reliquaries embossed the altars with incrusted gold and diamonds. Certainly at this auspicious moment gonnofs and arch-thieves, ruffians and sham Abrams thought far less of freeing the gipsy girl than they did of sacking Notre-Dame. We would even be willing to believe that to a goodly number of them Esmeralda was but a mere pretext,—if thieves require a pretext.

All at once, just as they gathered together about the battering-ram for a final effort, every man holding his breath and straining his muscles so as to lend all his strength to the decisive blow, a howl more frightful even than that which had risen and died away from beneath the rafter, again burst from their midst. Those who did not shriek, those who lived, looked up. Two streams of molten lead fell from the top of the building into the very thickest of the throng. The sea of men had subsided beneath the boiling metal which had made, at the points where it fell, two black and smoking holes in the crowd, as boiling water would in snow. About them writhed the dying, half consumed, and shrieking with agony. Around the two principal jets there were drops of this horrible rain which sprinkled the assailants, and penetrated their skulls like gimlets of flame. A leaden fire riddled the poor wretches as with countless hailstones.

The clamour was heartrending. They fled pell-mell, flinging the beam upon the corpses, the courageous with the timid, and the square was cleared for the second time.

All eyes were turned to the top of the church. What they saw was most strange. Upon the top of the topmost gallery, higher than the central rose-window, a vast flame ascended between the two belfries with whirling sparks,—a vast flame, fierce and strong, fragments of which were ever and anon borne away by the wind with the smoke. Below this flame, below the dark balustrade with its glowing trefoils, two spouts, terminating in gargoyles, vomiting unintermittent sheets of fiery rain, whose silvery streams shone out distinctly against the gloom of the lower part of the cathedral front. As they approached the ground, these jets of liquid lead spread out into sheaves, like water pouring from the countless holes of the rose in a watering-pot. Above the flame, the huge towers, each of which showed two sides, clear and trenchant, one all black, the other all red, seemed even larger than they were, from the immensity of the shadow which they cast, reaching to the very sky. Their innumerable carvings of demons and dragons assumed a mournful aspect. The restless light of the flames made them seem to move. There were serpents, which seemed to be laughing, gargoyles yelping, salamanders blowing the fire, dragons sneezing amid the smoke. And among these monsters, thus wakened from their stony slumbers by the flame, by the noise, there was one that walked about, and moved from time to time across the fiery front of the burning pile like a bat before a candle.

Doubtless this strange beacon would rouse from afar the woodcutter on the hills of Bicêtre, in alarm at seeing the gigantic shadow of the towers of Notre-Dame cast flickering upon his moors.

The silence of terror fell upon the Vagrants, and while it lasted nothing was heard save the cries of consternation uttered by the canons shut up in the cloisters, and more restive than horses in a burning stable, the stealthy sound of windows hastily opened and more hastily closed, the bustle and stir in the Hospital, the wind roaring

through the flames, the last gasp of the dying, and the constant pattering of the leaden rain upon the pavement.

Meantime, the leaders of the Vagrants had withdrawn to the porch of the Gondelaurier house, and were holding council. The Duke of Egypt, seated on a post, gazed with religious awe at the magical pile blazing in the air at the height of two hundred feet. Clopin Trouillefou gnawed his brawny fists with rage.

"Impossible to enter!" he muttered between his teeth.

"An old witch of a church!" growled the aged gipsy Mathias Hungadi Spicali.

"By the Pope's whiskers!" added a grey-haired old scamp who had served his time in the army, "here are church-spouts that beat the portcullis of Lectoure at spitting molten lead."

"Do see that demon walking to and fro before the fire!" exclaimed the Duke of Egypt.

"By the Rood!" said Clopin, "it's that damned bell-ringer; it's Quasimodo!"

The gipsy shook his head. "I tell you that it is the spirit Sabnac, the great marquis, the demon of fortifications. He takes the form of an armed soldier, with a lion's head. He turns men to stones, with which he builds towers. He commands fifty legions. It is surely he; I recognize him. Sometimes he is clad in a fine gown of figured gold made in the Turkish fashion."

"Where is Bellevigne de l'Etoile?" asked Clopin.

"He is dead," replied a Vagrant woman.

Andry le Rouge laughed a foolish

laugh. "Notre-Dame makes plenty of work for the hospital," said he.

"Is there no way to force that door?" cried the King of Tunis, stamping his foot.

The Duke of Egypt pointed sadly to the two streams of boiling lead which still streaked the dark façade like two long phosphorescent spindles.

"Churches have been known to defend themselves before," he observed with a sigh. "St. Sophia, at Constantinople, some forty years ago, thrice threw down the crescent of Mahomet merely by shaking her domes, which are her heads. Guillaume de Paris, who built this church, was a magician."

"Must we then go home discomfited like a pack of wretched lackeys?" said Clopin, "and leave our sister here, to be hanged by those cowled wolves to-morrow!"

"And the sacristy, where there are cartloads of gold?" added a Vagabond whose name we regret that we do not know.

"By Mahomet's beard!" cried Trouillefou.

"Let us make one more trial," added the Vagabond.

Mathias Hungadi shook his head. "We shall not enter by the door. We must find the weak spot in the old witch's armour,—a hole, a back gate, any joint."

"Who'll join us?" said Clopin. "I shall have another try. By the way, where is that little student Jehan, who put on such a coat of mail?"

"He is probably dead," answered some one; "we don't hear his laugh."

The King of Tunis frowned: "So much the worse. There was a stout

heart beneath that steel. And Master Pierre Gringoire?"

"Captain Clopin," said Andry le Rouge, "he took to his heels when we had only come as far as the Pont-aux-Changeurs."

Clopin stamped his foot. "By the Mass! he urges us on, and then leaves us in the lurch! A cowardly prater, helmeted with a slipper!"

"Captain Clopin," said Andry le Rouge, who was looking down the Rue du Parvis, "there comes the little student."

"Pluto be praised!" said Clopin. "But what the devil is he lugging after him?"

It was indeed Jehan, running as fast as was possible under the weight of his heavy armour and a long ladder which he dragged sturdily over the pavement, more breathless than an ant harnessed to a blade of grass twenty times its own length.

"Victory! *Te Deum!*" shouted the student. "Here's the ladder belonging to the longshoremen of St. Landry's wharf."

Clopin approached him:—

"Zounds, child! what are you going to do with that ladder?"

"I've got it," replied Jehan, panting and gasping. "I knew where it was,—under the shed at the lieutenant's house. There's a girl there who knows me, who thinks me a perfect Cupid. I took advantage of her folly to get the ladder, and I have the ladder, odds bodikins! The poor girl came down in her shift to let me in."

"Yes," said Clopin; "but what will you do with the ladder now that you have got it?"

Jehan looked at him with a mischievous, cunning air, and cracked his fingers like so many castanets. At that moment he was sublime. He had on his head one of those enormous fifteenth-century helmets, which terrified the foe by their fantastic crests. It bristled with ten iron beaks, so that he might have disputed the tremendous cognomen of δεϰέμϐολος, with Nestor's Homeric vessel.

"What shall I do with it, august King of Tunis? Do you see that row of statues with their foolish faces yonder, above the three porches?"

"Yes; what then?"

"That is the gallery of the kings of France."

"What is that to me?" said Clopin.

"Wait a bit! At the end of that gallery there is a door which is always on the latch, and with this ladder I will climb to it, and then I am in the church."

"Let me go up first, boy!"

"Not a bit of it, comrade; the ladder is mine. Come, you may be second."

"May Beelzebub strangle you!" said the surly Clopin. "I'll not be second to any man."

"Then, Clopin, seek a ladder for yourself;" and Jehan set out at full speed across the square, dragging his ladder after him, shouting,—

"Help, lads, help!"

In an instant the ladder was lifted, and placed against the railing of the lower gallery, over one of the side doors. The crowd of Vagrants, uttering loud cheers, thronged to the foot of it, eager to ascend; but Jehan maintained his right, and was first to set foot upon the rounds. The journey was long and slow. The gallery of the kings of France is now some sixty feet above the pavement. The eleven steps leading to the door made it still higher at the time of our story. Jehan climbed slowly, hampered by his heavy armour, clinging to the ladder with one hand and his cross-bow with the other. When he reached the middle, he cast a melancholy glance downwards at the poor dead Canters who bestrewed the steps.

"Alas!" said he, "there's a heap of corpses worthy of the fifth book of the Iliad!" Then he resumed his ascent. The Vagrants followed him; there was one upon every round. As this undulating line of cuirassed backs rose through the darkness, it looked like a serpent with scales of steel rearing its length along the church. Jehan, who represented the head, whistled shrilly, thus completing the illusion.

At last the student touched the balcony, and nimbly strode over it, amid the applause of the assembled Vagrants. Thus master of the citadel, he uttered a shout of joy, and all at once paused, petrified. He had seen behind one of the royal statues Quasimodo and his glittering eye lurking in the shadow

Before a second assailant could set foot upon the gallery, the terrible hunchback leaped to the top of the ladder, seized, without a word, the ends of the two uprights in his strong hands, raised them, pushed them from the wall, balancing for a moment, amid screams of agony, the long, pliant ladder loaded with Vagrants from top to bottom, and then suddenly, with superhuman force, hurled the clustering mass of men into the square. There was an instant when the boldest trembled. The ladder plunged backward, for a moment stood erect, and seemed to hesitate, then tottered, then all at once, describing a frightful arc of eighty feet in radius, fell headlong on the pavement with its burden of bandits, more swiftly than a drawbridge when the chains which hold it are broken. There was an awful volley of curses, then all was hushed, and a few mutilated wretches crawled away from under the heap of dead.

A clamour of rage and pain followed the first cries of triumph among the besiegers. Quasimodo looked on unmoved, leaning upon the balustrade. He seemed like some long-haired old king at his window.

Jehan Frollo, for his part, was in a critical situation. He was alone in the gallery with the dreadful ringer, parted from his companions by a perpendicular wall eighty feet high. While Quasimodo juggled with the ladder, the student hurried to the postern, which he supposed would be open. Not at all. The deaf man, on entering the gallery had fastened it behind him. Jehan then hid himself behind a stone king, not daring to breathe, and eyeing the monstrous hunchback with terror, like the man who, making love to the wife of the keeper of a menagerie, went one night to see her by appointment, climbed the wrong wall, and abruptly found himself face to face with a white bear.

For a few moments the deaf man paid no heed to him; but finally he turned his head and started. He had just seen the student.

Jehan prepared for a rude encounter; but the deaf man stood motionless: he had merely turned, and was looking at the youth.

"Ho! ho," said Jehan, "why do you fix that single melancholy eye so steadfastly upon me?"

As he said this, the young scamp slyly adjusted his cross-bow.

"Quasimodo," he cried, "I am going to change your name! Henceforth you shall be called 'the blind!'"

The arrow flew. The winged bolt whizzed through the air, and was driven into the hunchback's left arm. It disturbed Quasimodo no more than a scratch would have done the statue of King Pharamond. He put his hand to the dart, pulled it forth, and quietly broke it across his great knee; then he let the two pieces fall to the ground rather than threw them down. But Jehan had no time to fire a second shot. The arrow broken, Quasimodo drew a long breath, leaped like a grasshopper, and came down upon the student, whose armour was flattened against the wall by the shock.

Then by the dim light of the torches a terrible thing might have been seen.

Quasimodo with his left hand grasped both Jehan's arms, the poor fellow making no resistance, so hopeless did he feel that it would be. With his right hand the deaf man removed from him one after the other, in silence and with ominous slowness, all the pieces of his armour,—the sword, the daggers, the helmet, the cuirass, and the brassarts. He looked like a monkey picking a nut as he dropped the student's iron shell, bit by bit, at his feet.

When the youth found himself stripped, disarmed, naked, and helpless in those terrible hands, he did not try to speak to that deaf man, but he laughed impudently in his face, and sang, with the bold unconcern of a lad of sixteen, the song then popular:—

"She's clad in bright array,
The city of Cambray.
Marafin plundered her one day—"

He did not finish. They saw Quasimodo upright on the parapet, holding the boy by the feet with one hand, and swinging him round like a sling over the abyss; then a sound was heard like a box made of bone dashed against a wall, and something fell, but caught a third of the way down upon a projection. It was a dead body which hung there, bent double, the back broken, the skull empty.

A cry of horror rose from the Vagrants.

"Vengeance!" yelled Clopin. "Sack!" replied the multitude. "Assault! assault!"

Then there was an awful howl, intermingled with all languages, all dialects, and all accents. The poor student's death filled the mob with zealous fury. Shame gained the upper hand, and wrath that they had so long been held in check before a church by a hunchback. Rage found ladders, multiplied torches, and in a few moments Quasimodo, in despair, beheld that fearful swarm mounting on all sides to attack Notre-Dame. Those who had no ladders had knotted ropes; those who had no ropes scrambled up by the jutting sculptures. They clung to one another's rags. There was no way to resist this rising tide of awful figures; fury gleamed from their fierce faces; their grimy foreheads streamed with perspiration; their eyes gleamed; all these grimaces, all these deformities beset Quasimodo. It seemed as if some other church had sent its gorgons, its mediæval animals, its dragons, its demons, and its most fantastic carvings, to lay siege to Notre-Dame. A stratum of living monsters seemed to cover the stone monsters of the cathedral front.

Meantime, the square was starred with a thousand torches. The scene of confusion, hitherto lost in darkness, was suddenly ablaze with light. The square shone resplendent, and cast a red glow upon the heavens; the bonfire kindled upon the high platform still burned, and lighted up the city in the distance. The huge silhouette of the two towers, outlined afar upon the housetops of Paris, formed a vast patch of shadow amid the radiance. The city seemed to be aroused. Distant alarm-bells sounded. The Vagrants howled, panted, swore, climbed higher and higher; and Quasimodo, powerless against so many foes, shuddering for the gipsy girl, seeing those furious faces approach nearer and nearer to his gallery, implored Heaven to grant a miracle, and wrung his hands in despair.

Chapter V

THE RETREAT WHERE LOUIS OF FRANCE SAYS HIS PRAYERS

THE reader may remember that a moment before he caught sight of the nocturnal band of Vagrants, Quasimodo, while inspecting Paris from the top of his belfry, saw but one light still burning, and that gleamed from a window in the highest story of a tall dark structure close beside the Porte Saint-Antoine. This building was the Bastille;

that starry light was the candle of Louis XI.

King Louis XI. had actually been in Paris for two days. He was to set out again two days later for his fortress of Montilz-les-Tours. His visits to his good city of Paris were rare and brief; for he never felt that he had enough trap-doors, gibbets, and Scotch archers about him there.

He had that day come to sleep at the Bastille. The great chamber, five fathoms square, which he had at the Louvre, with its huge chimney-piece adorned with twelve great beasts and thirteen great prophets, and his great bed eleven feet by twelve, suited him but ill. He was lost amid all these grandeurs. This good, homely king preferred the Bastille, with a tiny chamber and a simple bed. And then, the Bastille was stronger than the Louvre.

This tiny room, which the king reserved to his own use in the famous state-prison, was spacious enough, after all, and occupied the topmost floor of a turret adjoining the keep. It was a circular chamber, carpeted with mats of lustrous straw, ceiled with beams enriched with *fleurs-de-lis* of gilded metal, with coloured interjoists wainscotted with rich woods studded with rosettes of white metal painted a fine bright green, compounded of orpiment and wood.

There was but one window,—a long arched opening latticed with brass wire and iron bars, and still further darkened by beautiful stained glass emblazoned with the arms of the king and queen, each pane of which was worth twenty-two pence.

There was but one entrance,—a modern door, with surbased arch, hung with tapestry on the inside, and on the outside decorated with a porch of bog-wood, a frail structure of curiously wrought cabinet-work, such as was very common in old houses some hundred and fifty years ago. "Although they are disfiguring and cumbersome," says Sauval, in despair, "still, our old folk will not do away with them, and retain them in spite of everything."

The room contained none of the furniture ordinarily found in such an apartment,—neither b e n c h e s, nor trestles, nor common box stools, nor more elegant stools mounted on posts and counter-posts, at four pence each. There was only one chair,—a folding-chair with arms,—and a very superb one it was: the wood was painted with roses on a red ground, the seat was of scarlet Spanish leather, trimmed with heavy silk fringe and studded with countless golden nails. The solitary chair showed that but one person had a right to be seated in that room. Besides the chair, and very near the window there was a table covered with a cloth embroidered with figures of birds.

Upon this table were a standish spotted with ink, sundry parchments, a few pens, and a chased silver goblet. Farther away stood a stove, and a prayer-desk of crimson velvet embossed with gold. Lastly, at the back of the room there was a simple bed of yellow and carnation-coloured damask, without tinsel or lace,—merely a plain fringe. This bed, famous for having borne the sleep,—or sleeplessness,—of Louis XI., might still be seen two hundred years ago, at the house of a councillor of state, where it was viewed by old Madame Pilou, celebrated in "Cyrus," under the name of "Arricidia" and of "Morality Embodied."

Such was the room known as "the retreat where Louis of France says his prayers."

At the moment when we introduce our reader to it, this retreat was very dark. The curfew had rung an hour before; it was night, and there was but one flickering wax candle placed on the table to light five persons grouped about the room.

The first upon whom the direct rays of the candle fell was a nobleman, magnificently dressed in scarlet breeches and jerkin striped with silver, and a loose coat with padded shoulders, made of cloth of gold brocaded in black. This splendid costume, upon which the light played, seemed to be frosted with flame at every fold. The man who wore it had his armorial bearings embroidered on his breast in gay colours, —a chevron with a deer passant at the base of the shield. The escutcheon was supported by an olive-branch dexter and a buck's horn sinister. This man wore at his belt a rich dagger, the silver-gilt handle of which was wrought in the shape of a crest, and surmounted by a count's coronet. He had an evil expression, a haughty mien, and a proud bearing. At the first glance his face revealed arrogance, at the second craft.

He stood bare-headed, a long scroll in his hand, behind the arm-chair in which sat, his body awkwardly bent, his knees crossed, his elbow on the table, a most ill-attired person. Imagine, indeed, upon the luxurious Spanish leather seat, a pair of knock knees, a couple of slender shanks meagrely arrayed in black woollen knitted stuff, a body wrapped in a fustian coat edged with fur, which had far more skin than hair; finally, to crown the whole, a greasy old hat, of the poorest quality of black cloth, stuck round with a circlet of small leaden images. This, with a dirty skull-cap, which showed scarce a single hair, was all that could be seen of the seated personage. His head was bent so low upon his breast that nothing could be distinguished of his face, which was wholly in shadow, unless it might be the tip of his nose, upon which a ray of light fell, and which was clearly a long one. By the thinness of his wrinkled hand, he was evidently an old man. This was Louis XI.

Some distance behind them, two men clad in Flemish fashion chatted together in low tones. They were not so entirely in the shadow but that any one who had been present at the performance of Gringoire's play could recognize them as two of the chief Flemish envoys, Guillaume Rym, the wise pensionary of Ghent, and Jacques Coppenole, the popular hosier. It will be remembered that these two men were connected with Louis XI.'s secret policy.

Lastly, at the farther end of the room, near the door, stood in the gloom, motionless as a statue, a sturdy man with thickset limbs, in military trappings, his doublet embroidered with armorial bearings, whose square face, with its goggle eyes, immense mouth, and ears hidden under two broad penthouses of straight, lank hair, partook at once of the character of the dog and the tiger.

All were uncovered save the king.

The gentleman nearest to the king was reading a lengthy document, to which his Majesty seemed listening most attentively. The two Flemings whispered together.

"Zounds!" grumbled Coppenole, "I am weary with standing; is there no chair here?"

Rym replied by a shake of the head, accompanied by a prudent smile.

"Zounds!" resumed Coppenole, utterly miserable at being obliged to lower his voice; "I long to sit down on the floor, with my legs crossed, in true hosier style, as I do in my own shop at home."

"Beware how you do so, Master Jacques."

"Bless me! Master Guillaume! must we be on our feet forever here?"

"Or on our knees," said Rym.

At this moment the king spoke. They were silent.

"Fifty pence for the coats of our lackeys, and twelve pounds for the cloaks of the clerks of our crown. That's it! pour out gold by the ton! Are you mad, Olivier?"

So saying, the old man lifted his head. The golden shells of the collar of Saint Michel glistened about his neck. The light of the candle fell full upon his thin, peevish profile. He snatched the paper from his companion's hands.

"You will ruin us!" he cried, running his hollow eye over the scroll. "What is all this? What need have we for so vast an establishment? Two chaplains at ten pounds a month each, and an assistant at one hundred pence! A valet at ninety pounds a year! Four head cooks at six-score pounds a year each; a roaster, a soup-maker, a sauce-maker,

an under cook, a keeper of the stores, two stewards' assistants, at ten pounds a month each! Two scullions at eight pounds! A groom and his two helpers at twenty-four pounds a month! A porter, a pastry-cook, a baker, two wagoners, each sixty pounds a year! And the farrier, six-score pounds! And the master of our exchequer chamber, twelve hundred pounds! And the comptroller five hundred! And I know not how many more! 'Tis sheer madness! Our servants' wages plunder France! All the treasures of the Louvre will melt away before such a wasting fire of expense! We will sell our plate! And next year, if God and Our Lady [here he raised his hat] grant us life, we will take our diet-drinks from a pewter pot!"

With these words he cast a glance at the silver goblet which sparkled on the table. He coughed, and continued,—

"Master Olivier, princes who reign over great domains, such as kings and emperors, should never suffer extravagant living in their houses; for thence the fire spreads to the provinces. Therefore, Master Olivier, forget this not. Our expenses increase yearly. The thing displeases us. What, by the Rood! until '79 they never exceeded thirty-six thousand pounds; in '80 they amounted to forty-three thousand six hundred and nineteen pounds,—I have the figures in my head; in '81 they were sixty-six thousand six hundred and eighty pounds; and this year, by my faith! they will come to eighty thousand pounds! Doubled in four years! monstrous!"

He paused for lack of breath; then he went on angrily,—

"I see around me none but people

fattening on my leanness! You suck crowns from me at every pore!"

All were silent. His rage must be allowed free vent. He continued:—

"It is like that petition in Latin from the nobles of France, that we would re-establish what they call the charges on the crown! Charges, indeed! crushing charges! Ah, gentlemen! you say that we are not a king to reign *dapifero nullo, buticulario nullo!* We will show you, by the Rood! whether we be a king or no!"

Here he smiled with a sense of his power; his bad humour moderated, and he turned towards the Flemings:

"Mark you, gossip Guillaume, the head pantler, the chief cellarer, the lord chamberlain, the lord seneschal, are not worth so much as the meanest lackey; remember that, gossip Coppenole. They are good for nothing. As they thus hang uselessly around the king, they remind me of the four Evangelists about the dial of the great clock on the Palace, which Philippe Brille has just done up as good as new. They are gilded over, but they do not mark the hour, and the hands go on as well without them."

For a moment he seemed lost in thought, and added, shaking his aged head:—

"Ho! ho! by Notre-Dame, I am no Philippe Brille, and I will not re-gild my lordly vassals! Go on, Olivier!"

The person thus addressed took the scroll from his royal master's hands, and began to read again in a loud voice:—

"To Adam Tenon, clerk to the keeper of the seals of the provosty of Paris, for the silver, fashioning, and engrav-ing of said seals, which have been new made by reason of the others preceding being old and worn out, and no longer fit for use, twelve Paris pounds.

"To Guillaume Frère, the sum of four pounds four Paris pence for his labour and cost in nourishing and feeding the pigeons in the two dovecots of the Hôtel des Tournelles, for the months of January, February, and March of this present year; for the which he hath expended seven sextaries of barley.

"To a Grey Friar, for confessing a criminal, four Paris pence."

The king listened in silence. From time to time he coughed; then he raised the goblet to his lips, and swallowed a mouthful with a wry face.

"In this year have been made by order of the courts and by sound of trumpet, in the public places of Paris, fifty-six proclamations; the account yet to be made up.

"For quest and search in sundry places, both in Paris and elsewhere, for funds said to be concealed there, but nothing found, forty-five Paris pounds."

"A crown buried to unearth a penny!" said the king.

"For setting six panes of white glass at the Hôtel des Tournelles, in the place where the iron cage is, thirteen pence; for making and delivering, by the king's command, on muster-day, four escutcheons with the arms of our said lord wreathed all around with roses, six pounds; for two new sleeves to the king's old doublet, twenty pence; for a box of grease to grease the king's boots, fifteen farthings; for rebuilding a sty to lodge the king's black swine, thirty Paris pounds; sundry partitions, planks, and gratings made for the safe-keeping of the lions at the Hôtel Saint-Pol, twenty pounds."

"Here be costly beasts," said Louis XI. "Never mind, 't is a luxury which befits a king. There is one big tawny lion that I love for his pretty tricks. Have you seen him, Master Guillaume? Princes must needs keep these rare wild beasts. We kings should have lions for lapdogs, and tigers instead of cats. Grandeur beseems a crown. In the time of Jupiter's pagans, when the people offered an hundred sheep and an hundred oxen to the gods, emperors gave an hundred lions and an hundred eagles. That was fierce and very fine. The kings of France have ever had these roarings round their throne; nevertheless, my subjects must do me the justice to say that I spend far less money in that way than my predecessors, and that I am much more moderate as regards lions, bears, elephants, and leopards. Go on, Master Olivier. We merely wished to say this much to our Flemish friends."

Guillaume Rym bowed low, while Coppenole, with his sullen air, looked like one of those bears to which his Majesty referred.

The king did not notice him. He wet his lips with the liquid in the goblet, and spat the brew out again, saying "Faugh! what a disagreeable diet-drink!" The reader continued:—

"For feeding a rascally tramp, kept under lock and key in the little cell at the shambles for six months, until it should be decided what to do with him, six pounds and four pence."

"What's that?" interrupted the king; "feed what should be hanged! By the Rood! I will not pay one penny for his keep! Olivier, settle the matter with Master d'Estouteville, and this very night make me preparations for this gallant's wedding with the gallows. Go on."

Olivier made a mark with his thumb-nail against the item of the rascally tramp, and resumed:—

"To Henriet Cousin, chief executioner of Paris, the sum of sixty Paris pence, to him adjudged and ordered by the lord provost of Paris, for having bought, by order of the said provost, a broad-sword for the execution and decapitation of all persons condemned by the courts for their demerits, and having it furnished with a scabbard and all thereunto appertaining; and likewise for having the old sword sharpened and repaired, it having been broken and notched in doing justice upon my lord Louis of Luxembourg, as herein more fully set down—"

The king interrupted. "Enough; I cheerfully order the sum to be paid. There are expenses which I never regard; I have never regretted such moneys. Continue."

"For repairing a great cage—"

"Ah!" said the king, grasping the arms of his chair with both hands, "I knew that I came here to the Bastille for a purpose. Stay, Master Olivier; I desire to see this cage for myself. You may read the costs while I examine it. Gentlemen of Flanders, come and look at it; it is a curious sight."

Then he rose, leaned upon his reader's arm, signed to the mute who stood at the door to go before him, to the two Flemings to follow him, and left the room.

The royal party was increased at the door of the retreat by men-at-arms weighed down with steel, and slender pages bearing torches. It proceeded for some time through the interior of the gloomy keep, perforated with staircases and corridors in the thickness of the walls. The captain of the Bastille walked at the head of the procession, and ordered the gates to be thrown open before the bent and feeble old king, who coughed as he moved along.

At every wicket gate all heads were forced to stoop, except that of the old man bowed by age. "Hum!" he mumbled, for he had lost all his teeth, "we are all ready for the door of the tomb. A low door needs a stooping passenger."

At last, after passing through a final gate so encumbered with locks that it took a quarter of an hour to open it, they entered a lofty, spacious, vaulted hall, in the middle of which they saw, by the light of the torches, a huge and massive cube of masonry, iron, and wood. The interior was hollow. It was one of those famous cages meant for prisoners of state, which were known by the name of "the king's daughters." In its sides were two or three small windows, so closely grated with heavy iron bars that the glass was entirely hidden. The door was a great flat stone slab, such as are used for tombs,—one of those doors used for entrance only. But here, the dead man was a living being.

The king walked slowly around the little structure, carefully examining it, while Master Olivier, who followed him, read aloud:—

"For repairing a great cage of heavy wooden joists, girders, and timbers, being nine feet long by eight in breadth, and seven feet high between the planks, planed, and clamped with strong iron clamps, which has been placed in a room in one of the towers of the Bastille Saint-Antoine, in which cage is put and kept, by command of our lord the king, a prisoner formerly dwelling in a worn-out and crazy old cage. There were used for the said new cage ninety-six horizontal beams and fifty-two uprights, ten girders eighteen feet long. Nineteen carpenters were employed for twenty days, in the court of the Bastille, to square, cut, and fit all the said wood."

"Quite fine heart of oak," said the king, rapping on the timber with his knuckles.

". . . There were used in this cage," continued the other, "two hundred and twenty large iron clamps, of eight and nine feet, the rest of medium length, with the screws, roller-bolts, and counter-bands requisite for said clamps, all the aforesaid iron weighing three thousand seven hundred and thirty-five pounds; besides eight large iron bolts serving to fasten the said cage, with the nails and clamp-irons, weighing all together two hundred and eighteen pounds; not to mention the iron gratings for the windows of the room wherein the cage was placed, the iron bars on the door, and other items—"

"Here's a mighty deal of iron," said the king, "to restrain the lightness of one mind!"

". . . The whole amounts to three hundred and seventeen pounds five pence and seven farthings."

"By the Rood!" exclaimed the king.

At this oath, which was Louis XI.'s favourite imprecation, some one seemed to waken within the cage: chains rattled loudly against the wood-work, and a faint voice, which appeared to issue from the tomb, cried: "Sire! Sire! Pardon!" But no one could see the person uttering these words.

"Three hundred and seventeen pounds five pence and seven farthings!" repeated Louis XI.

The piteous voice which issued from the cage had chilled the blood of all present, even that of Master Olivier himself. The king alone appeared as if he had not heard it. At his command Master Olivier resumed his reading, and his Majesty calmly continued his inspection of the cage.

"Moreover, there has been paid to a mason who made the holes to receive the window-bars, and the floor of the room in which the cage stands, forasmuch as the floor could not have borne this cage by reason of its weight, twenty-seven pounds and fourteen Paris pence—"

The voice again began its moan:—

"Mercy, Sire! I swear that it was my lord Cardinal of Angers, and not I, who plotted the treason."

"The mason charges well!" said the king. "Go on, Olivier!"

Olivier continued:—

"To a joiner, for window-frames, bedstead, close stool, and other items, twenty pounds two Paris pence—"

The voice continued likewise:—

"Alas! Sire! will you not hear me? I protest that it was not I who wrote that thing to my lord of Guyenne, but his highness Cardinal Balue!"

"The joiner is dear," observed the king. "Is that all?"

"No, Sire. To a glazier, for the window-panes in said chamber, forty-six pence eight Paris farthings."

"Have mercy, Sire! Is it not enough that all my worldly goods were given to my judges, my silver plate to M. de Torcy, my books to Master Pierre Doriolle, my tapestries to the Governor of Roussillon? I am innocent. For fourteen years I have shivered in an iron cage. Have mercy, Sire! You will find your reward in heaven."

"Master Olivier," said the king, "what is the sum total?"

"Three hundred and sixty-seven pounds eight pence three Paris farthings."

"By'r Lady!" cried the king. "What an extravagant cage!"

He snatched the scroll from Master Olivier's hands, and began to reckon up the items himself upon his fingers, looking by turns at the paper and the cage. Meantime, the prisoner's sobs were plainly to be heard. It was a doleful sound in the darkness, and the by-standers paled as they gazed into one another's faces.

"Fourteen years, Sire! full fourteen years! ever since the month of April, 1469. In the name of the Blessed Mother of God, Sire, hear me! You have enjoyed the warmth of the sun all these years. Shall I, poor wretch, never again behold the light of day? Pity me, Sire! Be merciful. Clemency is a goodly and a royal virtue, which turns aside the stream of wrath. Does your Majesty believe that it will greatly content a king in the hour of his death, to reflect that he has never let any offence go unpunished? Moreover, Sire, I never did betray your Majesty; it was my lord of Angers. And I wear about my leg a very heavy chain, and a great ball of iron at the end of it, far heavier than is reasonable. Ah, Sire, have pity upon me!"

"Olivier," said the king, shaking his head, "I observe that these fellows charge me twenty pence the hogshead for plaster, which is worth only twelve. Have this account corrected."

He turned his back on the cage, and prepared to leave the room. The miserable prisoner guessed by the receding torches and noise that the king was departing.

"Sire! Sire!" he cried in tones of despair.

The door closed. He saw nothing more, he heard nothing save the harsh voice of the jailor singing in his ears the song:—

"Master Jean Balue,
Has quite lost view
Of his bishoprics cherished.
My lord of Verdun
Has not a single one;
Every one hath perished."

The king silently reascended to his retreat, and his train followed him, terrified by the prisoner's last groans. All at once his Majesty turned to the governor of the Bastille.

"By the way," said he, "was there not some one in that cage?"

"Zounds, Sire, yes!" replied the governor, lost in amaze at such a question.

"Who, then?"

"The Bishop of Verdun."

The king was better aware of this than any one else; but this was his way.

"Ah!" said he, with an innocent semblance of thinking of it for the first time, "Guillaume de Harancourt, the friend of Cardinal Balue,—a merry devil of a bishop!"

A few moments later the door of the retreat was reopened, then closed again upon the five persons whom we saw there at the beginning of this chapter, and who resumed their places, their low-voiced conversation, and their former attitudes.

During the king's absence a number of despatches had been laid on the table, and he now broke the seals. Then he rapidly read them one after the other, motioned to Master Olivier, who seemed to perform the office of his minister, to take a pen, and without imparting the contents of the despatches to him, began to dictate answers in an undertone, the latter writing them down, kneeling uncomfortably at the table.

Guillaume Rym watched him.

The king spoke so low that the Flemings caught but a few detached and scarcely intelligible fragments, such as:—

". . . keep up fertile places by commerce and sterile ones by manufactures. Show the English lords our four bombards, the London, Brabant, Bourg-en-Bresse, and Saint-Omer. . . Artillery occasions war to be more wisely waged at the present time. . . To Monsieur de Bressuire, our friend. . . . Armies cannot be maintained without tribute," etc.

Once he raised his voice:—

"By the Rood! the King of Sicily seals his letters with yellow wax, like a king of France. We may be wrong to allow him this privilege. My fair cousin of Burgundy gave no armorial bearings upon a field gules. The greatness of a house is ensured by holding its prerogatives intact. Note that, gossip Olivier."

Again:—

"Oho!" said he, "an important message this! What would our brother the emperor have?" And running his eye over the missive, he interrupted his reading with constant exclamations: "Surely the Germans are so great and powerful that 't is scarcely credible. But we are not unmindful of the old proverb: The finest country is Flanders; the fairest duchy, Milan; the most beauteous kingdom, France. Is it not so, Sir Flemings?"

This time Coppenole bowed with Guillaume Rym. The hosier's patriotism was tickled.

The last despatch made Louis XI. frown.

"What's this?" he exclaimed. "Complaints and requisitions against our garrisons in Picardy! Olivier, write with speed to Marshal de Rouault: That discipline is relaxed. That the men-at-arms of the ordnance, the nobles of the ban, the free-archers, and the Swiss guards do infinite injury to the peasants. That the soldiers, not content with the goods which they find in the houses of the tillers of the soil, constrain them, by heavy blows of bludgeons and sticks, to seek throughout the town for wine, fish, spices, and other articles of luxury. That the king is well aware of all this. That we intend to preserve our people from all unseemly acts, larceny, and pillage. That this is our sovereign will by Our Lady! That, moreover, it likes us not that any min-

strel, barber, or serving man-at-arms should go arrayed like a prince, in velvet, silken cloth, and rings of gold. That these vanities are hateful in the sight of God. That we content ourselves—we who are a gentleman of high degree—with one cloth doublet at sixteen pence the Paris ell. That soldiers' servants may well come down to that also. We command and order these things. To Monsieur de Rouault, our friend. Good!"

He dictated this letter in a loud voice, in a firm tone, and by fits and starts. Just as he ended it, the door opened and admitted a new personage, who rushed into the room in extreme alarm, shouting,—

"Sire! Sire! the people of Paris have risen in revolt!"

The grave face of Louis XI. was convulsed; but every visible sign of emotion passed away like a flash of lightning. He restrained himself, and said with calm severity,—

"Gossip Jacques, you enter somewhat abruptly!"

"Sire! Sire! there is a revolt!" replied the breathless gossip Jacques.

The king, who had risen, took him roughly by the arm and whispered in his ear in a manner to be heard by him alone, with concentrated rage, and a sidelong glance at the Flemings,—

"Hold your tongue, or speak low!"

The new-comer understood, and began to tell him in a low voice a very incoherent tale, to which the king listened with perfect composure, while Guillaume Rym drew Coppenole's attention to the new-comer's face and dress, his furred hood (*caputia fourrata*), his short epitoge (*epitogia curta*), and his black velvet gown, which bespoke a president of the Court of Accounts.

This person had no sooner given the king a few details, than Louis XI. cried with a burst of laughter,—

"Indeed! Speak up boldly, gossip Coictier! Why do you talk so low? Our Lady knows that we hide nothing from our good Flemish friends."

"But, Sire—"

"Speak up boldly!"

Gossip Coictier was dumb with surprise.

"So," resumed the king,—"speak, sir, —there is a commotion among the common people in our good city of Paris?"

"Yes, Sire."

"And it is directed, you say, against the Bailiff of the Palace of Justice?"

"It looks that way," said the gossip, who still stammered and hesitated, utterly astounded by the sudden and inexplicable change which had been wrought in the king's sentiments.

Louis XI. added: "Where did the watch encounter the mob?"

"Moving from the chief haunt of the beggars and vagrants towards the Pont-aux-Changeurs. I met them myself on my way hither to execute your Majesty's orders. I heard certain of the number shouting, 'Down with the Bailiff of the Palace!'"

"And what is their grievance against the bailiff?"

"Ah!" said gossip Jacques, "that he is their lord."

"Really!"

"Yes, Sire. They are rascals from the Court of Miracles. They have long inveighed against the bailiff, whose vassals they are. They refuse to recognize him either as justiciary or road-surveyor."

"Ay, say you so!" returned the king, with a smile of satisfaction which he vainly strove to disguise.

"In all their petitions to Parliament," added gossip Jacques, "they claim that they have but two masters,—your Majesty and their God, who is, I believe, the devil."

"Hah!" said the king.

He rubbed his hands; he laughed that inward laugh which makes the face radiant; he could not disguise his joy, although he tried at times to compose himself. No one understood his mood, not even Master Olivier. He was silent for a moment, with a pensive but contented air.

"Are they strong in numbers?" he asked suddenly.

"Indeed they are, Sire," replied gossip Jacques.

"How many?"

"At least six thousand."

The king could not help exclaiming, "Good!" He added, "Are they armed?"

"With scythes, pikes, hackbuts, mattocks, and all sorts of dangerous weapons."

The king seemed by no means alarmed at this account. Gossip Jacques felt obliged to add,—

"If your Majesty send not promptly to the bailiff's aid, he is lost."

"We will send," said the king, with an assumed expression of seriousness. "It is well. Certainly we will send. The bailiff is our friend. Six thousand! They are determined knaves. Their boldness is marvellous, and we are greatly wroth at it; but we have few people about us to-night. It will be time enough in the morning."

Gossip Jacques exclaimed, "Straightway, Sire! The bailiff's house may be sacked twenty times over, the seigniory profaned, and the bailiff hanged, ere then. For the love of God, Sire, send before to-morrow morning!"

The king looked him in the face. "I said to-morrow." It was one of those looks which admit of no reply. After a pause, Louis XI. again raised his voice. "Gossip Jacques, you must know— What was—" He corrected himself. "What is the bailiff's feudal jurisdiction?"

"Sire, the Bailiff of the Palace has jurisdiction from the Rue de la Calandre to the Rue de l'Herberie, the Place Saint-Michel, and the places commonly called the Mureaux, situated near the church of Notre-Dame des Champs [here the king lifted the brim of his hat], which residences are thirteen in number; besides the Court of Miracles, the lazaretto known as the Banlieue, and all the highway beginning at this lazarhouse and ending at the Porte Saint-Jacques. Of these divers places he is road-surveyor, high, low, and middle justiciary, and lord paramount."

"Hey-day!" said the king, scratching his left ear with his right hand; "that is a goodly slice of my city. And so the bailiff was king of all that?"

This time he did not correct himself. He continued to muse, and as if speaking to himself, said,—

"Have a care, Sir Bailiff! You had a very pretty piece of our Paris in your grasp."

All at once he burst forth. "By the Rood! Who are all these people who claim to be commissioners of highways, justiciaries, lords, and masters in our midst; who have their toll-gate in every bit of field, their gibbet and their hangman at every cross-road among our people, in such fashion that, as the Greek believed in as many gods as there were fountains, and the Persian in as many as he saw stars, the Frenchman now counts as many kings as he sees gallows? By the Lord! this thing is evil, and the confusion likes me not. I would fain know whether it be by the grace of God that there are other inspectors of highways in Paris than the king, other justice than that administered by our Parliament, and other emperor than ourselves in this realm! By the faith of my soul! the day must come when France shall know but one king, one lord, one judge, one headsman, even as there is but one God in paradise!"

He again raised his cap, and went on, still meditating, with the look and tone of a hunter loosing and urging on his pack of dogs: "Good! my people! bravely done! destroy these false lords! do your work. At them, boys! at them! Plunder them, capture them, strip them! Ah, you would fain be kings, gentlemen? On, my people, on!"

Here he stopped abruptly, bit his lip, as if to recall a thought which had half escaped him, bent his piercing eye in turn upon each of the five persons who stood around him, and all at once, seizing his hat in both hands, and staring steadily at it, he thus addressed it: "Oh, I would burn you if you knew my secret thoughts!"

Then again casting about him the

attentive, anxious glance of a fox returning by stealth to his earth, he added,—

"It matters not; we will succour the
bailiff. Unfortunately, we have but few
troops here to send forth at this moment
against so large a populace. We must
needs wait until to-morrow. Order shall
be restored in the City, and all who are
taken shall be strung up on the spot."

"By-the-bye, Sire!" said gossip
Coictier, "I forgot it in my first dismay,
—the watch has caught two stragglers
of the band. If it please your Majesty
to see these men, they are here."

"If it please me to see them!" cried
the king. "Now, by the Rood! do you
forget such things! Run quickly, you,
Olivier! go and fetch them."

Master Olivier went out, and returned
a moment after with the two prisoners,
surrounded by archers of the ordnance.
The first had a fat, stupid face, with
a drunken and astonished stare. He
was dressed in rags, and bent his knee
and dragged his foot as he walked. The
second was a pale, smiling fellow, whom
the reader already knows.

The king studied them for an instant
without speaking, then abruptly addressed the first:—

"Your name?"

"Gieffroy Pincebourde."

"Your business?"

"A Vagabond."

"What part did you mean to play in
that damnable revolt?"

The Vagabond looked at the king,
swinging his arms with a dull look. His
was one of those misshapen heads,
where the understanding flourishes as
ill as the flame beneath an extinguisher.

"I don't know," he said. "The others
went, so I went too."

"Did you not intend outrageously to
attack and plunder your lord the Bailiff
of the Palace?"

"I know that they were going to take
something from some one. That's all
I know."

A soldier showed the king a pruning-
bill, which had been found upon the
fellow.

"Do you recognize this weapon?"
asked the king.

"Yes, it is my bill; I am a vine-
dresser."

"And do you acknowledge this man
as your companion?" added Louis XI.,
pointing to the other prisoner.

"No. I do not know him."

"Enough," said the king. And
beckoning to the silent, motionless
person at the door, whom we have already pointed out to our readers:—

"Friend Tristan, here is a man for
you."

Tristan l'Hermite bowed. He gave
an order in a low voice to two archers,
who led away the poor Vagrant.

Meantime the king approached the
second prisoner, who was in a profuse
perspiration. "Your name?"

"Sire, Pierre Gringoire."

"Your trade?"

"A philosopher, Sire!"

"How dared you, varlet, go and beset
our friend the Bailiff of the Palace, and
what have you to say about this upris-
ing of the people?"

"Sire, I had naught to do with it."

"Come, come, rascal! were you not
taken by the watch in this evil
company?"

"No, Sire; there is a mistake. It was
an accident. I write tragedies. Sire, I
entreat your Majesty to hear me. I am

a poet. It is the melancholy whim of people of my profession to roam the streets after dark. I passed this way to-night. It was a mere chance. I was wrongfully arrested; I am innocent of this civil storm. Your Majesty sees that the Vagabond did not recognize me. I conjure your Majesty—"

"Silence!" said the king, betwixt two gulps of his diet-drink. "You stun me."

Tristan l'Hermite stepped forward, and pointing at Gringoire, said,—

"Sire, may we hang this one too?"

It was the first time that he had spoken.

"Pooh!" negligently answered the king. "I see no reason to the contrary."

"But I see a great many!" said Gringoire.

Our philosopher was at this moment greener than any olive. He saw by the king's cold and indifferent manner that his only resource was in something very pathetic, and he threw himself at the feet of Louis XI., exclaiming with frantic gestures,—

"Sire, your Majesty will deign to hear me. Sire, let not your thunders fall upon so small a thing as I! The thunderbolts of God never strike a lettuce. Sire, you are an august and very mighty monarch; have pity on a poor honest man, who would find it harder to kindle a revolt than an icicle to emit a spark. Most gracious lord, magnanimity is a virtue meet for kings and royal beasts. Alas! rigour does but anger the minds of men; the fierce blasts of winter could not make the traveller doff his cloak, while the sun shining down, little by little warmed him to such a degree that he stripped to his shirt. Sire, you are the sun. I

protest to you, my sovereign lord and master, that I am not of the company of the Vagrants. I am neither disorderly nor a thief. Rebellion and brigandage are not of Apollo's train. I am not one to rush into those clouds which burst in thunders of sedition. I am a faithful vassal of your Majesty. A good subject should feel the same jealousy for the glory of his king that the husband feels for the honour of his wife, the same affection with which the son responds to his father's love; he should burn with zeal for his house; for the increase of his service. Any other passion which possessed him would be mere madness. Such, Sire, are my political maxims. Do not, therefore, judge me to be a rebel and a plunderer, by my ragged dress. If you will but pardon me, Sire, I will wear it threadbare at the knees in praying to God for you night and morning! Alas! I am not exceeding rich, 'tis true. I am indeed rather poor; but not vicious, for all that. It is not my fault. Every one knows that great wealth is not to be derived from literature, and that the most accomplished writers have not always much fire in winter. Pettifoggers get all the grain, and leave nothing but the chaff for the rest of the learned professions. There are forty most excellent proverbs about the tattered cloak of the philosopher. Oh, Sire, clemency is the only light which can illumine the interior of a great soul! Clemency bears the torch for all the other virtues. Without her, they are but blind, and gropers after God. Mercy, which is the same thing as clemency, produces those loving subjects who are the most potent body.

guard of princes. What matters it to you,—to you whose majesty dazzles all who behold it,—if there be one poor man the more upon the earth, a poor innocent philosopher floundering in the darkness of calamity, with an empty stomach and an empty purse? Besides, Sire, I am a scholar. Great kings add a pearl to their crown when they encourage letters. Hercules did not disdain the title of Musagetes. Matthias Corvinus favoured Jean of Monroyal, the ornament of mathematics. Now, it is a poor way of protecting letters, to hang the learned. What a blot upon Alexander's fame if he had hanged Aristotle! The deed would not have been a tiny patch upon the visage of his reputation to enhance its beauty, but a malignant ulcer to disfigure it. Sire, I wrote a most fitting epithalamium for the Lady of Flanders, and my lord the most august Dauphin. That is no fire-brand of rebellion. Your Majesty sees that I am no mere scribbler, that I have studied deeply, and that I have much natural eloquence. Pardon me, Sire. By so doing, you will perform an act of gallantry to Our Lady; and I vow that I am mightily frightened at the very idea of being hanged!"

So saying, the much distressed Gringoire kissed the king's slippers, and Guillaume Rym whispered to Coppenole, "He does well to crawl upon the floor. Kings are like Jupiter of Crete,—they have no ears but in their feet." And, regardless of the Cretan Jove, the hosier responded, with a grave smile, his eye fixed on Gringoire: "Oh, 'tis well done! I fancy I hear Councillor Hugonet begging me for mercy."

When Gringoire paused at last for lack of breath, he raised his head, trembling, to the king, who was scratching with his nail a spot on the knee of his breeches; then his Majesty drank from the goblet of ptisan. He spoke not a word, however, and the silence tortured Gringoire. At last the king looked at him. "What a dreadful bawler!" said he. Then, turning towards Tristan l'Hermite: "Bah! let him go!"

Gringoire fell backwards, overcome with joy.

"Scot-free!" grumbled Tristan. "Don't your Majesty want me to cage him for a while?"

"Friend," rejoined Louis XI., "do you think it is for such birds as these that we have cages made at an expense of three hundred and sixty-seven pounds eight pence three farthings? Let this wanton rascal depart incontinently, and dismiss him with a beating."

"Oh," cried Gringoire, "what a noble king!"

And for fear of a contrary order, he hastened towards the door, which Tristan opened for him with a very bad grace. The soldiers followed, driving him before them with sturdy blows, which Gringoire bore like the true Stoic philosopher that he was.

The king's good humour, since the revolt against the bailiff was announced to him, appeared in everything he did. This unusual clemency was no mean proof of it. Tristan l'Hermite, in his corner, wore the surly look of a dog who has seen a bone, but had none.

The king, meantime, merrily drummed the march of Pont-Audemer with his fingers on the arm of his chair. He was a dissembling prince, but more skilled in hiding his troubles than his joy. These outward manifestations of delight at any good news sometimes went to extraordinary lengths,—as on the death of Charles the Bold, when he vowed a silver balustrade to Saint-Martin of Tours; and on his accession to the throne, when he forgot to order his father's obsequies.

"Ha, Sire!" suddenly exclaimed Jacques Coictier, "what has become of that sharp fit of illness for which your Majesty summoned me?"

"Oh," said the king, "indeed, I suffer greatly, good gossip. I have a ringing in my ears, and cruel pains in my chest."

Coictier took the king's hand, and began to feel his pulse with a knowing air.

"See, Coppenole," said Rym in a low voice; "there he is, between Coictier and Tristan. They make up his entire court,—a doctor for himself, a hangman for the rest of the world!"

As he felt the king's pulse, Coictier assumed a look of more and more alarm. Louis XI. watched him with some anxiety. Coictier's face darkened visibly. The king's feeble health was the worthy man's only source of income, and he made the most of it.

"Oh, oh!" he muttered at last. "This is serious enough."

"Is it not?" said the frightened king.

"*Pulsus creber, anhelans, crepitans, irregularis,*" added the physician.

"By the Rood!"

"This might take a man off in less than three days."

"By'r Lady!" cried the king. "And the remedy, good gossip?"

"I must reflect, Sire."

He examined the king's tongue, shook his head, made a wry face, and in the midst of these affections said suddenly,—

"Zounds, Sire, I must tell you that there is a receivership of regales vacant, and that I have a nephew."

"I give my receivership to your nephew, gossip Jacques," replied the king; "but cool this fire in my breast."

"Since your Majesty is so graciously inclined," rejoined the doctor, "you will not refuse me a little help towards building my house in the Rue Saint-André des Arcs."

"Hey!" said the king.

"I have come to the end of my means," continued the doctor, "and it would really be a pity that my house should have no roof; not for the sake of the house, which is very plain and ordinary, but for the paintings by Jehan Fourbault, which enliven the walls. There is a Diana flying in the air, so excellently done, so delicate, so dainty, so natural in action, the head so nicely coifed and crowned with a crescent, the flesh so white, that she leads into temptation all those who study her too curiously. There is also a Ceres. She, too, is a very lovely divinity. She is seated upon sheaves of grain, and crowned with a gay garland of wheat-ears intertwined with purple goat's-beard and other flowers. Nothing was ever seen more amorous than her eyes, rounder than her legs, nobler than her mien or more graceful than her draperies. She is one of the most innocent and perfect beauties ever produced by mortal brush!"

"Wretch!" groaned Louis XI.; "what are you driving at?"

"I must have a roof over these paint-ings, Sire; and although it will cost but a trifle, I have no more money."

"How much will your roof cost?"

"Why, a roof of copper, embellished and gilded, two thousand pounds, at the utmost."

"Ah, the assassin!" cried the king; "he never draws me a tooth that is not priceless."

"Am I to have my roof?" said Coictier.

"Yes; and go to the devil! but cure me first."

Jacques Coictier bowed low and said,—

"Sire, a repellant alone can save you. We will apply to your loins the great specific, composed of cerate, Armenian bole, white of egg, vinegar, and oil. You will continue your diet-drink, and we will answer for your Majesty."

A lighted candle attracts more than one moth. Master Olivier, seeing the king so liberally inclined, and thinking the moment opportune, advanced in his turn: "Sire!"

"What is it now?" said Louis XI.

"Sire, your Majesty knows that Master Simon Radin is dead?"

"Well?"

"He was King's Councillor for the Treasury."

"Well?"

"Sire, his post is vacant."

As he said this, the haughty face of Master Olivier lost its arrogant look, and assumed a mean and grovelling expression. This is the only change of which a courtier's features are capable. The king looked him full in the face, and said drily, "I understand."

He added,—

"Master Olivier, Marshal Boucicaut once said, 'There are no good gifts save those from the king, no good fishing save in the sea.' I see that you are quite of ! opinion. Now, hear this; we have an excellent memory. In '68, we made you groom of our chamber; in '69, keeper of the castle of the Pont Saint-Cloud, at a salary of one hundred pounds Tours (you wished them to be Paris pounds); in November, '73, by letters given at Gergeole, we appointed you keeper of the woods at Vincennes, in place of Gilbert Acle, esquire; in '75, warden of the forest of Rouvray-lez-Saint-Cloud, in the place of Jacques le Maire; in '78, we graciously settled upon you, by letters-patent sealed with green wax, a rental of ten Paris pounds, for yourself and your wife, to be derived from the Place-aux-Marchands, situated in the Saint-Germain School; in '79, warden of the forest of Senart, in place of that poor Jehan Daiz; then, captain of the Château de Loches; then, governor of Saint-Quentin; then, captain of the Pont de Meulan, of which you style yourself count; of the five pence fine paid by every barber who shall shave a cus-tomer upon a holiday, three pence go to you, and we take the remainder. We were pleased to change your name of Le Mauvais, which too strongly re-sembled your face. In '74, we granted you, to the great displeasure of our nobles, armorial bearings of countless hues, which make your breast shimmer like that of a peacock. By the Rood! are you not sated yet? Is not the draught of fishes fine enough, and miraculous enough; and do you not fear lest another salmon should sink your boat? Pride will be your ruin, my friend. Pride is always hard pressed by ruin and shame. Consider this, and be silent."

These words, uttered in a severe tone, restored its wonted insolence to Master Olivier's face.

"Good!" he muttered almost audibly; "it is plain that the king is ailing to-day; he gives the doctor everything."

Louis XI., far from being irritated by this sally, replied with much gentleness. "Stay; I forgot that I had also made you my ambassador to Mistress Marie at Ghent. Yes, gentlemen," added the king, turning to the Flemings, "this fellow has been an ambassador. There, my gossip," he continued, addressing Master Olivier, "let us not quarrel; we are old friends. It is very late; we have finished our work. Shave me."

Our readers have doubtless ere now recognized in Master Olivier the dread Figaro whom Providence, the greatest of all dramatists, so artistically added to the long and bloody comedy of Louis XI.'s reign. This is not the place for us to attempt any portrait of this strange figure. The royal barber went by three names. At court he was politely termed Olivier le Daim; by the people, Olivier le Diable: his real name was Olivier le Mauvais.

Olivier le Mauvais, then, stood motionless, casting sulky glances at the king, and looking askance at Jacques Coictier.

"Yes, yes; the doctor!" he muttered.

"Well, yes, the doctor!" rejoined Louis XI., with rare good-nature; "the doctor has more influence than you. That is natural enough; he has a hold

upon our whole body, while you only take us by the chin. There, my poor barber, cheer up. Why, what would you say, and what would become of your office, if I were such a king as King Chilpêric, whose favourite trick it was to pull his beard through his hand? Come, gossip, look to your work; shave me! Go, fetch the necessary tools."

Olivier, seeing that the king was in a jesting mood, and that it was impossible to put him out of temper, left the room to obey his orders, grumbling as he went.

The king rose, stepped to the window, and suddenly opening it with strange agitation, clapped his hands, exclaiming,—

"Oh, yes, there is a red glow in the sky over the City! The bailiff is burning; it can be nothing else. Ah, my good people! 'tis thus at last you help me to crush their lordships!"

Then turning to the Flemings: "Gentlemen, come and look. Is not that a fire which flares so high?"

The two men of Ghent approached.

"A great fire," said Guillaume Rym.

"Oh," added Coppenole, whose eyes flashed, "that reminds me of the burning of the lord of Hymbercourt's house! There must be a fine riot yonder!"

"Do you think so, Master Coppenole?" And the face of Louis XI. was almost as full of joy as that of the hosier. " 'T will be hard to suppress it, eh?"

"By the Mass, Sire! your Majesty will make great gaps in many a company of troops in doing it."

"Oh, I! that's quite another thing," rejoined the king. "If I chose—"

The hosier answered boldly,—

"If this rebellion be what I suppose, you may choose to no purpose, Sire."

"Friend," said Louis XI., "two companies of my ordnance and the discharge of a serpentine would win an easy victory over the groundlings."

The hosier, in spite of the signs made to him by Guillaume Rym, seemed determined to oppose the king.

"Sire, the Swiss were groundlings too. My lord duke of Burgundy was a great gentleman, and he despised that vulgar mob. At the battle of Grandson he cried, 'Gunners, fire upon those low-lived villains!' and he swore by Saint George. But magistrate Scharnachtal fell upon the proud duke with his club and his people, and at the onslaught of the peasants with their bull-hides, the brilliant Burgundian army was broken like a pane of glass by a stone. Many knights were killed that day by base clowns; and my lord of Château-Guyon, the grandest noble in Burgundy, was found dead beside his great grey charger in a small marshy meadow."

"Friend," replied the king, "you talk of battles. This is only a mutiny; and I will quell it with a single frown whenever it pleases me."

The other answered indifferently,—

"That may be, Sire. In that case it will merely be because the people's hour has not yet come."

Guillaume Rym felt obliged to interfere:—

"Master Coppenole, you are speaking to a powerful king."

"I know it," gravely answered the hosier.

"Let him talk, friend Rym," said the king. "I like such frankness. My father, Charles VII., said that Truth

was sick. I, for my part, thought she had died, without a confessor. Master Coppenole has undeceived me."

Then, laying his hand familiarly upon Coppenole's shoulder, he added,—

"You were saying, Master Jacques—"

"I was saying, Sire, that perhaps you were right,—that the people's hour had not yet come in this land."

Louis XI. looked searchingly at him:—

"And when will that hour come, sirrah?"

"You will hear it strike."

"By what o'clock, pray?"

Coppenole, with his homely, peaceful face, drew the king to the window.

"Listen, Sire! Here you have a donjon, a bell-tower, cannon, burghers, soldiers. When the bell rings, when the cannon growl, when the donjon falls with a crash, when burghers and soldiers shout and slay one another, then the hour will strike."

The king's face became dark and thoughtful. For an instant he stood silent; then he gently patted the thick donjon wall, as he might have caressed the flank of his favourite horse.

"Oh, no!" he said; "you will not crumble so easily, will you, my good Bastille?"

Then, turning with an abrupt gesture to the daring Fleming,—

"Did you ever see a revolt, Master Jacques?"

"I made one," said the hosier.

"And how," said the king, "do you set to work to make a revolt?"

"Ah!" replied Coppenole, "it is not very difficult. There are a hundred ways of doing it. In the first place, discontent must be rife in the town:

that is not an uncommon occurrence. And then you must consider the character of the inhabitants. The men of Ghent are always ready to rebel; they always love the prince's son, never the prince. Well, I will suppose that one morning somebody comes into my shop and says: Friend Coppenole, this thing or that thing has happened,—the Lady of Flanders is resolved to maintain the Cabinet; the high bailiff has doubled the tax on vegetables or something else; whatever you please. I drop my work on the spot; I leave my shop, and I run out into the street, crying, 'Storm and sack!' There is always some empty hogshead lying about. I mount upon it, and I proclaim aloud, in the first words that come to me, all that distresses me; and when you belong to the people, Sire, there is always something to distress you. Then there is a gathering of the clans; there are shouts; the alarm-bell rings; the people disarm the troops and arm themselves; the marketmen join in; and so it goes on. And it will always be so, so long as there are nobles in the seigniories, burghers in the towns, and peasants in the country."

"And against whom do you rebel in this way?" asked the king. "Against your bailiffs; against your liege-lords?"

"Sometimes; that depends on circumstances. Against the duke, too, at times."

Louis XI. reseated himself, and said with a smile,—

"Ah! here they have got no farther than the bailiffs."

At this instant Olivier le Daim returned. He was followed by two pages carrying various articles of the king's toilet; but what struck Louis XI. was

the fact that he was also accompanied by the provost of Paris and the captain of the watch, who seemed dismayed. The spiteful barber also looked dismayed, but was inwardly pleased. He was the first to speak:—

"Sire, I crave your pardon for the disastrous news I bring!"

The king turned so quickly that he tore the matting on the floor with the legs of his chair.

"What do you mean?"

"Sire," replied Olivier le Daim, with the malicious look of a man who rejoices to strike a severe blow, "this rising of the people is not directed against the Bailiff of the Palace."

"And against whom, then?"

"Against you, Sire."

The old king rose to his feet as erect as a young man.

"Explain yourself, Olivier! And look to your head, my friend; for I swear by the cross of Saint-Lô that if you lie to us at this hour, the same sword which cut off the head of my lord Luxembourg is not too dull to chop off yours!"

The oath was a tremendous one; Louis XI. had never but twice in his life sworn by the cross of Saint-Lô.

Olivier opened his lips to answer.

"On your knees!" fiercely interrupted the king. "Tristan, watch this man!"

Olivier knelt, and said coldly,—

"Sire, a witch was condemned to death by your parliamentary court. She took refuge in Notre-Dame. The people desire to take her thence by force. The provost and the captain of the watch, who have just come from the scene of the insurrection, are here to give me the lie if I speak not truly. The people are besieging Notre-Dame."

"Indeed!" said the king in a low voice, pale and trembling with rage. "Notre-Dame! So they lay siege to my good mistress, Our Lady, in her own cathedral! Rise, Olivier; you are right. I give you Simon Radin's office. You are right; it is I whom they attack. The witch is in the safe-keeping of the church; the church is in my safe-keeping; and I was foolish enough to believe that they were assaulting the bailiff. It is myself!"

Then, made young by fury, he began to pace the floor with hasty strides. He laughed no longer; he was terrible to behold; he came and went; the fox was turned to a hyæna. He seemed to have lost all power of speech; his lips moved, and his fleshless hands were clinched. All at once he raised his head, his hollow eye seemed filled with light, and his voice flashed forth like a clarion:—

"Do your work well, Tristan! Do your work well with these scoundrels! Go, Tristan my friend; kill! kill!"

This outburst over, he sat down again, and said with cold and concentrated wrath,—

"Here, Tristan! There are with us in this Bastille Viscount de Gif's fifty lances, making three hundred horse: take them. There is also M. de Châteaupers' company of archers of our ordnance: take them. You are provost-marshal; you have your own men: take them. At the Hôtel Saint-Pol you will find forty archers of the Dauphin's new guard: take them. And with all these soldiers you will hasten to Notre-Dame. Ah, you commoners of Paris, so you would attack the Crown of France, the

sanctity of Notre-Dame, and the peace of this republic! Exterminate them, Tristan! exterminate them! and let not one escape but for Montfaucon."

Tristan bowed. "It is well, Sire."

After a pause he added, "And what shall I do with the witch?"

This question gave the king food for thought.

"Ah," said he, "the witch! D'Estouteville, what was the people's pleasure in regard to her?"

"Sire," replied the provost of Paris, "I fancy that as the people desire to wrest her from her shelter in Notre-Dame, it is her lack of punishment that offends them, and they propose to hang her."

The king seemed to muse deeply; then, addressing Tristan l'Hermite: "Very well, good gossip; exterminate the people, and hang the witch!"

"That's it," whispered Rym to Coppenole, "punish the people for their purpose, and then fulfil that purpose."

"It is well, Sire," answered Tristan. "If the witch be still in Notre-Dame, shall we disregard the sanctuary, and take her thence?"

"By the Rood! Sanctuary!" said the king, scratching his ear. "And yet this woman must be hanged."

Here, as if struck by a sudden thought, he fell upon his knees before his chair, doffed his hat, put it on the seat, and gazing devoutly at one of the leaden images with which it was loaded, he exclaimed, with clasped hands: "Oh, Our Lady of Paris, my gracious patroness, pardon me! I will only do it this once. This criminal must be punished. I assure you, Holy Virgin, my good mistress, that she is a witch, and unworthy of your generous protection. You know madame, that many very pious princes have infringed upon the privileges of the Church for the glory of God and the needs of the State. Saint Hugh, Bishop of England, allowed King Edward to capture a magician in his church. Saint Louis of France, my master, for the same purpose violated the church of St. Paul; and Alphonso, son of the King of Jerusalem, the Church of the Holy Sepulchre itself. Forgive me this once, Our Lady of Paris! I will never do so again, and I will give you a fine new silver statue, like the one I gave Our Lady of Ecouys last year. Amen."

He made the sign of the cross, rose, put on his hat, and said to Tristan,—

"Make haste, friend; take Châteaupers with you. Ring the alarm! Quell the mob! Hang the witch! That is all. And I expect you to pay the costs of hanging. You will render me an account thereof. Come, Olivier, I shall not go to bed to-night; shave me."

Tristan l'Hermite bowed, and left the room. Then the king dismissed Rym and Coppenole with a gesture, and the words,—

"God help you, my good Flemish friends. Go, take a little rest; the night is passing, and we are nearer morn than evening."

Both retired, and on reaching their apartments under the escort of the captain of the Bastille, Coppenole said to Guillaume Rym,—

"Ahem! I have had enough of this coughing king. I have seen Charles of Burgundy drunk, and he was not so bad as Louis XI. sick."

"Master Jacques," replied Rym, " 'tis because the wine of kings is less cruel than their diet-drink."

CHAPTER VI

"THE CHIVE IN THE CLY"

On leaving the Bastille, Gringoire ran down the Rue Saint-Antoine with the speed of a runaway horse. On reaching the Porte Baudoyer, he walked straight up to the stone cross in the middle of the square, as if he had been able to distinguish in the darkness the figure of a man in a black dress and cowl, who sat upon the steps of the cross.

"Is it you, master?" said Gringoire.

The black figure rose.

" 'Sdeath! You make my blood boil, Gringoire. The man on the tower of Saint-Gervais has just cried half-past one."

"Oh," rejoined Gringoire, "it is not my fault, but that of the watch and the king. I have had a narrow escape. I always just miss being hanged; it is my fate."

"You just miss everything," said the other; "but make haste. Have you the password?"

"Only fancy, master, that I have seen the king! I have just left him. He wears fustian breeches. It was quite an adventure."

"Oh, you spinner of words! What do I care for your adventure? Have you the watchword of the Vagrants?"

"I have; never fear. It is 'the Chive in the Cly.' "

"Good! Otherwise we could not make our way to the church. The Vagrants block the streets. Luckily, it appears that they met with considerable resistance. We may yet be there in time."

"Yes, master; but how are we to get into Notre-Dame?"

"I have the key to the towers."

"And how shall we get out?"

"There is a small door, behind the cloisters, which opens upon the Terrain, and thence to the water. I have the key, and I moored a boat there this morning."

"I had a pretty escape from being hanged!" repeated Gringoire.

"Come, be quick!" said the other.

Both went hurriedly towards the City.

CHAPTER VII

CHÂTEAUPERS TO THE RESCUE

THE reader may perhaps recall the critical situation in which we left Quasimodo. The brave deaf man, assailed on every hand, had lost, if not all courage, at least all hope of saving not himself (he did not think of himself), but the gipsy. He ran frantically up and down the gallery. Notre-Dame was about to be captured by the Vagrants. Suddenly, the gallop of horses filled the neighbouring streets, and with a long train of torches and a broad column of horsemen riding at full speed with lances lowered, the furious sound burst into the square like a whirlwind:—

"France! France! Hew down the clodpolls! Châteaupers to the rescue! Provosty! provosty!"

The terrified Vagrants wheeled about.

Quasimodo, who heard nothing, saw the naked swords, the torches, the pikeheads, the horsemen, at whose head he recognized Captain Phœbus. He saw the confusion of the Vagrants,—the alarm of some, the consternation of the stoutest-hearted,—and he derived so much strength from this unexpected succour, that he hurled from the church the foremost assailants, who were already bestriding the gallery rails.

The king's troops had actually arrived.

The Vagrants fought bravely; they defended themselves desperately. Taken in flank from the Rue Saint-Pierre aux Bœufs, and in the rear from the Rue du Parvis, driven close against Notre-Dame, which they were still assailing, and which Quasimodo was defending, at once besiegers and besieged, they were in the singular situation in which Count Henri d'Harcourt afterwards found himself at the famous siege of Turin, in 1640,—between Prince Thomas of Savoy, whom he was besieging, and the Marquis de Leganez, who was blockading him. *"Taurinum obsessor idem et obsessus,"* as his epitaph says.

The conflict was frightful. As Père Mathieu puts it, "wolf's flesh needs dog's teeth." The king's cavaliers, among whom Phœbus de Châteaupers comported himself most valiantly, gave no quarter, and the edge of the sword slew those who escaped the thrust of the lance. The Vagrants, ill-armed, foamed and bit. Men, women, and children flung themselves upon the cruppers and breast-pieces of the horses, and clung to them like cats with tooth and nail. Others blinded the archers by blows of their torches; others again struck iron hooks into the riders' necks and pulled them down, cutting into pieces those who fell.

One man had a large shining scythe,

with which he mowed the legs of the horses. It was a frightful sight. He sang a nasal song, and swept his scythe ceaselessly to and fro. At every stroke he cut a broad swath of dismembered limbs. He advanced thus into the thickest of the cavalry, with the calm deliberation, swaying of the head, and regular breathing of a mower cutting down a field of grain. This was Clopin Trouillefou. A shot from an arquebus at last laid him low.

Meantime, windows were again opened. The neighbours, hearing the battle-shouts of the king's men, joined in the skirmish, and from every story bullets rained upon the Vagrants. The square was filled with thick smoke, which the flash of musketry streaked with fire. The front of Notre-Dame was vaguely visible through it, and the decrepit hospital the Hôtel-Dieu, with a few wan patients looking down from the top of its roof dotted with dormer-windows.

At last the Vagrants yielded. Exhaustion, lack of proper arms, the terror caused by the surprise, the musketry from the windows, the brave onslaught of the king's men, all combined to crush them. They broke through the enemy's ranks, and fled in every direction, leaving the square heaped with corpses.

When Quasimodo, who had not stopped fighting for a single instant, saw this rout, he fell upon his knees and raised his hands to heaven; then, mad with joy, he ran, he climbed with the swift motion of a bird to that little cell, all access to which he had so intrepidly defended. He had but one thought now: that was, to kneel before her whom he had saved for the second time.

When he entered the cell he found it empty.

BOOK XI

MARRIAGE

CHAPTER I

THE LITTLE SHOE

WHEN the Vagrants attacked the church, Esmeralda was asleep.

Soon the ever-increasing noise about the building, and the anxious bleating of her goat, which waked before she did, roused her from her slumbers. She sat up, listened, looked about; then, alarmed by the light and commotion, hurried from her cell to see what it all meant. The aspect of the square, the vision which she beheld, the disorder and confusion of this night attack, the hideous rabble bounding hither and thither like an army of frogs half seen in the darkness, the croaking of the hoarse mob, the few red torches moving and dancing in the darkness like will-o'-the-wisps sporting on the misty surface of a marsh,—the whole scene produced upon her the effect of a weird battle waged by the phantoms of the Witches' Sabbath and the stone monsters of the Church. Imbued from infancy with the superstitious notions of the gipsy tribe, her first thought was that she had surprised the strange beings of the night in their sorceries. Thus she ran back to her cell in affright to hide her head, and implore her pillow to send her some less horrid nightmare.

Little by little, however, the first fumes of fear vanished; from the ever-increasing tumult, and from various other tokens of reality, she felt that she was beset, not by spectres, but by human beings. Then her terror, without being augmented, changed its nature. She reflected upon the possibility of a popular revolt to tear her from her refuge. The idea of again losing life, hope, and Phœbus, whom she still hoped to win in the future, her own absolute defencelessness, all flight cut off, no help at hand, her forlorn condition, her isolation,—these thoughts and countless others overwhelmed her. She fell upon her knees, her face buried in the bed-clothes, her hands clasped above her head, full of agony and apprehension, and, gipsy, pagan, and idolater though she was, she began with sobs to entreat mercy of the good Christian God, and to pray to her hostess, Our Lady. For, believe in nothing though one may, there are moments in life when one belongs to the creed of whatever church is nearest.

She lay thus prostrate for a very long time, trembling indeed, far more than she prayed, chilled by the ever-advancing breath of that frantic mob, wholly ignorant of the meaning of their unbridled rage, knowing not what was on foot, what was being done, what object that throng had in view, but foreseeing some terrible issue.

In the midst of her anguish she heard steps close at hand. She turned. Two men, one of whom carried a lantern, entered her cell. She uttered a faint shriek.

"Fear nothing," said a voice which was not unknown to her; "it is I."

"Who are you?" she asked.

"Pierre Gringoire."

That name calmed her fears. She raised her eyes, and saw that it was indeed the poet; but beside him stood a black figure veiled from head to foot, which silenced her.

"Ah!" replied Gringoire in reproachful tones, "Djali knew me before you did!"

The little goat, in fact, did not wait for Gringoire to pronounce his name. He had no sooner entered, than she rubbed herself fondly against his knees, covering the poet with caresses and white hairs,—for she was shedding her coat. Gringoire returned her caresses.

"Who is that with you?" said the gipsy in a low voice.

"Never fear," replied Gringoire; "it's a friend of mine."

Then the philosopher, placing his lantern on the ground, crouched upon the flagstones, and enthusiastically exclaimed, as he clasped Djali in his arms,—

"Oh, 'tis a pretty creature, doubtless more remarkable for her neatness than her size, but ingenious, subtle, and learned as any grammarian of them all! Come, my Djali, let us see if you have forgotten any of your cunning tricks!

Show us how Master Jacques Charmolue does—"

The man in black would not let him finish. He stepped up to him and gave him a rude shove on the shoulder. Gringoire rose.

"True," said he; "I forgot that we are in haste. Still, that's no reason, master mine, for handling people so roughly. My dear child, your life is in danger, and Djali's too. They want to hang you again. We are your friends, and are come hither to save you. Follow us."

"Is it true?" cried she, distractedly.

"Yes, quite true. Come quickly!"

"I will," she stammered. "But why doesn't your friend speak?"

"Ah!" said Gringoire, "that's because his father and mother were queer people, and brought him up to be silent."

She was forced to rest content with this explanation. Gringoire took her by the hand; his companion picked up the lantern and went on before. The girl was dizzy with dread. She let them lead her away. The goat followed them with leaps of delight, so rejoiced to see Gringoire once more that she made him stumble every moment by thrusting her horns between his legs.

"Such is life," said the philosopher at each escape from falling; "it is often our best friends who cause our downfall!"

They rapidly descended the tower stairs, traversed the church, full of solitude and gloom, but echoing with the din without in frightful contrast to the peace within, and came into the cloister courtyard by the Porte-Rouge. The cloister was deserted; the canons had fled to the bishop's palace to pray together; the court was empty, save for a few timid lackeys hiding in dark corners. They made their way towards the door which led from this courtyard to the Terrain. The man in black opened it with a key which he had about him. Our readers know that the Terrain was a strip of ground enclosed with walls on the City side, and belonging to the Chapter of Notre-Dame, which formed the extreme eastern end of the island in the rear of the church. They found this enclosure quite forsaken. Here there was already less noise in the air. The sound of the Vagrant's assault reached them more faintly, less harshly. The fresh wind which followed the course of the stream stirred with a perceptible rustle the leaves of the one tree planted at the tip of the Terrain. However, they were still very close to the danger. The nearest buildings were the Episcopal palace and the church. There was plainly great commotion within the palace. The gloomy mass was furrowed with lights, which flew from one window to another, as when you burn paper a dark structure of ashes remains, upon which bright sparks trace countless grotesque figures. Beside it the huge towers of Notre-Dame, thus viewed from the rear with the long nave upon which they are built, outlined in black against the vast red light which filled the square, looked like two monstrous andirons for a fire of the Cyclops.

In all directions, so much of Paris as could be seen shimmered in blended light and shade. Rembrandt has just such backgrounds in some of his pictures.

The man with the lantern walked straight to the end of the Terrain.

There, on the very edge of the water, were the worm-eaten remains of a picket-fence with laths nailed across, to which a few withered branches of a low vine clung like the fingers of an open hand. Behind, in the shadow of this trellis, a small boat was hidden. The man signed to Gringoire and his companion to enter it. The goat followed them. The man stepped in last; then he cut the hawser, shoved off from the shore with a long boat-hook, and seizing a pair of oars, seated himself in the bow, rowing with all his strength towards the middle of the stream. The Seine runs very swiftly at this point, and he had some difficulty in clearing the end of the island.

Gringoire's first care on entering the boat, was to take the goat upon his knees. He sat down in the stern; and the young girl, whom the stranger inspired with indescribable fears, took her place beside the poet.

When our philosopher felt the boat moving, he clapped his hands, and kissed Djali between her horns.

"Oh," said he, "here we are all four saved!"

He added, with the look of a deep thinker, "One is sometimes indebted to fortune, sometimes to cunning, for the happy issue of a great undertaking."

The boat proceeded slowly towards the right bank. The young girl watched the stranger with secret dread. He had carefully covered the light of his dark-lantern, and was but dimly visible, in the gloom, like a ghost in the bow of the boat. His cowl, still drawn down, formed a sort of mask over his face; and every time that he opened his arms, with their wide hanging black sleeves, in rowing, they looked like the broad wings of a bat. Moreover, he had not yet breathed a word. The only sound in the boat was that of the oars, mingled with the ripple of the water against the side of the boat.

"By my soul!" suddenly exclaimed Gringoire, "we are as gay and lively as so many owls! We're as silent as Pythagoreans or fishes! By the Rood! my friends, I wish one of you would speak to me. The human voice is music to the human ear. I am not the author of that remark, but Didymus of Alexandria is, and famous words they are. Certes, Didymus of Alexandria is no mean philosopher. One word, my pretty child,—say one word to me, I implore. By the way, you used to make a queer, funny little face; do you still make it? Do you know, my darling, that Parliament holds jurisdiction over all sanctuaries, and that you ran great risks in your cell in Notre-Dame? Alas! the little bird trochylus builds its nest in the jaws of the crocodile. Master, there's the moon peeping out again. How I hope they won't see us! We are doing a laudable deed in saving the damsel, and yet we should be hanged in the king's name if we were caught. Alas! human actions may be taken two ways. I am condemned for the same thing for which you are rewarded. Some admire Cæsar and blame Catiline. Isn't that so, master mine? What do you say to that philosophy? For my part, I possess the philosophy of instinct, of Nature (*ut apes geometriam*).— What! nobody answers me! What disagreeable tempers you both have! I must needs talk to myself. That's what we call

in tragedy a monologue. By the Rood!
—I must tell you that I've just seen
King Louis XI., and that I caught that
oath from him,—by the Rood, then,
they're still keeping up a fine howling
in the City! He's a wicked old villain
of a king. He's all muffled up in furs.
He still owes me the money for my
epithalamium, and he came precious
near hanging me to-night, which would
have bothered me mightily. He is
very stingy to men of merit. He really
ought to read the four books by Salvien
of Cologne, *'Adversus avaritiam.'* In
good sooth, he is a very narrow-minded
king in his dealings with men of letters,
and one who commits most barbarous
cruelties. He's a sponge to soak up
money squeezed from the people. His
economy is like the spleen, which grows
fat upon the leanness of all the other
members. Thus, complaints of the
hardness of the times become murmurs
against the sovereign. Under the reign
of this mild and pious lord, the gallows crack with their weight of victims,
the headsman's blocks grow rotten with
blood, the prisons are filled to bursting.
This king takes in money with one
hand and hangs men with the other.
He is pander to my lady Taxes and my
lord Gibbet. The great are stripped
of their dignities, and the small are
ceaselessly loaded with new burdens.
'Tis an extravagant prince. I do not
love this monarch. And how say you,
my master?"

The man in black suffered the babbling
poet to prate his fill. He continued to
struggle against the strong and angry
current which divides the prow of the
City from the stern of the Ile Notre-
Dame, which we now know as the Ile
Saint-Louis.

"By the way, master," suddenly observed Gringoire, "just as we made our
way into the square through the angry
Vagabonds, did your reverence note
that poor little devil whose brains your
deaf friend was about dashing out
against the railing of the gallery of
kings? I am near-sighted, and did
not recognize him. Do you know who
it could be?"

The stranger made no answer, but
he ceased rowing; his arms fell powerless; his head drooped upon his breast,
and Esmeralda heard him heave a convulsive sigh. She shuddered; she had
heard similar sighs before.

The boat, left to itself, drifted with
the current for some moments. But
finally the man in black drew himself
up, again seized the oars, and began
again to pull against the stream. He
rounded the end of the Ile Notre-Dame,
and bent his course towards the landing-
place of the Hay-market.

"Ah!" said Gringoire, "there's the
Barbeau house. There, master, look:
that collection of black roofs which form
such strange angles; there, beneath that
mass of low, stringy, streaked, and dirty
clouds, where the moon looks like the
yolk of a broken egg. 'Tis a handsome
house. It contains a chapel capped
by a tiny dome full of daintily wrought
decorations. Above it you may see the
bell-tower with its delicate tracery.
There is also a pleasant garden, consisting of a fish-pond, an aviary, an echo,
a mall, a labyrinth, a house for wild
beasts, and a quantity of shady alleys
most agreeable to Venus. There is also
a rascally tree, which goes by the name

of the Lovers' Retreat, because it once hid the meetings of a famous French princess and a gallant and witty constable of France. Alas! we poor philosophers are to a constable what a bed of cabbages and radishes is to the gardens of the Louvre. What does it matter, after all? Human life, for the great as well as for us, is made up of mingled good and ill. Grief goes ever hand in hand with gladness, as the spondee with the dactyl. Master, I must tell you the story of this Barbeau house. It ends in tragic fashion. It was in 1319, during the reign of Philip V., the longest of all the French kings. The moral of the story is, that the temptations of the flesh are hurtful and pernicious. Do not look too often at your neighbour's wife, much as your senses may be tickled by her beauty. Fornication is a very libertine thought. Adultery is curiosity about another's pleasure. Hollo! The noise seems to be growing louder over yonder!"

The din around Notre-Dame was indeed increasing rapidly. They paused and listened. They distinctly heard shouts of victory. All at once a hundred torches, which lit up the glittering helmets of men-at-arms, appeared upon all parts of the church,—upon the towers, galleries, and flying buttresses. These torches seemed searching for some one or something; and soon distant cries of, "The gipsy! The witch! Death to the gipsy!" fell plainly on the ears of the fugitives.

The wretched girl hid her face in her hands, and the unknown boatman began to row frantically for the shore. Meantime our philosopher reflected. He hugged the goat in his arms, and edged very gently away from the gipsy, who nestled closer and closer to him, as her only remaining protector.

Gringoire was certainly cruelly perplexed. He considered that the goat too, "according to the existing law," would be hanged if she were recaptured, which would be a great pity,—poor Djali! that it was quite too much of a good thing to have two condemned prisoners clinging to him at once; and, finally, that his companion asked nothing better than to take sole charge of the girl. A violent conflict went on within him, in which, like Jupiter in the Iliad, he alternately weighed the merits of the gipsy and the goat; and he gazed first at the one, then at the other, with tearful eyes, muttering, "After all, I cannot save you both!"

A shock warned them that the boat had reached shore. The ominous uproar still pervaded the City. The stranger rose, approached the gipsy, and tried to take her by the arm to help her to land. She repulsed him, and clung to Gringoire's sleeve, while he, in his turn, absorbed in the goat, almost pushed her from him. Then she sprang from the boat unaided. She was so distressed that she knew not what she was doing, or where she was going. She stood thus stupefied an instant, watching the water as it glided by. When she had somewhat recovered her senses, she was alone upon the wharf with the stranger. It seems that Gringoire had taken advantage of the moment of their landing, and stolen away with the goat into the throng of houses in the Rue Grenier-sur-l'Eau.

The poor gipsy shuddered when she found herself alone with this man. She tried to speak, to cry out, to call Gringoire; her tongue clove to the roof of her mouth, and no sound issued from her lips. All at once she felt the hand of the unknown upon her arm. It was a cold, strong hand. Her teeth chattered, she turned paler than the moonbeams which illumined her face. The man said not a word. He strode rapidly towards the Grève, holding her firmly by the hand. At that moment she vaguely felt that fate is an irresistible power. She had lost all control of her limbs; she suffered him to drag her along, running while he walked. The quay at this point rises abruptly from the river, but it seemed to her is if she were going down hill.

She looked in every direction. Not a single passer. The quay was absolutely deserted. She heard no sound, she perceived no stir save in the tumultuous and blazing City from which she was separated only by an arm of the Seine, and whence her name came to her joined with threats of death. The rest of Paris lay spread around her in great masses of shadow.

Meantime, the stranger drew her on in the same silence and with the same speed. She recognized none of the places through which she passed. As she went by a lighted window she made an effort, suddenly resisted him, and cried, "Help!"

The owner of the house opened the window, appeared in his shirt with his lamp, looked out upon the quay with a drowsy face, pronounced a few words which she did not catch, and closed the shutter. Thus her last glimmer of hope faded.

The man in black did not utter a syllable; he held her fast, and began to increase his speed. She resisted no longer, but followed him helplessly.

From time to time she mustered a little strength, and said in a voice broken by the unevenness of the pavement and the breathless haste with which she was borne along: "Who are you? Who are you?" He made no reply.

In this way they proceeded along the edge of the quay to an open square of considerable size. The moon shone faintly. They were in the Grève. In the middle stood a sort of black cross; it was the gallows. She recognized all this, and knew where she was.

The man stopped, turning to her, and lifted his cowl.

"Oh!" stammered she, frozen with fear; "I was sure that it must be he."

It was the priest. He looked like the ghost of himself. This was due to the moonlight. It seems as if by that light one could see only the spectres of things.

"Listen!" said he; and she trembled at the sound of that fatal voice which she had not heard for so long a time. He went on with the short, quick gasps which betray deep mental emotion: "Listen! We have reached our goal. I must speak with you. This is the Grève. This is a decisive point in our lives. Fate has delivered us over to each other. Your life is in my hands; my soul rests in yours. Beyond this place and this night all is dark. Hear me, then. I am going to tell you— But first, speak not to me of your Phœbus." (As he said this he came and went, like a man who cannot remain quietly in one place, dragging her after him.) "Speak not of him. If you but mention his name, I know not what I shall do, but it will be something terrible."

This said, like a body which has found its centre of gravity, he again stood still, but his words revealed no less emotion. His voice grew lower and lower.

"Do not turn away your head. Listen to me. It is a serious business. In the first place, I will tell you what has happened. It is no laughing matter, I assure you. What was I saying? Remind me! Ah! There is an order from Parliament which returns you to the scaffold. I have rescued you from the hangman's hands; but even now they are in pursuit of you. See!"

He stretched his arm towards the City. The search did, indeed, seem to be continued. The noise drew nearer; the tower of the lieutenant's house, directly facing the Grève, was full of light and bustle, and soldiers were seen running along the opposite quay with torches, shouting: "The gipsy! Where is the gipsy? Death! Death!"

"You see that they are in pursuit of you, and that I do not lie. I love you. Do not open your lips; rather, do not speak to me, if it be to tell me that you hate me. I am resolved never again to hear that. I have saved you.—Let me finish first.—I can save you wholly. Everything is ready. It is for you to choose. I can do as you would have me."

He interrupted himself excitedly: "No, that is not what I meant to say."

Then, running, and making her run after him,—for he did not loose his hold,—he went straight to the gibbet, and pointed to it.

"Choose between us," said he, coldly.

She tore herself from his grasp, and fell at the foot of the gibbet, throwing her arms about that dismal support; then she half turned her lovely head, and looked at the priest over her shoulder. She seemed a Holy Virgin at the foot of the cross. The priest remained motionless, his finger still raised to the gallows, his gesture unchanged as if he were a statue.

At last the gipsy said,—

"It is less horrible to me than you are."

Then he let his arm drop slowly, and gazed at the pavement in deep dejection.

"If these stones could speak," he murmured, "yes, they would say, 'There is a very miserable man.'"

He went on. The girl, kneeling before the gibbet, and veiled by her long hair, let him speak without interruption.

He had now assumed a gentle, plaintive tone, in painful contrast with the proud severity of his features.

"I love you. Oh, it is indeed true! Is there then no visible spark of that fire which burns my soul? Alas! girl, night and day; yes, night and day,—does this deserve no pity? It is a love which consumes me night and day, I tell you; it is torture. Oh, my suffering is too great to be endured, my poor child! It is a thing worthy of compassion, I assure you. You see that I speak gently to you. I would fain have you cease to feel such horror of me. After all, if a man love a woman, it is not his fault! Oh, my God! What! will you never forgive me? Will you always hate me? Is this the end? It is this that makes me wicked, I tell you, and horrible in my own sight! You do not even look at me! You are thinking of other things, perhaps, while I stand and talk to you, and both of us are trembling on the verge of eternity! But do not talk to me of your soldier! What! I might throw myself at your knees; what! I might kiss, not your feet, for that you would not suffer, but the ground beneath your feet; what! I might sob like a child: I might tear from my bosom, not words, but my heart and my very life, to show you how I love you; all would be in vain,—all! And yet your soul is full of gentleness and tenderness; you are radiant with the most beauteous mildness; you are all sweetness, goodness, mercy, and charm. Alas! you are unkind to me alone! Oh, what a freak of fate!"

He buried his face in his hands. The young girl heard his sobs. It was the first time she had seen him weep. Standing thus, shaken by sobs, he appeared more miserable and more suppliant than had he been on his knees. He wept thus for some time.

"Ah, well!" he added, his first tears over, "I can find no words to express my feelings; and yet I pondered well what I should say to you. Now, I tremble and shudder; I give way at the decisive moment; I feel that some superior power surrounds us, and I stammer. Oh, I shall fall to the ground if you do not take pity upon me, upon yourself! Do not condemn us both! If you knew how much I love you; what a heart mine is! Oh, what an abandonment of all virtue! what a desperate desertion of myself! A scholar, I scoff

at science; a gentleman, I disgrace my name; a priest, I make my missal a pillow of foul desires, grossly insult my God! All this for your sake, enchantress! to be worthy of your hell! And you reject the damned soul! Oh, let me tell you all! more still, something yet more horrible, oh, far more horrible—"

As he pronounced these last words, his look became quite wild. He was silent an instant, then resumed as if talking to himself, and in a firm voice,—

"Cain, what hast thou done with thy brother?"

There was another pause, and he added,—

"What have I done with him, Lord? I took him in my arms, I brought him up, I fed him, I loved him, I idolized him, and I killed him! Yes, Lord, for they have just now dashed his head, before my very eyes, against the stones of your temple, and it was because of me, because of this woman, because of her—"

His eye was haggard. His voice died away; he still repeated mechanically, over and over, at considerable intervals, like a bell prolonging its last vibration, "Because of her; because of her—"

Here his tongue ceased to articulate any distinct sound, although his lips still moved. All at once he gave way, and sank in a heap, lying motionless upon the ground, his head upon his knees.

A slight movement made by the girl to pull her foot from under him revived him. He slowly drew his hand over his hollow cheeks, and looked in amazement at his fingers, which were wet. "What!" he muttered, "have I wept?"

And turning quickly to the gipsy with indescribable anguish:—

"Alas! and you could coldly see me weep! Child, do you know that those tears are burning lava? Is it then really true,—in the man we hate, nothing moves us? You would see me die, and still laugh! One word,—only one word of pardon! Do not tell me that you love me, only tell me that you will try; that shall suffice, and I will save you. If not,—oh, time passes. I conjure you! by all that you hold sacred, do not wait until I am once more turned to stone, like the gibbet which also claims you! Think, that I hold the destinies of both in my hand; that I am mad,—it is terrible!—that I may let all fall; and that beneath us yawns a bottomless pit, wretched girl, wherein my fall shall follow yours through all eternity! One word of kindness,—but a single word!"

She opened her mouth to answer him. He threw himself upon his knees before her, to receive with adoration the words, perhaps relenting, which were about to fall from her lips. She said to him, "You are an assassin!"

The priest caught her fiercely in his arms, and began to laugh an abominable laugh.

"Well, yes, an assassin!" said he; "and you shall be mine. You will not have me for your slave, you shall have me for your master. You shall be mine! You shall be mine! I have a den whither I will drag you. You must follow me, you must needs follow me, or I will give you up to justice! You must die, my beauty, or be mine,—be the priest's, the apostate's, the assassin's! and that this night; do you hear me? Come! rejoice; come, kiss me, foolish girl! The tomb, or my bed!"

His eyes flashed with rage and desire. His impure lips reddened the neck of the young girl. She struggled in his arms. He covered her with frantic kisses.

"Do not bite me, monster!" she shrieked. "Oh, the hateful, poisonous monk! Let me go! I will tear out your vile grey hair, and throw it by handfuls in your face!"

He flushed, then paled, then released her, and looked at her gloomily. She thought herself victorious, and went on:—

"I tell you that I belong to my Phœbus, that 'tis Phœbus I love, that Phœbus alone is handsome! You, priest, are old! you are ugly! Begone!"

He uttered a violent cry, like the wretch to whom a red-hot iron is applied. "Then die!" he said, gnashing his teeth. She saw his frightful look, and strove to fly. He overtook her, shook her, threw her down, and walked rapidly towards the corner of the Tour-Roland, dragging her after him over the pavement by her fair hands.

Reaching it, he turned to her:—

"For the last time, will you be mine?"

She answered emphatically,—

"No!"

Then he called in a loud voice,—

"Gudule! Gudule! here is the gipsy girl! Avenge yourself!"

The young girl felt herself suddenly seized by the elbow. She looked. A fleshless arm was thrust from a loophole in the wall, and held her with an iron grip.

"Hold her fast!" said the priest; "it's the runaway gipsy. Do not let her go. I will fetch the officers. You shall see her hanged."

A guttural laugh from the other side of the wall replied to these bloody words: "Ha! ha! ha!" The gipsy saw the priest depart in the direction of the Pont Notre-Dame. The tramp of horses was heard coming from that quarter.

The girl recognized the spiteful recluse. Panting with terror, she tried to release herself. She writhed, she twisted herself in agony and despair; but the woman held her with unnatural strength. The thin bony fingers which bruised her flesh fastened about her arm like a vice. That band seemed riveted to her wrist. It was stronger than any chain, stronger than any pillory or iron ring; it was a pair of intelligent and living pincers issuing from a wall.

Exhausted, she sank back, and the fear of death took possession of her. She thought of the beauty of life, of youth, of the sight of the sky, of the various aspects of Nature, of the love of Phœbus, of all that was behind her and of all that was rapidly coming upon her, of the priest who would denounce her, of the hangman who would soon arrive, of the gallows which was already there. Then terror rose to the very roots of her hair, and she heard the melancholy laugh of the recluse, as she whispered in her ear,—

"Ha! ha! ha! You shall be hanged!"

She turned, almost fainting, to the window, and saw the savage face of the nun through the bars.

"What have I done to you?" she asked feebly.

The recluse made no answer; she began to mumble in angry, mocking sing-song, "Gipsy girl! gipsy girl! gipsy girl!"

The luckless Esmeralda veiled her face with her hair, seeing that it was no human being with whom she had to deal.

All at once the recluse exclaimed, as if the gipsy's question had taken all this time to penetrate her troubled brain:—

"What have you done to me, do you say? Ah! What have you done to me, indeed, you gipsy! Well, listen, and I will tell you. I had a child, even I! Do you hear? I had a child,—a child, I say! A pretty little girl! My Agnès," she repeated, her wits wandering for a moment, and kissing something in the gloom. "Well, are you listening, gipsy? They stole my child; they took my child from me; they ate my child! That is what you have done to me."

The young girl answered, as innocently as the lamb in the fable,—

"Alas! I probably was not even born then!"

"Oh, yes!" rejoined the recluse, "you must have been born. You had a hand in it. She would have been about your age! There! For fifteen years I have been in this hole; for fifteen years I have suffered; for fifteen years I have prayed; for fifteen years I have dashed my head against these four walls. I tell you, 'twas the gipsies who stole her from me,—do you hear?—and who gnawed her bones. Have you a heart? Fancy what it is to have a child who plays at your knee; a child who sucks your breast; a child who sleeps in your arms. It is such a helpless, innocent thing! Well, that,—that's what they took from me, what they killed for me! The good God knows it well! Now it is my turn; I will slaughter the Egyptians. Oh, how I would bite you, if the bars did not prevent me! My head is too big to pass through them! Poor little thing! they took her while she slept! And if they waked her when they snatched her up, all her shrieks were vain; I was not there! Ah, gipsy mothers, you ate my child! Come, look at yours!"

Then she began to laugh, or gnash her teeth, for the two things were much the same in that frenzied face. Dawn was at hand. An ashen light faintly illumined the scene, and the gallows became more and more distinctly visible in the centre of the square. From the other side, towards the Pont Notre-Dame the poor prisoner imagined she heard the tramp of approaching horsemen.

"Madame," she cried, clasping her hands and falling on her knees, dishevelled, frantic, mad with fright,— "Madame, have pity! they are coming. I never harmed you. Would you see me die so horrible a death before your very eyes? You are merciful, I am sure. It is too awful! Let me save myself! Let me go! Have mercy! I cannot die thus!"

"Give me back my child!" said the recluse.

"Mercy! mercy!"

"Give me back my child!"

"Let me go, in Heaven's name!"

"Give me back my child!"

Upon this, the girl sank down, worn out and exhausted, her eyes already having the glazed look of one dead.

"Alas!" she stammered forth, "you seek your child, and I seek my parents."

"Give me my little Agnès!" continued Gudule. "You know not where she is? Then die! I will tell you all. I was a prostitute; I had a child, they took my child from me. It was the gipsies who did it. You see that you must die. When your gipsy mother comes to claim you, I shall say, 'Mother, look upon that gibbet!—Or else restore my child!' Do you know where she is,—where my little girl is? Stay, I will show you. Here's her shoe,—all that is left me. Do you know where the mate to it is? If you know, tell me, and if it is only at the other end of the world, I will go on my knees to get it."

So saying, with her other hand, stretched through the bars, she showed the gipsy the little embroidered shoe. It was already light enough to distinguish the shape and colours.

"Show me that shoe," said the gipsy shuddering. "My God! my God!"

And at the same time with her free hand she hastily opened the little bag adorned with green glass beads, which she wore about her neck.

"That's it! that's it!" growled Gudule; "search for your devilish spells!"

All at once she stopped short, trembled from head to foot, and cried out in a voice which came from her inmost soul, "My daughter!"

The gipsy had drawn from the bag a tiny shoe, precisely like the other. A strip of parchment was fastened to the little shoe, upon which these verses were written:

"When the mate to this you find,

Her arms to thee shall ope a mother kind."

Quick as a flash of lightning the recluse compared the two shoes, read the inscription on the parchment, and pressed her face, beaming with divine rapture, to the window-bars exclaiming,—

"My daughter! my daughter!"

"Mother!" replied the gipsy.

Here we must forbear to set down more.

The wall and the iron grating parted the two. "Oh, the wall!" cried the recluse. "Oh, to see her and not to kiss her! Your hand! your hand!"

The girl put her arm through the window; the recluse threw herself upon the hand, pressed her lips to it, and stood lost in that kiss, the only sign of life being an occasional sob which heaved her bosom. Yet she wept torrents of tears in silence, in the darkness, like rain falling in the night. The poor mother poured out in floods upon that idolized hand the dark, deep fountain of tears within her heart, into which all her grief had filtered, drop by drop, for fifteen years.

Suddenly she rose, flung her long grey hair back from her face, and without a word began to shake the bars of her cell more fiercely than a lioness. They held firm. Then she brought from one corner a large paving-stone which served her as a pillow, and hurled it against them with such violence that one of them broke, flashing countless sparks. A second blow utterly destroyed the old iron cross which barricaded her window. Then with both hands she pulled out and demolished the rusty fragments. There are

moments when a woman's hands seem endowed with supernatural strength.

A passage being cleared,—and it took les than a minute to do the work,—she seized her daughter by the waist and dragged her into the cell. "Come, let me draw you out of the abyss!" she murmured.

When her daughter was in the cell, she placed her gently on the ground, then took her up again, and bearing her in her arms as if she were still her little Agnès, she paced to and fro in the narrow space, frantic, mad with joy, singing, shouting, kissing her daughter, talking to her, bursting into laughter, melting tears, all at once, and with the utmost passion.

"My daughter! my daughter!" she cried. "I've found my daughter! Here she is! The good God has restored her to me. Come, all of you! Is there no one here to see that I've found my daughter? Lord Jesus, how beautiful she is! You made me wait fifteen years, my good God, but it was to make her more beautiful for me! Then the gipsies did not eat her! Who told me so? My little girl! my little girl! kiss me. Those good gipsies! I love gipsies. It is really you. Then that was why my heart leaped within me every time you passed; and I thought it was hate! Forgive me, Agnès, forgive me. You thought me very cruel, didn't you? I love you. Have you still the same little mark on your neck? Let us see. She has it still. Oh, how beautiful you are! It was I who gave you those big eyes, miss. Kiss me. I love you. I care not now if other mothers have children; I can laugh them to scorn. They may come. Here is mine. Here's her neck, her eyes, her hair, her hand. Find me another as lovely! Oh, I tell you she'll have plenty of lovers, this girl of mine! I have wept for fifteen years. All my beauty has left me and gone to her. Kiss me."

She made her a thousand other extravagant speeches, their only merit being in the tone in which they were uttered, disordered the poor girl's dress until she made her blush, smoothed her silken hair with her hand, kissed her foot, her knee, her forehead, her eyes, went into ecstasies over each and all. The young girl made no resistance, but repeated ever and anon, in a low tone and with infinite sweetness, "Mother!"

"Look you, my little one," went on the recluse, interrupting each word with kisses,—"look you; I shall love you dearly. We will go away; we shall be very happy. I have inherited something at Rheims, in our native country. You know, at Rheims? Oh, no! you don't remember; you were too little. If you only knew how pretty you were at four months old! Tiny feet, which people, out of curiosity, came all the way from Epernay, full seven leagues off, to see! We will have a field and a house. I will put you to sleep in my bed. My God! my God! who would ever have believed it? I've found my daughter!"

"Oh, mother!" said the girl, at last recovering sufficient strength to speak in spite of her emotion, "the gipsy woman told me it would be so. There was a kind gipsy woman of our tribe who died last year, and who always took care of me as if she had been my nurse. It was she who hung this bag about my neck. She always said to me, 'Little one, guard this trinket well.

It is a precious treasure; it will help you to find your mother. You wear your mother around your neck.' The gipsy foretold it!"

The nun again clasped her daughter in her arms.

"Come; let me kiss you! You said that so prettily. When we are in our own country, we will give these little shoes to the Child Jesus in the church; we surely owe that much to the kind Blessed Virgin. Heavens! what a sweet voice you have! When you spoke to me just now, it was like music. Oh, my Lord God, I have found my child! But is it credible,—all this story? Nothing can kill one, for I have not died of joy."

And then she again began to clap her hands, to laugh, and cry.

"How happy we shall be!"

At this moment the cell rang with the clash of arms and the galloping feet of horses, which seemed to come from the Pont Notre-Dame, and to be advancing nearer and nearer along the quay. The gipsy threw herself into the nun's arms in an agony.

"Save me! save me, mother! I hear them coming!"

The recluse turned pale.

"Heavens! What do you say? I had forgotten; you are pursued! Why, what have you done?"

"I know not," replied the unhappy child; "but I am condemned to die."

"To die!" said Gudule, tottering as if struck by lightning. "To die!" she repeated slowly, gazing steadily into her daughter's face.

"Yes, mother," replied the desperate girl, "they mean to kill me. They are coming now to capture me. That gallows is for me! Save me! save me! They come! Save me!"

The recluse stood for some moments motionless, as if turned to stone; then she shook her head doubtingly, and all at once burst into loud laughter; but her former frightful laugh had returned:—

"Ho! ho! No; it is a dream! Oh, yes; I lost her, I lost her for fifteen years, and then I found her again, and it was but for an instant! And they would take her from me again! Now that she is grown up, that she is so fair, that she talks to me, that she loves me, they would devour her before my eyes,—mine, who am her mother! Oh, no; such things cannot be! The good God would not suffer them."

Here the cavalcade seemed to pause, and a distant voice was heard, saying,—

"This way, Master Tristan; the priest says that we shall find her at the Rat-Hole!" The tramp of horses began again.

The recluse sprang up with a despairing cry.

"Save yourself! save yourself, my child! I remember now! You are right; it is your death! Horror! Malediction! Save yourself!"

She thrust her head from the window, and rapidly withdrew it.

"Stay!" she said in a low, curt, and mournful tone, convulsively clasping the hand of the gipsy, who was more dead than alive. "Stay! do not breathe! There are soldiers everywhere. You cannot go; it is too light."

Her eyes were dry and burning. She stood for a moment speechless; then she strode up and down the cell, pausing at intervals to tear out handfuls

of her grey hair. Suddenly she said: "They are coming; I will speak to them. Hide yourself in this corner; they will not see you. I will tell them that you have escaped; that I let you go, by my faith!"

She laid her daughter—for she still held her in her arms—in a corner of the cell which was not visible from without. She made her crouch down, carefully arranged her so that neither hand nor foot protruded beyond the shadow, loosened her black hair, which spread over her white gown to hide it, put before her her jug and paving-stone,—the only articles of furniture which she had,—imagining that they would conceal her; and when this was done, feeling calmer, she knelt and prayed. Day, which was but just breaking, still left many shadows in the Rat-Hole.

At that instant the voice of the priest—that infernal voice—passed very close to the cell, shouting, —

"This way, Captain Phœbus de Châteaupers!"

At that name, at that voice, Esmeralda, huddling in her corner, made a movement.

"Do not stir!" said Gudule.

She had hardly finished speaking when a riotous crowd of men, swords, and horses, halted outside the cell. The mother rose hastily, and placed herself before the window in such a way as to cut off all view of the room. She saw a numerous band of armed men, on foot and on horseback, drawn up in the Grève. The officer in command sprang to the ground and came towards her.

"Old woman," said this man, who had an atrocious face, "we are looking for a witch, that we may hang her. We were told that you had her."

The poor mother assumed the most indifferent air that she could, and answered,—

"I don't know what you mean."

The other replied, "Zounds! Then what was that frightened archdeacon talking about? Where is he?"

"Sir," said a soldier, "he has disappeared."

"Come, now, old hag," resumed the commanding officer, "don't lie! A witch was left in your care. What have you done with her?"

The recluse dared not deny everything, lest she should rouse suspicion, and answered in a surly but seemingly truthful tone,—

"If you mean a tall girl who was thrust into my hands just now, I can only tell you that she bit me, and I let her go. There. Now leave me in peace."

The officer pulled a wry face.

"Don't lie to me, old scarecrow!" he replied. "I am Tristan l'Hermite, and I am the friend of the king. Tristan l'Hermite, do you hear?" he added looking round the Grève, " 'Tis a name familiar here."

"You might be Satan l'Hermite," responded Gudule, whose hopes began to rise, "and I could tell you nothing more, and should be no more afraid of you."

"Odds bodikins!" said Tristan, "here's an old gossip for you! Ah, so the witch girl escaped! And which way did she go?"

Gudule answered indifferently,—

"Through the Rue du Mouton, I believe."

Tristan turned his head, and signed to his troop to prepare to resume their march. The recluse breathed more freely.

"Sir," suddenly said an archer, "pray ask this old sorceress how the bars of her window came to be so twisted and broken."

This question revived the miserable mother's anguish. Still, she did not lose all presence of mind.

"They were always so," she stammered.

"Nonsense!" rejoined the archer; "only yesterday they formed a beautiful black cross which inspired pious thoughts in all who looked upon it."

Tristan cast a side-glance at the recluse.

"It seems to me that our friend looks embarrassed."

The unfortunate woman felt that everything depended upon her putting a good face on the matter, and, with death in her soul, she began to laugh. Mothers have such courage.

"Pooh!" said she, "that man is drunk. 'Twas more than a year ago that the tail of a cart full of stones was backed into my window and destroyed the grating. And, what's more, I scolded the carter roundly."

"That's true," said another archer; "I was here at the time."

There are always people everywhere who have seen everything. This unexpected testimony from the archer encouraged the recluse, who during this interrogatory felt as if she were crossing a precipice on the sharp edge of a knife.

But she was condemned to a continual alteration between hope and fear.

"If it was done by a cart," returned the first soldier, "the broken ends of the bars would have been driven inward; but they are bent outward."

"Ho! ho!" said Tristan; "your nose is as sharp as that of any inquisitor at the Châtelet. Answer him, old woman!"

"Good heaven!" she cried, at her wits' end, and in a voice which despite al her efforts was tearful, "I swear, sir, that it was a cart which broke those bars. You heard that man say he saw it; and besides, what has that to do with your gipsy?"

"Hum!" growled Tristan.

"The devil!" added the soldier, flattered by the provost's praises; "the fractures in the iron are quite fresh!"

Tristan shook his head. She turned pale.

"How long ago did you say this affair of the cart occurred?"

"A month,—perhaps a fortnight, sir. I'm sure I don't remember."

"She said it was a year, just now," observed the soldier.

"That looks queer!" said the provost.

"Sir," she cried, still pressing close to the window, and trembling lest their suspicions should lead them to put in their heads and examine the cell,—"sir, I swear it was a cart that broke these bars; I swear it by all the angels in paradise! If it was not a cart, may I be damned forever: and may God renounce me."

"You seem very ready to swear!" said Tristan, with his searching glance.

The poor woman felt her courage sink. She was in a state to commit any folly, and with terror she realized she was saying what she ought not to say.

Here another soldier ran up, shouting,—

"Sir, the old fagot lies. The witch did not escape through the Rue du Mouton. The chain has been stretched across the street all night, and the chain-keeper has seen no one pass."

Tristan, whose face grew more forbidding every instant, addressed the recluse:—

"What have you to say to this?"

She still strove to brave this fresh contradiction.

"I don't know, sir; I may have been mistaken. I dare say, indeed, that she crossed the water."

"That is in the opposite direction," said the provost. "However, it is not very likely that she would wish to return to the City, where she was closely pursued. You lie, old woman!"

"And then," added the first soldier, "there is no boat either on this side of the water or on the other."

"Perhaps she swam across," replied the recluse, disputing the ground inch by inch.

"Can women swim?" said the soldier.

"Odds bodikins! old woman! you lie! you lie!" angrily rejoined Tristan. "I have a great mind to let the witch go, and hang you in her stead. A quarter of an hour of the rack may wring the truth from your lips. Come! follow us!"

She seized eagerly upon his words:—

"As you like, sir. So be it, so be it! The rack. I am willing. Take me. Be quick; be quick. Let us be off at once. Meantime," thought she, "my daughter may escape."

"Zounds!" said the provost; "so greedy for the rack! I don't understand this mad-woman!"

An old grey-headed serjeant of the watch stepped from the ranks, and addressing the provost, said,—

"Mad, indeed, sir! If she let the gipsy go, it was not her fault, for she has no liking for gipsies. For fifteen years I have done duty on the watch; and I have heard her curse the gipsy women nightly with endless execrations. If the girl of whom we are in search is, as I suppose, the little dancer with the goat, she particularly detests her."

Gudule made an effort, and said,—

"Particularly."

The unanimous testimony of the men belonging to the watch confirmed the old serjeant's statement. Tristan l'Hermite, despairing of learning anything from the recluse, turned his back upon her, and with unspeakable anxiety she saw him move slowly towards his horse.

"Come," he muttered, "we must be off. Let us resume our search. I shall not sleep until this gipsy girl be hanged."

Still, he hesitated some time before mounting his horse. Gudule trembled between life and death as she saw him glance about the square with the restless air of a hunting-dog, which scents the lair of the wild beast and refuses to depart. At last he shook his head and leaped into his saddle. Gudule's terribly overladen heart swelled, and she said in a low voice, with a glance at her daughter, at whom she had not dared to look while the soldiers were there, "Saved!"

The poor girl had crouched in her corner all this time, without moving or breathing, staring death in the face. She had lost none of the scene between Gudule and Tristan, and each of her mother's pangs had found an echo in her own soul. She had heard the successive snappings of the thread which held her suspended over the abyss: twenty times she had felt that it must break, and now at last she began to breathe freely, and to hope that her footing was secure. At this instant she heard a voice say to the provost,—

" 'Sblood! Mr. Provost, it is no business for a soldier to hang witches. The mob still rages yonder. I must leave you to your own devices. You will not object to my rejoining my company, who are left without a captain."

This voice was that of Phœbus de Châteaupers. She underwent an indescribable revulsion of feeling. So he was there,— her friend, her protector, her stay, her refuge, her Phœbus! She rose, and before her mother could prevent her, flew to the window, crying,—

"Phœbus! help, my Phœbus!"

Phœbus was no longer there. He had just galloped round the corner of the Rue de la Coutellerie. But Tristan was not yet gone.

The recluse flung herself upon her daughter with a roar. She dragged her violently back, digging her nails into her neck. A tigress does not look twice when the safety of her young is in question. But it was too late. Tristan had seen her.

"Ha! ha!" cried he, with a laugh which bared all his teeth, and made his face like the muzzle of a wolf, "two mice in the trap!"

"I thought as much," said the soldier.

Tristan clapped him on the shoulder,—

"You are a famous cat! Come," he added, "where is Henriet Cousin?"

A man who had neither the dress nor the manner of a soldier stepped from the ranks. He wore a motley garb of brown and grey; his hair was smooth and lank, his sleeves were of leather, and in his huge hand was a bundle of rope. This man always accompanied Tristan, who always accompanied Louis XI.

"My friend," said Tristan l'Hermite, "I presume that this is the witch we are seeking. You will hang her for me. Have you your ladder?"

"There is one yonder under the shed of the Pillar House," replied the man. "Are we to do the business on this gallows?" he continued, pointing to the stone gibbet.

"Yes."

"Ho! ho!" rejoined the man, with a coarse laugh even more bestial than that of the provost; "we shan't have far to go."

"Despatch!" said Tristan; "you can laugh afterwards."

Meantime, since Tristan had seen her daughter, and all hope was lost, the recluse had not spoken a word. She had cast the poor gipsy, almost lifeless, into the corner of the cell, and resumed her place at the window, her hands clinging to the sides of the frame like two claws. In this position her eyes wandered boldly over the soldiers, the light of reason having once more faded from them. When Henriet Cousin approached her refuge, she glared so savagely at him that he shrank back.

"Sir," said he, returning to the provost, "which am I to take?"

"The young one."

"So much the better; for the old one seems hard to manage."

"Poor little dancer with the goat!" said the old serjeant of the watch.

Henriet Cousin again advanced to the window. The mother's eye made his own fall. He said somewhat timidly,—

"Madame,—"

She interrupted him in very low but furious tones:

"What do you want?"

"Not you," said he; "it is the other."

'What other?"

"The young one."

She began to wag her head, crying,—

"There's nobody here! there's nobody here! there's nobody here!"

"Yes, there is!" rejoined the hangman, "and you know it well. Let me have the young one. I don't want to harm you."

She said with a strange sneer,—

"Ah! you don't want to harm me!"

"Let me have the other, madame; it is the provost's will."

She repeated with a foolish look,—

"There's nobody here!"

"I tell you there is!" replied the hangman; "we all saw that there were two of you."

"Look then!" said the recluse, with a sneer. "Put your head in at the window."

The hangman scrutinized the mother's nails, and dared not venture.

"Despatch!" cried Tristan, who had ranged his men in a ring around the Rat-Hole, and himself sat on horseback near the gibbet.

Henriet returned to the provost once more, utterly out of countenance. He had laid his rope on the ground, and awkwardly twirled his hat in his hands.

"Sir," he inquired, "how am I to get in?"

"Through the door."

"There is none."

"Through the window."

"It is too small."

"Then make it bigger," angrily exclaimed Tristan. "Have you no pick-axes?"

From the back of her den, the mother, ever on the alert, watched them. She had lost all hope, she knew not what she wished, but they should not have her daughter.

Henriet Cousin went to fetch his box of tools from the shed of the Pillar House. He also brought out the trestles, which he at once set up against the gibbet. Five or six of the provost's men armed themselves with picks and levers, and Tristan moved towards the window with them.

"Old woman," said the provost in a stern voice, "surrender that girl with a good grace."

She looked at him like one who does not understand.

" 'Sblood!" added Tristan, "why should you prevent that witch from being hanged, as it pleases the king?"

The wretched woman began to laugh wildly.

"Why? She is my daughter!"

The tone in which she uttered that word made even Henriet Cousin shudder.

"I am sorry," replied the provost, "but it is the king's good pleasure."

She shrieked with redoubled laughter,—

"What is your king to me? I tell you she is my daughter!"

"Make a hole in the wall," said Tristan.

It was only necessary to remove one course of stones under the window, in order to make an opening of sufficient size. When the mother heard the picks and levers undermining her fortress, she uttered an awful scream; then she began to pace her cell with frightful speed,— one of the habits of a wild beast which she had acquired in her cage. She said no more, but her eyes flamed. The soldiers were chilled to the marrow.

All at once she caught up her paving stone, laughed, and hurled it with both hands at the workmen. The stone, ill aimed (for her hands trembled), struck no one and fell at the feet of Tristan's horse. She ground her teeth.

Meantime, although the sun had not yet risen, it was broad daylight; a lovely pink tint illumined the worm-eaten old chimneys of the Pillar House. It was the hour when the windows of the earliest risers in the great city open joyously upon the roofs. Some few country people, some fruiterers going to market on their donkeys, began to pass through the Grève; they paused a moment at sight of this cluster of soldiers huddled in front of the Rat-Hole, looked at them in surprise, then went their way.

The recluse had seated herself beside her daughter, covering her with her body, her eye fixed, listening to the poor girl, who never stirred, but murmured softly the one word, "Phœbus! Phœbus!" As the work of the destroyers progressed, the mother mechanically moved back, pressing the young girl closer and closer against the wall. All at once she saw the stones (for she was on the watch and never took her eyes from them) quiver, and she heard Tristan's voice urging the labourers on. Then she woke from the stupor into which she had sunk, exclaiming,—and, as she spoke, her voice now pierced the ear like a saw, then stammered as if all the curses which she uttered crowded to her lips at once:

"Ho! ho! ho! But this is horrible! You are robbers! Do you really mean to take my daughter from me? I tell you it is my daughter! Oh, cowards! Oh, base hangmen! Vile assassins! Help! help! Fire! Will they thus take my child? Then, what is he whom men call the good God?"

Then turning to Tristan, with foaming mouth, haggard eyes, on all fours like a panther, and bristling with rage:—

"Come and take my daughter! Do you not understand that this woman tells you it is her daughter? Do you know what it is to have a child of your own? Have you no mate, O lynx? Have you never had a cub? And if you have little ones, when they howl does nothing stir within you?"

"Down with the stones," said Tristan; "they are loosened."

The levers lifted the ponderous course of stone. It was, as we have said, the mother's last bulwark.

She threw herself upon it, tried to hold it up. She scratched it with her nails; but the heavy block, set in motion by six men, escaped from her grasp and slid gently to the ground along the iron levers.

The mother, seeing that an entrance was effected, fell across the opening, barricading the breach with her body, wringing her hands, beating her head against the flagstones, and shrieking in a voice hoarse with fatigue and scarcely audible,—

"Help! Fire! Fire!"

"Now, seize the girl," said Tristan, still unmoved.

The mother glared at the soldiers in so terrible a fashion that they would much rather have retreated than advanced.

"Come, come," repeated the provost. "Here, Henriet Cousin!"

No one stirred a step.

The provost swore:—

"By the Cross! my soldiers! Afraid of a woman!"

"Sir," said Henriet, "do you call that a woman?"

"She has a lion's mane!" said another.

"Come!" resumed the provost, "the gap is broad enough. Go in three abreast, as at the breach of Pontoise. Have done with it, by the head of Mahomet! The first who recoils I'll cut in two!"

Thus placed between the provost and the mother, both alike menacing, the soldiers hesitated an instant; then, making their choice, they advanced upon the Rat-Hole.

When the recluse saw this, she rose suddenly to her knees, shook her hair back from her face, then let her thin, bleeding hands fall upon her thighs. Great tears started one by one from her eyes; they trickled down a wrinkle in her cheeks, like a torrent down the bed which it has worn for itself. At the same time she spoke, but in a voice so suppliant, so sweet, so submissive, and so full of pathos, that more than one old fire-eater about Tristan wiped his eyes.

"Gentlemen! soldiers! one word. I must say one thing to you. She is my daughter, you see,—my dear little daughter whom I lost! Listen. It is quite a story. You must know that I was once very friendly with the soldiers. They were always kind to me in the days when little boys threw stones at me because I led a light life. Do you see? You will leave me my child, when you know all! I am a poor woman of the town. The gipsies stole her away from me. I kept her shoe for fifteen years. Stay; here it is. That was the size of her foot. Paquette Chantefleurie, at Rheims,—Rue Folle-Peine! Perhaps you knew her once. That was I. When you were young, you led a merry life; there were fine doings then. You will take pity on me, won't you, gentlemen? The gipsies stole her from me; they kept her hidden from me for fifteen years. I thought she was dead. Only fancy, my kind friends, I thought she was dead. I have spent fifteen years here, in this cave, with never a spark of fire in winter. That was hard to bear, that was. The poor, dear little shoe! I have shed so many tears that the good God heard me. Last night he gave me back my girl. The good God wrought a miracle. She was not dead. You will not take her from me, I am sure. If it were only myself, I would not complain; but for her, a child of sixteen! Let her have time to see the sun! What has she done to you? Nothing at all. No more have I. If you only knew that I have nobody but her, that I am old,

that she is a blessing sent down to me by the Holy Virgin! And then, you are all so kind! You did not know that she was my daughter; now you know it. Oh, I love her! Mr. Provost, I would rather have a hole through my heart than a scratch on her finger. You look like a good, kind gentleman! What I tell you, explains the whole thing, doesn't it? Oh, if you ever had a mother, sir! You are the captain; leave me my child! Remember that I pray to you on my knees, as one prays to Jesus Chirst! I ask nothing of any one; I am from Rheims, gentlemen; I have a little field there, left me by my uncle, Mahiet Pradon. I am not a beggar. I want nothing, but I must have my child! Oh, I must keep my child! The good God, who is master of us all, never gave her back to me for nothing! The king! you say the king! It can't give him much pleasure to have my little girl killed! And besides, the king is good! It's my daughter! It's my daughter, my own girl! She is not the king's! she is not yours! I will go away! we will both go away! After all, they will let two women pass,—a mother and her daughter! Let us pass! we are from Rheims! Oh, you are very kind, serjeants! I love you all. You will not take my dear little one from me; it is impossible, isn't it? Utterly impossible! My child, my child!"

We will not try to give any idea of her gestures, of her accent, of the tears which she swallowed as she spoke, of her hands which she clasped and then wrung, of the heartrending smiles, the pathetic glances, the groans, the sighs, the agonizing and piercing cries which the mingled with her wild, incoherent, rambling words. When she ceased, Tristan l'Hermite frowned, but it was to hide a tear that dimmed his tigerish eye. However, he conquered this weakness, and said curtly,—

"It is the king's command."

Then he bent down to Henriet Cousin and said in a low voice,—

"Put an end to this!"

Perhaps the terrible provost himself felt his heart fail him.

The hangman and his men entered the cell. The mother made no resistance. She only dragged herself towards her daughter and threw herself heavily upon her.

The gipsy saw the soldiers coming. The horror of death revived her.

"My mother!" she cried in tones of unspeakable distress; "my mother! They are coming! Defend me!"

"Yes, my love. I will defend you!" replied her mother, in a feeble voice; and clasping her closely in her arms, she covered her with kisses. The two, prostrate on the ground, mother and daughter, were a sight worthy of pity.

Henriet Cousin seized the girl just below her beautiful shoulders. When she felt his hand, she shrieked and fainted. The hangman, whose big tears fell drop by drop upon her, tried to raise her in his arms. He strove to loose her mother's hold, she having, as it were, knotted her hands about her daughter's waist; but she clung so closely to her child that it was impossible to part them. Henriet Cousin therefore dragged the girl from the cell, and her mother after her. The mother's eyes were also closed.

At this moment the sun rose, and

there was already a considerable crowd of people in the square, looking on from a little distance to see who was being thus dragged over the pavement to the gallows,—for this was Provost Tristan's way at hangings. He had a mania for hindering the curious from coming too close.

There was no one at the windows. Only, far off, on the top of the Notre-Dame tower overlooking the Grève, two men were to be seen darkly outlined against the clear morning sky, apparently watching the proceedings.

Henriet Cousin paused with his burden at the foot of the fatal ladder, and, scarcely breathing, so strongly was he moved to pity, he passed the rope around the girl's beautiful neck. The unhappy creature felt the horrible contact of the hemp. She raised her eyelids, and saw the fleshless arm of the stone gibbet stretched above her head. Then she shook off her torpor, and cried in a sharp, shrill voice, "No, no, I will not!" Her mother, whose head was buried and lost in her child's garments, did not speak a word; but her entire body was convulsed by a shudder, and she lavished redoubled kisses upon her child. The hangman took advantage of this moment quickly to unclasp her arms from the prisoner. Whether from exhaustion or despair, she submitted. Then he took the girl upon his shoulder, over which the charming creature fell gracefully, bent double over his large head. Then he put his foot upon the ladder to ascend.

At this instant the mother, crouching on the pavement, opened wide her eyes. Without a cry, she sprang up with a terrible look; then, like a wild beast leaping upon its prey, she threw herself upon the hangman's hand, and bit it. It was a flash of lightning. The hangman yelled with pain. They ran to his aid. With some difficulty they withdrew his bleeding hand from between the mother's teeth. She maintained a profound silence. The men pushed her away with some brutality, and observed that her head fell heavily on the pavement. They lifted her up; she fell back again. She was dead.

The hangman, who had not let go his hold of the girl, resumed his ascent of the ladder.

CHAPTER II

LA CREATURA BELLA BIANCO VESTITA

WHEN Quasimodo saw that the cell was empty, the gipsy gone, that while he was defending her she had been carried off, he tore his hair, and stamped with rage and surprise; then he ran from one end to end of the church in search of his sovereign lady, uttering strange howls, as he went, scattering his red hair upon the pavement. It was just at the moment when the royal archers entered Notre-Dame in triumph, also in search of the gipsy. Quasimodo helped them, without suspecting—poor deaf fellow! —their fatal purpose; he supposed that the enemies of the gipsy were the Vagrants. He himself guided Tristan l'Hermite to every possible hiding-place, opened secret doors, false altar-backs, and inner sacristies for him. Had the wretched girl still been there he must have betrayed her.

When the fatigue of unsuccessful search discouraged Tristan, who was not easily discouraged, Quasimodo continued to search alone. Twenty, nay, a hundred times he went the round of the church, from one end to the other, from top to bottom, upstairs, downstairs, running, calling, crying, sniffing, ferreting, rummaging, poking his head into every hole, thrusting a torch into every vault, desperate, mad. No wild beast which had lost its mate could be wilder or more frantic.

Finally when he was sure, very sure, that she was no longer there, that all was over, that she had been stolen from him, he slowly climbed the tower stairs, —those stairs which he had mounted with such eagerness and delight on the day when he saved her. He passed by the same places, with hanging head, voiceless, tearless, almost breathless. The church was again deserted, and had relapsed into its usual silence. The archers had left it to track the witch into the City. Quasimodo, alone in that vast cathedral, so crowded and so noisy but a moment previous, returned to the room where the gipsy had for so many weeks slept under his watchful care.

As he approached it, he fancied that he might perhaps find her there. When, at the turn of the gallery opening upon the roof of the side-aisle, he caught sight of the narrow cell with its tiny door and window nestling under a huge flying buttress, like a bird's nest under a branch, his heart failed him,—poor man!—and he leaned against a pillar lest he should fall. He imagined that she might perhaps have returned; that a good genius had undoubtedly brought her back; that the cell was too quiet, too safe, and too attractive for her not to be there; and he dared not take another step for fear of destroying his illusion. "Yes," he said to himself, "she is asleep, or saying her prayers. I won't disturb her."

At last he summoned up all his courage, advanced on tiptoe, looked, entered. Empty,—the cell was still empty. The unhappy deaf man slowly walked about it, lifted the bed and looked under it, as if she might be hidden between the mattress and the stones; then he shook his head, and stood staring stupidly. All at once he trampled his torch furiously under foot, and without a word, without a sigh, he threw himself headlong against the wall, and fell fainting on the floor.

When he came to his senses, he flung himself upon the bed; he rolled upon it; he kissed frantically the place, still warm, where the young girl had slept; he lay there for some moments as motionless as if about to die; then he rose, streaming with perspiration, panting, insensate, and began to beat his head against the wall with the frightful regularity of the clapper of one of his own bells, and the resolution of a man who is determined to dash out his brains. At last he fell exhausted for the second time; he dragged himself from the cell on his knees, and crouched before the door in an attitude of wonder.

Thus he remained for more than an hour without stirring, his eye fixed upon the empty cell, sadder and more pensive than a mother seated between an empty cradle and a coffin. He did not utter a word; only at long intervals a sob shook his whole body convulsively; but it was a dry, tearless sob, like summer lightning, which is silent.

It seems that it was then that, seeking in his desolate thoughts to learn who could have been the unlooked-for ravisher of the gipsy, his mind reverted to the archdeacon. He remembered that Don Claude alone had a key to the staircase leading to the cell. He recalled his midnight attempts upon the girl,—the first, in which he, Quasimodo, had helped him; the second, which he had foiled. He remembered a thousand details, and soon ceased to doubt that the archdeacon had stolen the gipsy from him. However, such was his respect for the priest, his gratitude, his devotion, his love for the man were so deeply rooted in his heart, that they resisted, even at this moment, the claws of jealousy and despair.

He considered that the archdeacon had done this thing, and the thirst for blood and murder which he would have felt for another were turned in the poor deaf man to added grief where Claude Frollo was concerned.

Just as his thoughts were thus concentrated upon the priest, as dawn whitened the flying buttresses, he saw on the upper story of Notre-Dame, at the angle formed by the outer railing which runs round the chancel, a moving figure. The figure was walking towards him. He recognized it. It was the archdeacon.

Claude advanced with grave, slow pace. He did not look before him as he walked. He was going towards the north tower; but his face was turned aside towards the right bank of the Seine, and he held his head erect, as if trying to see something over the roofs. The owl often carries its head in this crooked position; it flies towards one point, and looks in another. The priest thus passed above Quasimodo without seeing him.

The deaf man, petrified by this sudden apparition, saw him disappear through the door of the staircase in the north tower. The reader knows that this tower is the one from which the Hôtel de Ville is visible. Quasimodo rose, and followed the archdeacon.

Quasimodo climbed the tower stairs, intending to go to the top, to learn why the priest was there; yet the poor ringer knew not what he, Quasimodo, meant to do or say, or what he wished. He was full of fury, and full of fear. The archdeacon and the gipsy struggled for the mastery in his heart.

When he reached the top of the tower, before issuing from the shadow of the stairs and stepping upon the platform, he looked carefully about to see where the priest was. The priest stood with his back to him. There is an open balustrade around the platform of the belfry tower; the priest, whose eyes were riveted upon the city, leaned against that one of the four sides of the railing which overlooks the Pont Notre-Dame.

Quasimodo, stealthily advancing behind him, gazed abroad to see what he was watching so closely.

But the priest's attention was so fully absorbed that he did not hear the deaf man's step at his side.

Paris is a magnificent and charming sight, and especially so was the Paris of that day, viewed from the top of the towers of Notre-Dame in the cool light of a summer dawn. The day might have been one of the early days of July. The sky was perfectly clear. A few tardy stars were fading out at different points, and there was a single very brilliant one in the east, in the brightest part of the sky. The sun was just rising. Paris began to stir. A very white, very pure light threw into strong relief all the outlines which its countless houses present to the east. The monstrous shadows of the steeples spread from roof to roof from one end of the great city to the other. There were already certain quarters filled with chatter and noise,—here the stroke of a bell, there the blow of a hammer, yonder the intricate jingle and clatter of a passing cart. Already smoke rose here and there from the sea of roofs, as from the fissures in a vast volcano. The river, whose waters wash the piers of so many bridges and the shores of so many islands, was rippled with silvery folds. Around the city, outside the ramparts, the view was lost in a wide ring of fleecy vapours, through which the indefinite line of the plains and the graceful swell of the hills were vaguely visible. All sorts of sounds floated confusedly over the half-awakened city. Towards the east, the morning breeze chased across the sky a few white flakes torn from the fleece of mist upon the hills.

In the cathedral square certain good women, milkjug in hand, pointed with amaze to the strange dilapidation of the great door of Notre-Dame, and the two rivulets of lead congealed in the crevices of the sandstone. These were the only remaining signs of the tumult of the night. The bonfire kindled by Quasimodo between the towers had gone out. Tristan had already had the square cleared and the dead bodies thrown into the Seine. Kings like Louis

XI. are careful to wash the pavement quickly after a massacre.

Outside the tower rail, exactly under the point where the priest had paused, there was one of those fancifully carved gutters with which Gothic edifices bristle; and in a chink of this gutter were two pretty gilly-flowers in full bloom, waving and seeming almost alive in the breeze, as they playfully saluted each other. Above the towers, aloft, far away in the depths of the sky, were little twittering birds.

But the priest heard and saw none of these things. He was one of those men for whom there are no day-dreams, or birds, or flowers. In all that immense horizon, which assumed so many and such varied aspects about him, his gaze was centred on a single point.

Quasimodo burned to ask him what he had done with the gipsy; but the archdeacon seemed at this instant to have left the world far behind him. He was evidently passing through one of those critical moments of life when a man would not feel the earth crumble beneath him. His eyes fixed constantly upon a certain spot, he stood motionless and silent; and there was something so fearful about his silence and his motionlessness, that the shy bell-ringer shuddered before it, and dared not disturb him. Only—and this was one way of questioning the archdeacon—he followed the direction of his glance, and in this manner the eye of the unfortunate deaf man fell upon the Grève.

Thus he saw what the priest was watching. The ladder was reared beside the permanent gallows. There were a few people in the square, and a number of soldiers. A man dragged across the pavement a white object to which something black was fastened. This man stopped at the foot of the gallows.

At this point something took place which Quasimodo could not quite make out. Not because his one eye had not retained its great range, but there was a knot of soldiers which hindered him from seeing everything. Besides, at this instant the sun rose, and such a flood of light burst from the horizon that it seemed as if every pinnacle in Paris, spires, chimneys, and gables, were set on fire at once.

Meantime, the man continued to climb the ladder. Then Quasimodo saw him again distinctly. He had a woman across his shoulder,—a young girl dressed in white; this girl had a knotted rope around her neck. Quasimodo recognized her.

It was she!

The man reached the top of the ladder. There he arranged the noose. Here the priest, to see the better, knelt upon the balustrade.

All at once the man pushed the ladder quickly from him with his heel; and Quasimodo, who had scarcely breathed for some moments past, saw the unfortunate girl dangling from the end of the rope, a dozen feet from the ground, the man crouching above her, pressing his feet against her shoulders to weigh her down. The rope revolved rapidly several times, and Quasimodo saw a horrible shudder run through the gipsy's frame. The priest, on his part, with outstretched neck and starting eyes, watched that dreadful group of man and girl,—of the spider and the fly.

At the most awful moment a demoniac laugh—a laugh impossible to a mere man—broke from the livid lips of the priest. Quasimodo did not hear this laughter, but he saw it.

The ringer shrank back a few paces behind the archdeacon, and then, suddenly rushing furiously upon him, with his huge hands he hurled Don Claude into the abyss over which he leaned.

The priest cried, "Damnation!" and fell.

The gutter below arrested his fall. He clung to it with desperate hands, and, as he opened his mouth for a second shriek, he saw, looking over the edge of the balustrade, above his head, the terrible, avenging face of Quasimodo.

Then he was silent.

The abyss was beneath him. A fall of more than two hundred feet,—and the pavement.

In this dreadful situation the archdeacon said not a word, uttered not a groan. He merely writhed about the gutter making incredible efforts to climb up it, but his hands had no grip upon the granite, his feet scratched the blackened wall without finding a foothold. Those who have visited the Towers of Notre-Dame know that the stone projects directly below the balustrade. It was against this swell that the wretched archdeacon exhausted himself in frantic struggles. He was working, not upon a perpendicular wall, but upon a wall which sloped away from beneath him.

Quasimodo had only to stretch forth his hand to save him from the gulf; but he did not even look at him. He looked at the Grève; he looked at the gibbet; he looked at the gipsy girl.

The deaf man leaned his elbows on the railing, in the very place where the archdeacon had been the moment previous, and there, never removing his gaze from the only object which at this instant existed for him, he stood motionless and mute as if struck by lightning, and a river of tears flowed silently from that eye which until then had shed but a single tear.

Meantime, the archdeacon gasped. His bald head streamed with perspiration, his nails bled against the stone, his knees were flayed against the wall.

He heard his cassock, by which he hung to the spout, crack and rip at every jerk he gave it. To complete his misfortunes, this spout terminated in a leaden pipe which was bending beneath the weight of his body. The archdeacon felt this pipe slowly giving way. The miserable creature said to himself that when his cassock was torn through, when the lead bent completely, he must fall; and terror took possession of him. Sometimes he gazed wildly at a sort of narrow platform some ten feet below him, formed by certain carvings which jutted out; and he implored Heaven, from the depths of his distressed soul, to permit him to end his life upon that space two feet square, were it to last a hundred years. Once he looked down into the abyss, into the square; when he raised his head his eyes were shut and his hair was erect.

There was something frightful in the silence of the two men. While the archdeacon, a few feet beneath him, was agonizing in this horrible fashion, Quasimodo wept, and watched the Grève.

The archdeacon, seeing that all his struggles merely weakened the frail support which remained to him, resolved to move no more. He clung there, hugging the gutter, scarcely breathing, never stirring, his only movement being that mechanical heaving of the chest experienced in dreams when we think that we are falling. His eyes were fixed in a wide stare of anguish and amaze. Little by little, however, he lost ground; his fingers slipped from the spout; the feebleness of his arms and the weight of his body increased more and more. The bending lead which supported him, every moment inclined a notch nearer to the abyss.

He saw below him a fearful sight,— the roof of Saint-Jean le Rond as small as a card bent double. He gazed, one after another, at the impassive sculptures on the tower, like him suspended over the precipice, but without terror for themselves or pity for him. All around him was of stone: before his eyes, gaping monsters; below, far down in the square, the pavement; above his head, Quasimodo weeping.

Groups of curious citizens had gathered in the square, calmly trying to guess what manner of madman it might be who amused himself in so strange a manner. The priest heard them say, — for their voices reached him clear and shrill,—"But he will break his neck!"

Quasimodo was weeping.

At last the archdeacon, foaming with rage and fright, knew that all was in vain. However, he summoned up his remaining strength for a final effort.

He braced himself against the gutter, set his knees against the wall, hooked his hands into a chink in the stones, and succeeded in climbing up perhaps a foot; but this struggle made the leaden pipe upon which he hung, bend suddenly. With the same effort his cassock tore apart. Then, feeling that everything had failed him, his stiffened and trembling hands alone retaining a hold upon anything, the unfortunate wretch closed his eyes and loosened his grasp of the gutter. He fell. Quasimodo watched him fall.

A fall from such a height is seldom perpendicular. The archdeacon, launched into space, at first fell head downward, with outstretched arms; then he rolled over and over several times; the wind wafted him to the roof of a house, where the unhappy man broke some of his bones. Still, he was not dead when he landed there. The ringer saw him make another effort to clutch the gable with his nails; but the slope was too steep, and his strength was exhausted. He slid rapidly down the roof, like a loose tile, and rebounded to the pavement. There, he ceased to move.

Quasimodo then raised his eye to the gipsy, whose body he could see, as it swung from the gibbet, quivering beneath its white gown in the last death-throes; then he again lowered it to the archdeacon, stretched at the foot of the tower, without a trace of human shape, and he said, with a sob which heaved his mighty breast, "Oh, all that I ever loved!"

Chapter III

MARRIAGE OF PHŒBUS

Towards evening of the same day, when the bishop's officers came to remove the mangled body of the archdeacon from the pavement, Quasimodo had vanished from Notre-Dame.

Many rumours were rife concerning the accident. No one doubted that the day had come when, according to their compact, Quasimodo—that is to say the devil—was to carry off Claude Frollo, —that is to say the sorcerer. It was supposed that he had destroyed the body in taking the soul, as a monkey cracks the shell to eat the nut.

Accordingly the archdeacon was not buried in consecrated ground.

Louis XI. died the following year, in the month of August, 1483.

As for Pierre Gringoire, he contrived to save the goat, and he achieved some success as a tragic author. It seems that after dipping into astrology, philosophy, architecture, hermetics, and all manner of follies, he returned to writing tragedies, the most foolish of all things. This he called "making a tragic end." In regard to his dramatic triumphs, we read in 1483, in the Accounts of the Ordinary. "To Jehan Marchand and Pierre Gringoire, carpenter and composer, who made and composed the mystery performed at the Châtelet in Paris, on the entry of the legate, ordered the personages, dressed and habited the same as the said mystery required, and likewise made the necessary scaffoldings for the same, one hundred pounds."

Phœbus de Châteaupers also came to a tragic end: he married.

Chapter IV

MARRIAGE OF QUASIMODO

We have already said that Quasimodo disappeared from Notre-Dame on the day of the death of the gipsy and the archdeacon. Indeed, he was never seen again; no one knew what became of him.

During the night following the execution of Esmeralda, the hangman's assistants took down her body from the gibbet, and carried it, as was customary, to the vaults at Montfaucon.

Montfaucon, as Sauval states, was "the most ancient and most superb gibbet in the kingdom." Between the suburbs of the Temple and Saint-Martin, about three hundred and twenty yards from the walls of Paris, a few cross-bow shots from the village of La Courtille, at the top of a gentle, almost imperceptibly sloping hill, yet high enough to be seen for a distance of several leagues, was a building of singular shape, looking much like a Celtic cromlech, and where human sacrifices were also offered up.

Imagine, at the top of a chalk-hill a parallelopipedon of masonry fifteen feet high, thirty broad, and forty long, with a door, an outer railing, and a platform; upon this platform sixteen huge pillars of unhewn stone, thirty feet high, ranged in a colonnade around three of the four sides of the base which supported them, connected at the top by stout beams from which at intervals hung chains; from all these chains swung skeletons; round about it, in the plain, were a stone cross and two gibbets of secondary rank which seemed to spring up like shoots from the central tree; above all this, in the sky, a perpetual flight of ravens: such was Montfaucon.

At the close of the fifteenth century the awful gibbet, which dated from 1328, was already very much decayed; the beams were worm-eaten, the chains rusty, the pillars green with mould; the courses of hewn stone gaped widely at the joints, and grass grew upon the platform where no foot ever trod; the structure cast a horrid shadow against the sky, particularly at night, when the moon shone feebly upon those white skulls, or when the breeze stirred chains and skeletons, and made them rattle in the darkness. The presence of this gibbet was enough to give the entire neighbourhood an evil name.

The stone base of the odious structure was hollow. It had been made into a vast vault, closed by an antique grating of battered iron, into which were cast not only the human remains taken from the chains at Montfaucon, but the bodies of all the unfortunates executed upon the other permanent gallows throughout Paris. In this deep charnel-house, where so many mortal remains and so many crimes rotted together, many of the great ones of the earth, many innocent beings, have laid their bones, from Enguerrand de Marigni, who was the first victim of Montfaucon, and who was an upright man, down to Admiral de Coligni, who was the last, and who was likewise a good man.

As for the mysterious disappearance of Quasimodo, all that we have been able to discover is this:—

Some two years or eighteen months after the events which close this story, when search was made in the vault at Montfaucon for the body of Olivier le Daim, who had been hanged two days previous, and to whom Charles VIII. had accorded permission to be buried at Saint-Laurent in better company, among all those hideous carcasses two skeletons were found locked in a close embrace. One of the two, which was that of a woman, still had about it some fragments of a gown, of stuff once white, and about its neck was a necklace of grains of adrezarach, with a little silk bag, adorned with green glass beads, which was open and empty. These articles were doubtless of so little value that the hangman had not cared to remove them. The other skeleton, which held this in so close an embrace, was that of a man. It was noticed that his spine was curved, his head close between his shoulder-blades, and one leg shorter than the other. Moreover, his neck was not broken, and it was evident that he had not been hanged. The man to whom these bones belonged must therefore have come hither himself and died here. When an attempt was made to loose him from the skeleton which he clasped, he crumbled into dust.

THE END

Last Days of a Condemned Man

CONDEMNED to death!

These five weeks have I dwelt with this idea,—always alone with it, always frozen by its presence, always bent under its weight.

Formerly (for it seems to me rather years than weeks since I was free) I was a being like any other; every day, every hour, every minute had its idea. My mind, youthful and rich, was full of fancies, which it developed successively, without order or aim, but weaving inexhaustible arabesques on the poor and coarse web of life. Sometimes it was of youthful beauties, sometimes of unbounded possessions, then of battles gained, next of theatres full of sound and light, and then again the young beauties, and shadowy walks at night beneath spreading chestnut-trees. There was a perpetual revel in my imagination: I might think on what I chose,—I was free.

But now,—I am a Captive! Bodily in irons in a dungeon, and mentally imprisoned in one idea,—one horrible, one hideous, one unconquerable idea! I have only one thought, one conviction, one certitude,—

Condemned to death!

Whatever I do, that frightful thought is always here, like a spectre, beside me, —solitary and jealous, banishing all else, haunting me for ever, and shaking

me with its two icy hands whenever I wish to turn my head away or to close my eyes. It glides into all forms in which my mind seeks to shun it; mixes itself, like a horrible chant, with all the words which are addressed to me; presses against me even to the odious gratings of my prison. It haunts me while awake, spies on my convulsive slumbers, and re-appears, a vivid incubus, in my dreams!

I have just started from a troubled sleep in which I was pursued by this thought, and I made an effort to say to myself, "Oh, it was but a dream!"

Well, even before my heavy eyes could read the fatal truth in the dreadful reality which surrounds me,—on the damp and reeking dungeon-walls, in the pale rays of my night-lamp, in the rough material of my prison-garb, on the sombre visage of the sentry, whose cap gleams through the grating of the door,—it seems to me that already a voice has murmured in my ear,—

"Condemned to death!"

FIVE weeks have now elapsed since I was tried,—found guilty,—sentenced.

Let me endeavour to recall the circumstances which attended that fatal day.

It was a beautiful morning at the close of August. My trial had already lasted three days; my name and accusation had collected each morning a knot of spectators, who crowded the benches of the Court, as ravens surrounded a corpse. During three days all the assembly of judges, witnesses, lawyers, and officers had passed and repassed as a phantasmagoria before my troubled vision.

The two first nights, through uneasiness and terror, I had been unable to sleep; on the third I had slept, from fatigue and exhaustion. I had left the jury deliberating at midnight, and was taken back to the heap of straw in my prison, where I instantly fell into a profound sleep,—the sleep of forgetfulness. These were the first hours of repose I had obtained after long watchfulness.

I was buried in this oblivion when they sent to have me awakened, and my sound slumber was not broken by the heavy step and iron shoes of the jailor, by the clanking of his keys. or the rusty grating of the lock; to rouse me from my lethargy it required his harsh voice in my ear, his rough hand on my arm.

"Come," shouted he, "rise directly!"

I opened my eyes, and started from my straw bed: it was already daylight. At this moment, through the high and narrow window of my cell, I saw on the ceiling of the next corridor (the only firmament I was allowed to see) that yellow reflection by which eyes accustomed to the darkness of a prison recognize sunshine. And oh, how I love sunshine!

"It is a fine day!" said I to the jailor.

He remained a moment without answering me, as if uncertain whether it was worth while to expend a word; then, as if with an effort, he coolly murmured, "Very likely."

I remained motionless, my senses half sleeping, with smiling lips, and my eyes fixed on that soft golden reflection which reverberated on the ceiling.

"What a lovely day!" I repeated.

"Yes," answered the jailor; *"they are waiting for you."*

These few words, like a web which stops the flight of an insect, flung me back into the reality of my position. I pictured to myself instantly, as in a flash of lightning, that sombre Court of Justice, the Bench of Judges, in their robes of sanguine hue, the three rows of stupid-looking witnesses, two gendarmes at the extremity of my bench; black robes waving, and the heads of the crowd clustering in the depth of the shadow, while I fancied that I felt upon me the fixed look of the twelve jurymen, who had sat up while I slept.

I rose: my teeth chattered, my hands trembled, my limbs were so weak that at the first step I had nearly fallen; however, I followed the jailor slowly.

Two gendarmes waited for me at the door-way of the cell; they replaced my fetters, to which I yielded mechanically, as in a dream.

We traversed an interior court, and the balmy air of morning reanimated me. I raised my head: the sky was cloudless, and the warm rays of the sun (partially intercepted by the tall chimneys) traced brilliant angles of light on the high and sombre walls of the prison. It was indeed a delicious day.

We ascended a winding staircase; we passed a corridor, then another, then a third, and then a low door was opened. A current of hot air, laden with noise, rushed from it; it was the breath of the crowd in the Court of Justice which I then entered.

On my appearance the hall resounded with the clank of arms and the hum of voices; benches were moved noisily; and while I crossed that long chamber between two masses of people who were walled in by soldiers, I painfully felt myself the centre of attraction to all those fixed and gaping looks.

At this moment I perceived that I was without fetters, but I could not recall where or when they had been removed.

At length I reached my place at the bar, and there was a deep silence. The instant that the tumult ceased in the crowd, it ceased also in my ideas: a sudden clearness of perception came to me, and I at once understood plainly, what until then I could not discover in my confused state of mind, that *the decisive moment was come!* I was brought there to hear my *sentence!*

Explain it who can: from the manner in which this idea came to my mind, it caused me no terror! The windows were open; the air, and the sounds of the City came freely through them; the room was as light as for a wedding; the cheerful rays of the sun traced here and there the luminous forms of the windows, sometimes lengthened on the flooring, sometimes spreading on a table, sometimes broken by the angles of the walls; and from the brilliant square of each window the rays fell through the air in dancing golden beams.

The Judges at the extreme of the hall bore a satisfied appearance, probably from the anticipation of their labours being soon completed. The face of the President, softly lighted by a reflected sunbeam, had a calm and amiable expression; and a young counsel conversed almost gaily with a handsome woman who was placed near him.

The Jury alone looked wan and exhausted, but this was apparently from the fatigue of having sat up all night. Nothing in their countenances indicated men who would pass sentence of death.

Opposite to me a window stood wide open. I heard laughter in the Market for Flowers beneath; and on the sill of the window a graceful plant, illumined by sunshine, played in the breeze.

How could any sinister idea be formed amongst so many soothing sensations? Surrounded by air and sunshine, I could think of nought save freedom. Hope shone within me, as the day shone around me; and I awaited my sentence with confidence, as one daily calculates on liberty and life.

In the meantime my counsel arrived; after taking his place he leaned towards me with a smile.

"I have hopes!" said he.

"Oh, surely!" I replied in the same light tone.

"Yes," returned he; "I know nothing as yet of the verdict, but they have doubtless acquitted you of premeditation, and then it will be only *hard labour for life!*"

"What do you mean, sir?" replied I indignantly; "I would prefer death!"

Then the President, who had only waited for my counsel, desired me to rise. The soldiers carried arms; and, like an electric movement, all the assembly rose at the same instant. The Recorder, placed at a table below the

Tribunal, read the verdict, which the Jury pronounced during my absence.

*   *   *   *   *   *

A sickly chill passed over my frame; I leaned against the wall to avoid falling.

"Counsel, have you anything to say why this sentence should not be passed?" demanded the President.

I felt that *I* had much to urge, but I had not the power,—my tongue was cleaving to my mouth.

My counsel then rose. His endeavour appeared to be, to mitigate the verdict of the Jury, and to substitute the punishment of hard labour for life,—by naming which he had rendered me so indignant! This indignation must again have been powerful within me to conquer the thousand emotions which distracted my thoughts. I wished to repeat aloud what I had already said to him, but my breath failed, and I could only grasp him by the arm, crying with convulsive strength, "No!"

The Attorney-General replied against my counsel's arguments, and I listened to him with a stupid satisfaction. The Judges then left the Court; soon returned, and the President read my sentence.

"*Condemned to death!*" cried the crowd; and as I was led away the assembly pressed on my steps with avidity, while I walked on, confused, and nearly in unconsciousness. A revolution had taken place within me. Until that sentence of Death I had felt myself breathe, palpitate, exist, like other beings. Now I felt clearly that a barrier existed between me and the world. Nothing appeared to me under the same aspect as hitherto. Those large and luminous windows, that fair sunshine, that pure sky,—all was pale and ghastly, the colour of a winding sheet. Those men, women, and children who pressed on my path seemed to me like phantoms.

At the foot of the stairs a black and dirty prison-cart was waiting; as I entered it, I looked by chance around.

"The Condemned Prisoner!" shouted the people, running towards the cart.

Through the cloud which seemed to me to interpose between me and all things, I distinguished two young girls who gazed at me with eager eyes.

"Well," said the youngest, clapping her hands, "*it will take place in six weeks.*"

THIRD PAPER

CONDEMNED to death!

Well, why not? I remember once reading, "All mankind are condemned to death, with indefinite respites." How then is my position altered?

Since my sentence was pronounced, how many are dead who calculated upon a long life! How many are gone before me, who, young, free, and in good health, had fully intended to be present at my execution! How many, between this and then, perhaps, who now walk and breathe in the fresh air any where they please, will die before me!

And then, what has life for me, that I should regret? In truth, only the dull twilight and black bread of a prison, a portion of meagre soup from the trough of the convicts; to be treated rudely,—*I*, who have been refined by education; to be brutalized by turnkeys without feeling; not to see a human being who thinks me worthy of a word, or whom I could address; incessantly to shudder at what I have done, and what may be done to me,—these are nearly the only advantages of which the executioner can deprive me!

Ah! still it is horrible.

FOURTH PAPER

THE black cart brought me here to this hideous Bicêtre Prison.

Seen from afar, the appearance of that edifice is rather majestic. It spreads to the horizon in front of a hill, and at a distance retains something of its ancient splendour,—the look of a Royal Palace. But as you approach it, the Palace changes to a ruin, and the dilapidated gables shock the sight. There is a mixture of poverty and disgrace soiling its royal façades; without glass or shutters to the windows, but massive crossed-bars of iron instead, against which is pressed, here and there, the ghastly face of a felon or a madman.

FIFTH PAPER

WHEN I arrived here the hand of force was laid on me, and numerous precautions were taken: neither knife nor fork was allowed for my repasts; and a strait-waistcoat—a species of sack made of sail-cloth—imprisoned my arms. I had sued to annul my sentence, so the jailors might have for six or seven weeks their responsibility; and it was requisite to keep me safe and healthful for the Guillotine!

For the first few days I was treated with a degree of attention which was horrible to me,—the civilities of a turnkey breathe of a scaffold. Luckily, at the end of some days, habit resumed its influence; they mixed me with the other prisoners in a general brutality, and made no more of those unusual distinctions of politeness which continually kept the executioner in my memory.

This was not the only amelioration. My youth, my docility, the cares of the Chaplain of the prison, and above all some words in Latin which I addressed to the keeper, who did not understand them, procured for me a walk once a week with the other prisoners, and removed the strait-waistcoat with which I was paralyzed. After considerable hesitation they have also given me pens, paper, ink, and a night-lamp. Every Sunday after Mass I am allowed to walk in the Prison-court at the hour of recreation; there I talk with the prisoners, which is inevitable. They make boon companions, these wretches. They tell me their adventures,—enough to horrify one; but I know they are proud of them. They also try to teach me their mystic idioms,—an odious phraseology grafted on the general language, like a hideous excrescence; yet sometimes it has a singular energy, a frightful picturesqueness. To be hung is called "marrying the widow," as though the rope of the gallows were the widow of all who had been executed! At every instant mysterious, fantastic words occur, base and hideous, derived one knows not whence; they resemble crawling reptiles. On hearing this language spoken, the effect is like the shaking of dusty rags before you.

These men at least pity me, and they alone do so. The jailors, the turnkeys, —and I am not angry with them—gossip and laugh, and speak of me in my presence as of a mere animal.

SIXTH PAPER

I SAID to myself, "As I have the means of writing, why should I not do it? But of what shall I write? Placed between four walls of cold and bare stone, without freedom for my steps, without horizon for my eyes, my sole occupation mechanically to watch the progress of that square of light which the grating of my door marks on the sombre wall opposite, and, as I said before, ever alone with one idea,—an idea of crime, punishment, death,—can I have anything to *say,* I who have no more to *do* in this world; and what shall I find in this dry and empty brain which is worthy the trouble of being written?

"Why not? If all around me is monotonous and hueless, is there not within me a tempest, a struggle, a tragedy? This fixed idea which possesses me, does it not take every hour, every instant a new form, becoming more hideous as the time approaches? Why should I not try to describe for myself all the violent and unknown feelings I experience in my outcast situation? Certainly the material is plentiful; and, however shortened my life may be, there will still be sufficient in the anguish, the terrors, the tortures, which will fill it from this hour until my last, to exhaust my pen and ink! Besides, the only means to decrease my suffering in this anguish will be to observe it closely; and to describe it will give me an occupation. And then, what I write may not be without its use. This journal of my sufferings, hour by hour, minute by minute,

torment after torment, if I have strength to carry it on to the moment when it will be *physically* impossible for me to continue,—this history necessarily unfinished, yet as complete as possible, of my sensations, may it not give a grand and deep lesson? Will not there be in this process of agonizing thought, in this ever increasing progress of pain, in this intellectual dissection of a condemned man, more than one lesson for those who condemned? Perhaps the perusal may render them less heedless, when throwing a human life into what they call 'the scale of justice.' Perhaps they have never reflected on the slow succession of tortures conveyed in the expeditious formula of a sentence of death. Have they ever paused on the important idea, that in the man whose days they shorten there is an immortal spirit which had calculated on life, a soul which is not prepared for death? No! they see nothing but the execution, and doubtless think that for the condemned there is nothing anterior or subsequent!"

These sheets shall undeceive them. Published, perchance, some day, they will call their attention a few moments to the suffering of the mind; for it is this which they do not consider. They triumph in the power of being able to destroy the body, almost without making it suffer. What an inferior consideration is this! What is mere physical pain compared to that of the mind? A day will come,—and perhaps these memoirs, the last revelations of a solitary wretch, will have contributed—

That is, unless after my death the wind carries away these sheets of paper into the muddy court, or unless they melt with rain when pasted to the broken window of a turnkey.

SEVENTH PAPER

SUPPOSE that what I write might one day be useful to others,—might make the Judge pause in his decision, and might save the wretched (innocent or guilty) from the agony to which I am condemned,—why should *I* do it? What matters it? When my life has been taken, what will it be to me if they take the lives of others? Have I really thought of such folly?—to throw down the scaffold which I had fatally mounted!

* * * * * *

What! sunshine, spring, fields full of flowers and birds, the clouds, trees, nature, liberty, life,—these are to be mine no more!

Ah, it is myself I must try to save! Is it really true that this cannot be, that I must die soon,—to-morrow, to-day perhaps; is it all thus? Oh, heavens! what a dreadful idea,—of destroying myself against the prison wall!

EIGHTH PAPER

LET me consider what time generally elapses between the condemnation and the execution of a prisoner.

Three days of delay, after sentence is pronounced, for the prisoner's final plea to annul it.

The plea forgotten for a week in a Court of Assize, before it is sent to the Minister; a fortnight forgotten at the Minister's, who does not even know that there are such papers, although he is supposed to transmit them, after examination, to the "Cour de Cassation."

Then classification, numbering, registering; the guillotine-list is loaded, and none must go before their turn! A fortnight more waiting; then the Court assembles, rejects twenty pleas together, and sends all back to the Minister, who sends them back to the Attorney-General, who sends them back to the executioner; this would take three more days.

On the morning of the fourth day the Deputies of the Attorney-General and Recorder prepare the order of execution; and the following morning, from day-break, is heard the noise of erecting the scaffold, and in the cross-streets a commotion of hoarse voices.

Altogether *six weeks*. The young girl's calculation was right! I have now been at least five weeks (perhaps six, for I dare not reckon) in this fatal prison; nay, I think I have been even three days more.

NINTH PAPER

I HAVE just made my will; what was the use of this? I have to pay my expenses, and all I possess will scarcely suffice. A forced death is expensive.

I leave a mother, I leave a wife, I leave a child,—a little girl of three years old, gentle, delicate, with large black eyes and chestnut hair. She was two years and one month old when I saw her the last time.

Thus after my death there will be three women without son, without husband, without father,—three orphans in different degrees; three widows by act of law.

I admit that I am justly punished; but these innocent creatures, what have they done? No matter; they will be dishonoured, they will be ruined; and this is justice!

It is not much on account of my poor old mother that I feel thus wretched; she is so advanced in years, she will not survive the blow; or if she still linger a short time, her feelings are so blunted that she will suffer but little.

Nor is it for my wife that I feel the most. She is already in miserable health, and weak in intellect; her reason will give way, in which case her spirit will not suffer while the mind slumbers as in death.

But my daughter, my child, my poor little Mary, who is laughing, playing, singing, at this moment, and who dreams of no evil! Ah, it is the thought of her which unmans me!

TENTH PAPER

HERE is the description of my prison; eight feet square; four walls of granite, with a flagged pavement; on one side a kind of nook by way of alcove, in which is thrown a bundle or straw, where the prisoner is supposed to rest and sleep, dressed, winter, as in summer, in slight linen clothing. Over my head, instead of curtains, a thick canopy of cobwebs, hanging like tattered pennons. For the rest, no windows, not even a ventilator; and only one door, where iron hides the wood. I mistake; towards the top of the door there is a sort of window, or rather an opening of nine inches square, crossed by a grating, and which the turnkey can close at night. Outside, there is a long corridor lighted and aired by means of narrow ventilators high in the wall. It is divided into compartments of masonry, which communicate by a series of doors; each of these compartments serves as an antechamber to a dungeon, like mine. In these dungeons are confined felons condemned by the Governor of the Prison to hard labour. The three first cells are kept for prisoners under sentence of death, as being nearest to the goal, therefore most convenient for the jailor. These dungeons are the only remains of the ancient Bicêtre Castle, such as it was built in the fifteenth centry by the Cardinal of Winchester, he who caused Jeanne of Arc to be burned. I overheard this description from some persons who came to my den yesterday, to gratify their curiosity, and who stared at me from a distance as at a wild beast in a menagerie. The turnkey received five francs for the exhibition.

I have omitted to say that night and day there is a sentry on guard outside the door of my cell; and I never raise my eyes towards the square grating without encountering his eyes, open, and fixed on me.

ELEVENTH PAPER

As there is no appearance of daylight, what is to be done during the night? It occurred to me that I would arise and examine, by my lamp, the walls of my cell. They are covered with writings, with drawings, fantastic figures, and names which mix with and efface each other. It would appear that each prisoner had wished to leave behind him some trace here at least. Pencil, chalk, charcoal,—black, white, grey letters; sometimes deep carvings upon the stone. If my mind were at ease, I could take an interest in this strange book, which is developed page by page, to my eyes, on each stone of this dungeon. I should like to recompose these fragments of thought; to trace a character for each name; to give sense and life to these mutilated inscriptions,—these dismembered phrases.

Above where I sleep there are two flaming hearts, pierced with an arrow; and beneath is written "Amour pour la vie." Poor wretch! it was not a long engagement.

Beyond this, a three-sided cocked hat, with a small figure coarsely done beneath, and the words, "Vive l'Empereur!"

On the opposite wall is the name of "Papavoine." The capital *P* is worked in arabesques and embellished with care.

A verse of a popular drinking-song.

A Cap of Liberty, cut rather deeply into the stone, with the words beneath of "Bories, La République!"

Poor young man! he was one of the four subaltern officers of La Rochelle. How horrible is the idea of their (fancied) political necessity, to give the frightful reality of the guillotine for an opinion, a reverie, an abstraction!—And I! *I* have complained of its severity!— I who have really committed crime

Ah, what have I seen! I can go no farther in my research! I have just discovered, drawn with chalk in the corner of the wall, that dreadful image, the representation of that scaffold, which even at this moment is perhaps being put up for my execution! The lamp had nearly fallen out of my trembling hands!

TWELFTH PAPER

I RETURNED precipitately to sit on my straw bed; my head sunk on my knees. After a time, my childish fear was dissipated, and a wild curiosity forced me to continue the examination of my walls.

Besides the name of Papavoine, I tore away an enormous cobweb, thick with dust, and filling the angle of the wall. Under this web there were four or five names perfectly legible, among others of which nothing remained but a smear on the wall,—DAUTAN, 1815. POULAIN, 1818. JEAN MARTIN, 1821. CASTAING, 1823.

As I read these names, frightful recollections crowded on me. *Dautan* was the man who cut his brother in quarters, and who went at night to Paris and threw the head into a fountain, and the body into a sewer. *Poulain* assassinated his wife. *Jean Martin* shot his father with a pistol as the old man opened a window. And *Castaing* was the physician who poisoned his friend; and while attending the illness he had caused, instead of antidote, gave him more poison. Then, next to these names, was Papavoine, the horrible madman who stabbed children to death in his phrenzy.

"These," I exclaimed, as a shudder passed over me, "these, then, have been my predecessors in this cell. Here, on the same pavement where I am, they conceived their last thoughts,—these fearful homicides! Within these walls, in this narrow square, their last steps turned and re-turned, like those of a caged wild-beast. They succeeded each other at short intervals; it seems that this dungeon does not remain empty. They have left the place warm,—and it is to me they have left it. In my turn I shall join them in the felons' cemetery of Clamart, where the grass grows so well!"

*   *   *   *   *   *

I am neither visionary nor superstitious, but it is probable these ideas caused in my brain a feverish excitement; for, whilst I thus wandered, all at once these five fatal names appeared as though written in flames on the dark wall; noises, louder and louder, burst on my ears; a dull red light filled my eyes, and it seemed to me that my cell became full of men,—strangers to me. Each bore his severed head in his left hand, and carried it by the mouth, for the hair had been removed; each raised his right hand at me, *except the parricide.*

I shut my eyes in horror, and then I saw all even more distinctly than before!

Dream, vision, or reality, I should have gone mad if a sudden impression had not recalled me in time. I was near fainting, when I felt something cold crawling over my naked foot. It was the bloated spider, whom I had disturbed. This recalled my wandering senses. Those dreadful spectres, then, were only the fumes of an empty and convulsed brain. The sepulchre is a prison from whence none escape. The door of the tomb opens not inwards!

*   *   *   *   *   *

THIRTEENTH PAPER

I HAVE lately witnessed a hideous sight. As soon as it was day, the prison was full of noise, I heard heavy doors open and shut; the grating of locks and bolts; the clanking of bunches of keys; the stairs creaking from top to bottom with quick steps; and voices calling and answering from the opposite extremes of the long corridors. My neighbours in the dungeons, the felons at hard labour, were more gay than usual. All in the prison seemed laughing, singing, running, or dancing; I— alone silent in this uproar, alone motionless in this tumult—listened in astonishment.

A jailor passed; I ventured to call and ask him "if there were a Fête in the Prison."

"A Fête, if you choose to call it so," answered he; "this is the day that they fetter the galley-slaves who are to set off to morrow for Toulon. Would you like to see them? It would amuse you."

For a solitary recluse, indeed, a spectacle of any kind was an event of interest, however odious it might be; and I accepted the "amusement."

The jailor, after taking the usual precautions to secure me, conducted me into a little empty cell, without a vestige of furniture, and only a grated window, —but still a real window, against which one could lean, and through which one could actually perceive the sky! "Here," said he, "you will see and hear all that happens. You will be 'alone in your box,' like the King!"

He then went out, closing on me locks, bolts, and bars.

The window looked into a square and rather wide court, on every side of which was a large six-storied stone edifice. Nothing could seem more wretched, naked, and miserable to the eye than this quadruple façade, pierced by a multitude of grated windows, against which were pressed a crowd of thin and wan faces, placed one above the other, like the stones of a wall; and all, as it were, framed in the intercrossings of iron bars. They were prisoners, spectators of the ceremony, until their turn came to be the actors.

All looked in silence into the still empty court; among these faded and dull countenances there shone, here and there, some eyes which gleamed like sparks of fire.

At twelve o'clock, a large gateway in the court was opened. A cart, escorted by soldiers, rolled heavily into the court, with a rattling of irons. It was the Convict-guard with the chains.

At the same instant, as if this sound awaked all the noise of the prison, the spectators of the windows, who had hitherto been silent and motionless, burst into cries of joy, songs, menaces, and imprecations, mixed with hoarse laughter. It was like witnessing a masque of Demons; each visage bore a grimace, every hand was thrust through the bars, their voices yelled, their eyes flashed, and I was startled to see so many gleams amidst these ashes. Meanwhile the galley-sergeants quietly began their work. One mounted on the cart, and threw to his comrades the fetters, the iron collars, and the linen clothing; while others stretched long chains to the end of the court and the Captain tried each link by striking it on the pavement,—all of which took place under the mocking raillery of the prisoners, and the loud laughter of the convicts for whom they were being prepared.

When all was ready, two or three low doors poured forth into the court a collection of hideous, yelling, ragged men; these were the galley-convicts.

Their entry caused increased pleasure at the windows. Some of them, being 'great names' among their comrades, were saluted with applause and acclamation, which they received with a sort of proud modesty. Several wore a kind of hat of prison straw, plaited by themselves, and formed into some fantastic shape; these men were always the most applauded.

One in particular excited transports of enthusiasm,—a youth of seventeen, with quite a girlish face. In his prison he had made himself a straw dress, which enveloped him from head to foot; and he entered the court, jumping a somerset with the agility of a serpent. He was a mountebank condemned for theft, and there was a furious clapping of hands, and a volley of cheers, for him.

At length the names were called in alphabetical order, and they went to stand two and two, companions by similar initials; so that even if a convict had a friend, most likely their chains would divide them from suffering together.

Whilst they were exchanging their worn-out prison-garments for the thin and coarse clothing of the galleys, the weather, which had been hitherto uncertain, became suddenly cold and cloudy, and a heavy shower chilled their thin forms, and saturated their vesture.

A dull silence succeeded to their noisy bravadoes; they shivered, their teeth chattered, and their limbs shook in the wet clothes.

One convict only, an old man, retained a sort of gaiety. He exclaimed laughing, while wiping away the rain, and shaking his fist at the skies, "This was not in the playbill!"

When they had put on their miserable vestments, they were taken in bands of twenty or thirty to the corner of the court where the long chains were extended. At every interval of two feet in these chains were fastened short transverse chains, and at the extremity of each of the latter was attached a square iron collar, which opened by means of a hinge in the centre and closed by an iron bolt, which is riveted, for the whole journey, on the convict's neck. The convicts were ordered to sit down in the mud on the inundated pavement; the iron collars were fitted on them, and two prison-blacksmiths, with portable anvils, riveted the hard, unheated metal with heavy iron hammers.

This was a frightful operation, and even the most hardy turned pale! Each stroke of the hammer, aimed on the anvil resting on their backs, makes the whole form yield; the failure of its aim, or the least movement of the head, might launch them into eternity.

When this operation was finished, the convicts rose simultaneously. The five gangs joined hands, so as to form an immense circle, and thus ran round and round in the court with a rapidity that the eye could hardly follow. They sung some couplets, in their own idiom, to a melody which was sometimes plaintive, sometimes furious, often interrupted by hoarse cries and broken laughter, like delirious ravings, while the chains, clanking together in cadence, formed an accompaniment to a song more harsh than their own noise. A large trough was now brought in; the guards, striking the convicts to make them discontinue their dance, took them to the trough, in which was swimming I know not what sort of herbs in some smoking and dirty-looking liquid. Having partaken of it, they threw the remainder on the pavement, with their black bread, and began again to dance and sing. This is a liberty which is allowed to them on the day they are fettered and the succeeding night.

I gazed on this strange spectacle with such eager and breathless attention, that I totally forgot my own misery. The deepest pity filled my heart, and their laughter made me weep.

Suddenly, in the midst of a profound reverie into which I had fallen, I observed the yelling circle had stopped, and was silent. Then every eye was turned to the window which I occupied. "The Condemned! the Condemned!" shouted they, pointing their fingers at me; and their bursts of laughter were redoubled.

I was thunderstruck. I know not where they knew me, or how I was recognized.

"Good day! good night!" cried they, with their mocking sneer. One of the youngest, condemned to the Galleys for life, turned his shining, leaden face on me, with a look of envy, saying, "He is lucky! he is to be *clipped!* Good-bye, Comrade!"

I cannot describe what passed within me. I was indeed their "comrade!" The Scaffold is Sister to the Galleys. Nay, I was even lower than they were; the convicts had done me an honour. I shuddered: yes! their "comrade!" I remained at the window, motionless, as if paralyzed; but when I saw the five gangs advance, rushing towards me with phrases of disgusting cordiality; when I heard the horrible din of their chains, their clamours, their steps at the foot of my wall, it seemed to me that this knot of demons were scaling my cell! I uttered a shriek; I threw myself against the door violently, but there was no means of flight. I knocked, I called with mad fury. Then I thought I heard, still nearer, the horrid voices of the convicts. I thought I saw their hideous heads appearing on a level with the window; I uttered another shriek of anguish, and fainted.

*   *   *   *   *   *

FOURTEENTH PAPER

WHEN my consciousness returned it was night; I was lying on a truckle bed; a lamp which swung from the ceiling enabled me to see a line of beds similar to mine, and I therefore judged that I had been taken to the Infirmary. I remained a few moments awake, but without thought or recollection, totally engrossed by the happiness of being again in a bed. Certainly, in former days, this prison-hospital bed would have made me shrink with disgust; but I am no longer the same individual. The sheets were brown, and coarse to the touch, the blanket thin and ragged, and there was but one straw mattress.

No matter! I could stretch my limbs at their ease between these coarse sheets; and under this blanket, thin as it was, I felt the gradual decrease of that horrible chill in the marrow of my bones, to which I had lately been accustomed.—I slept again.

A loud noise awakened me at daylight. The noise came from without; my bed was beside the window, and I sat up to see from what it arose. The window looked into the large Court of the Bicêtre, which was full of people. Two lines of veterans had difficulty in keeping the crowd away from a narrow passage across the Court. Between this double rank of soldiers, five long wagons, loaded with men, were driven slowly jolting at each stone; it was the departure of the convicts.

These wagons were open, and each gang occupied one. The convicts, in consequence of their iron collars being attached to the centre chain, are obliged to sit back to back, their feet hanging over the sides of the wagon; the centre chain stretched the whole length of the cart, and on its unfastened end the Sergeant stood with his loaded musket. There was a continual clanking of the prisoners' chains, and at each plunge of the wagon their heads and pendant limbs were jolted violently. A quick penetrating rain chilled the air, and made their wet slight vesture cling to their shivering forms. Their long beards and short hair streamed with wet; their complexions were saturnine; they were shivering, and grinding their teeth with mingled rage and cold. But they had no power of moving; once riveted to that chain, each becomes a mere fraction of that hideous whole which is called the Gang. Intellect must abdicate,—the fetters condemn it to death; and the mere animal must not even hunger but at certain hours. Thus fixed, the greater part half clad, with bare heads, and no rest for their feet, they begin their journey of twenty-five days; the same sort of wagons, the same portion of dress being used in scorching July as in the cold rains of November. One would almost think that man wishes Heaven to take part in his office of executioner.

Between the crowd and the convicts a horrible dialogue was maintained,— abuse on one side, bravadoes on the other, imprecations from both; but at a sign from the Captain I saw the sticks of the Guard raining indiscriminate blows into the wagon, on heads or shoulders, and all returned to that kind of external calm which is called "order." But their eyes were full of vengeance, and their powerless hands were clenched on their knees.

The five wagons, escorted by mounted gendarmes and guards on foot, passed slowly under the high arched door of the Bicêtre. The crowd followed them: all vanished like a phantasmagoria, and by degrees the sounds diminished of the heavy wheels, clanking fetters, and the yells of the multitude uttering maledictions on the journey of the convicts. And such was their happy beginning!

What a proposition my counsel made! The Galleys! I was right to prefer death; rather the Scaffold than what I had seen!

FIFTEENTH PAPER

UNFORTUNATELY I was not ill; therefore the next day I was obliged to leave the Infirmary to return to my dungeon.

Not ill? No truly, I am young, healthful, and strong; the blood flows freely in my veins; my limbs obey my will; I am robust in mind and body, constituted for a long life. Yes, all this is true; and yet, nevertheless, I have an illness, a fatal illness,—an illness given by the hand of man!

Since I came out of the Infirmary a vivid idea has occupied me,—a thought which affects me to madness; namely, that I might have escaped, had they left me there! Those Physicians, those Charity Sisters seemed to take an interest in me. "To die so young! and by such a death!" One would have imagined they pitied me by their pressing round my bed. Bah! it was curiosity! I have no chance now! My plea will be rejected, because all was legal; the witnesses gave correct evidence, the counsel pleaded well, the Judges decided carefully. I do not reckon upon it, unless— No! folly; there is no hope. The plea is a cord which holds you suspended over an abyss, and which you feel giving way at each instant until it breaks. It is as if the axe of the Guillotine took six weeks to fall.

If I could obtain my pardon!— pardon! From whom, for what, and by what means? It is impossible that I should be pardoned. They say *an example is requisite.*

SIXTEENTH PAPER

DURING the few hours I passed at the Infirmary, I seated myself at a window in the sunshine (for the afternoon had become fine), and I enjoyed all the sun which the gratings of the window would allow me.

I sat thus, my heavy and fevered head within my hands, my elbows on my knees, my feet on the bar of the chair; for dejection had made me stoop, and sink within myself, as if I had neither bone nor muscular power.

The stifling air of the prison oppressed me more than ever; I still fancied the noise from the convicts' chains rung in my ears; I was almost overcome. I wished that some guardian spirit would take pity on me, and send even a little bird to sing there, opposite, on the edge of the roof.

I know not if it were a spirit of good or evil which granted my wish; but almost at the moment I uttered it, I heard beneath my window a voice,— not that of a bird, but far better,—the pure, fresh, *velvet* voice of a young girl of fifteen!

I raised my head with a start; I listened with avidity to the song she sung. It was a slow and plaintive air, —a sad yet beautiful melody. As I gathered the sense of the words, I cannot describe my pain and disappointment, while the stanzas of prison-dialect marred the sweet music.

I heard no more. I could listen to no more. The meaning, half-hidden, half-evident, of this horrible lament,— the struggle between the felon and the police; the thief he meets and despatches for his wife; his dreadful explanation to her: "I have sweated an oak" ("I have assassinated a man"); the wife who goes to Versailles with a petition, and the King indignantly exclaiming that he "will make the guilty man dance where there is no floor!"— and all this sung to the sweetest air, and by the sweetest voice that ever soothed human ear! I was shocked, disgusted, overcome. It was a repulsive idea that all these monstrous words proceeded from a fresh rosy mouth: it was like the slime of a snail over a rosebud!

I cannot express what I felt; I was at once pained and gratified. The idiom of crime, a language at once sanguinary and grotesque, united to the voice of a young girl, that graceful transition from the voice of childhood to the voice of woman,—all these deformities of words delightfully sung, cadenced, rounded!

Ah, how infamous is a prison! It contains a venom which assails all within its pestilential reach. Everything withers there, even the song of a girl of fifteen!

If you find a bird within its courts, it has mud on its wing. If you gather a beauteous flower there, it exhales poison!

SEVENTEENTH PAPER

WHILST I was writing, my lamp faded, daylight appeared, and the clock of the chapel struck six.

* * * * *

What can be the meaning of what has since happened? The turnkey on duty came into my cell; he took off his cap, bowed to me, apologized for disturbing me, and making an effort to soften his rough voice, inquired what I wished to have for my breakfast—

A shudder has come over me. *Is it to take place to-day?*

EIGHTEENTH PAPER

I FEEL that it *is* for to-day!

The Governor of the prison himself came to visit me. He asked me how he could serve or accommodate me; he expressed a hope that I had no complaint to make respecting him or his subordinates; and he inquired with interest regarding my health, and how I had passed the night. On leaving me, he called me "Sir!"

Oh, it surely is for to-day!

NINETEENTH PAPER

THE Governor of the prison thinks I have no cause of complaint against him or his jailors. He is right, and it would be wrong of me to complain; they have done their duty, they have kept me safe; and then they have been complaisant at my arrival and departure. Ought I not to be satisfied?

This Governor, with his benign smile, his soft words, his eye which flatters and spies, his coarse heavy hands,—he is the incarnation of a prison!

Ah, hapless creature! what will become of me? What will they do with me?

TWENTIETH PAPER

Lo! I am calm. All is finished—quite finished! I am relieved from the dreadful anxiety into which I was thrown by the Governor's visit; for I confess I still felt hope. Now, thank Heaven! hope is gone.

Let me record what has happened.

At half-past six the door of my cell was opened; an old man with white hair was entered, dressed in a brown great-coat.

He unfastened it, and beneath I saw the black cassock and bands of a priest. He was not the usual Chaplain to the prison, and I thought this appeared ominous. He seated himself opposite to me, with a quiet smile; then shook his head, and raised his eyes to heaven. I understood him.

"My son!" said he, "are you prepared?"

I answered, in a low tone, "I am not prepared—but I am ready."

Then my sight became troubled; a chill damp pervaded my frame. I felt the veins on my temples swelling, and a confused murmur in my ears.

Whilst I vacillated on my chair as though asleep, the old man continued speaking,—at least, so it appeared to me, for I think I remember seeing his lips move, and his hand raised.

The door opened again; the noise of the lock roused me from my reverie, and the Priest from his discourse. A person dressed in black entered, accompanied by the Governor of the prison, and bowed profoundly to me; he carried a roll of paper.

"Sir," said he, with a courteous smile, "I have the honour to bring you a message from the Attorney-General."

The first agitation was over; all my presence of mind returned, and I answered in a firm tone, "Read on, Sir."

He then read a long, technically-expressed paper, the purport of which was the rejection of my plea. "The execution will be to-day," added he; "we shall leave this for the Conciergerie Prison at half-past seven. My dear Sir, will you have the extreme goodness to accompany me at that hour?"

For some instants I had no longer listened to him; for while his eyes were fixed on the paper the Governor was occupied talking to the Priest; and I looked at the door which they had left half open! . . . Ah, hapless me! Four sentinels in the corridor. Again I was asked when I would be ready to go.

"When you please," I said; "at your own time."

"I shall have the honour of coming for you, then, in half an hour," said he, bowing; and all the party withdrew.

Oh, for some means of escaping, Good heavens! any means whatever! I *must* make my escape! I must! Immediately! By the doors, by the windows, by the roof! Even though in the struggle I should destroy myself!

Oh, rage! demons! malediction! It would take months to pierce this wall with efficient tools. And I have not one nail, nor one hour!

TWENTY-FIRST PAPER

CONCIERGERIE PRISON.

HERE I am transferred, then. Let me record the details. At half-past seven the messenger again presented himself at the threshold of my dungeon. "Sir," said he, "I wait for you."

Alas! and I saw that four others did the same! I rose, and advanced one step. It appeared to me I could not make a second. My head was so heavy, and my limbs so feeble; but I made an effort to conquer my weakness, and assumed an appearance of firmness.

Prior to leaving the cell, I gave it a final look; I had almost become attached to it. Besides, I left it empty and open, which gives so strange an appearance to a dungeon.

It will not be long untenanted. The turnkeys said they expected some one this evening,—a prisoner who was then being tried at the Court of Assizes.

At the turn of the corridor the Chap-lain rejoined us; he had just breakfasted.

At the threshold of the goal, the Governor took me by the hand; he had reinforced my escort by four veterans.

By the door of the Infirmary a dying old man exclaimed, "Good-bye, we shall soon meet again!"

We arrived in the courtyard, where I could breathe again freely, and this refreshed me greatly; but we did not walk long in the open air. The carriage was stationed in the first court. It was the same which had brought me there, —a sort of oblong van, divided into two sections by a transverse grating of close wire. Each section had a door; one in the front, one in the back of the cart; the whole so dirty, so black, so dusty, that the hearse for paupers is a state carriage by comparison! Before I buried myself in this moving tomb, I cast a look round the yard,—one of those despairing looks which seem to ask a miracle. The court was already encumbered with spectators. Like the day when the convicts departed, there was a slight, chilling shower of the season; it is raining still, and doubtless there will be rain all the day,—which will last when I am no more! We entered the van. The messenger and a gendarme, in the front compartment, the Priest, myself, and a gendarme in the other, with four mounted gendarmes around the carriage. As I entered it, an old grey-eyed woman who stood near exclaimed, "I like seeing this, even better than seeing the galley convicts!"

I can conceive this. It is a spectacle more easily taken in at one view. Nothing divides the attention; there is but one man, and on this isolated being there is as much misery heaped as on all the other convicts together. The van passed with a dull noise under the gateway, and the heavy doors of the Bicêtre were closed after us. I felt myself moving, but in stupor, like a man fallen into a lethargy, who can neither move nor cry out, and who fancies he feels that he is being buried alive. I listened vaguely to the peals of bells on the collars of the post-horses which drew the van, the iron wheels grating over various substances in the road, the cracking whips of the postillion, the galloping of the gendarmes round the carriage,— all seemed like a whirlwind which bore me away.

My mind was so stupefied with grief that I only conceived ideas as in a dream. I saw the blue towers of Nôtre-Dame in the distance. "Those who will be on the tower with the flag will see my execution well," said I to myself, smiling stupidly.

I think it was at that moment that the Priest addressed me again; I patiently let him speak. I had already in my ears the noise of the wheels, the galloping horses, and the postillion's whip; therefore it was only one more incomprehensible noise. I listened in silence to that flow of monotonous words, which deadened my thoughts, like the murmur of a brook; and they passed before my torpid mind, always varied yet always the same, like the crooked elms we passed by the roadside. The short and jerking voice of the messenger in the front of the van suddenly aroused me.

"Well, Chaplain," said he, in almost a gay tone, "what news have you to-day?"

The Chaplain, who spoke to me without ceasing, and who was deafened by the carriage, made no answer.

"Well, well! how the van rattles; one can hardly hear oneself. What was I saying to you, Chaplain! Oh, aye!— do you know the great news of Paris to-day?"

I started as if he were speaking to me.

"No," said the priest, who had at last heard him, "I have not had time to read the papers this morning: I shall see them this evening. When I am occupied in this way all day, I order my servant to keep the papers, and I read them on my return."

"Bah!" replied the other, "it is impossible that you have not heard what I mean. The news of Paris—the news of this morning."

It was now my turn to speak; and I said, "I know what you mean."

The Messenger looked at me. "You? really! and pray what is your opinion about it?"

"You are inquisitive," said I.

"How so, sir?" replied he. "Every one should have a political opinion: I esteem you too much to suppose that you are without one. As to myself, I am quite in favour of re-establishing the National Guard. I was a serjeant in my company; and, faith! it was very agreeable to—"

I interrupted him by saying, "I did not think this was the subject in question."

"What did you suppose, then? You professed to know the news."

"I spoke of something else with which Paris is also occupied to-day."

The fool did not understand, and his curiosity was awakened.

"More news! Where the deuce could *you* learn news. What is it, my dear sir? Do you know what it is, Chaplain? Do let me hear all about it, I beg. I like news, you see, to relate to the President; it amuses him."

He looked from one to the other, and obtained no answer.

"Well," said he, "what are you thinking of?"

"I am thinking," said I, "that I shall be past thinking, this evening."

"Oh, that's it," returned he. "Come, come, you are too sad. Mr. Castaing conversed on the day of his execution."

Then, after a pause, he continued: "I accompanied Mr. Papavoine on his last day. He wore his otter-skin cap, and smoked his cigar. As for the young men of La Rochelle, they only spoke among themselves, but still they spoke. As for you, I really think you are too pensive, young man."

"Young man?" I repeated. "I am older than you; every quarter of an hour which passes makes me a year older."

He turned round, looked at me some minutes with stupid astonishment, and then began to titter.

"Come, you are joking; older than I am? why, I might be your grandfather."

"I have no wish to jest," I answered gravely. He opened his snuff-box.

"Here, my good sir, don't be angry. Take a pinch of snuff, and don't bear malice."

"Do not fear," said I; "I shall not have long to bear it against you."

At this moment the snuff-box which he extended to me came against the grating which separated us. A jolt caused it to strike rather violently, and it fell, wide open, under the feet of the gendarme.

"Curse the grating!" said the messenger; then turning to me, he added, "Now, am I not unlucky? I have lost all my snuff!"

"I lose more than you," said I.

As he tried to pick up his snuff, he muttered between his teeth, "More than I! that's very easily said. No more snuff until I reach Paris! It's terrible."

The Chaplain then addressed him with some words of consolation; and I know not if I were pre-occupied, but it seemed to be to be part of the exhortation of which the commencement had been addressed to me.

By degrees conversation increased between the Chaplain and the officer; and I became again lost in thought. The vas was stopped for a minute before the toll-gate, and the inspector examined it. Had it contained a sheep or an ox which was going to be slaughtered, they would have required some money; but a human head pays no duty!

We passed through the gates, and the carriage trotted quickly through those old and crooked streets of the Faubourg St. Marceau and the city, which twist and cross each other like the many paths of an ant-hill. On the pavement of these narrow streets the rolling of the wheels became so noisy and rapid that I could hear no other sound, though I saw that people exclaimed, as the van passed, and bands of children followed its track. I fancied also I occasionally saw in the cross-streets ragged men displaying in their hands a bundle of printed papers, their mouths open as if vociferating something, while the passers stopped to purchase.

Half-past eight struck by the palace clock as we arrived in the court of the Conciergerie Prison. The sight of its wide staircase, its dark chapel, its sombre gates, made me shudder; and when the carriage stopped, I fancied the beatings of my heart stopped also.

But I collected my strength; the door was opened; with the rapidity of lightning I jumped from the moving prison, and passed between two lines of soldiers; already there was a crowd formed on my path.

TWENTY-SECOND PAPER

ALL my resolution abandoned me when I reached the low doors, private stairs, and interior corridors, which are only entered by the condemned. The Officer still accompanied me: the Priest had left me for a couple of hours—perchance to read the papers!

I was then taken to the Governor, into whose charge the Officer gave me. They made an exchange. The Director told him to wait a moment, as he had some "game" for him to take back in the Van to the Bicêtre. No doubt it was the man condemned to-day. He is to sleep to-night on the bundle of straw which I have not had time to wear out.

"Oh, very well," said the Officer to the Governor, "I will wait with pleasure; we can make out the two papers together, and it will be very convenient."

They then placed me in a small room adjoining the Governor's office, and left me, locked in, alone.

I know not of what I was thinking, or

how long I had been there, when a sudden and loud burst of laughter in my ear dispersed my reverie.

I raised my eyes with a start. I was no longer alone in the cell; a man was beside me. He was about fifty-five years old, middle-sized, wrinkled, stooping, and bald: with a sinister cast in his grey eyes, and a bitter sneer on his countenance; he was dirty, half clothed, ragged, disgusting.

We looked at each other steadfastly for some moments; he prolonging his bitter laugh, while I felt half astonished, half alarmed.

"Who are you?" said I to him at last.

"That is a funny question," said he. "I am a *friauche*."

"A friauche?" said I; "what does that mean?"

This question redoubled his merriment.

"Why," cried he, in the midst of a shout of laughter, "it means that they will play the same game with my head in six weeks hence, as they will with thine in six hours! Ha! ha! ha! thou seem'st to understand now!"

And truly I was pale, and my hair stood on end. This, then, was the other condemned prisoner, the one just sentenced, whom they expected at the Bicêtre; the heir of my cell.

He continued: "Never mind! Here's *my* history. I am son of a famous thief; it is a pity that they gave him one day a hempen cravat; it was during the 'reign of the Gallows by the grace of Heaven.' At six years of age I had neither father nor mother; in summer I turned somersets in the dust on the high-road, that carriage-travellers might throw me money; in winter I walked with naked feet in the mud, in ragged clothes, and blowing on my purple hands to excite pity. At nine years old I began to use my fingers; at times I emptied a pocket or a reticule; at ten years old I was a pilferer: then I made acquaintances, and at seventeen I became a thief. I broke into a shop, I robbed the till; I was taken and sent to the Galleys. What a hard life that was! Sleeping on bare boards, drinking plain water, eating black bread, dragging a stupid fetter which was of no use; sun-strokes and whip-strokes: and then all the heads are kept shaved, and I had such fine chestnut hair! Never mind! I served my time; fifteen years. That wears one famously!

"I was two-and-thirty years old; one fine morning they gave me a map of the road, a passport, and sixty-six francs, which I had amassed in my fifteen years at the Galleys, working sixteen hours a-day, thirty days a-month, twelve months a-year. Never mind! I wished to be an honest man with my sixty-six francs; and I had finer sentiments under my rags than you might find beneath the cassock of a priest. But deuce take the passport! It was yellow, and they had written upon it 'Freed convict.' I was obliged to show this at every village, and to present it every week to the mayors of the towns through which I was ordered to pass. A fine recommendation! a galley-convict! I frightened all the folk, and little children ran away, and people locked their doors. No one would give me work; I expended the last of my sixty-six francs,—and then— one must live. I showed my arms, fit for labour; the people shut their doors.

I offered my day's work for fifteen sous, for ten sous, for five sous! and no one would have me. What could be done? One day being hungry, I knocked my elbow through a baker's window; I seized on a loaf, and the baker seized on me. I did not eat the loaf, yet I was condemned to the Galleys for life, with three letters branded on my shoulder; I'll show them to you if you like. They call that sort of justice *the relapse*. So here I was, a returned horse. I was brought back to Toulon, —this time among the Green-caps (galley-slaves for life); so now I decided to escape. I had *only* three walls to pierce, two chains to break, and I had one nail! I escaped. They fired the signal gun; for we convicts are, like the Cardinals of Rome, dressed in red, and they fire cannons when we depart! Their powder went to the sparrows! This time, no yellow passport, but then no money either. I met some comrades in the neighbourhood who had also served their time or broken their chains. Their captain proposed to me to join the band. They killed on the highways. I acceded, and I began to kill to live. Sometimes we attacked a Diligence, sometimes it was a post-chaise, sometimes a grazier on horseback. We took the money, we let the horses go, and buried the bodies under a tree, taking care that their feet did not appear; and then we danced on the graves, so that the ground might not seem fresh broken.

I grew old this way, hiding in the bushes, sleeping in the air, hunted from wood to wood, but at least free and my own master. Everything has an end, and this like the rest; the gendarmes one night caught us at our tricks; my comrades escaped; but I, the oldest, remained under the claw of these cats in cocked hats. They brought me here. I had already mounted all the steps of the justice-ladder, except one. Whether I had now taken a handkerchief or a life was all the same for me. There was but one 'relapse' to give me,—the executioner. My business has been short: faith, I began to grow old and good for nothing. My father *married the widow* (was hanged); I am going to retire to the Abbey of Mont-à-Regret (the Guillotine); that's all, comrade!"

I remained stupefied during the recital. He laughed louder than at the beginning, and tried to take my hand. I drew back in horror.

"Friend," cried he, "you don't seem game. Don't be foolish on the scaffold: d' ye see? There is one bad moment to pass on the board, but that's so soon done. I should like to be there to show you the step! Faith, I've a great mind not to plead, if they will finish me with you to-day. The same Priest will serve us both. You see I'm a good fellow, eh? I say, shall we be friends?"

Again he advanced a step nearer to me.

"Sir," I answered, repulsing him, "I decline it."

Fresh bursts of laughter at my answer.

"Ha, ha, ha! Sir, you must be a Marquis."

I interrupted him, "My friend, I require reflection: leave me in peace."

The gravity of my tone rendered him instantly thoughtful. He shook his grey and nearly bald head, while he murmured between his teeth, "I understand now,—the Priest!"

After a few minutes' silence, he said to me, almost timidly,—

"Sir, you are a Marquis; that is all very well; but you have on such a nice great-coat, which will not be of much use to you. The Executioner will take it. Give it to me, and I will sell it for tobacco."

I took off my great-coat, and gave it to him. He began to clap his hands with childish joy; then looking at my shirt-sleeves, and seeing that I shivered, he added, "You are cold, Sir; put on this; it rains, and you will be wet through; besides, you ought to go decently on the wagon!"

While saying this, he took off his coarse, grey woollen jacket, and put my arms into it, which I allowed him to do unconsciously. I then leaned against the wall, and I cannot describe the effect this man had on me. He was examining the coat which I had given him, and uttered each moment an exclamation of delight. "The pockets are quite new! The collar is not in the least worn! It will bring me at least fifteen francs. What luck! I shall have tobacco during all my six weeks."

The door opened again. They were come to conduct me to the room where the condemned finally await their execution; and the guard was also come to take the other prisoner to the Bicêtre. He placed himself, laughingly, amongst them, and said to the gendarmes,—

"I say, don't make a mistake! We have changed skins, the gentleman and I; don't take me in his place. That won't suit me at all, now that I can have tobacco for six weeks!"

TWENTY-THIRD PAPER

THAT old scoundrel! he took my great-coat from me, for I did not give it to him; and then he left me this rag, his odious jacket. For whom shall I be taken?

It was not from indifference, or from charity, that I let him take it. No; but because he was stronger than I! If I had refused, he would have beaten me with those great coarse hands. Charity, indeed! I was full of bad feeling; I should like to have strangled him with my own hands, the old thief! —to have trampled him under my feet.

I feel my heart full of rage and bitterness, and my nature turned to gall: the approach of violent death renders one wicked.

TWENTY-FOURTH PAPER

THEY brought me into an empty cell. I asked for a table, a chair, and writing materials. When all these were brought, I asked for a bed. The turnkey eyed me with astonishment, and seemed mentally to say, "What will be the use of it?" However they made up a chaff bed in the corner. But at the same time a gendarme came to install himself in what was called my chamber. Are they afraid that I would strangle myself with the mattress?

TWENTY-FIFTH PAPER

IT is ten o'clock.

Oh, my poor little girl! In six hours more thy Father will be dead,—something to be dragged about the tables of lecturing rooms; a head to be cast by one party, a trunk to be dissected by another; then all to be thrown together into a bier, and despatched to the felons' burial-ground. This is what they are going to do with thy Father; yet none of them hate me, all pity me, and all could save me! They are going to kill me, Mary, to kill me in cold blood, —a ceremonial for the general good. Poor little girl! thy Father, who loved thee so well, thy Father who kissed thy little white neck, who passed his hands so fondly through the ringlets of thy silken hair, who danced thee on his knee, and every evening joined thy two little hands to pray to God!

Who will do all this for thee in future? Who now will love thee? My darling child, what wilt thou do for my presents, pretty play things, and kisses? Ah, unfortunate Orphan! What wilt thou do for food and raiment?

If the Jury had seen thee, my pretty little Mary, they would have understood it was wrong to kill the Father of a child three years old.

And when she grows up, what will become of her? Her Father will be one of the disgraces of Paris. She will blush for me and at hearing my name; she will be despised, rejected, reviled, on account of him who loved her with all the tenderness of his heart. Oh, my little Mary, whom I so idolized! can it be true that thou wilt encounter shame and horror through me?

Oh! can it be true that I shall die before the close of day? Those distant shouts which I hear, that mass of animated spectators who are already hastening to the Quays, those gendarmes preparing in their barracks,—is it all for me? Yes, I—myself am going to die?—

this actual self which is here, which lives, moves, breathes,—this self which I touch and can feel!

TWENTY-SIXTH PAPER

If I even knew how *it* is built, and in what way one dies upon it; but it is horrible I do not know this.

The very name of it is frightful, and I cannot understand how I have hitherto been able to write and utter it. The idea I attach to this hateful name is vague, undefined, and therefore more sinister. I construct and demolish in my mind continually its hideous scaffolding.

I dare not ask a question about it; yet it is dreadful not to know what it is, and how to act. I fancy there is a sort of hollow, and that you are laid on your face, and—

Ah, my hair will be white before my head falls!

TWENTY-SEVENTH PAPER

I had a glimpse of *it* once. I was passing by the Grève in a carriage, about eleven o'clock, one morning, when a crowd impeded our progress. I looked out of the window; a dense throng of men, women, and children filled the place and the neighbouring streets. Above the crowd I saw a kind of frame of red wood, which three men were building. I turned away my head with disgust. Close to the carriage there was a woman who said to a child, "Now, look! the axe slides badly; they are going to grease the slide with a candle-end."

They are probably doing the same now. Eleven o'clock has just struck. No doubt they are greasing the slide.

Oh, unhappy creature! this time I shall not turn away my head.

TWENTY-EIGHTH PAPER

Oh for a pardon! My reprieve! Perhaps I shall be pardoned. The King has no dislike to me. I wish to see my lawyer! He was right, and I should prefer the galleys. Five years of the galleys,—nay, twenty years, or even the galleys for life. Yes, and to be branded with letters! But it would let me have a reprieve of my life! A galley-slave can move, come and go, and see the sunshine.

Oh! I must see my lawyer; he shall discover some new plea to urge in mitigation of my sentence.

How can I thus write when every point of his eloquence has already failed, and been unanswerably refuted!

TWENTY-NINTH PAPER

The Priest returned. He has white hair, a very gentle look, a good and respectable countenance, and is a charitable man. This morning I saw him empty his purse into the hands of the prisoners. Whence is it then that his voice causes no emotion, and he does not ever seem affected by his own theme? Whence is it that he had as yet said nothing which has won on my intellect or my heart?

This morning I was bewildered; I scarcely heard what he said; his words seemed to me useless, and I remained indifferent; they glided away like those drops of rain off the window-panes of my cell.

Nevertheless, when he came just now to my room, his appearance did me good. Amongst all mankind he is the only one who is still a brother for me, I reflected; and I felt an ardent thirst for good and consoling words.

When he was seated on the chair, and I on the bed, he said to me,—

"My son,—"

This word opened my heart. He continued:

"My son, do you believe in God?"

"Oh, yes, Father!" I answered him.

"Do you believe in the holy Catholic, Apostolic, and Roman Church?"

"Willingly," said I.

"My son," returned he "you have an air of doubt."

Then he began to speak. He spoke a long time; he uttered a quantity of words. Then, when he had finished, he rose, and looked at me for the first time since the beginning of his discourse, and said "Well?"

I protest I had listened to him with avidity at first, then with attention, then with consideration.

I also rose and said, "Sir, leave me for a time, I beg of you."

He asked. "When shall I return?"

"I will let you know, Sir."

Then he withdrew in silence, but shaking his head as though inwardly exclaiming, "An Unbeliever."

No! low as I have fallen, I am *not* an unbeliever. God is my witness that I believe in Him. But how did that old man address me? Nothing to be felt, nothing to affect me, nothing to draw forth tears, nothing which sprung from his heart to enter into mine,—

nothing which was addressed from himself to myself.

On the contrary, there was something vague, inaccentuated, applicable to any case and to none in particular: emphatic where it should have been profound, flat where it ought to have been simple; a species of sentimental sermon and theological elegy. Now and then a quotation in Latin; here and there the names of Saint Augustine and Saint Gregory, and others of the Calendar. And throughout he had the air of reciting a lesson which he had already twenty times repeated; seeming to go over a theme almost obliterated in his memory from being so long known; but not one look in his eyes, not one accent in his voice, to indicate that *he* was interested!

And how could it be otherwise? This Priest is the head Chaplain of the Prison; his calling is to console and exhort,—that is, he lives by it. Condemned felons are the spring of his eloquence; he receives their confession, and prays with them, because he keeps his place by it. He had advanced in years in conducting men to death from his youth, he has grown accustomed to that which makes others shudder. The dungeon and scaffold are every-day matters with him.

He receives notice the preceding evening that he will have to attend some one the following day, at a certain hour. He asks, "Is it for the Galleys or an execution?" and he asks no more respecting them, but comes next day as a matter of course.

Oh that they would bring me, instead of this man, some young curate, some aged Priest, taken by chance from the nearest parish! Let them find him at his devotional studies, and without warning, say to him, "There is a man who is going to die, and it is reserved for you to console him. You must be there when they bind his hands; you must take a place in the fatal cart, with your crucifix, and conceal the executioner from him. You must pass with him through that horrible crowd which is thirsting for his execution; you must embrace him at the foot of the scaffold, and you must remain there until his soul has flown!"

When they have said this, let them bring him hither, agitated, palpitating, all shuddering from head to foot. Let me throw myself into his arms; then kneel at his feet, and he will weep, and we will weep together; and he will be eloquent, and I shall be consoled, and my heart will unburthen itself into his heart,—and I shall receive the blessed hope of Redemption, and he will take my Soul!

THIRTIETH PAPER

BUT that old man, what is he to me? What am I to him? Another individual of an unhappy class, a shadow of which he has seen so many; another unit to add to his list of executions.

I have been wrong, perhaps, not to attend to him more; it is he who is good, while I am the reverse. Alas! it was not my fault. The thought of my violent death has spoiled and hardened all within me.

They have just brought me food, as if I could possibly wish for it! I even tried to eat, but the first mouthful fell untasted from my lips.

THIRTY-FIRST PAPER

SINCE then a strange circumstance happened. They came to relieve my good old gendarme, with whom, ungrateful egotist that I am, I did not even shake hands. Another took his place; a man with a low forehead, heavy features, and stupid contenance. Beyond this I paid no attention, but seated myself at the table, my forehead resting on my hands, and my mind troubled by thought. A light touch on my shoulder made me look round. It was the new gendarme, with whom I was alone, and who addressed me pretty nearly in these terms:—

"Criminal, have you a kind heart?"

"No!" answered I, impatiently. The abruptness of my answer seemed to disconcert him. Nevertheless, he began again, hesitatingly,—

"People are not wicked for the pleasure of being so?"

"Why not?" answered I. "If you have nothing but that to say to me, leave me in peace. What is your aim?"

"I beg your pardon, Criminal," he returned; "I will only say two words, which are these: If you could cause the happiness of a poor man, and that it cost you nothing, would you not do so?"

I answered gravely, "Surely, you cannot allude to me as having power to confer happiness?"

He lowered his voice and assumed a mysterious air, which ill-suited with his idiotic countenance.

"Yes, Criminal, yes,—happiness! fortune!" whispered he; "all this can come to me through you. Listen here, I am a poor gendarme; the service is heavy, the pay is light; my horse is my own, and ruins me. So I put into the lottery as a counterbalance. Hitherto I have only missed by not having the right numbers. I am always very near them. If I buy seventy-six, number seventy-seven comes up a prize. Have a little patience, if you please; I have almost done. Well, here is a lucky opportunity for me. It appears, Criminal, begging your pardon, that you are to be executed to-day. It is a certain fact that the dead who are destroyed that way see the lottery before it is drawn on earth. Promise that your spirit shall appear to me to-morrow evening, to give me three numbers,—three good ones, eh? What trouble will it be to you? and I am not afraid of ghosts. Be easy on that point. Here's my address: Popincourt Barracks, staircase A, No. 26, at the end of the corridor. You will know me again, won't you? Come even to-night, if it suits you better."

I would have disdained to reply to such an imbecile, if a mad hope had not crossed my mind. In my desperate position there are moments when one fancies that a chain may be broken by a hair.

"Listen," said I to him, acting my part as well as a dying wretch could. "I can indeed render thee richer than the King. I can make thee gain millions, on one condition."

He opened his stupid eyes.

"What, what? I will do anything to please you, Criminal."

"Then instead of three numbers I promise to tell you four. Change coats with me."

"Oh, is that all?" cried he undoing the first hooks of his uniform cheerfully.

I rose from my chair; I watched all his movements with a beating heart. I already fancied the doors opening before the uniform of a gendarme; and then the prison—the street—the town—left far behind me! But suddenly he turned round with indecision, and asked,—

"I say,—it is not to go out of this?"

I saw that all was lost; nevertheless, I tried one last effort, useless as it was foolish.

"Yes, it is," said I to him; "but as thy fortune will be made—"

He interrupted me.

"Oh, law, no! on account of my numbers! To make them good, you must be dead, you know!"

I sat down again, silent, and more desponding, from all the hope that I had conceived.

THIRTY-SECOND PAPER

I SHUT my eyes, covered them with my hands, and sought to forget the present in the past. In a rapid reverie, the recollections of childhood and youth came back one by one, soft, calm, smiling, like islands of flowers on the black gulf of confused thoughts which whirled through my brain.

I was again a child,—a laughing, healthy schoolboy, playing, running, shouting with my brothers, in the broad green walks of the old garden where my first years were passed.

And then, four years later, behold me there again, still a child, but a passionate dreamer. And there is a young girl in the garden,—a little Spaniard, with large eyes and long hair, her dark polished skin, her rosy lips and cheeks, the Andalusian of fourteen, named *Pepa*. Our mothers had told us to "go and run together;" we had talked instead. Only the year before, we used to play and quarrel and dispute together. I tyrannized over Pepita for the best apple in the orchard; I beat her for a bird's nest. She cried; I scolded her, and we went to complain of each other to our mothers. But now—she was leaning on my arm, and I felt proud and softened. We walked slowly, and we spoke low. I gathered for her some flowers, and our hands trembled on meeting. She spoke to me of the birds, of the sky above us, of the crimson sunset behind the trees; or else of her school-fellows, her gown and ribbons. We talked in innocence, but we both blushed. The child had grown into a young girl. After we had walked for some time, I made her sit down on a bank; she was smiling. I was serious.

"Sit down there," said she, "there is still daylight; let us read something. Have you a book?"

I happened to have a favourite volume with me. I drew near her, and opened it by chance. She leaned her shoulder against mine, and we began to read the same page. Before turning the leaf, she was always obliged to wait for me. My mind was less quick than hers. "Have you finished?" she would ask, when I had only just commenced. Then our heads leaned together, our hair mixed, our breath gradually mingled. and at last our lips met.

When we again thought of continuing our reading it was starlight. I shall remember that evening all my life!

Oh, heaven! All *my* life!

THIRTY-THIRD PAPER

THE clock had just struck some hour, —I do not know which. I do not hear the strokes plainly. I seem to have the peal of an organ in my ears. It is the confusion of my last thoughts. At this final day, when I look back over the events of life, I recall my crime with horror; but I wish to have still longer to repent of it. I felt more remorse after my condemnation; since then it seems as if there were no space but for thoughts of death. But now, oh, how I wish to repent me thoroughly! When I had lingered for a minute on what had passed in my life, and then came back to the thought of its approaching termination, I shuddered as at something new. My happy childhood, my fair youth,—a golden web with its end stained. If any read my history, after so many years of innocence and happiness, they will not believe in this execrable year, which began by a crime, and will close by an execution. It would appear impossible.

And nevertheless, oh, — imperfection of human laws and human nature!— I was not ill-disposed.

THIRTY-FOURTH PAPER

OH! to die in a few hours, and to think that a year ago, on the same day, I was innocent and at liberty, enjoying autumnal walks, wandering beneath the trees! To think that in this same moment there are in the houses around me, men coming and going, laughing and talking, reading newspapers, thinking of business; shopkeepers selling their wares, young girls preparing their ball-dresses for the evening; mothers playing with their children!

THIRTY-FIFTH PAPER

I REMEMBER once, when a child, going alone to see the belfry of Nôtre-Dame.

I was already giddy from having ascended the dark winding staircase, from having crossed the slight open gallery which unites the two towers, and from having seen Paris beneath my feet; and I entered the cage of stone and woodwork where the great bell is hung. I advanced with trembling steps over the ill-joined planks, examining at a distance that bell, so famous amongst the children and common people in Paris; and it was not without terror that I observed the slated pent-houses, which surrounded the belfry with inclined planes, were just on a level with my feet. Through the openings I saw, in a bird's-eye view, the street beneath, and the passengers diminished to the size of ants.

Suddenly the enormous bell resounded; its deep vibration shook the air, making the heavy tower rock, and the flooring start from the beams. The noise had nearly upset me. I tottered, ready to fall, and seemed on the point of slipping over the pent-houses. In an agony of terror I lay down on the planks, pressing them closely with both my arms,—speechless, breathless, with this formidable sound in my ears, while beneath my eyes was the precipice, a profound abyss, where so many quiet and envied passengers were walking.

Well, it appears to me as if I were again in that belfry; my senses seem again giddy and dazzled; the booming of that bell seems to press on my brain, and around me I no longer see that tranquil and even life which I had quitted (where other men walk still) except from a distance, and beyond a terrible abyss.

THIRTY-SIXTH PAPER

IT is a quarter past one o'clock.

The following are my sensations at present: a violent pain in my head, my frame chilled, my forehead burning. Every time that I rise, or bend forward, it seems to me that there is a fluid floating in my head, which makes my brain beat violently against the bone.

I have convulsive startings, and from time to time my pen falls from my hand as if by a galvanic shock. My eyes ache and burn, and I suffer greatly in all my limbs.

In two hours and three-quarters hence, *all will be cured.*

THIRTY-SEVENTH PAPER

THEY say that it is nothing,—that one does not suffer; that it is an easy death. Ah! then, what do they call this agony of six weeks,—this summing-up in one day? What, then, is the anguish of this irreparable day, which is passing so slowly and yet so fast? What is this ladder of tortures which terminates in the scaffold? Are they not the same convulsions whether life is taken away drop by drop, or intellect extinguished thought by thought?

THIRTY-EIGHTH PAPER

IT is singular that my mind so often reverts to the King. Whatever I do, there is a voice within me which says,—

"There is, in this same town, at this same hour, and not far from hence, in another Palace, a man who also has guards to all his gates; a man alone, like thee, in the crowd,—with this difference, that he is as high as thou art low. His entire life is glory, grandeur, delight. All around him is love, respect, veneration; the loudest voices become low in speaking to him, and the proudest heads are bent. At this moment he is holding a Council of Ministers, where all coincide with his opinions; or else he thinks of the Chase to-morrow, or the Ball for this evening, feeling certain that the Fête will come, and leaving to others the trouble of his pleasures.

"Well, this man is of flesh and blood like thee! And in order that at this instant the scaffold should fall, and thou be restored to life, liberty, fortune, family, it would only be requisite for him to write his name at the foot of a piece of paper; or even that his carriage should meet thy fatal cart! And he is good, too, and perhaps would be glad to do it; and yet it will not be done!"

THIRTY-NINTH PAPER

WELL then, let me have courage with death,—let me handle this horrid idea, let me face it boldly. I will ask what it is, know what it demands, turn it in every sense, fathom the enigma, and look before-hand into the tomb.

* * * * * *

I have speculated upon Death and Eternity until my mind seems bewildered by its own horrible fantasies. My ideas wander. Oh, for a Priest,—a Priest who could instruct me! I must

have a Priest, and a crucifix to embrace. Alas! here is the same Priest again!

FORTIETH PAPER

AFTER a time, I begged of him to let me sleep. I threw myself on the bed. I had a fulness of blood in my head which made me sleep,—my last sleep on earth. I had a horible dream, from which I awoke in terror, shuddering and in agony.

The Chaplain was seated at the foot of my bed, reading prayers.

"Have I slept long?" I inquired of him.

"My son," said he, "you have slept an hour. They have brought your child, who is waiting in the next room; I would not allow them to awaken you."

"Oh," cried I, "my darling child! Let them bring in my idolized child!"

FORTY-FIRST PAPER

My child looked rosy and happy, and her large eyes were bright. Oh, she is so pretty! I drew her towards me; I raised her in my arms, and placing her on my knees, kissed her dear hair. I asked, "Why is her Mother not with her?" And I learnt that she was very ill, and my poor old mother also.

Mary looked at me with astonishment. Caressed, embraced, devoured with kisses, she submitted quietly; but, from time to time, cast an uneasy look towards her Nurse, who was crying in the corner.

At length I was able to speak.

"Mary," I exclaimed. "My own little Mary!" and I pressed her violently gainst my breast, which was heaving with sobs. She uttered a little cry, and then said, "Oh, you hurt me, sir."

"*Sir!*" It is nearly a year since she has seen me, poor child! She has forgotten me, face, words, voice; and then who could know me with this beard, this dress, and this pallor? What! already effaced from that memory,—the only one where I wished to survive! What! already, no longer a Father, am I condemned to hear no more that word, so soft in the language of children that it cannot remain in the language of men, "Papa?"

And yet to have heard it from that sweet mouth, once more,—only once more,—that is all that I would have asked in payment for the forty years of life they will take from me.

"Listen, Mary," said I to her, joining her two little hands in mine. "Do you not know me?"

She looked at me with her bright beautiful eyes and answered,—

"Oh, no, indeed."

"Look at me well," I repeated. "What! dost thou not know who I am?"

"Yes, sir," she answered. "You are a gentleman."

Alas! while loving one being on earth, loving with all your deep affection, having that being before you, who sees and looks at you, speaks and answers you, and yet knows you not! You wish for consolation but from this one being, who is the only one that does not know that you require it because you are going to die!

"Mary," I continued, "hast thou a papa?"

"Yes, sir," said the child.

"Well, then, dearest, where is he?"

She raised her large eyes in astonishment:—

"Ah, then you don't know, sir? Papa is dead."

Here she began to cry: I nearly let the little angel fall.

"Dead!" I exclaimed: "Mary, knowest thou what it is to be dead?"

"Yes, sir," she answered. "He is in earth and in Heaven;" and she continued of her own accord, "I pray to God for him morning and evening at mamma's knees."

I kissed her on her forehead.

"Mary, say to me thy prayer."

"I could not, sir; a prayer you do not say in the middle of the day. Come to-night to my house, and you shall hear me say it."

This was enough. I interrupted her.

"Darling Mary, it is *I* who am thy papa."

"You!" returned she.

I added, "Wouldst thou like me for thy papa?"

The child turned away. "No, sir; my papa was much prettier."

I covered her with kisses and tears. She tried to escape from my arms, crying,—

"Sir, you hurt me with your beard."

Then I replaced her on my knees, devouring her with my eyes, and continued,—

"Mary, canst thou read?"

"Yes," she answered, "I can read very well. Mamma makes me read my letters."

"Well, then, read a little to me," said I, pointing to a printed paper which she held crumpled in one of her dimpled hands.

She shook her pretty head, saying,—

"Oh, dear me! I can only read fables."

"But try, my darling. Come, open your paper."

She unfolded the paper, and began to spell with her finger, "s e n—sen,— TENCE—tence,—*Sentence.*" I snatched it from her hands. It was my own sentence of death she was reading to me!

Her nurse had bought the paper for a penny. To me it had cost more.

No words can convey what I felt; my violence had alarmed the child, who was ready to cry.

Suddenly she said to me,—

"Do give me back my paper; I want to play with it!"

I restored her to her nurse.

"Take her hence!" and I fell back in my chair, gloomy, desolate, in despair! Now they may come: I care for nothing more; the last fibre of my heart is broken.

FORTY-SECOND PAPER

THE Priest is kind; so is the jailor: tears came in their eyes when I sent away my child.

It is done. Now I must fortify myself, and think firmly of the Executioner, the cart, the gendarmes, the crowd in the street and the windows.

I have still an hour to familiarize myself with these ideas. All the people will laugh and clap their hands, and applaud; yet among those men, now free, unknown to jailors, and who run with joy to an execution,—in that throng there is more than one man destined to follow me sooner or later, on the scaffold.

More than one who is here to-day

on my account, will come hereafter on his own.

FORTY-THIRD PAPER

My little Mary. She is gone away to play; she will look at the crowd from the coach window, and already she thinks no more of the "Gentleman." Perhaps I may still have time to write a few pages for her, so that she may read them hereafter, and weep, in fifteen years hence, the sorrows of to-day. Yes, she shall know my history from myself, and why the name I leave her is tarnished.

FORTY-FOURTH PAPER

MY HISTORY

[NOTE. The pages which immediately followed this have not been found. Perhaps, as the next chapter seems to indicate, the Condemned had not time to write his history, as it was so late when he thought of it.]

FORTY-FIFTH PAPER

From a Chamber of the Town Hall.

THE Town Hall. Yes, I am here; the execrable journey is over. The place of execution is before me, and beneath the window, a horrible throng, laughing and yelling, while they await my appearance. My efforts at composure were vain; when above the heads of the crowd I saw the frightful scaffold, my heart failed. I expressed a wish to make my last declaration; so they brought me in here, and have sent for some law-officer to receive it. I am now waiting for him; so there is thus much gained. Here is what occurred, on my removal from the Conciergerie.

At three o'clock they came to tell me it was time. I trembled as if I had thought of any thing else during the last six hours, six weeks, six months. It produced on me the effect of something quite unexpected. They made me cross corridors, and descend stairs, they pushed me through a low door into a sombre room, narrow, arched, and scarcely lighted by a day of rain and fog. A chair was in the centre, on which I seated myself at their desire. Some persons were standing near the door; and beside the Priest and gendarmes, there were three men. The first of these, the tallest and oldest, was stout, with a red countenance. This was HE.

This was the Executioner,—the servant of the Guillotine; the others were his own servants. When I was seated, these walked quietly behind me; then suddenly I felt the cold of steel in my hair, and heard the grating action of scissors. My hair, cut carelessly, fell in heavy locks on my shoulders, and the executioner removed them gently with his coarse hand.

The parties in the room spoke in subdued tones. There was a heavy dull sound from without, which I fancied at first was caused by the river; but a shout of laughter soon proved to me it came from the crowd.

A young man near the window, who was writing with a pencil, in his pocket-book, asked one of the turnkeys, what was the name of the present operation? He was answered "The Toilet of the Condemned." From this I gathered that he was preparing the Report for to-morrow's newspaper. One of the servants then removed my waistcoat, and the other one taking my hands, placed them behind me, and I felt the knots of a cord rolled slowly round my wrists; at the same time the other took off my cravat. My linen,—the only remains of former times,—being of the finest quality, caused him a sort of hesitation for a moment; but at length he began to cut off the collar.

At this dreadful precaution, and the sensation of the steel touching my neck, a tremor passed over me, and a stifled groan escaped; the man's hand trembled.

"Sir," said he, "I beg your pardon; I fear I've hurt you."

The people shouted louder in the street. A tall red-faced man offered a handkerchief, steeped in vinegar, for me to inhale.

"Thank you," said I to him, in the firmest tone I could summon, "it is needless; I am recovered."

Then one man stooped down and fastened a small cord to my ankles, which restricted my steps; and this was again tied to the cord around my wrists; finally, the tall man threw my jacket over my shoullders, and tied the sleeves in front. All was now completed.

Then the Priest drew near with his Crucifix.

"Come, my son," said he.

The man raised me by my arms; and I walked, but my steps were weak and tottering. At this moment the folding doors were thrown open. A furious clamour, a chill breeze, and a strong white light reached me in the shade. From the extreme of the dark chamber I saw through the rain a thousand yelling heads of the expectant mass. On the right of the doorway, a range of mounted gendarmes; in front, a detachment of soldiers; on the left, the back of the cart, with a ladder. A hideous picture, with the appropriate frame of a prison-door.

It was for this dream moment that I had reserved my courage. I advanced a few steps, and appeared on the threshold.

"There he is! there he is!" bellowed the crowd. "He's come out at last!" and the nearest to me clapped their hands. Much as a king might be loved, there could not be more greeting for him.

The tall man first ascended the cart.

"Good morning, *Mr. Sampson!*" cried the children hanging by the lamp-posts. One of his servants next followed. "Bravo, *Tuesday!*" cried out the children, as the two placed themselves on the front seat.

It was now my turn, and I mounted with a firm step.

"He goes well to it!" said a woman beside the gendarmes.

This atrocious commendation gave me courage. The Priest took his seat beside me. They had placed me on the hindmost seat, my back towards the house. I shuddered at that last attention. There is a mixture of humanity in it.

I wished to look around me,—gendarmes before and behind: then crowd! crowd! crowd! A sea of heads in the street. The officer gave the word, and the procession moved on, as if pushed forward by a yell from the populace.

"Hats off! hats off!" cried a thousand voices together, as if for the King. Then I laughed horribly also myself, and said to the Priest, "Their hats— my head."

We passed a street which was full of public-houses, in which the windows were filled with spectators, seeming to enjoy their good places, particularly the women.

There were also people letting out tables, chairs, and carts; and these dealers in human life shouted out, "Who wishes for places?"

A strange rage seized me against these wretches, and I longed to shout out to them, "Do you wish for mine?"

The procession still advanced. At each step the crowd in the rear dispersed; and I saw, with my wandering eyes, that they collected again farther on, to have another view. I know not how it was, that notwithstanding the fog and the small white rain which crossed the air like gossamer, nothing which passed around escaped me; every detail brought its torture; words fail to convey my emotions. My great dread was lest I should faint. Last vanity! Then I endeavoured to confuse myself into being blind and deaf to all, except to the Priest, whose words I scarcely heard amidst the tumult. I took the Crucifix and kissed it.

"Have mercy on me," said I. "O my God!"

And I strove to engross myself with this thought.

But every shake of the cart disturbed me; and then I became excessively chilled, as the rain had penetrated my clothes. and my head was bare.

"Are you trembling with cold, my son?" demanded the Priest.

"Yes," answered I. "Alas! not only from cold."

At the turn to the Bridge, the women expressed pity at my being so young. We approached the fatal Quay. My hearing and sight seemed about to fail me. All those voices, all those heads at the windows, at doors, at shop fronts, on lamp-posts; these thirsting, and cruel spectators; this crowd where all knew me, and I knew none; this road paved and welled with human visages,—I was confounded, stupefied, senseless. There is something insupportable in the weight of so many looks being fixed upon one. I could scarcely maintain my place on the seat, and lent no further attention to the Priest. In the tumult which surrounded me, I no longer distinguished exclamations of pity from those of satisfaction, or the sounds of laughter from those of complaint. All formed together a noise in my ears like sounding brass.

My eyes read mechanically the signs over the shops.

Once I felt a painful curiosity to look round on *that* which we were approaching.

It was the last mental bravado, and the body would not aid it; for my neck remained paralyzed, and I could not turn it.

And the cart went on, on. The shops passed away; the signs succeeded each other,—written, painted, gilt; and the populace laughed while they tramped through the mud; and I yielded my mind, as persons do in sleeping. Suddenly this series of shops ended as we turned into the square; the voice of the mob became still more loud, yelling and joyous; the cart stopped suddenly, and I had nearly fallen on my face. The Priest held me up.

"Courage!" murmured he.

They next brought a ladder to the back of my cart. I leaned on the arm of the Priest and descended. I made one step, and turned round to advance another, but I had not the power; beyond the lamp I saw something startling. . . .

Oh, it was THE REALITY!

I stopped as if staggered by a blow.

"I have a last declaration to make," cried I, feebly.

And then they brought me up here.

I asked them to let me write my last wishes; and they unbound my hands; but the cord is here, ready to be replaced.

FORTY-SIXTH PAPER

A JUDGE, a Commissioner, a Magistrate,—I know not what was his rank, —has just been here.

I intreated him to procure my pardon; I begged it with clasped hands, and dragging myself on my knees at his feet.

He asked, with a fatal smile, if that were all I had to say to him?

"My pardon, my pardon!" I repeated. "Oh, for mercy's sake, five minutes more! Who knows, my pardon may come. It is so horrible at my age to die in this manner. Reprieves have frequently arrived even at the last moment! And to whom would they show mercy, sir, if not to me?"

That detestable Executioner! He came in to tell the Judge that the execution was ordered for a certain hour, which hour was at hand, and that he was answerable for the event.

"Oh, for mercy's sake! five minutes to wait for my pardon," cried I, "or I will defend myself."

The Judge and the Executioner went out. I am alone,—at least with only two gendarmes present.

That horrible throng, with its hyena cry! Who knows but that I shall escape from it, that I shall be saved? If my pardon,—it is impossible but that they will pardon me! Hark! I hear some one coming upstairs!

FOUR O'CLOCK.

Claude Gueux, King of Thieves

CLAUDE GUEUX was a poor workman, living in Paris about eight years ago, with his mistress and child. Although his education had been neglected, and he could not even read, the man was naturally clever and intelligent, and thought deeply over matters. Winter came with its attendant miseries,—want of work, want of food, want of fuel. The man, the woman, and the child were frozen and famished. The man turned thief. I know not what he stole. What signifies, as the result was the same; to the woman and child it gave three days' bread and warmth; to the man, five years' imprisonment. He was taken to Clairvaux,—the abbey now converted into a prison, its cells into dungeons, and the altar itself into a pillory. This is called progress.

Claude Gueux the honest workman, who turned thief from force of circumstances, had a countenance which impressed you,—a high forehead somewhat lined with care, dark hair already streaked with grey, deep-set eyes beam-

ing with kindness, while the lower part clearly indicated firmness mingled with self-respect. He rarely spoke, yet there was a certain dignity in the man which commanded respect and obedience. A fine character, and we shall see what society made of it.

Over the prison workshop was an inspector, who rarely forgot that he was a jailor also to his subordinates, handing them the tools with one hand, and casting chains upon them with the other. A tyrant, never using even self-reasoning; with ideas against which there was no appeal; hard rather than firm, at times he could even be jocular, doubtless a good father, a good husband, really not vicious, but *bad*. He was one of those men who never can grasp a fresh idea, who apparently fail to be moved by any emotion; yet with hatred and rage in their hearts they look like blocks of wood, heated on the one side but frozen on the other. This man's chief characteristic was obstinacy; and so proud was he of this very stubbornness that he compared himself with Napoleon,—an optical delusion, like taking the mere flicker of a candle for a star. When he had made up his mind to a thing, however absurd, he would carry out that absurd idea. How often it happens, that, when a catastrophe occurs, if we inquire into the cause we find it originated through the obstinacy of one with little ability, but having full faith in his own powers.

Such was the inspector of the prison workshop at Clairvaux,—a man of flint placed by society over others, who hoped to strike sparks out of such material; but a spark from a like source is apt to end in a conflagration.

The inspector soon singled out Claude Gueux, who had been numbered and placed in the workshop, and finding him clever, treated him well. Seeing Claude looking sad (for he was ever thinking of her he termed his wife), and being in a good humour, by way of pastime to console the prisoner he told him the woman had become one of the unfortunate sisterhood, and had been reduced to infamy; of the child nothing was known.

After a time Claude had accustomed himself to prison rule, and by his calmness of manner and a certain amount of resolution clearly marked in his face, he had acquired a great ascendency over his companions, who so much admired him that they asked his advice, and tried in all ways to imitate him. The very expression in his eyes clearly indicated the man's character; besides, is not the eye the window to the soul, and what other result could be anticipated than that the intelligent spirit should lead men with few ideas, who yielded to the attraction as the metal does to the loadstone? In less than three months Claude was the virtual head of the workshop, and at times he almost doubted whether he was king or prisoner, being treated sometimes like a captive pope, surrounded by his cardinals.

Such popularity ever has its attendant hatred; and though beloved by the prisoners, Claude was detested by the jailors. To him two men's rations would have been scarcely sufficient. The inspector laughed at this, as his own appetite was large; but what would be mirth to a duke, to a prisoner would be a great misfortune. When a free man, Claude Gueux could earn his daily four-pound loaf and enjoy it; but as a prisoner he daily worked, and for his labour received one pound and a-half of bread and four ounces of meat; it naturally followed that he was always hungry.

He had just finished his meagre fare, and was about to resume his labours, hoping in work to forget famine, when a weakly-looking young man came towards him, holding a knife and his untasted rations in his hand, but seemingly afraid to address him.

"What do you want?" said Claude, roughly.

"A favour at your hands," timidly replied the young man.

"What is it?" said Claude.

"Help me with my rations; I have more than I can eat."

For a moment Claude was taken aback, but without further ceremony he divided the food in two and at once partook of one half.

"Thank you," said the young man;

"allow me to share my rations with you every day."

"What is your name?" said Claude.

"Albin."

"Why are you here?" added Claude.

"I robbed."

"So did I," said Claude.

The same scene took place daily between this man old before his time (he was only thirty-six) and the boy of twenty, who looked at the most seventeen. The feeling was more like that of father and son than one brother to another; everything created a bond of union between them,—the very toil they endured together, the fact of sleeping in the same quarters and taking exercise in the same court yard. They were happy, for were they not all the world to each other?

The inspector of the workshop was so hated by the prisoners that he often had recourse to Claude Gueux to enforce his authority; and when a tumult was on the point of breaking out, a few words from Claude had more effect than the authority of ten warders. Although the inspector was glad to avail himself of this influence, he was jealous all the same, and hated the superior prisoner with an envious and implacable feeling, —an example of might over right, all the more fearful as it was secretly nourished. But Claude cared so much for Albin that he thought little about the inspector.

One morning as the warders were going their rounds one of them summoned Albin, who was working with Claude, to go before the inspector.

"What are you wanted for?" said Claude.

"I do not know," replied Albin, following the warder.

All day Claude looked in vain for his companion, and at night, finding him still absent, he broke through his ordinary reserve and addressed the turnkey. "Is Albin ill?" said he.

"No," replied the man.

"How is it that he has never put in an appearance today?"

"His quarters have been changed," was the reply.

For a moment Claude trembled, then calmly continued, "Who gave the order?"

"Monsieur D——." This was the inspector's name.

On the following night the inspector, Monsieur D——, went his rounds as usual. Claude, who had perceived him from the distance, rose, and hastened to raise his woollen cap and button his gray woollen vest to the throat, —considered a mark of respect to superiors in prison discipline.

"Sir," said Claude, as the inspector was about to pass him, "has Albin really been quartered elsewhere?"

"Yes," replied the inspector.

"Sir, I cannot live without him. You know the rations are insufficient for me, and Albin divided his portion with me. Could you not manage to let him resume his old place near me?"

"Impossible; the order cannot be revoked."

"By whom was it given?"

"By me."

"Monsieur D——," replied Claude, "on you my life depends."

"I never cancel an order once given."

"Sir, what have I ever done to you?"

"Nothing."

"Why, then," cried Claude, "separate me from Albin?"

"Because I do," replied the inspector, and with that he passed on.

Claude's head sank down, like the poor caged lion deprived of his dog; but the grief, though so deeply felt, in no way changed his appetite,—he was famished. Many offered to share their rations with him, but he steadily refused, and continued his usual routine in silence,—breaking it only to ask the inspector daily, in tones of anguish mingled with rage, something between a prayer and a threat, these two words; "And Albin?"

The inspector simply passed on, shrugging his shoulders; but had he only observed Claude he would have seen the evident change; noticeable to all present, and he would have heard these words, spoken respectfully but firmly:—

"Sir, listen to me; send my companion to me. It would be wise to do so, I can assure you. Remember my words!"

On Sunday he had sat for hours in the courtyard, with his head bowed in his hands, and when a prisoner called Faillette came up laughing, Claude said: "I am judging some one."

On the 25th of October, 1831, as the inspector went his rounds, Claude, to draw his attention, smashed a watch-glass he had found in the passage. This had the desired effect.

"It was I," said Claude. "Sir, restore my comrade to me."

"Impossible," was the answer.

Looking the inspector full in the face, Claude firmly added: "Now, reflect!

To-day is the 25th of October; I give you till the 4th of November."

A warder remarked that Claude was threatening Monsieur D——, and ought at once to be locked up.

"No, it is not a case of blackhole," replied the inspector, smiling disdainfully; "we must be considerate with people of this stamp."

The following day Claude was again accosted by one of the prisoners named Pernot, as he was brooding in the courtyard.

"Well, Claude, you are sad indeed; what are you pondering over?"

"I fear some evil threatens that good Monsieur D——," answered Claude.

Claude daily impressed the fact on the inspector how much Albin's absence affected him, but with no result save four-and-twenty hours' solitary confinement. On the 4th of November he looked round his cell for the little that remained to remind him of his former life. A pair of scissors, and an old volume of the "Emile," belonging to the woman he had loved so well, the mother of his child,—how useless to a man who could neither work nor read!

As Claude walked down the old cloisters, so dishonoured by its new inmates and its fresh whitewashed walls, he noticed how earnestly the convict Ferrari was looking at the heavy iron bars that crossed the window, and he said to him: "To-night I will cut through those bars with these scissors," pointing to the pair he still held in his hand.

Ferrari laughed incredulously, and Claude joined in the mirth. During the day he worked with more than ordinary ardour, wishing to finish a straw hat, which he had been paid for in advance by a tradesman at Troyes,—M. Bressier.

Shortly before noon he made some excuse to go down into the carpenters' quarters, a story below his own, at the time the warders were absent. Claude received a hearty welcome, as he was equally popular here as elsewhere.

"Can any one lend me an axe?" he said.

"What for?"

Without exacting any promises of secrecy he at once replied: "To kill the inspector with to-night."

Claude was at once offered several; choosing the smallest, he hid it beneath his waistcoat and left. Now, there were twenty-seven prisoners present, and not one of those men betrayed him; they even refrained from talking upon the subject among themselves, waiting for the terrible even which must follow.

As Claude passed on he saw a young convict of sixteen yawning idly there, and he strongly advised him to learn how to read. Just then Faillette asked what he was hiding.

Claude answered unhesitatingly: "An axe to kill Monsieur D—— to-night; but can you see it?"

"A little," said Faillette.

At seven o'clock the prisoners were locked in their several workshops. It was then the custom for the warders to leave them, until the inspector had been his rounds.

In Claude's workshop a most extraordinary scene took place, the only one of the kind on record. Claude rose and addressed his companions, eighty-four in number, in the following words:—

"You all know Albin and I were like brothers. I liked him at first for sharing his rations with me, afterwards because he cared for me. Now I never have sufficient, though I spend the pittance I earn in bread. It could make no possible difference to the inspector, Monsieur D——, that we should be together; but he chose to separate us simply from a love of tormenting, for he is a bad man. I asked again and again for Albin to be sent back, without success; and when I gave him a stated time, the 4th of November, I was thrust into a dungeon. During that time I became his judge, and sentenced him to death on November the 4th. In two hours he will be here, and I warn you I intend to kill him. But have you anything to say?"

There was a dead silence. Claude then continued telling his comrades, the eighty-one thieves, his ideas on the subject,—that he was reduced to a fearful extremity, and compelled by that very necessity to take the law into his own hands; that he knew full well he could not take the inspector's life without sacrificing his own, but that as the cause was a just one he would bear the consequences, having come to this conclusion after two months' calm reflection; that if they considered resentment alone hurried him on to such a step they were at once to say so, and to state their objections to the sentence being carried out.

One voice alone broke the silence which followed, saying, "Before killing the inspector, Claude ought to give him a chance of relenting."

"That is but just," said Claude, "and he shall have the benefit of the doubt."

Claude then sorted the few things a poor prisoner is allowed, and gave them to the comrades he mostly cared for after Albin, keeping only the pair of scissors. He then embraced them all,—some not being able to withhold their tears at such a moment. Claude continued calmly to converse during this last hour, and even gave way to a trick he had as a boy, of extinguishing the candle with a breath from his nose. Seeing him thus, his companions afterwards owned that they hoped he had abandoned his sinister idea. One young convict looked at him fixedly, trembling for the coming event.

"Take courage, young fellow," said Claude, gently; "it will be but the work of a minute."

The workshop was a long room with a door at both ends, and with windows each side overlooking the benches, thus leaving a pathway up the centre for the inspector to review the work on both sides of him. Claude had now resumed his work,—something like Jacques Clement, who did not fail to repeat his prayers.

As the clock sounded the last quarter to nine, Claude rose and placed himself near the entrance, apparently calm. Amidst the most profound silence the clock struck nine; the door was thrown open, and the inspector came in as usual alone, looking quite jovial and self-satisfied, passing rapidly along, tossing his head at one, grinding words out to another, little heeding the eyes fixed so fiercely upon him. Just then he heard Claude's step, and turning quickly round said,—

"What are you doing here? Why are you not in your place?" just as he would have spoken to a dog.

Claude answered respectfully, "I wish to speak to you, sir."

"On what subject?"

"Albin."

"Again!"

"Always the same," said Claude.

"So then," replied the inspector, walking along, "you have not had enough with twenty-four hours in the blackhole."

Claude, following him closely, replied: "Sir, return my companion to me!"

"Impossible!"

"Sir," continued Claude, in a voice which would have moved Satan, "I implore you to send Albin back to me; you will then see how I will work. You are free, and it would matter but little to you; you do not know the feeling of having only one friend. To me it is everything, encircled by the prison walls. You can come and go at your pleasure; I have but Albin. Pray let him come back to me! You know well he shared his food with me. What can it matter to you that a man named Claude Gueux should be in this hall, having another by his side called Albin? You have but to say 'Yes,' nothing more. Sir, my good sir, I implore you, in the name of Heaven, to grant my prayer!"

Claude, overcome with emotion, waited for the answer.

"Impossible!" replied the inspector, impatiently; "I will not recall my words. Now go, you annoyance!" And with that he hurried on towards the outer door, amidst the breathless silence maintained by the eighty-one thieves.

Claude, following and touching the inspector, gently asked: "Let me at least know why I am condemned to death. Why did you separate us?"

"I have already answered you; because I chose," replied the inspector.

With that he was about to lift the latch, when Claude raised the axe, and without one cry the inspector fell to the ground, with his skull completely cloven from three heavy blows dealt with the rapidity of lightning. A fourth completely disfigured his face, and Claude, in his mad fury, gave another and a useless blow; for the inspector was dead.

Claude, throwing the axe aside, cried out, "Now for the other!"

The other was himself; and taking the scissors, *his wife's*, he plunged them into his breast. But the blade was short, and the chest was deep, and vainly he strove to give the fatal blow. At last, covered with blood he fell fainting across the dead. Which of the two would be considered the victim?

When Claude recovered consciousness he was in bed, surrounded by every care and covered with bandages. Near him were Sisters of Charity, and a recorder ready to take down his deposition, who with much interest inquired how he was. Claude had lost a great deal of blood; but the scissors had done him a bad turn, inflicting wounds not one of which was dangerous; the only mortal blows he had struck were on the body of Monsieur D——. Then the interrogatory commenced.

"Did you kill the inspector of the prison workshop at Clairvaux?"

"Yes," was the reply.

"Why did you do so?"

"Because I did."

Claude's wounds now assumed a more serious aspect, and he was prostrated with a fever which threatened his life. November, December, January, February passed, in nursing and preparations, and Claude in turn was visited by doctor and judge,—the one to restore him to health, the other to glean the evidence needful to send him to the scaffold.

On the 16th of March, 1832, perfectly cured, Claude appeared in court at Troyes, to answer the charge brought against him. His appearance impressed the court favourably; he had been shaved and stood bareheaded, but still clad in prison garb. The court was well guarded by a strong military guard, to keep the witnesses within bounds, as they were all convicts. But an unexpected difficulty occurred; not one of these men would give evidence; neither questions nor threats availed to make them break their silence, until Claude requested them to do so. Then they in turn gave a faithful account of the terrible event; and if one, from forgetfulness or affection for the accused, failed to relate the whole facts, Claude supplied the deficiency. At one time the women's tears fell fast.

The usher now called the convict Albin. He came in trembling with emotion and sobbing painfully, and threw himself into Claude's arms. Turning to the Public Prosecutor, Claude said,—

"Here is a convict who gives his food to the hungry," and stooping, he kissed Albin's hand.

All the witnesses having been examined, the counsel for the prosecution then rose to address the court. "Gentlemen of the jury, society would be utterly put to confusion if a public prosecution did not condemn great culprits like him, who, etc."

After a long address by the prosecution, Claude's counsel rose. Then followed the usual pleading for and against, which ever takes place at the criminal court.

Claude in his turn gave evidence, and every one was astonished at his intelligence; there appeared far more of the orator about this poor workman than the assassin. In a clear and straightforward way he detailed the facts as they were,—standing proudly there, resolved to tell the whole truth. At times the crowd was carried away by his eloquence. This man, who could not read, would grasp the most difficult points of argument, yet treat the judges with all due deference. Once Claude lost his temper, when the counsel for the prosecution stated that he had assassinated the inspector without provocation.

"What!" cried Claude, "I had no provocation? Indeed! A drunkard strikes me,—I kill him; then you would allow there was provocation, and the penalty of death would be changed for that of the galleys. But a man who wounds me in every way during four years, humiliates me for four years, taunts me daily, hourly, for four years, and heaps every insult on my head,— what follows? You consider I have had no provocation! I had a wife for whom I robbed,—he tortured me about her. I had a child for whom I robbed,—he taunted me about this child. I was hungry, a friend shared his bread with me,—he took away my friend. I begged him to return my friend to me,—he cast me into a dungeon. I told him how much I suffered,—he said it wearied him to listen. What then would you have me do? I took his life; and you look upon me as a monster for killing this man, and you decapitate me; then do so."

Provocation such as this the law fails to acknowledge, because the blows have no marks to show.

The judge then summed up the case in a clear and impartial manner,— dwelling on the life Claude had led, living openly with an improper character; then he had robbed, and ended by being a murderer. All this was true. Before the jury retired, the judge asked Claude if he had any questions to ask, or anything to say.

"Very little," said Claude. "I am a murderer, I am a thief; but I ask you, gentlemen of the jury, why did I kill? Why did I steal?"

The jury retired for a quarter of an hour, and according to the judgment of these twelve countrymen—*gentlemen of the jury,* as they are styled—Claude Gueux was condemned to death. At the very outset several of them were much impressed with the name of Gueux (vagabond), and that influenced their decision.

When the verdict was pronounced, Claude simply said: "Very well; but there are two questions these gentlemen have not answered. Why did this man steal? What made him a murderer?"

He made a good supper that night, exclaiming, "Thirty-six years have now passed me." He refused to make any appeal until the last minute, but at the instance of one of the sisters who had nursed him he consented to do so. She in her fulness of heart gave him a five-franc piece.

His fellow-prisoners, as we have already noticed, were devoted to him, and placed all the means at their disposal to help him to escape. They threw into his dungeon, through the air-hole, a nail, some wire, the handle of a pail: any one of these would have been enough for a man like Claude to free himself from his chains. He gave them all up to the warder.

On the 8th of June, 1832, seven months and four days after the murder, the recorder of the court came, and Claude was told that he had but one hour more to live, for his appeal had been rejected.

"Indeed," said Claude, coldly; "I slept well last night, and doubtless I shall pass my next even better."

First came the priest, then the executioner. He was humble to the priest, and listened to him with great attention, regretting much that he had not had the benefit of religious training, at the same time blaming himself for much in the past.

He was courteous in his manner to the executioner; in fact he gave up all, —his soul to the priest, his body to the executioner.

While his hair was being cut, some one mentioned how the cholera was spreading, and Troyes at any moment might become a prey to this fearful scourge. Claude joined in the conversation, saying, with a smile, "There is one thing to be said,—I have no fear of the cholera!" He had broken half of the scissors,—what remained he asked the jailor to give to Albin; the other half lay buried in his chest. He also wished the day's rations to be taken to his friend. The only trifle he retained was the five-franc piece that the sister had given him, which he kept in his right hand after he was bound.

At a quarter to eight, the dismal procession usual in such cases left the prison. Pale, but with a firm tread Claude Gueux slowly mounted the scaffold, keeping his eyes fixed on the crucifix the priest carried,—an emblem of the Saviour's suffering. He wished to embrace the priest and the executioner, thanking the one and pardoning the other; the executioner simply repulsed him. Just before he was bound to the infernal machine, he gave the five-franc piece to the priest, saying, "For the poor."

The hour had scarcely struck its eight chimes, when this man, so noble, so intelligent, received the fatal blow which severed his head from his body.

A market-day had been chosen for the time of execution, as there would be more people about, for there are still in France small towns that glory in having an execution. The guillotine that day remained, inflaming the imagination of the mob to such an extent that one of the tax-gatherers was nearly murdered. Such is the admirable effect of public executions!

We have given the history of Claude Gueux's life, more to solve a difficult problem than for aught else. In his life there are two questions to be considered,—before his fall, and after his fall. What was his training, and what was the penalty? This must interest society generally; for this man was well gifted, his instincts were good. Then what was wanting? On this revolves the grand problem which would place society on a firm basis. *What nature has begun in the individual, let society carry out.* Look at Claude Gueux. An intelligent and most noble-hearted man, placed in the midst of evil surroundings, he turned thief. Society placed him in a prison where the evil was yet greater, and he ended with becoming a murderer. Can we really blame him, or ourselves?—questions which require deep thought, or the result will be that we shall be compelled to shirk this most important subject. The facts are now before us, and if the government gives no thought to the matter, what are the rulers about?

The Deputies are yearly much occupied. It is important to shift sinecures and to unravel the budget; to pass an Act which compels me, disguised as a soldier, to mount guard at the Count de Lobau's, whom I do not know, and to whom I wish to remain a stranger, or to go on parade under the command of my grocer, who has been made an officer. I wish to cast no reflections on the patrol, who keep order and protect our homes, but on the absurdity of making such parade and military hubbub about turning citizens into parodies of soldiers.

Deputies or ministers! it is important that we should sound every subject, even though it end in nothing; that we should question and cross-question what we know but little about. Rulers and legislators! you pass your time in classical comparisons that would make a village schoolmaster smile. You assert that it is the habits of modern civilization that have engendered adultery, incest, parricide, infanticide, and poisoning,—proving that you know little of Jocasta, Phedra, Œdipus, Medea, or Rodoguna, The great orators occupy themselves with lengthy discussions on Corneille and Racine, and get so heated in literary argument as to make the grossest mistakes in the French language. Very important indeed all this is, but we consider there are subjects of far greater consequence. In the midst of such useless arguments, what answer would the Deputies give if one rose and gravely addressed t h e m in the following words:—

"Silence, all those who have been speaking! silence, I say! You consider yourself acquainted with the question? You know nothing about it. The question is this: In the name of justice, scarcely a year ago, a man at Panners was cut to pieces; at Dijon a woman's head was taken off; in Paris, at St. Jacques, executions take place without number. This is the question! Now take your time to consider it, and you who argue over the buttons of the National Guards, whether they should be white or yellow, and if *security* is preferable to *certainty!*

"Gentlemen of the Right, gentlemen of the Left, the great mass of the people suffer! Whether a republic or a monarchy, the fact remains the same,—the people suffer! The people are famished, the people are frozen. Such misery leads them on to crime: the galleys take the sons, houses of ill-fame the daughters. You have too many convicts, too many unfortunates.

"What is the meaning of this social

gangrene? You are near the patient: treat the malady. You are at fault: now study the matter more deeply.

"When you pass laws, what are they but expedients and palliatives? Half your codes result from routine.

"Branding but cauterizes the wound, and it mortifies, and what is the end? You stamp the crime for life on the criminal; you make two friends of them, two companions—inseparables. The convict prison is a blister which spreads far worse matter than ever it extracts; and as for the sentence of death, when carried out it is a barbarous amputation. Therefore, branding, penal servitude, and sentence of death are all of one class; you have done away with the branding, banish the rest. Why keep the chain and the chopper now you have put aside the hot iron? Farinace was atrocious, but he was not ridiculous.

"Take down that worn ladder that leads to crime and to suffering. Revise your laws; revise your codes; rebuild your prisons; replace your judges. Make laws suited to the present time.

"You are bent on economy; do not be so lavish in taking off the heads of so many during the year. Suppress the executioner; you could defray the expenses of six hundred schoolmasters with the wages you give your eighty executioners. Think of the multitude; then there would be schools for the children, workshops for the men.

"Do you know that in France there are fewer people who know how to read than in any other country in Europe? Fancy, Switzerland can read, Belgium can read, Denmark can read, Greece can read, Ireland can read—and France cannot read! It is a crying evil.

"Go into your convict prisons, examine each one of these condemned men, and you will observe by the profile, the shape of the head, how many could find their type in the lower animals. Here are the lynx, the cat, the monkey, the vulture, the hyena. Nature was first to blame, no doubt: but the want of training fostered the evil. Then give the people a fair education, and what there is of good in these ill-conditioned minds, let that be developed. People must be judged by their opportunities. Rome and Greece were educated: then brighten the people's intellect.

"When France can read, then give the people encouragement for higher things. Ignorance is preferable to a little ill-directed knowledge; and remember, there is a book of far greater importance than the 'Compère Mathieu,' more popular than the 'Constitutionnel,' and more worthy of perusal than the charter of 1830,—that is the Bible.

"Whatever you may do for the people, the majority will always remain poor and unhappy. Theirs the work, the heavy burden to carry, to endure: all the miseries for the poor, all the pleasures for the rich.

"As such is life, ought not the State to lean to the weaker and helpless side?

"In the midst of all this wretchedness, if you but throw hope in the balance, let the poor man learn there is a heaven where joy reigns, a paradise that he can share, and you raise him; he feels that he has a part in the rich man's joys. And this was the teaching Jesus gave, and He knew more about it than Voltaire.

"Then give to those people who work, and who suffer here, the hope of a different world to come, and they will go on patiently; for patience follows in the footsteps of hope.

"Then spread the Gospel in all our villages, let every cottage have its Bible; the seed thus sown will soon circulate. Encourage virtue, and from that will spring so much that now lies fallow.

"The man turned assassin under certain circumstances, if differently influenced would have served his country well.

"Then give the people all encouragement; improve the masses, enlighten them, guard their morals, make them useful, and to such heads as those you will not require to use cold steel."

Monster and Infanticide

GUERNSEY

M. MARTIN, the queen's provost in Guernsey, came to see me on my arrival. I returned his visit on the 5th of December, 1858. He offered to accompany me to the prison which I was desirous to see.

We had gone by the streets which rise behind the Royal Court. When strolling about Saint Peter's Port, I had already remarked in the town, midway, a high wall, in which was a high gate with a G carved in the granite on the top of it. I said to myself, "That ought to be the prison. So it is."

The jailor received us. He is named Barbet; so the Guernsey malefactors call the prison the Hôtel Barbet. This man had the same frank, firm face, the same pleasant and determined manner which I had already remarked in many other jailors. His wife and daughter were preparing soup in the corner. Barbet took a heavy key, opened a grated door, and introduced us into a vast empty court, bounded on three sides by the high wall which had already attracted my attention. On the south the court is dominated by a new building of grey granite, the two-storied front of which is composed of two rows of seven arches superposed. Beneath the arches are the windows. Through the glass we perceive the heavy bars, painted white. That is the prison and those are the cells.

"Guernsey is an honest island," said the provost—a distinguished and intelligent man—a Non-comformist, an Independent, as Cromwell and Milton were. And he added, "We have at present only three prisoners, two men and a woman, out of a population of forty thousand."

One of the prisoners entered the court at that moment. He was a young man with a pleasing face, condemned to ten years of Botany Bay for robbery.

He was dressed in cloth trousers, a small blue paletot, and a cap.

The provost, who is also called the sheriff, and who in this capacity is governor of the prison, and accompanies the condemned to the scaffold—a circumstance which makes him averse to capital punishment—explained to me that the young man would not be transported, and that he would be free in a few days from his cellular prison.

The English "cellular prison," imbued and penetrated by the glacial spirit of English Protestantism, proves that severity and cold can be carried to a ferocious pitch. In one of the prisons—Millbank, I think—silence is imposed.

The sheriff told me that when visiting that prison he found in a cell a young man from Guernsey, whom he knew, who had been convicted of theft. When he saw the provost he clasped his hands and cried.

"Ah, monsieur, is my grandmother still alive?"

The provost had scarcely time to reply, when the jailor said to the agonized prisoner, "Hold your tongue!"

The young man died soon after. He passed from the prison to the tomb; from one silence to the other, and scarcely would perceive the change.

Beneath the seven arcades on the ground-floor are the debtors' cells. We entered them. They were unoccupied. A wooden bed, a paillasse, and a rug are all the prison authorities give to a debtor. The last debtor imprisoned was a Guernsey man, whose name has escaped me. He was put there by his wife, who kept him there ten years, gaining her own liberty by his imprisonment. At the end of ten years the husband paid his wife and got out. They lived together again, and the provost says do very well together.

There was no prisoner for debt there at the time; I must repeat this.

This prison is a silent testimony of approval to the Guernsey population. It contains twelve cells: six for debtors, six for ordinary offenders, besides two punishment-cells. There are also for the women two cells only, of which one is a punishment-cell.

One of the seven chambers on the ground-floor is the chapel, a small room without an altar, having a wooden pulpit for the chaplain in the left corner; and in front of the door, back to the window, four or five wooden benches with desks, upon which are scattered a few prayer-books.

On the first floor the criminals are imprisoned. We ascended. The jailor opened a well-lighted cell, furnished only with a wooden bed. At the foot of the bed the coverings were rolled up, and the blankets, like the counterpanes, are of coarse wool, only they seemed to me knitted. The paillasse had been removed, so that one could see the bedboard, on which a number of names and inscriptions had been cut and scratched with knives or nails. These formed a forest of almost obliterated letters. We distinguished among others the following words, which were more legible than the others:—

> GUERRE.
> HISTOIRE.
> CAIN.

Is not all crime included in those words? In a corner of the board there were some rudely-sketched ships in outline.

The cell behind this is a punishment-cell. There is only a plank bed in it, and a small window opening to the north. The last occupant had chalked on the wall a species of labyrinth, which made the jailor very angry. They had soiled the whiteness of his sepulchre for him.

All the cells were whitewashed.

The range of arcades in front of the cells form a sort of gallery, open to the air and southern sun, where the prisoners take exercise in wet weather.

There is in this gallery an old dilapidated bedstead, on which they mount, and can overlook the sea. "That is a great enjoyment for them," said the jailor. I stood upon the bedstead. I could see the island of Sark, and vessels on the horizon. I was desirous of visiting Tapner's cell. The sheriff conducted me thither.

This cell, and the punishment-cell near it, compose the female side.

When one is in the court facing the prison one sees that the first of the seven upper arcades to the left is barred towards the court and walled up towards the gallery. The small space between the railing and the wall was the special paddock of Tapner. There he paced backward and forward all day like a wild beast in a cage, in view of the other prisoners, but separated from them. The window looking into this cage is the window of his cell.

The door is thick, painted black, and bound with iron. Two great bolts above and below and a lock midway.

The jailor opened this door and let us in.

The cell, of the same dimensions as the others, about ten feet square, is clean, white, and well-lighted. The chimney at the bottom of the left angle cantwise, a bucket, a plank fixed to the wall facing the door; on the right of the door under the window is a wooden bedstead, of which one of the four posts is broken. On the bed a paillasse, a rug, and coarse woollen blankets.

This pallet was Tapner's bed. After his death it was given up to the women.

No fire might be lighted in the chimney without the doctor's orders.

At the moment we entered a woman was seated, or rather crouched, upon the bed, with her back to the door. I took my hat off. Mr. Tyrrell, a young English painter, who accompanied me, did the same.

This woman, the only prisoner at the time, was—so the sheriff told me—a thief, and more than that, an Irish-woman, added the jailor. She was a youngish woman, and kept on darning an old stocking, without appearing even to see us.

This woman, in whom the least curiosity was extinct, seemed to personify the sombre indifference of misery.

Tapner suffered in this cold, white, clear cell.

This John Charles Tapner, a kind of gentlemanly employé of the government, not having made use of the advantages of his education, reached the stages of robbery and assassination by drinking and debauchery. He was born of good family and of religious parentage, at Woolwich, in 1823. He died before he was thirty-one, on the 10th of February, 1854.

He lived with two sisters—married

to one, the lover of the other. He had insured his life for the full value of his appointment, £150 sterling, which absorbed all his income, and appeared to announce his intention of living by crime. The assurance was in his wife's name and his own, for the benefit of the survivor.

I asked, "Did the company pay it?"

"Eh? No," replied the sheriff.

"Has it relinquished or given to the poor the annual premiums which it received from Tapner?"

"Oh, no."

Under the virtuous pretext that there had been a crime, the company robbed the widow.

"Tapner appeared indifferent," said the provost, and he therefore concluded the man did not suffer. "That is a mistake," I said. "Do you not believe one is cold under the ice?"

The day before his death his likeness was taken. The apparatus was placed in the cage opening from his cell where there was plenty of sunlight. Tapner could not help laughing as he posed himself. A death's-head might as well have laughed.

"Do not laugh," said the provost to him; "keep serious. They will not recognize your portrait. You cannot laugh today; it is not possible."

It was so possible that he was laughing.

One day the provost lent him a prayer-book. "Read this, Tapner," said he, "if you are guilty." "I am not guilty," replied Tapner. "In any case," replied the provost, "you are a sinner, as we all are. You have not served God. Read this book." Tapner took it, and when the provost entered the cell an hour later he found him, book in hand, bathed in tears.

"His last interview with his wife was most distressing," said the provost. "Nevertheless, the woman was aware of his love-affair with her sister. But who can fathom all the mysteries of pardon?"

The night before my visit to the prison Mr. Pearce, one of the two chaplains who had attended Tapner on the day of his death, came to see me at Hauteville House with the provost. I asked Mr. Pearce, a very venerable and dignified gentleman, "Did Tapner know that I was interested in him?"

"Certainly, sir," replied Mr. Pearce "He was touched, and very grateful for your intervention, and he particularly wished you to be thanked on his behalf."

I note, as a characteristic detail of the liberty of the English Press, that at the time of Tapner's execution all the journals in the island had more or less demanded it, and were very much shocked by my letter to Lord Palmerston, agreeing in passing over in silence the facts which Mr. Pearce revealed to me.

"There is," said the provost to me, "another thing of which you are ignorant, and which was also passed over in silence. You think you completely failed in your intervention, and, nevertheless, you have gained an enormous victory, of which you have no idea. This island is like all England,—a country of tradition. What has been done yesterday must be done to-day, and done again to-morrow. Now, tradition ordained that the condemned man should go to the gallows with a cord round his neck. Tradition ordained that the gibbet should be erected on the beach, and that the condemned, to reach it, should march through the most public thoroughfares of the town,—there had not been an execution for twenty-five years,—and had been so arranged. So of course Tapner's execution must take place in the same way. After your letter they did not dare to do so. They said, let us hang the man, but in secret. They were ashamed; you did not tie the hands of Death, but you made him blush. They gave up the cord round the neck, the gibbet on the beach, the procession through the streets, and the crowd. They decided that Tapner should be hanged in private in the prison garden. Nevertheless, the law willed that the execution ought to be in public, and the matter was arranged by my signing tickets of admission for two hundred people. Feeling the same distress as they, and more, I agreed to all they decided. I signed the tickets for those who wanted them. Nevertheless, a difficulty presented itself,— the garden adjoining the prison is separated from it by the very wall of the open cell. The door of this garden is in College Street; to reach this door it was necessary for the condemned to leave the prison and walk about one hundred paces in public.

"They did not dare to have this done; so, to avoid it, they made a hole in the wall and let Tapner pass through it. Discretion prevailed."

I do not produce here the exact words of the sheriff, but the sense is the same.

"Well," said I, "conduct me to the garden."

"The breach is closed; the wall is rebuilt; I will take you round by the street."

At the moment of leaving the prison the jailor brought me some of the soup which is supplied to the prisoners, and inviting me to taste it, handed to me a large and very clean tin spoon. I tasted the soup, which is good and wholesome. The bread is excellent. I compared it in my mind to the horrible bread of the French prisons which they showed me at the Conciergerie, which is earthy, damp and viscous and fetid; often full of worms and mouldy.

It was raining; the weather was grey and lowering.

It was not really more than a hundred paces from the prison to the entrance of the garden. We turned to the left, up College Street, along the high black wall. All at once the provost stopped in front of a rather low door. On the panels of the door, which leads to the place where the man lost by drunkenness and ignorance met his death, there are several strips of old bills,—yellow, white, green,—relating to all kinds of things, and on which the rain that had effaced them, and the weather that had torn them to pieces, had only left two words distinguishable, — UNIVERSAL EDUCATION — TEMPERANCE.

The provost had a great key in his hand, and unlocked the door, which probably had not been opened since the day of the last execution, and which grated noisily on its hinges. We entered.

The provost shut the door behind us. We found ourselves in a narrow, square space, shut in on three sides by high walls, and opening on the fourth side on a steep staircase, which was dark, though in the open air. Opposite the staircase, the provost pointed out to me the repaired breach in the wall. Through that breach Tapner had passed; the staircase was the first ladder to the gibbet. He had mounted it. We mounted it. I do not know why I counted the steps at that moment; there were fourteen of them. This staircase leads to an oblong and narrow garden, overlooked by another, which forms a terrace. We ascend to this by seven granite steps like the fourteen we have already traversed.

At the top of these seven steps we are in full view of an enclosed open space, a hundred feet square, surrounded by low walls cut by two alleys, which form a cross in the centre. This is what they call the garden. Here Tapner was hanged.

The December sleet continued to fall; a few briers rustled in the wind. There were no flowers nor verdure in the garden, but only one little, thin, stunted fruit-tree at one of the four corners formed by the intersection of the walks. The whole appearance was heartrending. It was one of those sad places which the sun makes melancholy and the rain lugubrious.

There is no house in the garden. It is nobody's garden, except that of the spectre they have left there; it is deserted, abandoned, uncultivated, tragic. Other gardens surround and isolate it. It has no touch with the town, with life, with men—only with the prison. The houses in the low streets which surround it are visible afar off, and seem to have the appearance of looking over the wall into this ill-omened place.

Seeing on one side a sort of little walk, low, narrow, long, and rather deep,

on which abutted the first fourteen steps, and on the other this funereal garden, intersected by those two transversal alleys, it was impossible not to think of a ditch near which might be extended the mortuary cloth with the cross.

We have on our right a wall which is as high as the great wall where the gate is, and of which one sees the back from the street. A walk lower than the rest of the garden skirts this wall. A range of thick, rusty tenterhooks, and of long, thin wooden rods, silvered and polished by the frost, were fixed vertically to the wall at intervals of six to eight paces, indicating that formerly there had been an espalier here. It has now disappeared, and nothing of the rods is left, except a sort of skeleton.

A few paces on we reach a flight of three steps, which leads from the garden to the walk. Here we remark more rods on the wall. They reappear again a little farther on, leaving a space of fifteen feet unoccupied.

Here the provost stopped in silence. I saw that the rods were wanting, and I understood. This was where the scaffold had been erected. Looking up, one sees nothing except the broken glass upon the wall, and the round tower of the neighbouring church painted yellow and grey.

The scaffold was raised here. Tapner turned to the left, took the middle walk, and reached by one of the arms of the cross which the walks form the steps of the gibbet placed immediately above the three steps I have mentioned. He mounted on the platform, and thence, while he was saying his last prayer, he could see the sea-birds flying in the distance; the pale clouds of February, the ocean, the immensity yonder; and at the same time, by the opening in his mind at that dark hour, he could perceive the mystery, the unknown future, the escarpments of the tomb—God the immensity on high.

The gibbet was composed of two supports and a cross-bar; in the centre of this bar a rope with a knot at the end hung over a closed trap-door. On this trap, the snare of the law, Tapner was placed, and remained standing while the noose was adjusted around his neck. From the street behind the wall, from the College garden at the other side of the street, might have been seen the supports of the gibbet, the cord, the knot, and they could see the back of the condemned man until the trap-door was opened and he fell. Then he disappeared from the view of the spectators outside.

From the interior of the garden, and from the houses of which I have already spoken, they could see the rest.

The punishment was this frightful thing, as I said in my letter to Lord Palmerston. The provost recalled it to my mind, and confirmed all the details. He considered I had rather softened it down than amplified them.

At the moment Tapner fell the cord tightened, and he remained fifteen or twenty seconds motionless, and as if he were dead. The queen's proxy, the chaplain, the magistrates, believing that it was all over, or fancying that it had not commenced, hurried away, and the provost remained alone with the criminal, the executioner, and the curious spectators. I have described the agony of the unhappy wretch, and how the executioner had to drag him down by the feet.

Tapner dead—the law satisfied. It is now the turn of the superstitious; they never failed to come to the rendezvous which the gallows gives them. Epileptics came, and could not be prevented from seizing the convulsive hand of the dead man and passing it frantically over their faces. The dead man was cut down in an hour, and then it was a question who should steal the cord. The assistants threw it down, and each one claimed a piece; but the sheriff took it and threw it in the fire.

When it was burned, the people came and collected the cinders.

The wall against which the gibbet was erected supported a hut which occupied the south-east angle of the garden; thither they carried the corpse. They made ready a table, and a plasterer whom they found there made a cast of the man's face. The visage, violently deformed by strangulation, was recomposed, and had the expression of sleep. The cord removed, calmness returned. It appears as if death, even through punishment, wishes always to be kind, and that its last word should be peace.

I went to this hut; the door was open; it was a miserable cell, scarcely plastered, which served as a garden shed. Some tools were propped against the wall. The chamber was lighted by a window opening into the garden, and by another looking into the street, which had been closed up when Tapner was brought thither, and had not since been reopened. With the exception of the table, which had disappeared, the place was the same as when the corpse had been there. The closed window was then closed; the shutter which had been put up by the hangman remained shut. In front of this window was a piece of furniture, full of little drawers, some of which were missing. On this, beside a broken bottle and some dried flowers, stood one of these drawers full of plaster. It was the same plaster which had been used. I opened at hazard another drawer, and found more plaster, with the imprints of fingers. The floor was littered with yellow herbs and dead leaves. A net was thrown into a corner on a heap of dust. Near the door, in an angle of a wall, was a shovel, the gardener's shovel, probably, or the grave-digger's.

Towards four o'clock in the afternoon, the body being nearly cold, the sheriff put Tapner in the coffin. They did not bury him. They did not go to the expense of a winding-sheet; they simply nailed him down with his clothes on. In Guernsey the clothes of the deceased are his own property; not, as in London, the hangman's perquisite. At nightfall, ten or twelve persons only being present, they carried the coffin to the cemetery, where a grave had been dug in the morning.

"You must see everything," said the provost; so we went out, and I followed him. We plunged into the poor thoroughfares, and arrived in a narrow, steep, angular street lined with hovels, at the corner of which I read Lemarchand Street. The provost left me, went down a dark alley, and came back with the key, which seemed larger than the key of the garden. An instant after we stopped in front of a great black door opening in the centre.

My conductor opened this door, and we found ourselves in a sort of dark and lofty shed.

"Sir," said the provost, "look up; overhead is the gibbet of Beasse."

This Beasse, who was hanged in 1830, was a Frenchman; he had passed as a non-commissioned officer through the Spanish war of 1823 under the Duke of Angoulême; then, enriched by inheritance or otherwise, he retired to Guernsey. There, with his income of fifteen thousand francs, he was a gentleman. He bought a fine house, and became a grandee. In the evening he visited the bailiff, M. Daniel le Brocq.

When one went to see Beasse one found a man working in his garden sometimes. This gardener was the hangman. The hangman of Guernsey was a skilful horticulturist, isolated, and avoided by all. His fellow-creatures having shunned him, he turned to Nature, and was no less skilful in the garden than on the gallows. Beasse, having no prejudices, employed him.

Beasse then was in a good position on account of his money, even in view of the haughty aristocracy of Guernsey, even of the *forty* and the *sixty*.

One day they noticed that his servant was very stout. Then they saw that she was thinner. What had become of the child? The neighbours were aroused; rumours were circulated. The police paid Beasse a visit; two constables came with a doctor. The doctor visited the servant, who was in bed; then the constable said to Beasse, "The woman has been confined. There was a child; we must find it." Beasse, who up to that moment had declared he did not know what they wanted, took a shovel, went into a corner of his garden, and began to dig furiously. One of the constables, thinking that he wished to give a blow with the spade to the object and pass the mark as an accidental wound, took the spade himself and continued to dig more carefully. In a moment or so the child was discovered.

The poor little thing had one larding-pin buried in its throat and another in its anus. Beasse denied that he was the father of the child. He was tried, condemned to be hanged, and it was his friend, the bailiff, Daniel le Brocq, pronounced.

His goods were confiscated.

The provost, after relating this horrible narrative, said: "Beasse was deficient in coolness. By going himself to dig up the ground where the body was, he lost himself. He could easily have saved himself. He had only to say, 'The child is dead. I gave it to a beggar who passed to bury it. I gave him a sovereign. I don't know who he is, and I should not know him again.' No one could have proved the contrary. No one would have known what had become of the child, and they could not have condemned him; Guernsey being still ruled by the Norman custom, which insists on material proof,—*corpus delicti*—before condemnation."

The provost asked me, "Would you have advanced the question of the inviolability of human life for Beasse as you did for Tapner?"

"Unquestionably," I said. "This Tapner and this Beasse are miserable creatures, but the principles never assert their grandeur and beauty so well save when they defend those whom even pity does not defend."

At the time that Beasse was condemned the Revolution of 1830 broke out. He then said to the same M. Martin, now provost, "I would rather remain in France to be shot than in Jersey to be hanged."

Here is a detail. The bailiff was a friend of his, and had to pronounce on him; his gardener was the hangman who executed him. The bailiff did not hesitate. But the gardener was different. Perhaps the gardener had lost touch of hanging. Perhaps his hands, after training roses and lilies, were incapable of making nooses. Perhaps, quite honestly, this legalized slayer was kinder than the law, and was disinclined to stretch the neck of the man with whom he had broken bread. At any rate, the day after the sentence the hangman of Guernsey disappeared. He escaped in some smuggling cutter, and left Saint-Peter's. They sought for him; they searched the island; but he never returned.

It became necessary to advertise.

A man, an Englishman, was in prison for some offence. They offered him pardon if he would become the executioner, and hang Beasse as a commencement. Men call that a pardon. The man accepted. Justice breathed again. She had seen a moment when her death's-head had nothing to devour, not that the upper jaw, the judge, had failed, but because the lower jaw, the hangman, had disappeared.

The day of execution arrived.

They brought Beasse to the gallows, with the cord round his neck, through the streets on to the beach. He was the last who suffered in this way. On the scaffold, at the moment when the white cap was being pulled over his eyes, he turned towards the crowd, and as if he wished to leave one agony behind him, he threw at the spectators this phrase, which might have been spoken by a guilty as well as an innocent man: *"It is only crime that dishonours!"*

The platform was long in falling. They had no trap-door, and had to knock out a whole piece. It was fastened at the extremities to the planks by cords which it was necessary to cut on one side while it remained suspended on the other. The hangman,—the pardoned prisoner,—the same inexperienced wretch, who, twenty-five years later, hanged Tapner,—took an axe and cut the cord; but as he was nervous, he was a long time about it. The crowd murmured, and did not think of saving the culprit, though they nearly stoned the hangman.

I had this scaffold over my head.

I looked up, as the provost requested me to do.

The hut in which we were had a pointed roof, of which the interior framework was naked. Under the beams of this roof, and precisely overhead, were placed two long joists, which had been the support of Beasse's gibbet. At the upper end of those one could see the holes in which the transversal bar had been inserted, to which the cord was fastened. This bar had been taken out, and was lying with the joists. About the centre of these beams were nailed two kinds of wooden cushions, the projecting parts of which had sustained the platform of the gallows. These two beams, supported by the timberwork of the roof, themselves supported a massive, long, narrow plank,

from the ends of which ropes hung. This plank was the platform of the gibbet, and those cords were the same which the hangman had been so long cutting. Behind one could perceive a kind of step-ladder, with flat wooden steps, lying near the platform. Beasse had mounted this. All this hideous machine—supports, cross-beams, platform, ladder—were painted iron-grey, and seemed to have been used more than once. The impressions of ropes could be seen on the beams here and there; two or three long ladders of the ordinary form were leaning against the wall.

Near these ladders, in an angle to our right, the provost showed me a species of wooden trellis composed of many panels.

"What is that?" I asked him. "One would say it is a cage. It is, in fact, a cage."

"It is the pillory," he replied. "It is fifteen or twenty years since they used to put that up in the market-place and expose criminals in it. It is now out of date."

Like the gallows of Beasse, this cage was painted a dark grey. Formerly the cage was of iron; then it was made of wood, and painted black to resemble iron; then it was done away with. That is the history of all the old penalty, the future included.

Dust and darkness now cover this apparatus of terror. It might be one of the dark corners of oblivion. Spiders have found this pillory-cage a very good place to spin their webs in and to catch flies.

The platform of the old gibbet having acted badly for Beasse, they built a new one for Tapner. They adopted the English system of the trap, which opens under the patient. "An officer of the garrison invented for the opening of this trap a very ingenious mechanism," said the provost, "and he was executed."

I returned to the scaffold of Beasse. Looking again at one of the ends of the cord, I could see the grooves which the axe in the trembling hands of the hangman had made.

"Now, sir," said the provost, "turn round."

He pointed out in the other compartment of the shed, still up in the roof, a collection of beams having the red colour of the fir-trees. This was like a bundle of planks and beams thrown pell-mell together, among which one could distinguish a long and heavy ladder, with flat steps like the other, and which appeared to me enormous. They were all clean, new, fresh, and forbidding. This was the scaffold of Tapner.

One could see the beams, one might distinguish the cross-beam, one could count the planks of the platform and the steps of the ladder. I was considering from the same point of view the ladder which had borne Beasse and the ladder which Tapner had climbed. My eyes could not detach themselves from those steps, which spectres had ascended, and to which they joined in the distance, in my mind's eye, the sombre steps of the Infinite.

The shed in which we were is composed of two buildings, the geometrical plan of which presents a right angle, forms a T square. The opening of the square is occupied by a little triangular

court, which makes one think of the knife of the guillotine. Grass grows between the paving-stones. The rain was falling there; it was formidable.

This funereal shed formerly served as a stable for the country magistrates when they came to sit in the town. One can still see the numbers on the boxes in which they stabled their horses while they were on the bench. I stopped between the two posts marked 3 and 4. An old broken basket was lying on the ground at the bottom of the stall between the two posts; above this stall they had placed the largest beams of the gibbet.

"Why do they keep them there?" I said to the provost. "Why, what you have them do? They would warm a poor family for the whole winter."

Between the figures 3 and 4 one could perceive high up on the roof a startling object—the trap that opened under the feet of Tapner. One could see it underneath,—the massive black bolt, the hinges that turned upon eternity, and the two black joists which united the planks. One also distinguished the ingenious mechanism of which the provost had spoken. It is this too narrow trap which causes the agony. The culprit is caught by the shoulders and suspended. It is scarcely three feet square,—which is not sufficient space, because of the oscillations of the cord. However, the provost explained that Tapner had been badly pinioned, that he had been permitted the movement of his arms; better tied, he would have fallen straight and would not have moved. The guardian of the shed had entered and joined us while the provost was speaking. When he had finished the man added, "Yes, it was the bad pinioning of Tapner that did the mischief, otherwise it would have been magnificent."

Coming out of the shed, the provost begged to take leave of me, and Mr. Tyrrell offered to conduct me to the house of the plasterer who had taken a cast of Tapner. I accepted.

I know still so little of the streets of the town, which seems to be a labyrinth.

We traversed many of the high streets of Saint Peter Port, in which grass grows, and we descended a wide street which plunges into one of the four or five ravines by which the town is intersected. Opposite a house, before which two cypresses, trimmed in the shape of cones, are growing, there is a stonemason's. We entered the yard. At first sight, one is struck by the number of crosses and tomb-stones standing in the passage or against the walls. A workman, the only one in the shed, was fastening together some squares of faience. Mr. Tyrrell spoke to him in English. "Yes, sir," replied the workman, and he went to the planks in tiers at the end of the shed, searched among the plaster and the dust, and brought back in the one hand a mask and in the other a head. These were the mask and the head of Tapner. The mask had been coloured pink—the plaster of the head remained white. The mask had been modelled on the face having still the whiskers and the hair clinging to it; then they had shaved the head and had moulded the skull, the face and the neck naked. Tapner was as celebrated in Guernsey as Lacenaire had been in Paris.

As the provost had said, his face was strangely carved. It recalled to me, in a singular way, the admirable Hungarian violinist Reményi. The physiognomy was youthful and grave, the eyes shut as if in sleep, only a little foam sufficiently thick for the plaster to have taken the impression had remained at the corner of the upper lid, which gives to the face, when regarded for a long while, a sort of ironical sneer. Although the elasticity of the flesh made the neck at the moment of moulding very nearly the natural size, the mark of the cord was plainly visible, and the running knot, distinctly imprinted under the right ear, had left a hideous swelling.

I wanted to carry away this head. They sold it to me for three francs.

It remained to me to make the third pause on this dolorous way, for crime has its own as well as virtue.

"Where is Tapner's grave?" I asked Tyrrell.

He made a gesture and walked on; I followed him.

At Guernsey, as in all English cities, the cemetery is in the town in the midst of the streets. Behind the college, a massive building in English Gothic, which dominates the whole town, there is one of these cemeteries, the largest, perhaps, in Saint Peter Port. A street had been cut through it in the early years of the century, and it is now in two parts. On the western side lie the Guernsey people, on the eastern side the strangers.

We passed up the street through the cemetery, which, planted with trees, has scarcely any houses in it, and above the walls which border it one can see tomb-stones upright or flat on either side.

Mr. Tyrrell showed me an open door on the right, and said to me, "It is here."

We passed through into the strangers' portion of the cemetery.

We found ourselves in a long parallelogram, enclosed by walls, grass-grown, in which some tombs are scattered. There was no rain, the grass was damp, and the long grey clouds were sweeping slowly along the sky.

As we entered we heard the sound of a pickaxe. The noise ceased, and a living bust seemed to emerge from the ground at the end of the cemetery, and regard us in astonishment.

It was the grave-digger, who was digging a grave, and standing in it waist-deep.

He ceased working when he saw us, not being accustomed to the entrance of living bodies, and not being the landlord except in an hotel of the dead.

We walked towards him over the tombs. He was a young man. There was behind him a stone already mossy, and on which one could read:—

A ANDRÉ JASINSKI,
16th June, 1844.

As we were approaching him he resumed his work. When we reached the edge of the grave he looked up, saw us, and tapped the ground with his spade. The ground sounded hollow. The man said to us, "There is a dead body there which bothers us." Then we understood that he had met with an old grave in the course of digging a new one.

Having said that, without waiting our reply, and as if he were talking less to us than to himself, he bent down and commenced to dig without troubling himself any more about us. One would have said that his eyes were full of the darkness of the grave, and he could see us no longer.

I spoke to him.

"Are you the man," I said, "who buried Tapner?"

He straightened himself, and looked at me like a man who was searching in his memory.

"Tapner?" said he.

"Yes."

"The fellow who was hanged?"

"Yes; did you bury him?"

"No," replied the man. "It was Mr. Morris, the caretaker of the cemetery. I am only a digger myself."

There seems to be a hierarchy among grave-diggers.

I resumed—

"Can you point out the grave to me?"

"Whose grave?"

"Tapner's."

The man replied,—

"Close to the other man who was hanged."

"Show me the place."

He stretched his arm out of the grave, and indicated a spot near the gate by which we had entered,—a grassy corner, about fifteen paces square, where there were no tombs. The tomb-stones which filled the cemetery extended to the borders of this funereal square, and stopped there, as if it were a line it could not pass even in death. The nearest stone backed against the wall of the street bore this epitaph, below which one might read four lines in English, which were hidden by the bushes:—

TO THE MEMORY

OF

AMELIA,

DAUGHTER OF

JOHN AND MARY WINNECOMBE.

I entered into the solitary square which the grave-digger pointed out. I advanced slowly, my gaze bent on the ground. Suddenly I felt under my feet a hillock, which I had not seen because of the height of the grass. This was where they had buried Tapner.

Tapner's grave is very near the entrance to the cemetery, at the foot of a small hut, where the grave-diggers leave their tools. This hut adjoins, gable fashion, to a large building, of which the high door occupies the whole side. The wall which skirts the square in which Tapner is buried is skirted by a penthouse, under which are suspended four or five ladders, fastened with chains and padlocked. At the place where the ladders cease the tombs commence. The benediction and the malediction are side by side in the cemetery, but they do not mingle. Near the shed one distinguishes another eminence, more elongated, and not so prominent as that of Tapner. This is where Beasse is buried.

I spoke to the grave-digger.

"Do you know where the hangman lives who hanged Tapner?"

"The hangman is dead," he replied.

"When did he die?"

"Three months after Tapner."

"Did you bury him?"

"No."

"Is he here?"

"I don't think so."

"Do you know where he is?"

"I do not know."

I snatched a handful of grass from the grave of Tapner, put it in my pocket-book, and came away.

A Woman of the Streets

V. H. WAS elected to the Académie one Tuesday, 1841. Two days afterwards Madame de Girardin, who lived at that time in the Rue Laffitte, invited him to dinner.

At this dinner was Bugeaud, as yet only a general, who had just been appointed governor-general of Algeria, and who was just going out to his post.

Bugeaud was then a man of sixty-five years of age, vigorous, with a very fresh complexion, and pitted with small-pox. He had a certain abruptness of manner which was never rudeness. He was a mixture of rustic and man of the world, old-fashioned and easy mannered, having nothing of the heaviness of the old martinet, witty and gallant.

Madame de Girardin placed the general on her right and V. H. on her left. A conversation sprang up between the poet and the soldier, Madame de Girardin acting as interpreter.

The general was in very bad humour with Algeria. He maintained that this conquest precluded France from speaking firmly to Europe; that nothing was easier to conquer than Algeria, that the forces could easily be blockaded there, that they would be taken like rats, and that they would make but one mouthful; moreover, that it was very difficult to colonize Algeria, and that the soil was unproductive; he had examined the land himself, and he found that there was a distance of a foot and a half between each stalk of wheat.

"So then," said V. H., "that is what has become of what was formerly called the granary of the Romans! But even supposing it were as you say, I think our new conquest is a fortunate and grand affair. It is civilization trampling upon barbarism. It is an enlightened people which goes out to a people in darkness. We are the Greeks of the world; it is for us to illumine the world. Our mission is being accomplished, I only sing Hosanna! You differ from me, it is clear. You speak as a soldier, as a man of action. I speak as a philosopher and a thinker."

V. H. left Madame de Girardin rather early. It was on the 9th of January. It was snowing in large flakes. He had on thin shoes, and when he was in the street he saw that it was impossible to return home on foot. He went along the Rue Taitbout, knowing that there was a cab-rank on the boulevard at the corner of that street. There was no cab there. He waited for one to come. He was thus waiting, like an orderly on duty, when he saw a young man,

well and stylishly dressed, stoop and pick up a great handful of snow, and put it down the back of a woman of the streets who stood at the corner of the boulevard in a low-necked dress. The woman uttered a piercing shriek, fell upon the dandy, and struck him. The young man returned the blow, the woman responded, and the battle went on in a *crescendo*, so vigorously and to such extremities that the police hastened to the spot.

They seized hold of the woman and did not touch the man.

Seeing the police laying hands upon her, the unfortunate woman struggled with them. But when she was securely seized she manifested the deepest grief. While two policemen were pushing her along, each holding one of her arms, she shouted, "I have done no harm, I assure you! It is the gentleman who interfered with me. I am not guilty; I implore you leave me alone! I have done no harm, really, really!"

"Come, move on; you will have six months for this business."

The poor woman at these words, "You will have six months for this business," once more began to defend her conduct, and redoubled her supplications and entreaties. The policemen, not much moved by her tears, dragged her to a police-station in the Rue Chauchat, at the back of the Opéra.

V. H., interested in spite of himself in the unhappy woman, followed them, amid the crowd of people which is never wanting on such an occasion.

Arriving near the station, V. H. conceived the idea of going in and taking up the cause of the woman. But he said to himself that he was well known, that just then the newspapers had been full of his name for two days past, and that to mix himself up in such an affair was to lay himself open to all kinds of disagreeable banter. In short, he did not go in.

The office into which the girl had been taken was on the ground-floor, overlooking the street. He looked through the windows at what was going on. He saw the poor woman lie down upon the floor in despair and tear her hair; he was moved to pity, he began to reflect, and the result of his reflections was that he decided to go in.

When he set foot in the office a man who was seated before a table, lighted by a candle, writing, turned around and said to him in a sharp, peremptory tone of voice, "What do you want, sir?" "Sir, I was a witness of what took place just now; I come to make a deposition as to what I saw, and to speak to you in this woman's favour." At these words the woman looked at V. H. in mute astonishment, and as though dazed. "Your deposition, more or less interested, will be unavailing. This woman has been guilty of an assault in a public thoroughfare. She struck a gentleman. She will get six months' imprisonment for it."

The woman once more began to cry, scream, and roll over and over. Other women, who had come and joined her said to her, "We will come and see you. Never mind. We will bring you some linen things. Take that for the present." And at the same time they gave her money and sweetmeats.

"When you know who I am," said V. H., "you will, perhaps, change your

manner and tone, and will listen to me."

"Who are you, then?"

V. H. saw no reason for not giving his name.

He gave his name. The Commissary of Police, for he was a Commissary of Police, was prolific of excuses, and became as polite and deferential as he had before been arrogant; offered him a chair, and begged him to be good enough to be seated.

V. H. told him that he had seen with his own eyes a gentleman pick up a snowball and throw it down the back of the woman; that the latter, who could not even see the gentleman, had uttered a cry indicating sharp pain; that indeed she had attacked the gentleman, but that she was within her right; that apart from the rudeness of the act, the violent and sudden cold occasioned by the snow might, in certain circumstances, do the woman the most serious injury; that so far from taking away from this woman, who had possibly a mother or a child to support, the bread so miserably earned, it should rather be the man guilty of this assault upon her whom he should condemn to pay a fine; in fact, that it was not the woman who should have been arrested, but the man.

During this defence, the woman, more and more surprised, beamed with joy and emotion. "How good the gentleman is!" she said, "how good he is! I never knew so good a gentleman. But then I never saw him. I do not know him at all."

The Commissary of Police said to V. H.: "I believe all that you allege, but the policemen have reported the case, and there is a charge made out. Your deposition will be entered in the charge-sheet, you may be sure. But justice must take its course, and I cannot set the woman at liberty."

"What! After what I have just told you, and what is the truth—truth which you cannot and do not doubt—you are going to detain this woman? Then this justice is a horrible injustice!"

"There is only one condition on which I could end the matter, and that is that you would sign your deposition. Will you do so?"

"If the liberty of this woman depends on my signature, here it is."

And V. H. signed.

The woman continually repeated, "How good the gentleman is! How good he is!"

These unhappy women are astonished and grateful not only when they are treated with sympathy, they are none the less so when they are treated with justice.

Fieschi the Exploder

April 14, 1842.

In the Boulevard du Temple the house of Fieschi is being pulled down. The rafters of the roof are destitute of tiles. The windows, without glass or frames, lay bare the interior of the rooms. Inside, through the windows at the corner of the yard, can be seen the staircase which Fieschi, Pepin, and Morey went up and down so many times with their hideous project in their hands. The yard is crowded with ladders and carpenter's work, and the ground-floor is surrounded by a timber boarding.

What can be seen of Fieschi's room appears to have been embellished and decorated by the different lodgers who have inhabited it since. The walls and ceilings are covered with a paper sprinkled with a small pattern of green-ish hue; and upon the ceiling an ornamental beading, also papered, makes the outline of a Y. This ceiling is, however, already broken in and much cracked by the builder's pickaxe.

Upon the subject of the Fieschi trial I have from the chancellor himself, M. Pasquier, several details which are not known.

As long as Fieschi, after his arrest, thought that his accomplices were in sympathy with him he remained silent. One day he learned through his mistress, Nini Lassave, the one-eyed woman, that Morey said, "What a pity the explosion did not kill him!" From that moment Fieschi was possessed with hatred; he denounced Pepin and Morey, and was as assiduous in ruining them as he had previously been anxious to save them. Morey and Pepin were arrested. Fieschi became the energetic supporter of the prosecution. He entered into the most minute details, revealed everything, threw light on, traced, explained, unveiled, unmasked everything, and failed in nothing, never telling any falsehood, and caring little about putting his head under the knife provided the two other heads fell.

One day he said to M. Pasquier, "Pepin is such a fool that he entered in his account-book the money he gave me for the machine, setting down what it was to be used for. Make a search at the house. Take his account-book for the six first months of 1835. You will find at the head of a page an entry of this kind made with his own hand." His instructions are followed, the search is ordered, the book is found. M. Pasquier examines the book, the procurator-general examines the book; nothing is discovered. This seems strange. For the first time Fieschi was at fault. He is told of it: "Look again." Useless researches, trouble wasted. The commissioners of the court are reinforced by an old examining magistrate whom this affair makes a councillor at the Royal Court in Paris (M. Gaschon, whom the Chancellor Pasquier, in telling me all this, called Gâcon or Cachon). This judge, an expert, takes the book, opens it, and in two minutes finds at the top of a page, as stated, the memorandum which formed the subject of Fieschi's accusation. Pepin had been content to strike it through carelessly, but it remained perfectly legible. The president of the Court of Peers and the procurator-general, from a certain habit readily understood, had not read the passages which were struck through,

and this memorandum had escaped them.

The thing being discovered, Fieschi is brought forward, and Pepin is brought forward, and they are confronted with each other before the book. Consternation of Pepin, joy of Fieschi. Pepin falters, grows confused, weeps, talks of his wife and his three children; Fieschi triumphs. The examination was decisive, and Pepin was lost. The sitting had been long; M. Pasquier dismisses Pepin, takes out his watch, and says to Fieschi, "Five o'clock! Come, that will do for to-day. It is time for you to go to dinner." Fieschi leaped up: "Dinner! O, I have dined to-day. I have cut off Pepin's head!"

Fieschi was correct in the smallest particulars. He said one day that at the moment of his arrest he had a dagger upon him. No mention was to be found of this dagger in any of the depositions. "Fieschi," said M. Pasquier, "what is the use of telling lies? You had no dagger!" "Ah, president," said Fieschi, "when I arrived at the station-house I took advantage of the moment when the policemen had their backs turned to throw the dagger under the camp-bed on which I had to sleep. It must be there still. Have a search made. Those gendarmes are a filthy lot. They do not sweep underneath their beds." A visit was made to the station-house, the camp-bed was removed, and the dagger was found.

I was at the Peers' Court the day before his condemnation. Morey was pale and motionless. Pepin pretended to be reading a newspaper. Fieschi gesticulated while talking loudly and laughing. At one moment he rose and said, "My lords, in a few days my head will be severed from my body; I shall be dead, and I shall rot in the earth. I have committed a crime, and I render a service. As for my crime, I am going to expiate it; as for my service, you will gather the fruits of it. After me no more riots, no more assassinations, no more disturbances. I shall have sought to kill the king; I shall have succeeded in saving him." These words, the gesture, the tone of voice, the hour, the spot, struck me. The man appeared to me courageous and resolute. I said so to M. Pasquier, who answered me: "He did not think he was to die."

He was a bravo, a mercenary, nothing else. He had served in the ranks, and he mixed up his crime with some sort of military ideas. "Your conduct is very dreadful," M. Pasquier said to him; "to blow up perfect strangers, people who have done you no harm whatever,—passers-by." Fieschi coldly replied, "It is what is done by soldiers in an ambush."

Lecomte the Assassin

May 31, 1846.

THE Court of Peers is summoned to try the case of another attempt upon the person of the king.

On the 16th of April last the king went for a drive in the forest of Fontainebleau, in a *char à bancs*. At his side was M. de Montalivet, and behind him were the queen and several of their children. They were returning home towards six o'clock, and were passing by the walls of the Avon enclosure, when two gunshots were fired from the left. No one was hit. Rangers, gendarmes, officers of hussars who escorted the king, all sprang forward. A groom climbed over the wall and seized a man whose face was half masked with a neckerchief. He was an ex-Ranger-general of the forests of the Crown, who had been dismissed from his post eighteen months before for a grave dereliction of duty.

June 1, midday.

The orator's tribune and the president's chair have been removed.

The accused is seated on the spot where the tribune usually stands, and is placed with his back to a green baize curtain, placed there for the trial, between four gendarmes with grenadier's hats, yellow shoulder-straps, and red plumes. In front of him are five barristers, with white bands at their necks and black robes. The one in the centre has the Cross of the Legion of Honour and grey hair. It is Maître Duvergier, the *bâtonnier*. Behind the prisoner red benches, occupied by spectators, cover the semicircle where the chancellor usually presides.

The prisoner is forty-eight years of age; he does not appear to be more than about thirty-six. He has nothing in his appearance which would suggest the deed which he has done. It is one of those calm and almost insignificant countenances, which impress rather favourably than otherwise. General Voirol, who sits beside me, says to me, "He looks a good-natured fellow." However, a dark look gradually overspreads the face, which is somewhat handsome, although of a vulgar type, and he looks like an ill-natured fellow. From the seat which I occupy his hair and moustache appear black. He has a long face with ruddy cheeks. He casts his eyes almost continually downward; when he raises them, every now and then, he looks right up at the ceiling; if he were a fanatic, I should say up to heaven. He has a black cravat, a white shirt, and an old black frockcoat, with a single row of buttons, and wears no ribbon, although belonging to the Legion of Honour.

General Berthuzène leans forward towards me, and tells me that Lecomte yesterday remained quiet all day, but that he became furious when he was refused a new black frock-coat which he had asked for to *appear in before the High Court*. This is a trait of character.

While the names of the Peers were being called over his eyes wandered here and there. To the preliminary questions of the chancellor he replied in a low tone of voice. Some of the Peers called out, "Speak up!" The chancellor told him to look towards the Court.

The witnesses were brought in, among whom were one or two women, very stylishly dressed, and some peasant women. They are on my right, in the lobby on the left of the tribune. M. Decazes walks about among the witnesses. M. de Montalivet, the first witness, is called. He wears a red ribbon, together with two stars, one of a foreign order. He comes in limping, on account of his gout. A footman in a russet livery with a red collar assists him.

I have examined the articles brought forward in support of the indictment, which are in the right-hand passage. The gun is double-barrelled, with twisted barrels, the breech ornamented with arabesques in the style of the Renaissance; it is almost a fancy weapon. The blouse worn by the assassin is blue, tolerably well worn. The neckerchief with which he hid his face is a cotton neckerchief, coffee-coloured, with white stripes. On these articles is hung a small card bearing the signatures of the prosecuting officials and the signature of "Pierre Lecomte."

June 5.

During an interval in the sitting I observed the man from a short distance. He looks his age. He has the tanned skin of a huntsman and the faded skin of a prisoner. When he speaks, when he becomes animated, when he stands upright, his appearance becomes strange. His gesture is abrupt, his attitude fierce. His right eyebrow rises towards the corner of his forehead and gives him an indescribably wild and diabolical appearance. He speaks in a muffled but firm tone.

At one point, explaining his crime, he said,

"I stopped on the 15th of April at the Place du Carrousel. It was raining. I stood under a projecting roof and looked mechanically at some engravings. There was a conversation going on in the shop at the side, where there were three men and a woman. I listened mechanically also. I felt sad. Suddenly I heard the name of the king; they were talking of the king. I looked at these men. I recognized them as servants at the Castle. They said that the king would go the next day to Fontainebleau. At that instant my idea appeared. It appeared to me plainly, dreadfully. It left off raining. I stretched out my hand from beneath the projection of the roof. I found that it no longer rained, and I went away. I returned home to my room, to my little room, bare of furniture and wretched. I remained there alone for three hours. I mused, I pondered, I was very unhappy. My project continually recurred. And then the rain began to come down again. The weather was gloomy; a strong wind was blowing; the sky was nearly black. I felt like a madman. Suddenly I got up. It was settled. I had made up my mind. That is how the idea came into my head."

At another moment, when the chancellor said that the crime was without a motive, he said,—

"How so? I wrote to the king once, twice, three times. The king did not reply. Oh, then—"

He did not finish what he had to say, but his fist clutched the rail fiercely. At this moment he was terrific. He was a veritable wild man. He sits down. He is now composed; calm and fierce.

While the procurator-general spoke, he moved about like a wolf, and appeared furious. When his counsel (Duvergier) spoke, tears came into his eyes. They ran down his cheeks, heavy and perceptible.

June 6.
This is how it takes place. On his name being called in a loud voice by the clerk of the Court, each Peer rises and pronounces sentence also in a loud voice.

The thirty-two Peers who have voted before me have all declared for the parricide's penalty. One or two have mitigated this to capital punishment.

When my turn came, I rose and said,—

"Considering the enormity of the crime and the smallness of the motive, it is impossible for me to believe that the delinquent acted in the full possession of his moral liberty, of his will. I do not think he is a human creature having an exact perception of his ideas and a clear consciousness of his actions. I cannot sentence this man to any other punishment but imprisonment for life."

I said these words in very loud tones. At the first words all the Peers turned round and listened to me in the midst of a silence which seemed to invite me to continue. I stopped short there, however, and sat down again.

The calling of the names continued. The Marquis de Boissy said,—

"We have heard these solemn words. Viscount Victor Hugo has given utterance to an opinion which deeply impresses me, and to which I give my adhesion. I think, with him, that the delinquent is not in full possession of his reason. I declare for imprisonment for life."

The calling of the names continues with the lugubriously monotonous rejoinder: "Capital punishment, parricide's penalty."

Proceeding by seniority, according to the dates at which the members of the House have taken their seats, the list comes down to the names of the oldest Peers. Viscount Dubouchage being called in his turn, said,—

"Being already uneasy in my mind during the trial, owing to the manner of the accused, but fully convinced by the observations of M. Victor Hugo, I declare that, in my opinion, the delinquent is not of sound mind. Viscount Hugo gave the reasons for this opinion in a few words, but in a way which appears to me conclusive. I support him in his vote, and I declare, like himself, for imprisonment for life."

The other Peers, of whom a very small number remained, all voted for the parricide's penalty.

The chancellor, being called on last, rose and said,—

"I declare for the parricide's penalty. Now a second vote will be taken. The first vote is only provisional, the second alone is final. All are, therefore, at liberty to retract or confirm their votes. An opinion worthy of profound consideration in itself, not less worthy of consideration owing to the quarter whence it emanates, has been put forward with authority, although supported by a very small minority, during the progress of the voting. I think it right to declare here that during the continuance of the long inquiry preceding the prosecution, during seven weeks, I saw the accused every day; I examined him, pressed him, questioned him, and, as old Parliamentarians say, 'turned him around' in every direction. Never for a single moment was his calmness of perception obscured. I always found that he reasoned correctly according to the frightful logic of his deed, but without mental derangement, as also without repentance. He is not a madman: he is a man who knows what he wanted to do, and who admits what he has done. Let him suffer the consequences."

The second call has begun. The number of Peers voting for the parricide's penalty has increased. On my name being called I rose. I said,—

"The Court will appreciate the scruples of one in whose conscience such formidable questions are suddenly agitated for the first time. This moment, my lords, is a solemn one for all, for no one more than for myself. For eighteen years past I have had fixed and definite ideas upon the subject of irreparable penalties. Those ideas you are acquainted with. As a mere author I have published them; as a politician, with God's help I will apply them. As a general rule, irreparable penalties are repugnant to me; in no particular instance do I approve of them. I have listened attentively to the observations of the chancellor. They are weighty from so eminent a mind. I am struck by the imposing unanimity of this imposing assembly. But while the opinion of the chancellor and the unanimity of the Court are much, from the point of view of discussion, they are nothing in face of one's conscience. Before the speeches began I read, re-

read, studied all the documents of the trial; during the pleadings I studied the attitude, the looks, the gestures, I scrutinized the soul of the accused. Well, I tell this Court, composed as it is of just men, and I tell the chancellor, whose opinion has so much weight, that I persist in my vote. The accused has led a solitary life. Solitude is good for great, and bad for little minds. Solitude disorders those minds which it does not enlighten. Pierre Lecomte, a solitary man with a small mind, was necessarily destined to become a savage man with a disordered mind. The attempt upon the king, the attempt on a father, at such a time, when he was surrounded by his family; the attempt upon a small crowd of women and children, death dealt out haphazard, twenty possible crimes inextricably added to a crime determined upon,—there is the deed. It is monstrous. Now, let us examine the motive. Here it is: A deduction of twenty francs out of an annual allowance, a resignation accepted, three letters remaining unanswered. How can one fail to be struck by such a reconciliation and such an abyss? I repeat, in conclusion, in the presence of these two extremes, the most monstrous crime, the most insignificant motive, it is evident to me that the thing is absurd, that the mind which has made such a reconciliation and crossed such an abyss is an illogical mind, and that this delinquent, this assassin, this wild and solitary man, this fierce, savage being, is a madman. To a doctor, perhaps, he is not a madman; to a moralist he certainly is. I will add that policy is here in harmony with justice, and that it is always well to deny human reason

to a crime which revolts against nature, and shakes society in its foundations. I adhere to my vote."

The Peers listened to me with profound and sympathetic attention. M. de Boissy and M. Dubouchage remained firm, as I did.

There were two hundred and thirty-two voters. This is how the votes were distributed:—

196 for the parricide's penalty;
33 for capital punishment;
3 for imprisonment for life.

The entire House of Peers may be said to have been displeased at the execution of Lecomte. He had been condemned in order that he might be pardoned. It was an opportunity for mercy held out to the king. The king eagerly seized such opportunities, and the House knew this. When it learned that the execution had actually taken place it was surprised, almost hurt.

Immediately after the condemnation, the chancellor and Chief President Franck-Carré, were summoned by the king. M. Franck-Carré was the Peer who had been delegated to draw up the case. They went to the king in the chancellor's carriage. M. Franck-Carré, although he voted for the parricide's penalty, was open in favour of a pardon. The chancellor also leaned in this direction, although he would not declare himself on the subject. On the way he said to President Franck-Carré: "I directed the inquiry, I directed the prosecution, I directed the trial. I had some influence over the vote. I will not give my opinion on the subject of a pardon. I have enough responsibility as it is. They will do what they like."

In the cabinet of the king he respectfully adopted the same tone. He declined to commit himself to a definite opinion on the subject of a pardon. President Franck-Carré was explicit. The king saw what was the real opinion of the chancellor.

Maître Duvergier had conceived an affection for his client, as a barrister always does for the client he has to defend. It is a common result. The public prosecutor ends by hating the accused, and the counsel for the defence by loving him. Lecomte was sentenced on a Friday. On the Saturday M. Duvergier went to see the king. The king received him in a friendly manner, but said, "I will see about it; I will consider it. The matter is a grave one. My danger is the danger of all. My life is of consequence to France, so that I must defend it. However, I will think the matter over. You know that I detest capital punishment. Every time I have to sign the dismissal of an appeal for a pardon I am the first to suffer. All my inclinations, all my instincts, all my convictions are on the other side. However, I am a constitutional king; I have ministers who decide. And then naturally I must think a little of myself too."

M. Duvergier was dreadfully grieved. He saw that the king would not grant a pardon.

The Council of Ministers was unanimously in favour of the execution of the sentence of the Court of Peers.

On the following day, Sunday, M. Duvergier received by express a letter from the Keeper of the Seals, Martin du Nord, announcing to him that "the king thought it right to decide that the law should take its course." He was still under the influence of the first shock of hope definitively shattered when a fresh express arrived. Another letter. The Keeper of the Seals informed the *bâtonnier* that the king, wishing to accord to the condemned man, Pierre Lecomte, a *further* token of his good-will, had decided that the yearly allowance of the said Lecomte should revert to his sister for her lifetime, and that his Majesty had placed an immediate sum of three thousand francs at the disposal of the sister for her assistance. "I thought, M. le Bâtonnier," said the Keeper of the Seals, in conclusion, "that it would be agreeable to you to communicate yourself to the unhappy woman this evidence of the royal favour."

M. Duvergier thought he had made some mistake in reading the first letter. "A *further* token," he said to one of his friends, who was present. "I was mistaken, then. The king grants the pardon." But he re-read the letter, and saw that he had read it only too correctly. A *further token* remained inexplicable to him. He refused to accept the commission which the Keeper of Seals asked him to undertake.

As to the sister of Lecomte, she refused the three thousand francs and the pension; she refused them with something of scorn and also of dignity. "Tell the king," she said, "that I thank him. I should have thanked him better for something else. Tell him that I do not forget my brother so quickly as to take his spoils. This is not the boon that I expected of the king. I want nothing. I am very unhappy and miserable, I am nearly starving of hunger, but it pleases me to die like this, since my brother died like that. He who causes the death of the brother has no right to support the sister."

M. Marilhac plays throughout this affair a lugubriously active part. He was a member of the Commission of the Peers during the preliminaries to the trial. He wanted to omit from the brief for the prosecution the letter of Dr. Gallois, in which he spoke of Lecomte as a madman. It was at one moment proposed to suppress the letter.

Lecomte displayed some courage. At the last moment, however, on the night preceding the execution, he asked, towards two o'clock, to see the procurator-general, M. Hébert; and M. Hébert, on leaving him after an interview of a quarter of an hour, said, "He has completely collapsed; the mind is gone."

June 12.

I dined yesterday at the house of M. Decazes with Lord Palmerston and Lord Lansdowne.

Lord Palmerston is a stout, short, fair man, who is said to be a good talker. His face is full, round, broad, red, merry, and shrewd, slightly vulgar. He wore a red ribbon and a star, which I think is that of the Bath.

The Marquis of Lansdowne affords a striking contrast to Lord Palmerston. He is tall, dark, spare, grave, and courteous, with an air of breeding, a gentleman. He had a star upon his coat, and round his neck a dark-blue ribbon, to which hung a gold-enamelled decoration, round-shaped, and surmounted by the Irish harp.

M. Decazes brought these two gentlemen to meet me. We spoke for some minutes of Ireland, of bread-stuffs, and of the potato disease.

"Ireland's disease is graver still," I said to Lord Palmerston.

"Yes," he replied; "the Irish peasants are very wretched. Now, your country folk are happy. Ah, you are favoured by the skies! What a climate is that of France!"

"Yes, my lord," I rejoined; "but you are favoured by the sea. What a citadel is England!"

Lady Palmerston is graceful and talks well. She must have been charming at one time. She is no longer young. Lord Palmerston married her four years ago, after a mutual passion which had lasted for thirty years. I conclude from this that Lord Palmerston belongs a little to history and a great deal to romance.

At table I was between M. de Mantalivet and Alexandre Dumas. M. de Montalivet wore the cross of the Legion of Honour, and Alexandre Dumas the cross of an order which he told me was that of St. John, and which I believe to be Piedmontese.

I led up in conversation with M. de Montalivet to the event of the 16th of April. He was, it is well known, in the *char à bancs* by the king's side.

"What were you conversing with the king about at the moment of the report?" I said.

"I cannot remember," he replied. "I took the liberty of questioning the king upon this subject. He could not recall it either. The bullet of Lecomte destroyed something in our memory. All I know is that while our conversation was not important, we were very intent upon it. If it had not absorbed our attention we should certainly have perceived Lecomte when he stood up above us to fire; the king, at all events, would have done so, for I myself was turning my back somewhat to speak to the king. All that I remember is that I was gesticulating very much at the moment. When the first shot was fired, some one in the suite cried, 'It is a huntsman unloading his gun.' I said to the king, 'A strange kind of huntsman to fire the remains of his powder at kings.' As I finished speaking the second shot went off. I cried, 'It is an assassin!' 'Oh!' said the king, 'not so fast; do not let us judge too hastily. Wait, we shall see what it means.' You see in that the character of the king, do you not?

Calm and serene in the presence of the man who has just fired at him; almost kindly. At this moment the queen touched me gently on the shoulder; I turned round. She showed me, without uttering a word, the wadding of the gun which had fallen upon her lap, and which she had just picked up. There was a certain calmness in this silence which was solemn and touching.

"The queen, when the carriage leans over a little, trembles for fear she will be upset; she makes the sign of the cross when it thunders; she is afraid of a display of fireworks; she alights when a bridge has to be crossed. When the king is fired upon in her presence she is calm."

Henri the Regicide

July 29, midnight, 1846.

SUZANNE, the chambermaid, has just returned home.

She has been to the *fête* to see the fireworks. On coming in—she was radiant—she said, "Oh! what a lucky thing, madame! It was my cousin who arrested the man who fired upon the king." "What! Has any one fired at the king?" "Yes, and my cousin arrested the man. What a lucky thing! It was this evening, just now. The king was on the balcony. The man fired two pistol-shots together, and missed the king. Oh, how people applauded! The king was pleased. He pointed out himself where the smoke came from. But my cousin, who is a policeman in plain clothes, was there, close to the man. He only had to turn round. He took the man into custody." "What is his name?" "Joseph Legros." "The assassin?" "No, my cousin. He is a tall fellow. The man is little. I do not know his name. I have forgotten it. He looked sad; he pretended to be crying. When he was taken away he said, 'Oh dear! I must die, then.' He is fifty years old. Some gold was found on him. I should think he will have a bad time of it to-night. My cousin is delighted, and the curé also is delighted." (This is a canon of Nôtre-Dame who resides in the same building as the cousin in the police.) "What luck, eh! Madame, what luck!"

July 30.

There is close to here, in the Rue de Limoges, a house with a carriage-way of solemn and gloomy appearance, some old court-house, with a little square yard. On the left-hand side of the door is a great black board, in the centre of which are the Arms of France. Upon this board is an inscription in wooden letters, formerly gilt, and running thus:—

SOUVENIRS AND USEFUL ARTICLES
for Ladies.
OFFICE REQUISITES
of every kind.
MANUFACTORY OF FANCY ARTICLES
IN EMBOSSED STEEL
AND OTHER GOODS
8 — JOSEPH HENRI — 8

Joseph Henri is the assassin. He has a wife and three children.

On the right-hand side, in the courtyard there is a house-door, above which is seen:—

JOSEPH HENRI
THE WAREHOUSE IS ON THE FIRST FLOOR

The whole house is of a fallen and dismal appearance.

August 1.

The day before yesterday I went to inscribe my name at the palace of the king, who has gone to Eu. This is done upon a kind of register, with a green parchment back like a laundress's book. There are five registers, one for each member of the royal family. Every evening the registers are forwarded to the king, and the queen carefully reads them.

I do not suppose people inscribed their names at the residence of Louis XIV. or of Napoleon.

This reminds me of the first time I dined at the Tuileries. A month afterwards I met M. de Rémusat, who was among the guests, and who says, "Have you paid your visit of digestion?"

Homely manners are charming and graceful, but they go rather too far sometimes. I thoroughly understand royalty living a homely life, but this granted, I prefer the patriarchal style to the home style. Patriarchal life is as simple as homely life, and as majestic as royal life.

M. Lebrun, who came to leave his name at the same time as I did, was telling me that a few years ago the King of the Belgians was at the Tuileries. M. Lebrun goes to see him. He speaks to the hall porter. "Can I see the King of the Belgians, please?" "The King of the Belgians? Oh! yes, Sir, in the second courtyard, through the little door. Go up to the third floor and turn to the left along the corridor. The King of the Belgians is No. 9."

The Prince de Joinville lives in a little attic at the Tuileries. The Duke of Saxe-Coburg is lodged in the Louvre in a corridor. Like the King of the Belgians, he has his card nailed upon the door: "Duke of Saxe-Coburg."

August 25.

The trial of Joseph Henri begins to-day in the Court of Peers.

The prisoner is brought in after the Court is seated by four gendarmes, of whom two hold him by the arms. There were six to Lecomte. Joseph Henri is a little man, who appears over fifty years of age. He is dressed in a black frock-coat; he has a black silk waistcoat and black cravat, whiskers, black hair, a long nose. He wears eye-glasses.

He enters, bows three times to the Court, as an actor bows to the pit, and sits down. During the calling of the names he takes snuff with a profound look of ease.

The chancellor tells him to rise, and asks him his surname and Christian names. He replies in a low tone of voice, in a subdued and timid manner. "Speak louder," said the chancellor. The prisoner repeats his replies loudly and very distinctly. He looks like a worthy citizen who is taking out a passport, and who is being questioned by the government employé. He sits down and whispers a few words to his counsel, M. Baroche, *bâtonnier* of the order of barristers. There are five barristers at the bar. Among the crowd which throngs the semicircle behind the prisoner is a priest. Not far from the priest is a Turk.

The prisoner is so short that when he stands up he does not reach above the heads of the gendarmes seated beside him. From time to time he blows his nose loudly in a white handkerchief with blue squares. He has the appearance of a country registrar. His person altogether suggests something ineffably mild, sad, and subdued. Every now and then, however, he holds his head in his two hands, and a look of despair penetrates through the air of indifference. He is, in fact, despairing and indifferent at one and the same time.

When the procurator-general and the chancellor tell him that he is playing a part, he looks at them without any appearance of resentment, and like a man who does not understand.

He speaks a great deal, rather fast, sometimes in low, at others in very loud, tones. He appears to see things only through a veil, and to hear only through a screen. One would imagine there was a wall, barely transparent, between the real world and himself. He looks fixedly, just as if he is seeking to make out things and distinguish faces from behind a barrier. He utters rambling words in a subdued manner. They have a meaning, however, for a thoughtful person.

He concludes a long explanation thus: "My crime is without a stain. At present my soul is as in a labyrinth."

The procurator-general said to him, "I am not to be imposed on by you. You have an object, and that is to escape the death penalty by appearing to invite it, and in this way to secure some less grave penalty."

"Pooh!" he exclaimed; "how can you say so? Other penalties are a punishment, the penalty of death is annihilation."

He stood musing for a moment, and then added: "For eighteen years my mind has suffered. I do not know what state my mind is in; I cannot say. But you see I am not trying to play the madman."

"You had," the chancellor said, "ferocious ideas."

He replies: "I had no ferocious ideas; I had only ideas" (here he indicates with a gesture an imaginary flight of birds hovering round his head)

"which I thought came to me from God."

Then he remains silent for a moment, and continues, almost violently: "I have suffered a great deal,—a great deal" (folding his arms). "And do you think I suffer no longer?"

Objection is made to certain passages of what he has written.

"Just as you please. All that I have written I have written, written, written; but I have not read it."

At another moment he breaks out unexpectedly amid the examination with this: "I have beliefs. My principal belief is that there are rewards and punishments above."

The names of all the regicides, of Fieschi, of Alibaud, of Lecomte, are mentioned to him. His face becomes clouded, and he exclaims, "How is it you speak to me of all those whose names you have just mentioned?"

At this moment Viennet comes up behind me, and says, "He is not a madman, he is a fool."

For myself I should have said the precise contrary.

He is asked, "Why did you write to M. de Lamartine and M. Raspail?"

He replies, "Because I had read some of their writings, and they appeared to me to be philanthropists; and because I thought that philanthropy should not be found only in a pen point."

He frequently concludes his replies with this word, addressed to the Court, and uttered almost in a whisper, *"Appreciate!"*

The procurator-general recapitulates all the charges, and concludes by asking him, "What have you to say in reply?"

"I have no reply to make."

And he places his hand on his forehead as if he had a pain there.

In the midst of a long rambling statement, mingled here and there with flashes of intelligence, and even of thoughtfulness, he stops short to ask for a basin of soup, and gives a number of directions to the attendant who brings it to him. He has a fit of trembling which is plainly perceptible. He drinks a glass of water several times during the examination. He trembles so violently that he cannot carry the glass to his lips without holding it with both hands.

He calls the procurator-general "Monsieur le Procureur." When he speaks of the king he says "his Majesty."

During the very violent speech, for the prosecution, of the procurator-general he makes signs of approval. During the speech for the defence, of his counsel, he makes signs of disagreement. However, he listens to them with profound attention. At one point M. Hébert said, "The prisoner has no political animus. He even protests his respect and admiration for the king." Joseph Henri nods his head twice in token of assent. At another moment the procurator-general says that the prisoner wants to secure a ludicrously inadequate punishment. He says "No," with a shake of his head, and takes snuff.

During the temporary rising of the Court Villemain came to me in the reading-room, and said, "What do you think of all this? It seems to me that no one here is genuine,—neither the prisoner, nor the procurator-general, nor the chancellor. They all look to me as though they are shamming, and as

though not one of them says what he thinks. There is something false, equivocal, and confused in this affair."

During the trial Villemain contemplated Joseph Henri with fixed and melancholy interest.

August 27.

The deliberation began at twenty minutes past eight o'clock. The Peers, without swords or hats, sit with closed doors; only the clerks are present. On taking their seats the Peers cried out on all sides, "Open the ventilators; let us have some light; give us some air!"

The heat that was in the hermetically sealed room was over-powering.

Two questions were asked by the chancellor:—

"Is the prisoner Henri guilty of the attempt upon the life of the king? Is he guilty of an attempt upon the person of the king?"

I should not omit to say that during the calling of the names Langrenée said to me, "I shall be the only one of the diplomatic body who will not vote for the sentence of death." I congratulated him, and went and sat down again behind the bench occupied by Bussière.

Another Peer, one of the new ones, whom I did not know, left his seat, came towards me, and seated himself upon the empty chair at the side, saying to me, "You do not know me?" "No." "Well, I nursed you when you were little,—no higher than that, upon my knees. I am a friend of your father's. I am General Rapatel."

I remembered the name, which my father had often mentioned. I shook hands with the general. We conversed affectionately. He spoke to me of my childhood, I spoke to him of his great battles, and both of us became younger again. Then silence took place. The voting had begun.

The voting went on, on the question of an attempt on the life or an attempt on the person, without its being ascertained beforehand whether the difference in the crime involved any difference in the penalty. However, it was soon evident that those Peers who decided that it was an attempt on the person did not desire the death penalty, and the majority of this opinion became larger and larger.

As the second vote was about to be taken, I said: "It results from the deliberation on the whole, and from the earnest views which have been put forward, that, in the opinion of all the judges, the words 'person of the king' have a double sense, and that they signify the physical person and the moral person. These two senses, however, are distinct to the conscience, although they are confounded in the vote. The physical person has not been injured, has not been seriously menaced, as nearly all my noble colleagues are agreed. It is only the moral person who has been not only menaced, but even injured. Having given this explanation, and with this reserve, that it is perfectly understood that it is the moral person only that is injured, I associate myself with the immense majority of my colleagues, who declare the prisoner, Joseph Henri, guilty of an attempt upon the person of the king."

The clerk proclaimed the result:—
One hundred and twenty-two Peers decided for an attempt on the person; thirty-eight for an attempt on the life; four for an act of contempt.

The sitting was suspended for a quarter of an hour. The Peers left the Court, and became scattered in groups in the lobby. I conversed with M. de la Redorte, and I told him that if it came to the point I admitted State policy as well as justice, but on the condition that I should consider State policy as the human voice, and justice as the Divine voice. M. de Mornay came up to me and said that the *Anciens* abandoned the death penalty; that they were sensible of the feeling of the House, and gave way to it; but that, in agreement with the majority, they would vote for penal servitude for life, and I was asked to give my support to this vote. I said that it was impossible for me to do so; that I congratulated our *Anciens* on having abandoned the death penalty, but that I should not vote for penal servitude; that, in my opinion, the punishment exceeded the offence; that, moreover, it was not in harmony with the dignity of the Chamber or its precedents.

The sitting was resumed at half-past four.

When my turn came, I simply said, "Detention for life."

Several Peers gave the same vote. Thirteen in all. Fourteen voted the death penalty; a hundred and thirty-three penal servitude for life.

Several Peers said to me, "You ought to be satisfied; there is no death sentence. The judgment is a good one." I replied, "It might have been better."

The procurator-general and the advocate-general were brought in, in scarlet robes; then the public rushed in noisily. There were a number of men in blouses. Two women who were among the crowd were turned out. The names of the

Peers were called; then the chancellor read the judgment amid profound silence.

P. S.—September 12.

The punishment has not been commuted; the judgment will be carried out.

Joseph Henri, who had been transferred from the Luxembourg and from the Conciergerie to the prison of La Roquette, started the day before yesterday for Toulon in a prison-van with cells, accompanied by eight felons. While the irons were being placed upon him he was weak, and trembled convulsively; he excited the compassion of everybody. He could not believe that he was really a convict. He muttered in an underdone, "Oh dear! if I had but known!"

The Crypt of Pain

I REMEMBER that on Thursday, the 10th of September, 1846, St. Patient's day, I decided to go to the Académie. There was to be a public meeting for the award of the Montyon prize, with a speech by M. Viennet. Arriving at the Institute, I ascended the staircase rather irresolutely. In front of me ran up boldly and cheerfully, with the nimbleness of a schoolboy, a member of the Institute in full dress, with his coat buttoned up, tight-fitting, and nipped in at the waist,—a lean, spare man, with active step and youthful figure. He turned round. It was Horace Vernet. He had an immense moustache, and three crosses of different orders suspended from his neck. In 1846 Horace Vernet was certainly more than sixty years of age.

Arriving at the top of the staircase, he entered. I felt neither so young nor so bold as he, and I did not enter. In the street outside the Institute I met the Marquis of B. "You have just come away from the Académie?" he asked. "No," I replied; "one cannot come away without going in. And you, how is it you are in Paris?" "I have just come from Bourges." The Marquis, a very warm Legitimist, had been to see Don Carlos, son of him who took the title of Charles V. Don Carlos, whom the faithful called Prince of the Asturias, and afterwards King of Spain, and who was known to European diplomacy as the Count de Montemolin, looked with some amount of annoyance upon the marriage of his cousin, Doña Isabella, with the Infante Don Francisco d'Assiz, Duke of Cadiz, which had just been concluded at this very moment He plainly showed the Marquis how surprised he felt, and even let him see a letter addressed by the Infante to him, the Count de Montemolin, in which this phrase occurred, word for word: "I will abandon all thought of my cousin as long as you remain between her and me."

We shook hands, and M. de B. left me.

As I was returning by the Quai des Morfondus, I passed by the lofty old towers of Saint-Louis, and I felt an inclination to visit the prison of the Conciergerie at the Palais de Justice. It is impossible to say how the idea came into my head to go in and see how man had contrived to render hideous in the inside what is so magnificent on the outside. I turned to the right, however, into the little courtyard, and rang at the grating of the doorway. The door was opened; I gave my name. I had with me my peer's medal. A doorkeeper was put at my service to serve as a guide wherever I wished to go.

The first impression which strikes one on entering a prison is a feeling of darkness and oppression, diminished respiration and perception, something ineffably nauseous and insipid intermingled with the funereal and the lugubrious. A prison has its odour as it has its *chiaroscuro*. Its air is not air, its daylight is not daylight. Iron bars have some power, it would seem, over those two free and heavenly things,— air and light.

The first room we came to was no other than the old guard-room of Saint-Louis, an immense hall cut up into a large number of compartments for the requirements of the prison. Everywhere are elliptical-pointed arches and pillars with capitals; the whole scraped, pared, levelled, and marred by the hideous taste of the architects of the Empire and the Restoration. I make this remark once for all, the whole building having been served in the same fashion.

In this warder's room could still be seen on the right-hand side the nook where the pikes were stacked, marked out by a pointed moulding at the angle of the two walls.

The outer office in which I stood was the spot where the *toilet* of condemned criminals took place. The office itself was on the left. There was in this office a very civil old fellow, buried in a heap of cardboard cases, and surrounded by nests of drawers, who rose as I entered, took off his cap, lighted a candle, and said:

"You would like, no doubt, to see Héloïse and Abélard, sir?"

"By all means," I said; "there is nothing I should like better."

The old man took the candle, pushed on one side a green case bearing this inscription, "Discharges for the month," and showed me in a dark corner behind a great nest of drawers a pillar and capital, with a representation of a monk and a nun back to back, the nun holding in her hand an enormous phallus. The whole was painted yellow, and was called Héloïse and Abélard.

My good man continued:—

"Now that you have seen Héloïse and Abélard, you would, no doubt, like to see the condemned cell?"

"Certainly," I said.

"Show the gentleman the way," said the good man to the turnkey.

Then he dived once more into his cases. This peaceful creature keeps the register of the sentences and terms of imprisonment.

I returned to the outer office, where I admired as I passed by a very large and handsome shell-work table in the brightest and prettiest Louis XV. taste, with a marble border, but dirty, unsightly, daubed with colour which had once been white, and relegated to a dark corner. Then I passed through a gloomy room, encumbered with wooden bedsteads, ladders, broken panes of glass, and old window-frames. In this room the turnkey opened a door with a fearful noise of heavy keys and drawn bolts, and said, "That is it, sir."

I went into the condemned cell.

It was rather a large place, with a low, arched ceiling, and paved with the old stone flooring of Saint-Louis,—square blocks of lias-stone alternating with slabs of slate.

Some of the paving-stones were missing here and there. A tolerably large semicircular vent-hole, protected by its iron bars and projecting shaft, cast a pale and wan sort of light inside. No furniture, save an old cast-iron stove of the time of Louis XV., ornamented with panels in relief, which it is impossible to distinguish owing to the rust, and in front of the skylight a large arm-chair in oak, with an opening in the seat. The chair was of the period of Louis XIV., and covered with leather, which was partly torn away so as to expose the horse-hair. The stove was on the right of the door. My guide informed me that when the cell was occupied a folding bedstead was placed in it. A gendarme and a warder, relieved once every three hours, watched the condemned man day and night, standing the whole time, without a chair or bed, so that they might not fall asleep.

We returned to the outer office, which led to two more rooms,—the reception room of the privileged prisoners, who were able to receive their visitors without standing behind a double row of

iron bars, and the saloon of the barristers, who are entitled to communicate freely and in private with their clients. This "saloon,"—for so it was described in the inscription placed over the door, —was a long room, lighted by an opening in the wall, and furnished with long wooden benches like the other one. It appears that some young barristers had been guilty of abusing the privilege of a legal tête-à-tête. Female thieves and poisoners are occasionally very good-looking. The abuse was discovered, and the "saloon" was provided with a glazed doorway. In this way it was possible to see, although not to hear.

At this juncture the governor of the Conciergerie, whose name was Lebel, came up to us. He was a venerable old man, with some shrewdness in his looks. He wore a long frock-coat, and in his button-hole the ribbon of the Legion of Honour. He begged to be excused for not having ascertained before that I was in the place, and asked me to allow him to accompany me in the tour of inspection which I wished to make.

The outer office led through an iron barrier into a long, wide, and spacious vaulted passage.

"What is that?" I asked M. Lebel.

"That," he said, "was formerly connected with the kitchens of Saint-Louis. It was very useful to us during the riots. I did not know what to do with my prisoners. The Prefect of Police sent and asked me, 'Have you plenty of room just now? How many prisoners can you accommodate?' I replied, 'I can accommodate two hundred.' They sent me three hundred and fifty, and then said to me, 'How many more can you accommodate?' I thought they were joking. However, I made room by utilizing the Women's Infirmary. 'You can,' I said, 'send a hundred prisoners.' They sent me three hundred. This rather annoyed me; but they said, 'How many can you still find room for?' 'You can now send as many as you like.' Sir, they sent me six hundred! I placed them here; they slept upon the ground on trusses of straw. They were very excitable. One of them, Lagrange, the Republican from Lyons, said to me, 'Monsieur Lebel, if you will let me see my sister, I promise you I will make all the men keep quiet.' I allowed him to see his sister; he kept his word, and the place, with all its six hundred devils, became a little heaven. My Lyons men thus continued well behaved and civil until the day when, the House of Peers having begun to move in the matter, they were brought in contact, during the official inquiry, with the Paris rioters, who were of Sainte-Pélagie. The latter said to them, 'You must be mad to remain quiet like that. Why, you should complain, you should shout, you should be furious.' My Lyons men now became furious, thanks to the Parisians. They became perfect Satans! Oh, what trouble I had! They said to me, 'Monsieur Lebel, it is not because of you, but of the Government. We want to show our teeth to the Government.' And Reverchon then undressed himself and stood stark naked."

"He called that showing his teeth, did he?" I asked M. Lebel.

In the meantime the turnkey had opened the great railings at the far end of the corridor, then other railings and heavy doors, and I found myself in the heart of the prison.

I could see through the railed arches the men's exercise-yard. It was a tolerably large, oblong courtyard, above which towered on every side the high walls of Saint-Louis, nowadays plastered and disfigured. A number of men were walking up and down in groups of two or three; others were seated in the corners, upon the stone benches which surround the yard. Nearly all wore the prison dress,—large waistcoats with linen trousers; two or three, however, wore black coats. One of the latter was clean and sedate-looking, and had a certain indescribable air of a town-bred man. It was the wreck of a gentleman.

This yard had nothing repulsive-looking about it. It is true that the sun was shining brightly, and that everything looks smiling in the sun,—even a prison. There were two beds of flowers with trees, which were small, but of a bright green, and between the two beds, in the middle of the yard, an ornamental fountain with a stone basin.

This yard was formerly the cloister of the Palace. The Gothic architect surrounded the four sides with a gallery ornamented with pointed arches. The modern architects have covered these arches with masonry; they have placed steps and partitions in them and made two stories. Each arcade made one cell on the ground-floor and one on the first floor. These cells, clean and fitted with timber floorings, had nothing very repulsive about them. Nine feet long by six feet wide, a door opening on to the corridor, a window overlooking the ground, iron bolts, a large lock, and a railed opening in the door, iron bars to the window, a chain, a bed in the angle on the left of the door, covered with coarse linen and coarse blanketing, but very carefully and neatly made, —that is what these cells were like. It was recreation time. Nearly all the cells were open, the men being in the yard. Two or three, however, remained closed, and some of the prisoners— young workmen, shoemakers and hatters for the most part—were working there, making a great noise with their hammers. They were, I was told, hardworking and well-conducted prisoners, who preferred to do some work rather than go out for exercise.

The quarters of the privileged prisoners were above. The cells were rather larger, and, as a result of the greater liberty enjoyed here at a cost of *sixteen centimes* a day, rather less clean. As a general rule, in a prison, the greater the cleanliness the less liberty there is. These wretched beings are so constituted that their cleanliness is the token of their servitude. They were not alone in their cells; there were, in some cases, two or three together; there was one large room in which there were six. An old man with a kindly and honest-looking face was engaged in reading. He lifted up his eyes from his book when I entered, and looked at me like a country curé reading his breviary and seated upon the grass with the sky above his head. I made inquiries, but I could not discover of what this *good-man* was accused. Upon the whitewashed wall near the door these four lines were written in pencil:—

"Dans la gendarmerie,
Quand un gendarme rit,
Tous les gendarmes rient
Dans la gendarmerie."

Beneath them a parodist had added:—
"Dans la Conciergerie,
Quand un concierge rit,
Tous les concierges rient
Dans la Conciergerie."

M. Lebel called my attention in the yard to the spot where a prisoner had made his escape a few years before. The right angle formed by the two walls of the yard at the northernmost end had sufficed for the accomplishment of the man's purpose. He had planted his back in this angle, and drew himself up solely by the muscular force of his shoulders, elbows, and heels, as far as the roof, where he caught hold of a stove-pipe. Had this stove-pipe given way under his weight he would have been a dead man. On reaching the roof he climbed down again into the outer enclosure and fled. All this in broad daylight. He was captured again in the Palais de Justice. His name was Bottemolle. "Such an escape was deserving of better luck," said M. Lebel. "I was almost sorry to see him brought back."

At the beginning of the men's yard there was, on the left, a little office reserved for the chief warder, with a table placed at a right angle before the window, a leather-covered chair, and all kinds of cardboard cases and papers upon the table. Behind this table and chair was an oblong space of about eight feet by four. It was the site of the cell formerly occupied by Louvel. The wall which divided it from the office had been demolished. At a height of about seven feet the wall ended, and was replaced by an iron grating reaching to the ceiling. The cell was lighted only through this and through the window in the door, the light coming from the corridor of the office and not from the courtyard. Through this grating and through the window of the door Louvel, whose bed was in the corner at the far end, was watched night and day. For all that, moreover, two turnkeys were placed in the cell itself. When the wall was pulled down the architect preserved the door—a low-lying, door, armed with a great square lock and round bolt—and had it built into the outer wall. It was there I saw it.

I remember that in my early youth I saw Louvel cross the Pont-au-Change on the day on which he was taken to the Place de Grève. It was, I think, in the month of June. The sun shone brightly. Louvel was in a cart, with his arms tied behind his back, a blue coat thrown over his shoulders, and a round hat upon his head. He was pale. I saw him in profile. His whole countenance suggested a sort of earnest ferocity and violent determination. There was something harsh and frigid in his appearance.

Before we left the men's quarters M. Lebel said, "Here is a curious spot." And he made me enter a round, vaulted room, rather lofty, about fifteen feet in diameter, without any window or opening in the wall, and lighted only through the doorway. A circular stone bench stretched all round the chamber.

"Do you know where you are now?" asked M. Lebel.

"Yes," I replied.

I recognized the famous chamber of torture. This chamber occupies the ground-floor of the crenellated tower, —the smallest of the three round towers on the quay.

In the centre was an ominous and singular-looking object. It was a sort of long and narrow table of lias-stone, joined with molten lead poured into the crevices, very heavy, and supported on three stone legs. This table was about two and a half feet high, eight feet long, and twenty inches wide. On looking up I saw a great rusty iron hook fastened in the round stone which forms the key-stone of the arch.

This object is the rack. A leather covering used to be put over it, upon which the victim was stretched. Ravaillac remained for six weeks upon this table, with his feet and hands tied, bound at the waist by a strap attached to a long chain hanging from the ceiling. The last ring of this chain was slipped on to the hook which I still saw fixed above my head. Six gentlemen guards and six guards of the provost's department watched him day and night. Damiens was guarded like Ravaillac in this chamber, and tied down upon this table during the whole time occupied by the inquiry and the trial of his case. Desrues, Cartouche, and Voisin were tortured upon it. The Marchioness de Brinvilliers was stretched upon it stark naked, fastened down, and, so to speak, quartered by four chains attached to the four limbs, and there suffered the frightful "extraordinary torture by water," which caused her to ask, "How are you going to continue to put that great barrel of water in this little body?"

A whole dark history is there, having filtered, so to speak, drop by drop, into the pores of these stones, these walls, this vault, this bench, this table, this pavement, this door. There it all is; it has never quitted the place. It has been shut up there, it has been bolted up. Nothing has escaped from it, nothing has evaporated; no one has ever spoken, related, betrayed, revealed anything of it. This crypt, which is like the mouth of a funnel turned upside down, this case made by the hands of man, this stone box, has kept the secret of all the blood it has drunk, of all the shrieks it has stifled. The frightful occurrences which have taken place in this judge's den still palpitate and live, and exhale all sorts of horrible miasms. What a strange abomination is this chamber! What a strange abomination this tower placed in the very middle of the quay, without any moat or wall to separate it from the passer-by! Inside, the saws, the boots, the wooden horses, the wheels, the pincers, the hammers which knock in the wedges, the hissing of flesh touched with the red-hot iron, the spluttering of blood upon the live embers, the cold interrogatories of the magistrates, the despairing shrieks of the tortured man; outside, within four paces, citizens coming and going, women chattering, children playing, tradespeople selling their wares, vehicles rolling along, boats upon the river, the roar of the city, air, sky, sun, liberty!

It is a gloomy reflection that this tower without windows has always seemed silent to the passer-by; it made no more noise then than it does now. What must be the thickness of these walls for the sound of the street not to have reached the tower, and for the sound of the tower not to have reached the street!

I contemplated this table in particular with a curiosity filled with awe. Some of the prisoners had carved their names upon it. Towards the centre eight or ten letters, beginning with an *M*, and

forming a word which was illegible, were rather deeply cut. At one end had been written with a punch the name of "Merel." (I quote from memory, and may be mistaken, but I think that is the name.)

The wall was hideous in its nakedness. It seemed as though one felt its fearful and pitiless solidity. The paving was the same kind of paving as in the condemned cell,—that is to say, the old black and white stones of Saint-Louis in alternate squares. A large square brick stove had taken the place of the old heating furnace for the instruments of torture. This chamber is used in winter as a place of warmth for the prisoners.

We then proceeded to the women's building. After being in the prison for an hour, I was already so accustomed to the bolts and bars that I no longer noticed them, any more than the air peculiar to prisons, which suffocated me as I went in. It would be impossible, therefore, for me to say what doors were opened to enable us to walk from the men's to the women's quarters. I do not remember. I only recollect that an old woman, with a nose like a bird of prey, appeared at a railing and opened the gate to us, asking us if we wished to look round the yard. We accepted the offer.

The women's exercise yard was much smaller and much more gloomy than that of the men. There was only one bed of shrubs and flowers, a very narrow one, and I do not think there were any trees. Instead of the ornamental fountain there was a wash-house in the corner. A female prisoner with bare arms was inside washing her clothes. Eight or ten women were seated in the yard in a group, talking, sewing, and working. I raised my hat. They rose and looked at me with curiosity. They were for the most part apparently of the lower middle class, and presented the appearance of small shopkeepers about forty years of age. That appeared to be the average age. There were, however, two or three young girls.

By the side of the yard there was a little chamber into which we entered. There were two young girls there, one seated, the other standing. The one who was seated appeared ill; the other was tending her.

I asked, "What is the matter with that young girl?"

"Oh, it is nothing," said the other, a tall and rather handsome dark girl with blue eyes; "she is subject to it. She is not very well. She was often taken like it at Saint-Lazare. We were there together. I look after her."

"What is she charged with?" I continued.

"She is a servant. She stole six pairs of stockings of her employers."

Just then the invalid turned pale and fainted. She was a poor girl of sixteen or seventeen years of age.

"Give her some air," I said.

The big girl took her in her arms like a child, and carried her into the yard. M. Lebel sent for some ammonia.

"She took six pairs of stockings," he said; "but it is her third offence."

We returned to the yard. The girl lay upon the stones. The women crowded round her, and gave her the ammonia to smell. The old female warder took off her garters, while the big dark girl unlaced her clothing. As she undid her stays she said,—

"This comes over her every time she puts on stays. I will give you stays, you little fool!"

In those words, *little fool*, there was somehow or other a tone which was tender and sympathizing.

We left the place.

One of the peculiarities of the Conciergerie is that all the cells occupied by regicides since 1830 are in the women's quarters.

I entered, first of all, the cell which had been occupied by Lecomte, and which had just been tenanted by Joseph Henri. It was a tolerably large chamber, almost vast, well lighted, and having nothing of the cell about it but the stone floor, the door armed with the biggest lock in the Conciergerie, and the window,—a large railed opening opposite the door. This chamber was furnished as follows: in the corner near the window, a boat-shaped mahogany bedstead, four and a half feet wide, in the most imposing style of the Restoration; on the other side of the window a mahogany writing-table; near the bed a mahogany chest of drawers, with lacquered rings and handles; upon the chest of drawers a looking-glass, and in front of the looking-glass a mahogany clock in the form of a lyre, the face gilded and chased; a square carpet mat at the foot of the bed; four mahogany chairs covered with Utrecht velvet; between the bed and the writing-table a china stove. This furniture, with the exception of the stove, which would shock the taste of common-people, is the very ideal of a rich shopkeeper. Joseph Henri was dazzled by it. I asked what had become of this poor madman. After having been transferred from the Conciergerie to the prison of La Roquette, he had set out that very morning, in the company of eight felons, for the convict prison of Toulon.

The window of this cell looked out on the women's exercise yard. It was ornamented with a rusty old projecting shaft, full of holes. Through these holes could be seen what was going on in the yard,—an amusement for the prisoner not altogether without drawbacks for the women, who thought themselves alone and secluded from observation in the yard.

Near by was the cell formerly occupied by Fieschi and Alibaud. Ouvrard, who was the first to occupy it, had a marble chimney-piece placed in it (Sainte-Anne marble, black with white veins), and a large wooden partition forming a recess and dressing-room. The furniture was of mahogany, and very similar to that of the apartment of Joseph Henri. After Fieschi and Alibaud, this cell had had for its occupants the Abbé de Lamennais and the Marchioness de Larochejacquelein; then Prince Louis Napoleon; and, finally, that "stupid Prince de Berghes," as M. Lebel put it.

Opposite these two cells was the entrance to the Women's Infirmary, a long and broad chamber, too low-lying for its size. There were a score of beds there, with no one in the beds. I expressed surprise at this.

"I hardly ever have any invalids," said M. Lebel. "In the first place, the prisoners only stay here a short time. They come to await their trial, and go away immediately afterwards; if acquitted, at liberty; if convicted, to their destination. As long as they are here, the anticipation of their trial keeps them in a state of excitement which leaves room for nothing else. Yes, they have no time to get ill; they have another sort of feverishness than fever. At the period of the cholera, which was also the great period of riots, I had seven hundred prisoners here. They were everywhere,—in the doorways, in the offices, in the waiting-rooms, in the yards, on the beds, on straw, on the paving-stones. I said, 'Good heavens! It is to be hoped the cholera will not come in addition to all this.' Sir, I did not have a single man invalided."

There is certainly a moral in these facts. They show that strong mental excitement is a preservation against all ailments. In times of pestilence, while sanitary and hygienic measures should not be neglected, the people should be entertained by grand fêtes, grand performances, noble impressions. If no one troubled about the epidemic it would disappear.

"When they had, in the cells on the opposite side, a prisoner guilty of an attempt on the person of the king, the Women's Infirmary was converted into a guard-room. Here were installed fifteen or twenty warders, kept secluded from the outer world, like the prisoner himself, seeing no one, not even their wives, and this for the whole time of the preliminaries of the trial, sometimes six weeks, at others two months. That is what is done," added M. Lebel, from whom I had these details, "when I have regicides."

This phrase fell from him in the most natural manner possible; to him it was a sort of habit to have regicides.

"You spoke," I said, "in a contemptuous manner of the Prince de Berghes. What do you think of him?"

He wiped his eye-glasses on his sleeve, and replied:

"Oh, as for that, I do not think anything about him; he was a wretched, great simpleton, well-bred, with excellent manners, and a gentle expression, but a fool. When he arrived here I put him at first in this chamber, in this infirmary, which is of a good size, so that he might have space and air. He sent for me. 'Is my case a serious one, sir?' he asked. I stammered a few hesitating words. 'Do you think,' he added, 'that I shall be able to get away this evening?' 'Oh, no,' I said. 'Well, to-morrow, then?' 'Nor to-morrow,' I replied. 'What! do you really think they will keep me here for a week?' 'Perhaps longer.' 'More than a week! More than a week! My case really is a serious one, then? Do you think my case is serious?' He walked about in every direction, continuing to repeat this question, to which I never replied. His family, however, did not abandon him. The duchess his mother, and the princess his wife, came to see him every day. The princess, a very pretty little woman, asked if she might share his prison cell. I gave her to understand that this was impossible. As a matter of fact, what was his offence? Forgery, certainly; but without any motive. It was an act of stupidity, nothing more. The jury found him guilty because he was a prince. If he had been some rich tradesman's son, he would have been acquitted. After he was sentenced to three years' imprisonment, he was left here for some time with me, and then he was transferred to a sanitarium, of which a whole wing was secured for his exclusive use. He has been there nearly a year now, and he will be left there for six months longer; then he will be pardoned. So that his being a prince damaged him at his trial, but it benefits him in his imprisonment."

As we crossed the passage my guide stopped me and called my attention to a low door about four and a half feet in height, armed with an enormous square lock and a great bolt, very similar to the door of Louvel's cell. It was the door of the cell of Marie-Antoinette, —the only thing which had been preserved just as it was, Louis XVIII. having converted her cell into a chapel. It was through this door that the queen went forth to the Revolutionary Court; it was through it also that she went to the scaffold. The door no longer turned on its hinges. Since 1814 it had been fixed in the wall.

I have said that it had been preserved just as it was, but I was mistaken. It was daubed over with a fearful nankeen-coloured picture; but this is of no consequence. What sanguinary souvenir is there which has not been painted either a yellow or a rose-colour?

A moment afterwards I was in the chapel, which had formerly been a cell. If one could have seen there the bare stone floor, the bare walls, the iron bars at the opening, the folding-bedstead of the queen, and the camp-bedstead of the gendarme, together with the historic screen which separated them, it would have created a profound feeling of emotion and an unutterable impression. There were to be seen a little wooden altar, which would have been a disgrace to a village church, a coloured wall (yellow, of course), small stained-glass windows, as in a Turkish *café,* a raised wooden platform, and upon the wall two or three abominable paintings, in which the bad style of the Empire had a tussle with the bad taste of the Restoration. The entrance to the cell had been replaced by an archivault cut in the wall. The vaulted passage by which the queen proceeded to the Court had been walled up. There is a respectful vandalism that is even more revolting than a vindictive vandalism, because of its stupidity.

Nothing was to be seen there of what came under the eye of the queen, unless it was a small portion of the paved flooring, which the boards, fortunately, did not entirely cover. This floor was an old-fashioned, chevroned pavement of bricks, laid on horizontally, with the narrow side uppermost.

A straw chair, placed upon the platform, marked the spot where the bed of the queen had rested.

On coming away from this venerable spot, profaned by a foolish piety, I went into a large apartment at the side, which had been the place of incarceration for the priests during the Terror, and which had been converted into the chapel of the Conciergerie. It was very mean-looking, and very ugly, like the chapel-cell of the queen. The Revolutionary Court held its sittings above this apartment.

While walking about in the depths of the old building, I perceived here and there, through openings in the walls, immense cellars, mysterious and deserted chambers, with portcullises opening on to the river, fearful dungeons, dark passages. In these crypts spiders' webs abounded, as well as mossy stones, sickly gleams of light, vague, and distorted forms. I asked M. Lebel, "What is this place?" He replied, "This is no longer used." What had it been used for?

We had to go back through the men's yard. As we passed through it M. Lebel pointed out to me a staircase near the latrines. It was here that a murderer named Savoye, who had been condemned to the galleys, had hanged himself, not many days previously, to the railings of the baluster. "The jury have made a mistake," said this man; "I ought to have been condemned to death. I will settle the matter." He settled it by hanging himself. He was put under the special supervision of a prisoner who had been raised to the functions of a warder and whom M. Lebel dismissed.

While the governor of the Conciergerie furnished me with these details a decently dressed prisoner came up to us. He seemed to wish to be spoken to. I asked him several questions. He was a young fellow who had been a working embroiderer and lace-maker, afterwards the assistant to the Paris executioner,—what was formerly called the "headsman's valet,"—and finally, he said, a groom in the king's stables.

"Pray, sir, ask the governor not to have me put in the prison-dress, and to leave me my *fainéant.*" This word, which has to be pronounced *faignant,* means a cloth coat in the latest slang. He had, in fact, a tolerably good cloth coat. I obtained permission for him to keep it, and I got him into conversation.

He spoke very highly of M. Sanson, the executioner, his former master. M. Sanson lived in the Rue du Marais-du-Temple, in an isolated house, of which the jalousies were always closed. He received many visits. Numbers of English people went to see him. When visitors presented themselves at M. Sanson's they were introduced into an elegant reception-room on the ground-floor, *furnished entirely with mahogany,* in the midst of which there was an excellent piano, always open, and provided with pieces of music. Shortly afterwards M. Sanson arrived, and asked his visitors to be seated. The conversation turned upon one topic and another. Generally the English people asked to see the guillotine. M. Sanson complied with this request, no doubt for some consideration, and conducted the ladies and gentlemen to the adjoining street (the Rue Albouy, I think), to the house of the scaffold-manufacturer. There was a shed at this place, where the guillotine was permanently erected. The strangers grouped themselves around it, and it was made to *work.* Trusses of hay were guillotined.

One day an English family, consisting of the father, the mother, and three pretty daughters, fair and with rosy cheeks, presented themselves at Sanson's residence. It was in order to see the guillotine. Sanson took them to the carpenter's and set the instrument at work. The knife fell and rose again several times at the request of the young ladies. One of them, however,—the youngest,—was not satisfied with this.

She made the executioner explain to her, in the minutest details, what is called the *toilet of the condemned.*

Still she was not satisfied. At length she turned hesitatingly towards the executioner.

"Monsieur Sanson," she said.

"Mademoiselle," said the executioner.

"What is done when the man is on the scaffold? How is he tied down?"

The executioner explained the dreadful matter to her, and said, "We call that 'putting him in the oven.' "

"Well, Monsieur Sanson," said the young lady, "I want you to put me in the oven."

The executioner started. He gave an exclamation of surprise. The young lady insisted. "I fancy," she said, "that I should like to be able to say I have been tied down in it."

Sanson spoke to the father and mother They replied, "As she has taken a fancy to have it done, do it."

The executioner had to give in. He made the young Miss sit down, tied her legs with a piece of string, and her arms behind her back with a rope, fastened her to the swinging plank, and strapped her on with the leather strap. Here he wanted to stop. "No, no, that is not yet all," she said. Sanson then swung the plank down, placed the head of the young lady in the dreadful neck-piece, and closed it upon her neck. Then she declared she was satisfied.

When he afterwards told the story, Sanson said, "I quite thought she was going to say at last, 'That is not all; make the knife fall.' "

Nearly all the English visitors ask to see the knife which cut off the head of Louis XVI. This knife was sold for old iron, in the same way as all the other guillotine knives when they are worn out. English people will not believe it and offer to buy it of M. Sanson. If he had cared to trade in them, there would have been as many *knives of Louis XVI.* sold as walking-sticks of Voltaire.

From his anecdotes of Sanson, the fellow who said he had formerly been a groom at the Tuileries, wanted to proceed to anecdotes of the king. He had heard the conferences of the king with the ambassadors, etc. I did not trouble him. I thought of his being a Gascon, and an embroiderer, and his political revelations appeared to be only fancy articles of a superior description.

Up to 1826 the Conciergerie had no other entrance than a grating opening into the courtyard of the Palais de Justice. It was through this that criminals condemned to death came out. In 1826 was made the doorway which is to be seen upon the quay between the two great round towers. These two towers had, upon the ground-floor, like the tower of the torture-chamber, a room without a window. The two grotesque Gothic arches, without any voussoir or equilaterial triangle for a base, which are still admired here to this day, and which are masterpieces of ignorance, were opened in these splendid walls by a sort of stone-mason named Peyre, who held the office of architect to the Palais de Justice, and who mutilated, dishonoured, and disfigured the building as may be seen. These two rooms, thus lighted, make two fine circular apartments. Their walls are ornamented with inlaid Gothic arches of admirable purity, resting upon exquisite brackets. These charming triumphs of architecture and sculpture were never intended to see the light of day, and were made, strange to say, for horror and darkness.

The first of the two rooms—the nearest to the men's yard—had been converted into a dormitory for the warders. There were in it a dozen beds, arranged like the rays of a star, round a stove placed in the centre. Above each bed a plank, fixed in the wall through the delicate mullions of the architecture, held the personal belongings of the warders,—generally represented by a brush, a trunk, and an old pair of boots.

Over one of the beds, however, beside the pair of boots, which was not wanting in any single instance, was a little heap of books. I noticed this; it was explained to me. It was the library of a warder named Peiset, to whom Lacenaire had imparted literary tastes. This man, seeing Lacenaire constantly reading and writing, first admired and then consulted him. He was not without intelligence; Lacenaire advised him to study. Some of the books which were there were those of Lacenaire. Lacenaire gave them to him.

Peiset had bought a few other old books upon the quays; he took the advice of Lacenaire, who said, "Read this," or "Do not read that." By degrees the jailor became a thinker, and it was thus that an intelligence had been awakened and had expanded in this repulsive atmosphere.

The other room could only be entered by a door which bore this inscription: "Entrance reserved for the Governor." M. Lebel opened it for me very politely, and we found ourselves in his sitting-room. This apartment was, in fact, transformed into the governor's sitting-room. It was almost identical with the other, but differently furnished. This sitting-room was made up in extraordinary fashion. The architecture of Saint-Louis, a chandelier which had belonged to Ouvrard, hideous wall-paper in the Gothic arches, a mahogany writing-desk, some articles of furniture with unbleached calico coverings, an old legal portrait without any case or frame and nailed askew upon the wall, some engravings, some heaps of paper, a table loking like a counter; altogether, the room, thus furnished, had the characteristics of a palace, a prison-cell, and a shop-parlour. It was patibulary, magnificent, ugly, ridiculous, sinister, royal, and vulgar.

It was into this apartment that the visitors of the privileged prisoners were shown. At the time of his detention, of which many traces remained at the Conciergerie, M. Ouvrard used to see his friends here. The Prince de Berghes used to see his wife and mother here. "What does it matter to me if they do receive visitors here?" said M. Lebel. "They think themselves in a drawing-room, and they are none the less in a prison." The worthy man looked profoundly convinced that the Duchess and Princess de Berghes must have thought they were in a drawing-room.

It was there also that the chancellor, Duke Pasquier, was in the habit of preparing the preliminaries of the official inquiries confided to him in respect of the prosecutions before the House of Peers.

The governor's room communicated with this apartment. It was very mean and ugly looking. The species of den which served as his bedroom was solely dependent upon the doors for light and air,—that is to say, so far as I could see, for I passed rapidly through. It was clean, although of a rather mouldy-smelling cleanliness, and had all sorts of frames in the corners, and old-fashioned knick-knacks, and all those minutiæ which one sees in the rooms of elderly people. The dining-room was larger, and had windows. Two or three good-looking young ladies were seated there upon straw-bottomed chairs, and were at work under the eye of a lady of about fifty years of age. They rose with a modest and pleasant look as I passed, and their father, M. Lebel, kissed them on the forehead. Nothing stranger could be imagined than this Anglican Presbyterian's home, surrounded by the infamous interior of a prison, and walled round as it were and preserved in all its purity amid every vice, every crime, every disgrace, and every shame.

"But," I said to M. Lebel, "What has become of the hall of the chimney-pieces? Where is it?"

He appeared to turn it over in his mind like a person who fails to understand.

"The hall of the chimney-pieces? Did you say the hall of the chimney-pieces?"

"Yes," I rejoined, "a great hall which was under the *salle des pas perdus,* and there were in the four corners four enormous chimney-pieces, constructed in the thirteenth century. Why, I remember distinctly having come to see it some twenty years ago, in company with Rossini, Meyerbeer, and David d'Angers."

"Ah!" said M. Lebel, "I know what you mean. That is what we call the Kitchens of Saint-Louis."

"Well, the Kitchens of Saint-Louis then, if that is what you call them. But what has become of this hall? Besides the four chimney-pieces, it had some handsome pillars which supported the roof. I have not seen it even now. Has your architect, M. Peyre, hidden it away?"

"Oh, no. Only he has made some alterations in it for us."

These words, quietly uttered, made me shudder. The hall of the chimney-pieces was one of the most remarkable monuments of the Royal and domestic architecture of the Middle Ages. What might not a creature like the architect Peyre have done with it? M. Lebel continued:—

"We scarcely knew where to put our prisoners during the time when they have to undergo their preliminary examination. M. Peyre took the Kitchens of Saint-Louis and made a magnificent *souricière* with three compartments,— one for men, one for women, and one for the juveniles. He contrived this in the best manner possible, and he did not destroy the old hall to any great extent, I assure you."

"Will you take me to it?" I said to M. Lebel.

"By all means."

We passed through long, wide, low, and narrow corridors and passages. Here and there we came across a staircase crowded with gendarmes, and we saw pass, amid a hubbub of policemen and warders, some poor wretch whom the ushers handed to each other, at the same time saying to each other in a loud tone of voice the word *Disponsible*.

"What does that word convey?" I said to my guide.

"It means that he has a man whom the examining magistrate has done with,

and who is at the disposal of the gen-darme."

"To set him at liberty?"

"No, to take him back to prison."

At length the last door opened.

"Here you are," said the governor, "in the room you are looking for."

I look round.

I was in darkness.

I had a wall in front of my eyes.

My eyeballs, however, gradually became accustomed to the darkness, and after a few moments I distinguished on my right, in a recess, a lofty and magnificent chimney-piece in the shape of an inverted funnel, built of stone, and resting, by means of an open buttress of the most exquisite style, against a pillar which stood in face of it.

"Ah," I said, "here is one of the chimney-pieces. But where are the others?"

"This is the only one," replied M. Lebel, "which remains intact. Of the three others, two are completely destroyed, and the third is mutilated; it was necessary for a *souricière*. It is because we had to fill up the intervals between the pillars with stone-work. We had to put up partitions. The architect preserved this chimney-piece as a specimen of the architectural style of the period."

"And," I added, "of the folly of the architects of our time!" Thus there was no hall, but a number of compartments; and out of four chimney-pieces three were destroyed. This was effected under Charles X. This is what the sons of Saint-Louis made of the souvenirs of Saint-Louis.

"It is true," continued M. Lebel, "that this *souricière* might very well have been placed elsewhere. But then, you know, they did not think of that, and they had this hall available. However, they arranged it very well. It is divided by stone walls in longitudinal compartments, lighted each by one of the windows of the old hall. The first is that of the juveniles. Should you like to go in?"

A turnkey opened a heavy door with a peep-hole bored through it, by means of which the interior of the *souricière* could be watched, and we went in.

The juveniles' *souricière* was an oblong room, a parallelogram, provided with two stone benches on the two principal sides. There were three boys there. The eldest was rather a big boy. He appeared to be about seventeen years of age, and was clad in frightful old yellowish clothes.

I spoke to the youngest, who had a rather intelligent, although an enervated and degraded, face.

"What is your age, boy?"
"I am twelve, sir."
"What have you done to be in here?"
"I took some peaches."
"Where?"
"In a garden at Montreuil."
"By yourself?"
"No, with my friend."
"Where is your friend?"
He pointed out the other one, who was clad like himself in the prison material, and was a little bigger than himself, and said, "There he is."
"You got over a wall, then?"
"No, sir. The peaches were on the ground in the road."
"You only stooped down?"
"Yes, sir."
"And picked them up?"

"Yes, sir."
At this point M. Lebel leaned towards me, and said, "He has already been taught his lesson."

It was evident, in fact, that the child was telling a lie. There was neither decision nor candour in his look. He cast his eyes down obliquely as he looked at me, as a sharper examines his victim, and moreover with that delighted expression of a child who makes a man his dupe.

"You are not telling the truth, my lad," I resumed.
"Yes, I am, sir."
This "Yes, I am, sir," was said with that kind of impudence in which one feels that everything is wanting, even assurance. He added boldly, "And for that I have been sentenced to three years' imprisonment. But, *je'n rappelle.*"
"Have not your relatives come to claim you?"
"No, sir."
"And your friend, was he sentenced?"
"No, his relatives claimed him."
"He is a better boy than you, then?"
The boy hung down his head.

M. Lebel said to me, "He has been sentenced to be detained for three years in a House of Correction, to be brought up there,—acquitted, that is to say, for not having acted 'with discretion.' The misfortune and the grief of all the little vagabonds is to be under sixteen years of age. They have a thousand ways of trying to persuade the authorities that they are sixteen years of age, and guilty *with discretion.* In fact, when they are sixteen years and one day old they are punished with a few month's imprisonment for their pranks. If they are a day less than sixteen years old, they have three years' detention at La Roquette."

I gave a small sum of money to these poor little wretches, who perhaps were only wanting in education.

All things considered, society is more guilty towards them than they are guilty towards society. We may ask them, What have you done with our peaches? Very well. But they might reply, what have you done with our intelligence?

"Thank you, sir," said the youngster, putting the money in his pocket.

"I would have given you twice as much," I told him, "if you had not told a lie."

"Sir," said the boy, "I have been sentenced, but *j'en rappelle.*"

"It was bad to take peaches, but it was worse to tell a lie."

The child did not appear to understand.

"Je'n rappelle," he said.

We quitted the cell, and as the door was closed, the boy followed us with a look, while still repeating, *"J'en rappelle."* The two others did not breathe a word. The jailor bolted the door while muttering, "Keep quiet, my little *rats.*" This word reminded us that we were in a *"souricière."*

The second compartment was set apart for men, and was exactly similar to the first. I did not go in, but contented myself with looking through the peep-hole. It was full of prisoners, among whom the turnkey pointed out to me a youth with a prepossessing countenance, tolerably dressed, and wearing a thoughtful air. This was an individual named Pichery, the ringleader of a gang of thieves who were to be put on their trial in a few days' time.

The third slice cut out of the Kitchens of Saint-Louis was the women's jail. It was thrown open to us. I saw only seven or eight inmates, all more than forty years of age, with the exception of a youngish woman who still retained some remains of good looks. This poor creature hid herself behind the others. I understood this bashfulness, and I neither asked nor permitted any question. All kinds of little articles of women's luggage—baskets, flat baskets, work-bags, pieces of knitting just begun—encumbered the stone benches.

There were also great pieces of brown bread. I took up a piece of this bread. It was of the colour of road scrapings, smelled very nasty, and stuck to the fingers like birdlime.

"What is that?" I said to M. Lebel.

"It is the prison bread."

"Why, it is detestable!"

"Do you think so?"

"Look at it yourself."

"It is a contractor who supplies it."

"And who makes his fortune, does he not?"

"M. Chayet, Secretary at the Prefecture, has to examine the bread; he considers it very good,—so good that he does not have any other on his own table."

"M. Chayet," I said, "is wrong to judge the bread eaten by the prisoners by the bread he receives himself. If the speculator does send him every day a delicacy, that does not prove that he does not send filth to the prisoners."

"You are right; I will speak about it."

I learned afterwards that the quality of the bread had been looked into, and that an improvement had been effected.

On the whole, there was nothing remarkable in this cell, unless it was that the walls were covered all over with inscriptions in black marks. Here are the three which stood out prominently in larger letters than the others: "Corset." "Je suis codanée à six mois pour vacabonage." "Amour pour la vie."

The three doors of the compartments opened on the same passage,—a long dark corridor, at the two extremities of which, like two stone tiaras, were the rounded forms of the two chimney-pieces which had been preserved, and of which, as I had already said, there was only one which was perfect. The second had lost its principal ornament,—its buttress. Of the others all that remained visible was the sites on which they had stood in the corners of the juvenile compartment and the women's compartment.

It was upon the easternmost of these two latter chimney-pieces that the curious figure of the demon Mahidis was carved. The demon Mahidis was a Persian demon which Saint-Louis brought back from the Crusades. It was to be seen upon the chimney-piece with its five heads,—for he had five heads; and each of these five heads had composed one of those songs which are called *ragas* in India, and which are the oldest music known. These ragas are still celebrated and dreaded throughout Hindustan on account of their magic powers. There is no juggler who is bold enough to sing them. One of these ragas sung at nuddar makes the night fall instantly, and to conjure from the ground an immense circle of darkness, which spreads as far as the voice of the singer will carry. Another is called the Ihu-

puck raga. Whoever sings it perishes by fire. A tradition relates how the Emperor Akbar one day was smitten with a desire to hear this raga sung. He sent for a famous musician named Naïk-Gopaul, and said to him: "Sing me the Ihupuck raga." Thereupon the poor tenor, trembling from head to foot, falls upon the emperor's knees. The emperor had his whim, and was inflexible. The only concession the tenor could obtain was to be allowed to go and see his family for the last time. He sets out, returns to the town in which he lives, makes his will, embraces his old father and mother, says adieu to all that he loves in the world, and returns to the emperor. Six months elapsed. Eastern kings have melancholy and tenacious whims. "Ah, there you are, musician," said Shah Akbar, in a sad but friendly tone. "Welcome! You are going to sing me the Ihupuck raga." Naïk-Gopaul trembles, and implores once more. But the emperor is inexorable. It was winter-time. The Jumna was frozen over; people were skating upon it. Naïk-Gopaul has the ice broken, and gets into the water up to his neck. He begins to sing. At the second verse the water became warm, at the second stanza the ice melted, at the third stanza the river began to boil. Naïk-Gopaul was cooking; he was covered with blisters. Instead of singing, he cried, "Mercy, Sire!"

"Go on," said Akbar, who was no mean lover of music.

The poor wretch went on singing; his face was crimson, his eyes started out of his head, but he continued to sing, the emperor listening meanwhile with ecstasy. At length a few sparks shot out of the hair of the tenor, which stood on end.

"Mercy!" he cried, for the last time.

"Sing!" said the emperor.

He began the last stanza amid shrieks. Suddenly the flames burst forth from his mouth, then from his entire body, and the fire consumed him in the midst of the water. That is one of the habitual effects of the music of this demon Mahidis, who was represented upon the demolished chimney-piece. He had a wife named Parbutta, who is the author of what the Hindoos call the *sixth raga*. Thirty raginis, a music of a feminine and inferior character, were dictated by Boimba. It was to these three devils, or gods, that was due the invention of the gamut, composed of twenty-one notes, which forms the basis of the music of India.

As we withdrew three gentlemen in black coats, conducted by a turnkey, passed near us; they were visitors. "Three new members of the Chamber of Deputies," M. Lebel informed me in a whisper. They had whiskers and high cravats, and spoke like Provincial academicians. They were lavish in expressions of admiration; they were in ecstasies, more particularly at the work which had been done in the way of embellishing the prison and making it suitable to the requirements of the police authorities. One of them maintained that Paris was being prodigiously embellished, *thanks to the architects of taste who were modernizing (sic) the ancient buildings;* and he asserted that the Académie Française ought to make these Paris embellishments the subject of a prize competition in poetry. This set me thinking that M. Peyre has done for the Palais de Justice what M. Godde has done for Saint-Germain-des-Prés, and M. Debret for Saint-Denis; and while M. Lebel was giving some instructions to the warders, I wrote with a pencil upon a pillar of the hall of the chimney-pieces these verses, which might be sent in for the competition if ever the Académie should set up the competition desired by these gentlemen, and which, I hope, would secure the prize:—

"Un sizain vaut une longue ode
    Pour chanter Debret, Peyre, et
      Godde;
    L'oison gloussant, l'âne qui brait,
    Fètent Godde, Peyre, et Debret;
    Et le dindon, digne compère,
    Admire Debret, Godde, et Peyre."

As M. Lebel turned round, I finished. He conducted me to the outer door again, and I issued forth. As I went away, some one of a group of men in blouses behind me, who appeared to be waiting on the quay, said, "There is one of them who has been discharged. He is a lucky fellow."

It appears that I looked like a thief. However, I had spent two hours at the Conciergerie, the sitting of the Académie must still be going on, and I reflected, with much inward satisfaction, that if I had gone to it I should not have been "discharged" thus early.

Count Mortier the Madman

November 11, 1846

YESTERDAY Chancellor Pasquier comes to the house of Mme. de Boignes, and finds her in great agitation, holding a letter in her hand. "What is the matter, madame?" "This letter which I have received. Read it." The chancellor took the letter; it was signed "Mortier," and said, in effect, "Madame, when you read this letter my two children and myself will no longer be alive."

It was Count Mortier, a Peer of France, and formerly an ambassador, but where I cannot remember, who wrote. M. Pasquier was much concerned. M. Mortier was known as a confirmed hypochondriac. Four years ago, at Bruges, he ran after his wife with a razor in his hand, with the intention of killing her. A month ago he made a similar attempt, which led to a separation, by the terms of which M. Mortier retained the custody of the children, a little boy of seven years of age and a little girl of five. His hypochondria was caused, it appears, by jealousy, and developed into uncontrollable passion.

The chancellor sends for his carriage, and does not take a chair. "Where does M. Mortier live?" "In the Rue Neuve Saint-Augustin, in the Hôtel Chatham," said Mme. de Boignes.

M. Pasquier arrives at the Hôtel Chatham; he finds the staircase crowded, a commissary of police, a locksmith with his bunch of keys, the door barricaded. The alarm had been given. They were going to break open the door.

"I forbid you," said the chancellor. "You would exasperate him, and if the mischief were not yet done he would do it."

For some time, however, M. Mortier had not answered. There was nothing but a profound silence behind the door, —a terrible silence, for it seemed that if the children were still living they would be crying. "It seemed," said the chancellor, when he told me this to-day, "as if it was the door of a tomb."

The chancellor called out his name: "Count Mortier, it is I, M. Pasquier, the chancellor, your colleague. You know my voice, do you not?"

To this a voice replied, "Yes."

It was the voice of M. Mortier.

The on-lookers breathed again.

"Well," continued M. Pasquier, "you know me; open the door."

"No," replied the same voice. Then it obstinately refused to speak again. All was silent once more.

This happened several times. He replied, the dialogue continued, he refused to open, then he remained silent. Those outside trembled for fear that in these brief intervals of silence he might do the dreadful deed.

In the meantime the prefect of police had arrived.

"It is I, your colleague, Delessert, and your old friend." (They were school-fellows, I think.)

This parleying lasts for more than an hour. At length he consents to open the door provided they give him their word they will not enter. The word is given;

he half opens the door; they go in.

He was in the anteroom, with an open razor in his hand; behind him was the inner door of his rooms, locked and with the key removed. He appeared frenzied.

"If any one approaches me," he said, "there will be an end of him and me. I will remain alone with Delessert and speak to him; I consent to that."

A risky conversation this, with a furious man armed with a razor. M. Delessert, who behaved bravely, asked every one else to withdraw, remained alone with M. Mortier, and after a refusal, which lasted for a space of twenty minutes, persuaded him to put down the razor.

Once disarmed, he was secured.

But were the children dead or living? It was terrible to reflect upon. To all questions on the subject he replied, "It is nothing to do with you."

The inner door is broken open, and what is found at the farther end of the rooms? The two children, crouching under the furniture.

This is what had happened.

In the morning M. Mortier said to his children, "I am very unhappy. You love me, and I love you. I am going to die. Will you die with me?"

The little boy said, resolutely, "No, papa."

As for the little girl, she hesitated. In order to persuade her the father passed the back of the razor gently around her neck, and said to her, "There, my dear, it will not hurt you any more than that."

"Well, then, papa," said the child. "I do not mind dying."

The father goes out, probably to fetch a second razor. Directly he goes out,

the little boy rushes to the key, lays hold of it, shuts the door, and locks it twice on the inside.

Then he takes his sister to the furthermost end of the rooms and gets under the furniture with her.

The doctors declared that Count Mortier was a melancholy and dangerous madman. He was taken to a mad-house.

He had a mania, in fact, for razors. When he was seized he was searched; besides that which he had in his hand, one was found in each of his pockets.

On the same day the news arrived in Paris that my colleague, Count Bresson, had cut his throat at Naples, where he had recently been appointed Ambassador.

This was a grief to us all, and a great surprise. From a mere worldly point of view, Count Bresson wanted nothing. He was a Peer of France, an ambassador, a Grand Cross of the Legion of Honour. His son had lately been created a Duke in Spain. As an ambassador he had a salary of two hundred thousand francs a year. He was an earnest, kindly, gentle, intelligent, sensible man, very rational in everything, of high stature, with broad shoulders, a good square face, and at fifty-five years of age looked only forty; he had wealth, greatness, dignity, intelligence, health, and was fortunate in private as in public life. He killed himself.

Nourrit also went to Naples and killed himself.

It is the climate? Is it the marvellous sky?

Spleen is engendered just as much under a blue sky as under a gloomy sky, —more so, perhaps.

As the life of even the most prosperous man is always in reality more sad than gay, a gloomy sky is in harmony with ourselves. A brilliant and joyous sky mocks us. Nature in its sad aspects resembles us and consoles us; Nature, when radiant, impassive, serene, magnificent, transplendent, young while we grow old, smiling when we are sighing, superb, inaccessible, eternal, contented, calm in its joyousness, has in it something oppressive.

By dint of contemplating the sky,—ruthless, unrelenting, indifferent, and sublime,—one takes a razor and makes an end of it.

An Over-Night Criminal

THE prison for condemned convicts, built by the side of, and as a comparison to, the prison for youthful offenders, is a living and striking antithesis. It is not only that the beginning and the ending of the evil-doer face each other; there is also the perpetual confronting of the two penal systems,—solitary confinement and imprisonment in common. This is almost enough to decide the question. It is a dark and silent duel between the dungeon and the cell, between the old prison and the new.

On one side were all the condemned, pell-mell,—the child of seventeen with the old man of seventy; the prisoner of thirteen months with the convict for life; the beardless lad who has filched apples and the assassin of the highway, snatched from the Place Saint-Jacques and sent to Toulon in consequence of "extenuating circumstances;" the almost innocent and the quasi-condemned; the blue-eyed and the grey-beard; hideous, pestilential workshops, where they sewed and worked in semi-darkness, amid things dirty and foetid, without air, daylight, speech; without looking at each other; without interest; horrible, mournful spectres, some of whom terrified one by their age, and others by their youth.

On the other side a cloister, a hive, each worker in his cell, each sole in its alveole: an immense edifice of three stories, inhabited by neighbours who never saw each other; a town composed of small hermitages; nothing but children and children who do not know each other, who live years close to each other without ever hearing the echo of each other's foot-falls or the sound of their voices, separated by a wall, by an abyss: work, study, tools, books; eight hours sleep, one hour of repose, one hour of play, in a small walled court; prayers morning and evening: thought ever!

On one side the cesspool, on the other cultivation!

You enter a cell; you find a child standing up before a bench lighted by a dirty window, of which one square pane at the top can be opened. The child is clad in coarse serge; clean, grave, quiet. He ceases working and salutes. You question him; he replies with a serious gaze, and in subdued tones.

Some are making locks, a dozen a day; others are carving furniture, etc., etc. There are as many conditions as stories; as many workshops as corridors. The child can read and write besides. He has in prison a master for his brain as well as for his body.

You must not think that because of its mildness the prison is insufficient punishment. No; it is profoundly sad. All the prisoners have an appearance of punishment which is peculiar.

There are still many more criticisms to be passed; the cell system begins. It has almost all its improvements to come; but, incomplete and imperfect as it is at present, it is admirable when compared with the system of imprisonment in common.

The prisoner—a captive on all sides, and only at all free on the working side —interests himself in what he makes, whatever it may be. Thus, a lad who hated all occupations becomes a most furiously industrious mechanic. When one is in solitary confinement one manages to find light in the darkest dungeon.

The other day I was visiting the convict prison, and I said to the governor, who accompanied me:—

"You have a man condemned to death here now?"

"Yes, sir, a man named Marquis, who tried to murder a girl, Torisse, with intent to rob her."

"I should like to speak to that man," I said.

"Sir," replied the governor, "I am here to take your orders, but I cannot admit you into the condemned cell."

"Why not?"

"Sir, the police regulations do not permit us to introduce everybody into the cells of the condemned."

I replied, "I am not acquainted with the conditions of the police regulations, M. le Directeur de la Prison, but I know what the law permits. The law places the prisons under the authority of the Chambers, and the officials under the *surveillance* of the Peers of France, who can be called upon to judge them. Wherever it is possible that an abuse may exist, the legislature may come in and search for it. Evil may exist in the cell of a man condemned to death. It is therefore my duty to enter, and yours to open it."

The governor made no reply, and led me forward.

We skirted a small courtyard in which were some flowers, and which was surrounded by a gallery. This was the exercise-ground of the condemned prisoners. It was surrounded by four lofty buildings. In the center of one of the sides of the gallery there is a heavy door bound with iron. A wicket opened, and I found myself in a kind of ante-chamber, gloomy, and paved with stone. Before me were three doors,—one directly opposite me, the others on either hand: three heavy doors, pierced with a grating, and cased with iron. These three doors opened into three cells, appropriated to the use of the condemned criminals who awaited their fate after the double appeal to the judge and to the Supreme Courts. This generally means a respite of two months.

"We have never had more than two of these cells occupied at the same time," said the governor.

The door of the centre one was opened. It was that of the condemned cell then occupied.

I entered.

As I crossed the threshold a man rose quickly and stood up.

This man was at the other end of the cell. I saw him at once. A pale gleam of daylight which descended from a wide, deeply-set window above his head lighted it up from the back. His head was bare, his neck was bare; he had shoes on and a strait-waistcoat, and pantaloons of brown woollen stuff. The sleeves of this waistcoat, of thick grey linen, were tied in front. His hand could be distinguished resting on this, and holding a pipe quite full of tobacco. He was on the point of lighting this pipe at the moment the door was opened. This was the condemned man.

Nothing could be seen through the window but a glimpse of the rainy sky.

There was a moment's silence. I was too greatly moved to be able to speak.

He was a young man, evidently not more than twenty-two or twenty-three years old. His chestnut hair, which curled naturally, was cut short; his beard had not been trimmed. He had beautiful large eyes, but his glance was low and villainous, his nose flat, his temples prominent; the bones behind the ears large, which is a bad sign; the forehead low, the mouth coarse, and to the left of the cheek was that peculiar puffing which agony produces. He was pale; his whole face was contracted; nevertheless, at our entry he forced a smile.

He stood upright. His bed was on his left hand,—a kind of truckle-bed, in disorder, on which he had in all probability been extended just previously,—and to his right a small table of wood, coarsely painted a yellow hue, having for a top a plank painted to imitate marble. On this table were glazed earthenware dishes containing cooked vegetables and a little meat, a piece of bread, and a leathern pouch full of tobacco. A straw chair stood beside the table.

This was not the horrible cell of the Conciergerie. It was a good-sized room, fairly light, coloured yellow, furnished with the bed, table, and chair aforesaid, a faïence stove, and a shelf fitted in the angle of the wall opposite the window laden with old clothes and old crockery. In another corner there was a square chair, which replaced the ignoble tub of the old prisons.

Everything was clean, or nearly so, in good order, swept and garnished, and had that indescribable homeliness about it which deprives things of their unpleasantness as well as of their attractiveness. The barred window was open. Two small chains for supporting the sashes hung to two nails above the head of the condemned man. Near the stove two men stood,—a soldier, armed only with his sword, and a warder. Condemned criminals always have this escort of two men, who do not leave them night or day. The attendants are relieved every three hours.

I did not take in all these details at once. The condemned man absorbed all my attention.

M. Paillard de Villeneuve was with me. The governor broke the silence.

"Marquis," he said, pointing to me, "this gentleman is here in your interest."

"Sir," I said, "if you have any complaint to make, I am here to entertain it."

The condemned bowed, and replied with a smile which sat ill upon him, "I have no complaints, sir; I am very well here. These gentlemen [indicating his guardians] are very kind, and would willingly converse with me. The governor comes to see me from time to time."

"How do they feed you?" I asked.

"Very well, sir; I have double rations." Then he added, after a pause, "*We* have a right to double rations; and then I have white bread too."

I glanced at the piece of bread, which was white.

He added, "The prison bread is the only thing to which I have not been able to accustom myself. At Sainte-Pélagie, where I was detained, we formed a society of young men among ourselves, and so as not to mix with the others, to have white bread."

I replied, "Were you better off in Sainte-Pélagie than here."

"I was very well at Sainte-Pélagie, and I am very well here."

I continued, "You said you did not wish to mix with the others. What do you mean by 'the others'?"

"There were a great many common people there," he replied.

The condemned was the son of a porter in the Rue Chabanais.

"Is your bed comfortable?" I asked.

The governor lifted the coverings and said, "Yes, sir; a hair mattress, two mattresses, and two blankets."

"And two bolsters," added Marquis.

"Do you sleep well?" I asked.

He replied without hesitation, "Very well."

There was on the bed an open, torn volume.

"You read?"

"Yes, sir."

I took up the book. It was an "Abridgment of Geography and History," printed in the last century. The first pages and half the binding were wanting. The book was open at a description of the Lake of Constance.

"Sir," said the governor to me, "I lent him that book."

I turned to Marquis.

"Does this book interest you?"

"Yes, sir," he replied. "The governor has also lent me the 'Voyages of La Pérouse' and Captain Cook. I am very fond of the adventures of our great explorers. I have read them already, but I re-read them with pleasure, and I will read them again in one year, or in ten."

He did not say I *could* read them, but I *will* read them. For the rest, the poor young man was a good talker, and was fond of hearing himself speak. "Our great explorers" is textual. He talked like a newspaper. In all the rest of his remarks I remarked this absence of naturalness. Everything disappears in the face of death except affectation. Goodness vanishes, wickedness disappears, the benevolent man becomes bitter, the rude man polite, the affected man remains affected. A strange thing it is that death touches you, but does not give you simplicity.

He was a poor, vain workman; a bit of an artist, too much and too little, who had been destroyed by vanity. He had the idea of coming out and enjoying himself. He had stolen a hundred francs from his father's desk, and next day, after a course of pleasure and dissipation, he had killed a girl in order to rob her. This terrible ladder, which has so many steps that lead from domestic robbery to murder, from the paternal reprimand to the scaffold, criminals like Lacenaire and Poulmann take twenty years to descend; he, this young man, who was a lad but yesterday, had cleared them all in twenty-four hours! He had, as an old convict, a former school-master, said in the courtyard, jumped all the steps.

What an abyss is such a destiny!

He turned over the leaves for a few minutes, and I continued: "Have you never had any means of existence?"

He raised his head, and replied with some pride, "Yes, indeed, sir."

Then he proceeded. I did not interrupt him.

"I was a furniture-designer. I have even studied to be an architect. I am called Marquis. I was a pupil of M. Le Duc."

He referred to M. Viollet Le Duc, the architect of the Louvre. I remarked, in the complacent sequence of the word Marquis, "Le Duc!" However, he had not yet ended.

"I started a 'Journal of Design' for cabinet-makers. I had already made some progress. I wanted to give carpet-manufacturers designs in the Renaissance style, made according to the rules of the trade, which they never had. They are forced to content themselves with engravings of very incorrect styles."

"You had a good idea. Why did you not carry it out?"

"It miscarried, sir."

He spoke the words quickly, and added: "However, I do not mean to say that I wanted money. I had talent, I sold my designs; I would certainly have finished by selling them at my own price."

I could not help saying, "Then why—"

He understood, and answered: "I really cannot say. The idea crossed my mind. I should not be thought capable of that at this fatal day."

At the words "fatal day" he stopped, then continued, with a sort of carelessness:—

"I am sorry I have not some designs here; I would show them to you. I also painted landscapes. M. Le Duc taught me water-colour painting. I succeeded in the Cicéri style. I did things which you would have sworn were Cicéri's. I am very fond of drawing. At Sainte-Pélagie I drew the portraits of many of my companions in crayons only. They would not let me have my box of water-colours."

"Why?" I asked without thinking.

He hesitated. I was sorry I had put the question, for I divined the reason.

"Sir," he said, "it was because they fancied there was poison in the colours. They were wrong. They are water-colours."

"But," remarked the governor, "there is minium in the vermilion?"

"It is possible," he replied. "The fact is, they did not permit it, and I had to content myself with the crayons. The portraits were all good likenesses, too."

"And what do you do here?"

"I occupy myself."

He remained deep in thought after this reply, then he added, "I can draw well. This," indicating the strait-waistcoat, "does not interfere with me. In an extreme case one can draw." He moved his hand beneath his bonds as he spoke. "And then these gentlemen are very kind" (indicating the attendants). They have already offered to let me raise the sleeves. But I do something else,—I read."

"You see the chaplain, of course?"

"Yes, sir; he comes to see me."

Here he turned to the governor, and said, "But I have not yet seen the Abbé Montès."

That name in his mouth had a sinister effect on me. I had seen the Abbé Montès once in my life,—one summer day on the Pont-au-Change, in the cart which was carrying Louvel to the scaffold.

Nevertheless the governor replied, "Ah, dame! He is old; he is nearly eighty-six. The poor man is in attendance when he can."

"Eighty-six!" I exclaimed. "That is what is wanted so long as he has a little strength. At his age one is so near to God that one ought to speak very beautiful words."

"I will see him with pleasure," said Marquis, quickly.

"Sir," said I, "we must have hope."

"Oh!" said he, "do not discourage me. First, I have my petition to the Appeal Court, and then I have my demand *en grâce*. The sentence which has been pronounced may be quashed. I do not say that it is not just, but it is a little severe. They ought to have taken my age into consideration, and given me the benefit of extenuating circumstances. And then I have signed my petition to the king. My father, who comes to see me, bids me be at ease. M. Le Duc himself sent the petition to his Majesty. M. Le Duc knows me well; he knows his pupil Marquis. The king is not in the habit of refusing him anything. It is impossible that they will refuse me a pardon—I do not say a free pardon—but—"

He was silent.

"Yes," I said, "be of good courage; you have here your judges on one side, and your father on the other. But above you have also your father and your judge, who is God, who cannot feel the necessity to condemn you without at the same time experiencing the desire to pardon you. Hope, then."

"Thank you, sir," replied Marquis.

Again silence ensued.

Then I asked, "Do you require anything?"

"I would like to go out and walk in the yard a little oftener. That is all, sir. I only am allowed out for a quarter of an hour a day."

"That is not sufficient." I said to the governor. "Why is it so?"

"Because of our great responsibility," he replied.

"Well!" I exclaimed, "put four guards on duty if two do not suffice, but do not refuse this young man a little air and sunlight. A court in the centre of the prison, stocks and bars everywhere, four lofty walls surrounding it, four guards always there, the strait-waistcoat, sentinels at every wicket, two rounds, and two *enceintes* sixty feet high, what have you to fear? The prisoner ought to be allowed to walk in the courtyard when he asks permission."

The governor bowed, and said, "That is but just, sir. I will carry out your suggestions."

The condemned man thanked me with effusiveness.

"It is time for me to leave you," I said. "Turn to God, and keep up your courage, sir."

"I shall have good courage, sir."

He accompanied me to the door, which was then shut upon him. The governor conducted me into the next cell on the right. It was longer than the other. It contained only a bed and a utensil.

It was in here that Poulmann was confined. In the six weeks which he passed here he wore out three pairs of shoes walking up and down these boards. He never ceased walking, and did fifteen leagues a day in his cell. He was a terrible man.

"You have had Joseph Henri?" I asked.

"Yes, sir; but in the infirmary only. He was ill. He was always writing to the Keeper of the Seals, to the pro-curator-general, to the chancellor, to the Great Refoundary, letters,—letters of four pages, and in small close writing, too. One day I said to him, laughingly, 'It is fortunate that you are not compelled to read what you have written.' No one ever read them, evidently. He was a fool."

As I was leaving the prison the governor indicated to me the two "rounds," or encircling paths: high walls, a scanty herbage, a sentry-box at every thirty paces. He pointed out to me, under the very windows of the condemned cells, a place where two soldiers on duty had shot themselves the year before. They had blown their brains out with their rifles, and we could see the bullet-holes in the sentry-box. The rain had washed away the blood-stains from the wall. One man had killed himself because his officer, seeing him without his rifle, which he had left in the sentry-box, said to him in passing, "fifteen days in the *salle de police*." We never found out why the other man shot himself.

Praslin, Duchess-Slayer

August 18, 4 P.M., 1846.

I have this instant learned that the Duchess of Praslin was assassinated last night in her own mansion, No. 55 Rue St. Honoré.

August 20.

The Court of Peers is convened for to-morrow, to arraign M. de Praslin.

Saturday, August 21. Written at this sitting.

At seven minutes past two the public sitting opens. The Keeper of the Seals, Hébert, mounts the tribune, and reads the ordinance which constitutes the Court of Peers.

There are women on the benches; a man, stout and bald and white, of ruddy countenance, closely resembling Parmentier, is in the west tribune, and for a moment attracts the attention of the Peers.

The chancellor causes the tribunes to be evacuated; the Procurator-general Delangle is introduced, and the Advocate-general Bresson, in red robes. The chancellor remarks that the tribunes are not all empty, those of the reporters among others; he gets angry, and gives orders to the ushers. The tribunes are cleared with some difficulty.

M. de Praslin was arrested yesterday, and transferred to the prison of the chamber on the chancellor's warrant. He was committed this morning at daybreak. He is in the cell where M. Teste was.

It was M. de Praslin who, on the 17th of July, passed over the pen to sign the warrant for the arrest of MM. Teste and Cubières. A month after, exactly, on the 17th of August, he signed his own warrant with his dagger.

The Duke of Praslin is a man of middle height, and of rather commonplace appearance. He has a very gentle, but a very false, manner. He has a villainous mouth, and a horribly constrained smile. He is a fair, pallid man; pale, washed-out, like an Englishman. He is neither fat nor thin, nor goodlooking nor ugly. He has no signs of breeding in his hands, which are fat and thick. He has always the air of being about to say something which he never does say.

I have only spoken to him three or four times in my life. The last time we were ascending the great staircase together. I had informed him that I would interrogate the Minister of War if they did not pardon Dubois de Gennes, whose brother had been the duke's secretary. He said that he would support me.

He had not behaved well towards this Dubois de Gennes. He had put him aside very cavalierly. The duke undertook to present his petitions to the king with his own hands, and he put them in the post!

M. de Praslin did not speak in the Chamber. He voted sternly in the trial. He decided very harshly in the Teste affair.

In 1830 I occasionally met him at the house of the Marquis de Marmier, since duke. He was then only Marquis de Praslin, as his brother was alive. I had noticed the marquise, a good-looking stout woman,—a contrast to the marquis, who was then very thin.

The poor duchess was literally hacked to pieces with the knife, and stunned by the butt of the pistol. Allard, the successor to Vidocq, of the secret police, said, "It was clumsily done; trained assassins would have worked better; a man of the world did that!"

The Comte de Nocé came up to me in the robing-room, and said, "Do you understand? He had made a fire to burn his *robe de chambre.*"

I replied, "He had something to burn! It was not his *robe de chambre,* it was his brain."

A month ago the army received a blow in the case of General Cubières; the magistrature, in President Teste; now the old nobility has had its turn in the Duke of Praslin.

This must be put a stop to.

Sunday, 22.

At the present moment one can perceive, in the window of Mlle. de Luzzy, in Madame Lemaire's house, Rue du Harlay, in the court, the melon, the bouquet, and the basket of fruit which the duke brought from the country the very evening before the murder.

The duke is seriously ill. People say he is poisoned. Just now I heard a flower-girl say, "*Mon Dieu,* if only they do kill him, it will amuse me very much to read all the details in the paper every evening."

In his address to the Court, in secret sitting, the chancellor said the duty which devolved upon the Court, and upon him, was the most painful they had ever been called upon to perform. His voice literally changed while he spoke these words. Before the sitting commenced he came into the reading-room; I bade him good morning, and we shook hands. The old chancellor was overcome.

The chancellor also said, "Rumours of suicide and of escape are in circulation. *Messieurs les Paris* may rest assured. No precaution will be spared to ensure for the culprit, if he be found guilty, the public and legal punishment which he has incurred and deserves, and which he, in that case, cannot by any means escape."

They say that the procurator-general Delangle already repeats to his intimates his little "effective bit"—the description of the room after the crime had been committed there, the sumptuous furniture, the golden fringe, the silken hangings, etc.; there a pool of blood; here the open window, the rising sun, the trees, the garden as far as the eye could reach, the songs of the birds, the sunlight, etc.; then the corpse of the deceased duchess. Contrast! Delangle is astonished at the effect beforehand, and is dazzled by himself.

On the 17th Mlle. de Luzzy had dined at Mme. Lemaire's, at the under-teachers' table. She was pale, and appeared to be suffering. "What is the matter with you?" asked Mlle. Julie Rivière, one of her companions. Mlle. de Luzzy replied that she did not feel very well; that she had fainted that day in the Rue St. Jacques, but the doctor had not thought it necessary to bleed her.

Doctor Louis is the Praslin family practitioner. They called him to see the duke. The prefect of police made the doctor promise that he would only speak to the duke concerning his health. The precaution turned out to be quite needless. The duke would scarcely respond, even by signs, to the doctor's questions. He was in a strange torpor. M. Louis perceived that he had tried to poison himself by swallowing a narcotic.

M. Louis did not think he ought to be moved on the 20th. He thought that if the chancellor had him dragged to Luxembourg, notwithstanding his advice, it was in the hope that the duke would die on the way. I do not think so.

The populace is exasperated against the duke; the family is still more indignant that the populace. If he were to be judged by his family, he would be more severely condemned than by the Court of Peers, and more cruelly tortured than by the people.

August 21.

On Wednesday, when coming from the Académie with Cousin and the Count of Sainte-Aulaire, Cousin said, "You will see Mlle. de Luzzy; she is a rare woman. Her letters are masterpieces of wit and style. Her interrogatory is admirable; still, you will not read it except when translated by Canchy. If you had heard her you would have been astonished. No one has more grace, more tact or intelligence. If she wishes to write some day for us, we will give her, *par Dieu*, the Montyon Prize. For the rest, she is headstrong and impetuous; she is a woman at once wicked and charming."

I said to Cousin, "Ah, so you are in love with her?"

To which he replied, "Hée!"

"What do you think of the affair?" said M. de Sainte-Aulaire, addressing me.

"There must have been some motive. If not, the duke is a madman. The cause is in the duchess or in the mistress; but she is in the swim, otherwise the fact is impossible. There is at the bottom of such a crime as this either a very powerful reason or a great folly."

That was, in effect, my opinion. As for the ferocity of the duke, it is explained by his stupidity; he was a beast —and ferocious.

The populace have already coined the verb *Prasliner*—to *Prasliner* your wife.

The examining Peers visited the Praslin mansion the day before yesterday. The bedroom is still in the state it was left on the morning of the murder. The blood from red has turned to black; that is the only difference. This room gives one the horrors. One can see the terrible struggle and resistance of the duchess as they actually occurred. Everywhere are the prints of bloody hands passing from wall to wall, from one door to another, from one bell-pull to another. The unhappy woman, like a wild animal caught in a snare, must have rushed round and round the room, screaming and seeking an escape from the dagger-blows of the assassin.

From the gate in the Rue de Vaugirard one can see in the prison three windows which have *hottes*. These are the only ones. Three months ago they had neither bars nor *hottes*. The bars were placed for President Teste, and the *hottes* for the Duke of Praslin. Doctor Louis told me:

"The day after the murder, at half-past 2 a. m., I was called, and went to M. de Praslin's house. I knew nothing; judge my utter stupefaction. I found the duke in bed; he was already in custody. Eight women, who relieved each other every hour, never took their eyes from him. Four police agents were seated on chairs in a corner. I had noticed his condition, which was terrible. The symptoms declared cholera or poison. People accuse me of not having said at once he is poisoned. That would have denounced him and lost him. Poisoning is a tacit confession of guilt. 'You should have said so,' the chancellor remarked to me. I replied, 'Monsieur le Chancellor, where an opinion implies the condemnation of a person a doctor will not give it.'

"For the rest," continued M. Louis, "the duke was very gentle: he was passionately fond of his children, and passed his life with one of them on his knee, and sometimes one on his back too. The duchess was beautiful and intelligent; she had become an enormous size. The duke suffered terribly, but exhibited the greatest fortitude. Not a word, not a complaint in the midst of the tortures of the arsenic."

It would appear that M. de Praslin was a very well made man.

At the *post-mortem* the doctors were much struck. One of them exclaimed, "What a beautiful corpse!" He was a fine athlete, Doctor Louis told me.

The tomb in which they laid him bears a leaden plate, on which is the number 1054. A number after his death, as convicts have in life, is the only epitaph of the Duke of Choiseul-Praslin.

Mlle. Deluzy—not De Luzzy—is still in the Conciergerie. She walks about every day for two hours in the courtyard. Sometimes she wears a nankeen dress, sometimes a striped silk gown.

She knows that many eyes are fixed on her at the windows. People who watch her say she strikes attitudes. She is a source of amusement for M. Teste, whose window looks in to the court. She was still in confinement on the 31st.

Granier de Cassagnac, who had seen her, has given me a description of her. She has a very low forehead, her nose turns up a great deal, her hair is very light-coloured. Nevertheless, she is pretty. She looks straight at all who pass, seeking observation, and perhaps to fascinate them.

She is one of those women who neglect the heart in order to cultivate the wit. She is capable of follies, not from passion but from egotism.

August 30.

A sitting in which the Court is dissolved. At a quarter past one I enter the Chamber. There are but a few Peers present,—M. Villemain, M. Cousin, M. Thénard; some generals, General Fabvier among them; some former presidents, among them B. Barthe; there is also M. le Comte de Bondy, who bears a singular resemblance to, with better characteristics than, the Duke of Praslin.

I chat with General Fabvier, then for a long time with M. Barthe, of everything, and of those of the Chamber of Peers in particular. It is necessary to take up the subject to make the people sympathetic with it, and to make it sympathetic with the people. We spoke of the suicide of Alfred de Montesquiou.

In the cloak-room it was the general topic, as well as another sad incident: the prince of Eckmühl has been arrested during the night for having stabbed his mistress.

At two o'clock the chancellor rose; he had on his right the Duke Decazes, and on his left the Viscount Pontécoulant. He spoke for twenty minutes. The attorney-general was introduced.

There are about sixty Peers. The Duke of Brancas and the Marquis de Fontis are beside me.

M. Delangle laid down his brief for the prosecution, holding that the Court was dissolved by the death of the duke.

The attorney-general went out. The chancellor said, "Does any one claim the right to speak?"

M. de Boissy rose. He partly approved of what the chancellor had said. The poison had been taken before the Court of Peers had assembled, consequently no responsibility rested on the Court. Public opinion accused the Peers charged with the investigation of having winked at the poisoning.

COUNT LANJUINAIS. An opinion without any foundation.

BOISSY. But universal. [No, no.] I insist that it may be proved that no responsibility for the poisoning rests upon the chancellor, the investigating Peers, nor on the Courts.

THE CHANCELLOR. No one entertains such an opinion; the report of the *post-mortem* quite disposes of the question.

M. Cousin agreed with the chancellor, and, while sharing the anxiety of M. de Boissy, believed that there was no foundation for the rumour.

M. de Boissy persisted. He believed there had been complicity, but he did not accuse any of the officers of the Court.

M. Barthe rose, and gave way to the Duke Decazes, who related the circumstances of his interview with M. de Praslin the Tuesday he died, at 10 a. m.

This is the interview:—

"You suffer a great deal, my dear friend?" M. Decazes had said.

"Yes."

"It is your own fault. Why did you poison yourself?"

Silence.

"You have taken laudanum?"

"No."

"Then you have taken arsenic?"

The sick man looked up and said, "Yes."

"Who procured the arsenic for you?"

"No one."

"What do you mean? Did you buy it yourself at the chemist's?"

"I brought it from Praslin."

Silence. The Duke Decazes continued: "This is the time, for the sake of your family, your memory, your children, to speak. You confess to having taken poison. It is not to be supposed that an innocent person would deprive his nine children of their father when they are already motherless. You are guilty, then?"

Silence.

"At least you regret your crime. I beg of you to say if you deplore it."

The accused raised his eyes and hands to heaven, and said, with an agonized expression, "If I deplore it!"

"Then confess. Do not you wish to see the chancellor?"

The accused made an effort, and said, "I am ready."

"Well, then," said the duke, "I will go and inform him."

"No," replied the sick man, after a pause, "I am too weak to-day. To-morrow. Tell him to come to-morrow."

At half-past four that afternoon he was dead.

This could not be put into the pleadings, as it was a private conversation, which M. Decazes repeated because the Court was, in a sense, informal.

M. Barthe called attention to the fact that the poisoning took place on Wednesday, the 19th, and had not been renewed.

M. de Boissy wished to punish those who watched the duke so carelessly. He poisoned himself on Wednesday, at ten in the evening.

The chancellor said that M. de Boissy was mistaken; it was four in the afternoon. Besides, such things happen frequently in ordinary cases, and in the best guarded prisons.

The decree dissolving the Court was voted unanimously.

The Duke of Massa, after the vote, asked that the words "his wife" should be inserted in the sentence. There was a Dowager Duchess of Praslin. This was allowed.

The procurator-general was recalled, and sentence was read to him. The sitting broke up at five minutes to three.

Many Peers remained to chat in the hall. M. Cousin said to M. de Boissy, "You were right to ask for information. It was excellent."

M. Decazes added to his former statement the following details: When the duke was carried to the Luxembourg he was clad in a dressing-gown and trousers. During the journey he did not vomit; he only complained of a consuming thirst. When he arrived, at five in the afternoon, they undressed him and put him to bed at once. They did not give him back his dress until the next day, when they moved him into an adjacent room to be examined by the chancellor. After the examination they undressed him again, and put him to bed once more. It is therefore impossible that, even if he had some poison in his pockets, he could have taken it. It is true they did not search him; but that would have been futile. They watched his movements closely.

Hubert, The Spy

JERSEY.

YESTERDAY, the 20th of October, 1853, contrary to my custom, I went into the town in the evening. I had written two letters, one to Schœlcher in London, the other to Samuel in Brussels, and I wished to post them myself. I was returning by moonlight, about half-past nine, when, as I was passing the place which we call Tap et Flac, a kind of small square opposite Gosset the grocer's, an affrighted group approached me.

They were four refugees,—Mathé, a representative of the people; Rattier, a lawyer; Hayes, called Sans-Couture, a cobbler; and Henry, called little Father Henry, of whose profession I am ignorant.

"What is the matter with you?" I said, seeing them greatly agitated.

"We are going to execute a man," said Mathé, as he waved a roll of paper which he held in his hand.

Then they rapidly gave me the following details. Having retired since May from the society of refugees, and living in the country, all these facts were new to me.

In the month of April last a political refugee landed in Jersey. The innkeeper Beauvais, who is a generous-hearted fellow, was walking on the quay when the packet came alongside. He saw a man pale, exhausted, and in rags carry a little bundle. "Who are you?" said Beauvais. "A refugee." "What is your name?" "Hubert." "Where are you going?" "I

do not know." "You have no inn?" "I have no money." "Come home with me."

Beauvais took Hubert to his house, which is No. 20 Don Street.

Hubert was a man of about fifty, with white hair and black moustache. His face was marked with small-pox. His appearance was robust, his eyes intelligent. He said he had been a schoolmaster and a surveyor. He came from the department of the Eure; he had been exiled on the 2d of December.

He reached Brussels, where he came to see me; driven from Brussels, he went to London, and in London he lived in the last stage of misery. He had lived five months, five winter months, in what they call a *Sociale,* a sort of dilapidated hall, the doors and windows of which permit draughts, and the roof admits the rain. He had slept the two first months side by side with Bourillon, another refugee, on the stone floor in front of the fireplace.

These men lay on the flags without mattress or covering, without even a handful of straw, their wet, ragged clothes on their bodies. There was no fire. It was not till the end of the two months that Louis Blanc and Ledru-Rollin had given them some money to buy coal. When these men had some potatoes they boiled them and dined; when they had none they ate nothing at all.

Hubert, without money or bed, almost without shoes or clothing, lived there, slept on the stone, shivered continually, ate seldom, and never complained. He took his large share of the general suffering stoically, impassible, and in silence. He was a member of the Delegation Society; then he had quitted it, saying, "Félix Pyat is no socialist." Afterwards he joined the Revolutionary Society; but he left it, declaring that Ledru-Rollin was not a Republican.

On the 14th of September, 1852, the Prefect of the Eure wrote to him to agree to send in his submission. Hubert answered the prefect in a letter very outspoken, and full, as regards his "Emperor," of the coarsest terms, such as *clique, canaille, misérable.* He showed this letter, dated the 24th of September, to all the refugees he met, and posted it up in the room where the members of the Revolutionary Society used to meet.

On the 5th of February he saw his name in the "Moniteur" among the pardoned. Hubert was filled with indignation, and instead of returning to France he went to Jersey, declaring that there were better Republicans there than in London. So it came to pass that he disembarked at St. Heliers.

When he reached Beauvais's house, Beauvais showed him a room.

"I told you I had no money," said Hubert. "It is all the same," said Beauvais. "Give me a corner and a truss of straw in the granary." "I will give you my room and my bed in preference," said Beauvais.

At meal-time Hubert did not wish to take his place at table. Many refugees were living in Beauvais's house, where they breakfasted and dined for thirty-five francs a month.

"I have not thirty-five sous," said Hubert. "Give me a morsel at once. I will eat it at a corner of the kitchen-table."

Beauvais was annoyed. "By no means," he said; "you will dine with us, citizen." "And pay you—" "When you can." "Never, perhaps." "Well, then, never."

Beauvais procured for Hubert some pupils in the town, to whom he taught grammar and arithmetic, and with the produce of these lessons he compelled him to buy a coat and some shoes. "I have shoes," said Hubert. "Yes, you have shoes, but they have not any soles."

The refugees were moved at seeing Hubert's condition, and they assigned to him the ordinary assistance allotted to the necessitous who had no wife or child, namely, seven francs a week. With that and his lessons he existed. He had no more. Many people, Gaffney among others, offered him money, but he never would accept it. "No," he would say; "there are people more unfortunate than I."

He made himself very useful in Beauvais's house, occupying the least possible room, rising from the table before dinner was over, drinking no wine or brandy and refusing to have his glass filled. For the rest, he was an ardent communist, did not recognize any chief, declared the Republic was betrayed by Louis Blanc, Félix Pyat, and Ledru-Rollin; by me, proclaiming at the fall of Napoleon, whom he always called Badinguet, a six months' massacre to finish up with; compelling, by force of suffering and sternness, even from those who avoided him, a kind of respect, having about him some indescribable token of rough honesty. A moderate said of him to an enthusiast, "He is worse than Robespierre." The other replied, "He is better than Marat."

Now the mask was about to fall. The man was a spy.

The fact was discovered in this wise. Hubert, among the refugees, had an intimate friend named Hayes. One day, in the beginning of September, he took Hayes aside, and said to him, in a low and mysterious tone, "I am going away to-morrow." "You going away?" "Yes." "Where are you going to?" "To France." "What, to France?" "To Paris." "To Paris?" "They expect me there." "What for?" "For a blow." "How will you enter France?" "I have a passport." "From whom?" "From the consul." "In your own name?" "In my own name." "That is very odd." "You forgot that I was pardoned in February." "That's true; and the money?" "I have some." "How much?" "Twenty francs." "Are you going all the way to Paris with twenty francs?" "As soon as I reach Saint-Malo I will go as I can,—on foot, if necessary. If necessary I will not eat anything. I will go straight on by the shortest way."

Instead of taking the shortest, he took the longest way. From Saint-Malo he went to Rennes, from Rennes to Nantes, from Nantes to Angers, from Angers to Paris by the railway. He took six days on the journey. As he proceeded he saw in every town the democratic leaders,—Boué at Saint-Malo, Roche, Dr. Guépin and the Mangins at Nantes; Rioteau at Angers. He announced himself everywhere as being on a mission from the refugees of Jersey, and he easily gained assistance everywhere. He neither hid nor displayed his poverty; people could see it. At Angers he borrowed fifty francs from Rioteau, not having enough to go to Paris.

From Angers he wrote to a woman with whom he had lived in Jersey, one Mélanie Simon, a seamstress, lodging at No. 5 Hill Street, and who had actually lent him thirty-two francs for his journey. He had concealed this money from Hayes. He told this woman that she might write to him to No. 38, Rue de l'Ecole de Médecine; that he did not lodge there, but he had a friend who would forward his letters.

Arrived in Paris he went to see Goudchaux; he found, one knows not how, the dwelling of Boisson, the agent of the Ledru-Rollin faction. The said Boisson lived concealed in Paris. He presented himself to Boisson as an envoy from us, the refugees of Jersey, and entered into all the combinations of the party called the Party of Action.

Towards the end of September he disembarked in Jersey from the steamer "Rose." The day after his arrival he took Hayes aside and declared that a blow was about to be struck, and that if he, Hubert, had arrived some days sooner in Paris, the blow would have been struck then; that his advice, which had almost been accepted, had been to blow up a railway bridge while Badinguet's train was passing; that men and money were both ready, but that the people had no confidence except in the refugees, and that he was going to return to Paris for this purpose. As he had taken part in every blow dealt since 1830, he was not the man to back out of this; but he himself was not sufficient,—he required ten refugees, of good will, to put themselves at the head of the people when the time for action arrived, and he had come to seek them in Jersey. He ended by asking Hayes if he would be one of the ten. *"Parbleu!"* replied Hayes.

Hubert saw the refugees, and made them the same confidences with the same mystery, saying, "I have told no one but you." He enrolled, among others besides Hayes, Jego, who was recovering from typhoid fever, and Gigoux, to whom he declared that his name, Gigoux, would raise the masses.

Those he enlisted thus, with a view of taking them to Paris, said, "But the money?" "Rest easy," replied Hubert, "they have it. They will await you on the landing-stage. Come to Paris, the rest will settle itself. They will undertake to find a place for you."

Besides Hayes, Gigoux, and Jego, he interviewed Jarassé, Famot, Rondeaux, and others.

Since this dissolution of the General Society two societies of refugees were formed in Jersey,—the "Fraternelle" and the "Fraternité."

Hubert belonged to the "Fraternité," of which Gigoux was treasurer. He drew from it, as I have said, seven francs a week. He claimed from Gigoux that he should be paid the fourteen francs for the two weeks he was away, as he had been absent in the service of the Republic.

The day Hubert and those I have mentioned were to leave was fixed for Friday, the 21st of October.

However, a refugee named Rattier, a lawyer of Lorient, being one morning in the shop of Hurel, the tobacconist, saw entering a shop a man to whom he had never spoken, but whom he knew by sight. This man, perceiving him to be a Frenchman, said to him, "Citizen, have you change for a hundred-franc note?" "No," replied Rattier. The man unfolded a yellow paper, which he was holding in his hand, and presented it to the tobacconist, requesting change. The shopkeeper had not sufficient. During the colloquy Rattier recognized the paper as a Bank of France note for one hundred francs. The man went away, and Rattier said to Hurel, "Do you know that man's name?" "Yes," replied Hurel, "he is a French refugee named Hubert."

Almost at the same time Hubert, when paying for his lodging, took from his pocket a handful of shillings and half crowns.

Mélanie Simon claimed the thirty-two francs; he refused to pay her, and at the same time, by a strange sort of contradiction, he permitted her to see a pocketbook full, as Mélanie said afterwards, of yellow and blue papers. "These are bank-notes," said Hubert to her. "I have here three thousand five hundred francs."

Now the contradiction was explained. Hubert, about to return to France, wished to take Mélanie Simon with him; he refused to pay her, in order that she might go with him; and that she might go without anxiety, he showed her that he was rich.

Mélanie Simon did not wish to leave Jersey, and again demanded her thirty-two francs. Disputes arose; Hubert still refused. "Listen to me," said Mélanie:

"if you do not pay me, I have seen your money, I suspect you are a spy, and I will denounce you to the refugees."

Hubert laughed.

"Make them believe that of me," said he. *"Allons donc."*

He hoped to disabuse Mélanie Simon of this idea by putting a good face on the matter.

"My thirty-two francs," said Mélanie.

"Not a sou," replied Hubert.

Mélanie Simon went to find Jarassé, and denounced Hubert.

It seemed at first sight that Hubert was right. Among the refugees the idea was divided.

"Hubert a spy?" they said. "Nonsense!"

Beauvais recalled his sobriety and Gaffney his disinterestedness, Bisson his republicanism, Seigneuret his communism, Bourillon his five months they slept on the stones, Gigoux the assistance they had given him, Roumilhac his stoicism, and all of them his misery.

"I have seen him without shoes," said one.

"And I without a home," said another.

"And I without bread," added a third.

"He was my best friend," remarked Hayes.

Then Rattier related the incident of the one-hundred-franc note; the details of Hubert's journey leaked out by degrees. They asked themselves why this curious journey had been undertaken? They learned that he had passed from place to place with wonderful facility. A resident of Jersey declared that he had seen him walking on the quay of Saint-Malo among the custom-house officers and the gendarmes without their noticing him. Suspicion was awakened: Mélanie Simon proclaimed it on the house-tops; the wine-growing poet, Claude Durand, who was respected by all the proscribed, shook his head when speaking of Hubert.

Mélanie Simon told Jarassé of Hubert's letter, giving his address in Paris at No. 38, Rue de l'Ecole de Médecine, where a friend received his letters. Now, the son of Mathé, the representative, when he went to Paris some months before, had by a curious coincidence lodged in that very same house.

Jarassé having shown to Mathé Hubert's letter to Mélanie, the address and the friend attracted the attention of Mathé's son, who was present, and who declared that it was the house in which he had lodged. Among the lodgers there had been an agent of police named Philippi.

A portentous rumour began to circulate among the refugees.

Hayes and Gigoux, Hubert's friends, whom he had enrolled for Paris, said to him,—

"People are certainly talking." "About what?" said Hubert. "About Mélanie Simon and you." "Well, they say she is my mistress, I suppose." "No, they say that you are a spy." "Well, what of that?" "It will provoke an inquiry," said Hayes. "And a judgment," said Gigoux.

Hubert made no answer. His friends frowned.

Next day they pressed him again. He was silent. They returned to the charge. He almost refused to speak. The more he hesitated, the more they insisted. They finished up by declaring that he must clear the matter up.

Hubert, having no means of avoiding the inquiry, and perceiving that suspicion grew stronger, consented.

The refugees held their club meeting at Beauvais's house, in No. 20, Don Street.

Those idle and those out of work met there in a common room. Hubert posted in this room a declaration addressed to his brothers in exile, in which, in reference to the infamous calumnies spread concerning him, he placed himself at the disposal of all present seeking an inquiry, and demanding that he should be judged by all the refugees.

He wished the inquiry to take place immediately, reminding them that he wished to leave Jersey on Friday, the 21st of October, and concluded by saying, "The justice of the people ought to be prompt."

The last words of this proclamation were, "The Day is approaching. Signed, Hubert."

The society "Fraternité" to which Hubert belonged assembled, called an inquiry, and nominated five of its members to institute this dramatic process of proscription, namely, Mathé, Rattier, Rondeaux, Henry, and Hayes. Mathé, since his son's surprised exclamation, was convinced of the culpability of Hubert.

This commission, a regular judicial one, called witnesses, heard Gigoux and Jego, who had been enrolled by Hubert for Paris, Jarassé, Famot, to whom Hubert had spoken of the six months' massacre to finish up; collected the reports of Rattier and Hayes; called Mélanie Simon, confronted her with Hubert; read in evidence the letter written

by Hubert from Angers, which though torn, was pieced together; drew up an official report of everything. When confronted with Hubert, Mélanie Simon confirmed all her statements, and told him plainly that he was a Bonapartist spy.

Suspicions abounded, but the proofs were wanting.

Mathé said to Hubert, "You are going away on Friday?" "Yes." "You have a trunk?" "Yes." "What do you carry in that trunk?" "My old clothes and the copies of the Socialist and Republican publications." "Will you permit your trunk to be searched?" "Yes."

Rondeaux accompanied Hubert to Beauvais's house, where he lodged, and where his trunk was. It was opened. Rondeaux found in it some shirts and handkerchiefs, an old pair of trousers, and an old coat. Nothing more.

The absence of positive proof weakened the suspicions, and the opinion of the refugees went rather in Hubert's favour.

Hayes, Gigoux, and Beauvais defended him warmly.

Rondeaux told what he had found in the trunk.

"And the Socialist publications?" asked Mathé.

"I did not see any of them," replied Rondeaux.

Hubert said nothing.

However, the report of the searching of the trunk got about, and a carpenter of Queen Street said to Jarassé, I think it was. "But have you opened the double bottom?" "What double bottom?" "The double bottom of the trunk." "Do you mean to say that the trunk has a false bottom?" "Certainly."

"How do you know?" "Because I made it."

This was repeated to the commissioners. Mathé said to Hubert, "Your trunk has a false bottom?" "No doubt." "Why this double bottom?" "*Parbleu!* To hide the democratic writings which I carry about." "Why did you not tell Rondeaux of it?" "I did not think about it." "Will you permit us to see it?" "Yes."

Hubert gave his consent in the calmest manner in the world, giving answers in monosyllables and scarcely removing his pipe from his mouth. From his laconic answers his friends argued his innocence.

The commissioners decided that they would all be present at this inspection of the trunk. They set out. It was Thursday,—the day before that fixed by Hubert for his departure. "Where are we going?" asked Hubert.

"To Beauvais's house," said Rondeaux, "since your trunk is there." Hubert replied:—

"We are a numerous body; it will be necessary to break open the false bottom with a hammer; that will cause some commotion at Beauvais's house, where there are always a number of refugees. Let two of you come with me and carry the trunk to the carpenter's house, while the others await us there. As the carpenter made the false bottom, he will be able to remove it better than anybody else. All will then pass in the presence of the commission without scandal."

They consented to this. Hubert, assisted by Hayes and Henry, carried the trunk to the carpenter's shop; the false bottom was opened, a quantity of papers was found; they were Republican writings,—my speeches, the "Bagnes d'Afrique" of Ribeyrolles, the "Couronne Impériale" of Cahaigne.

They found there three or four passports of Hubert's, the last issued in France *on his order*. They found a complete set of documents relative to the interior organization of the revolutionary society organized in London by Ledru-Rollin, all that packed in with a mass of letters and old documents.

Among the latter they found two letters which seemed singular.

The former, dated the 24th of September, was addressed to the Prefect of the Eure, rejecting the amnesty offered with a prodigality of epithets. This was the letter which Hubert had shown to the refugees in London, and fixed up in their meeting-room.

The second letter, dated the 30th, only six days later, was addressed to the same person, and contained, under the guise of asking for money, clear offers of service to the Bonapartist Government.

These two letters contradicted each other; it was evident that only one of them was intended to be sent, and it appeared probable that this was not the former. According to all appearance, the second was the true letter; the first was merely a blind.

They showed them to Hubert, who continued to smoke his pipe calmly.

They put the letters on one side, and continued their examination of the papers.

A letter in Hubert's writing, commencing "My dear mother," fell into the hands of Rattier. He read the opening sentences, but as it seemed a family letter he was about to throw it down, when he perceived that the sheet was double. He opened it almost mechanically, and he felt as if lightning had flashed in his eyes. His gaze fell on the head of the second sheet on these words, in Hubert's handwriting, "To M. de Maupas, Minister of Police. Monsieur le Ministre."

Then followed the letter which they were about to read,—a letter signed "Hubert,"

To M. de Maupas,
Minister of Police at Paris.

M. LE MINISTRE,—I have received, under date of 14th of September last, with a view of making me return to France, a letter from M. le Préfet de l'Eure.

On the 24th and 30th of the same month I wrote two letters to M. le Préfet, neither of which has been answered.

Since then my name has been figured in the "Moniteur" in the list, according to the decree of the 5th of this month (February), but I was not ready to go at that time, as I wished to finish in London a pamphlet entitled "The Republican Refugees, and the Republic impossible by these same pretended Republicans." This pamphlet, full of truths and facts which no one could deny, will produce, I think, some effect in France, where I wish to have it printed. I had my passport *visé* for France yesterday; nothing of importance will keep me in England except that before leaving, if they will give me what is due to me, what I claim by my letter of the 30th of September.

M. le Préfet de l'Eure who was begged to communicate this letter to the proper person, should have laid it before the Government. I am waiting the solution of the matter, but seeing that so long a time has elapsed and I have received nothing, I have decided to address this letter to you, in the hope of obtaining an immediate settlement.

My address in London, England, is 17 Church Street, Soho Square.

And my name, Hubert Julien Damascène, geometrical surveyor of Henqueville, near Andelys (Eure).

(Signed)   HUBERT.
25th of February, 1853.

Rattier raised his eyes and looked at Hubert.

He had dropped his pipe. The perspiration stood on his forehead in great beads.

"You are a spy!" said Rattier.

Hubert, pale as death, fell into a chair without replying.

The members of the commission tied up the papers and went immediately to report the result to the Fraternity Society, which was then assembled.

It was on their way thither that I met them.

When these facts came to light, a sort of electric shock thrilled the refugees in the town. They ran about the streets, they ran against each other; the most excited was the most stupefied. That Hubert, whom they had trusted!

One fact added to the excitement. Thursday is the post-day when the papers from France arrive in Jersey. The news which they brought threw a lurid light upon Hubert. Three hundred arrests had been made in Paris. Hubert had seen Rocher of Nantes at Saint-Malo! Rocher had been arrested. He had seen Guépin and the Mangins at Nantes; the Mangins and Guépin had been arrested. He had seen Rioteau at Angers, and had borrowed money from him; Rioteau was arrested. He had seen Goudchaux and Boisson at Paris; Goudchaux and Boisson were arrested.

Facts and memories came in shoals. Gaffney, one of those who to the last moment had supported Hubert, related that, in 1852, he had forwarded contraband from London to Havre a parcel containing eighty copies of "Napoleon the Little." Hubert and an attorney of Rouen, a refugee named Bachelet, were in his room when he closed the parcel. He had made in their presence a calculation, from which it resulted that the parcel was to be sent to his mother's house to him, Gaffney, on the day when a friend previously notified would come and take it away. Hubert and Bachelet went out. After their departure Gaffney rectified his calculation, and found out that the parcel would arrive at his mother's house at Havre a day too soon. He wrote accordingly to his mother and his friend. The parcel arrived, and was taken away by his friend. On the day following, which had been fixed by Gaffney in the presence of Hubert and Bachelet, the police searched Madame Gaffney's house, with a view of finding the books which they said had been sent to her from London.

About ten o'clock in the evening twelve or fifteen refugees were assembled at Bauvais's house. Pierre Leroux, and a Jersey gentleman, M. Philippe Asplet, a constabulary officer, were seated in a corner. Pierre Leroux conversed with M. Asplet about table-turning.

Suddenly Henry entered and told them about the false bottom in the trunk, the letter to Maupas, the arrests in France; Hayes, Gigoux, and Rondeaux confirmed his statements.

At that moment the door opened and Hubert appeared. He came back to sleep, and as usual took his key from a peg in the common room.

"There he is;" cried Hayes.

They all rushed upon Hubert.

Gigoux struck him, Hayes seized him by the hair, Heurtebise held him by the throat, Beauvais drew his knife, Asplet arrested Beauvais's arm.

Beauvais told me an hour later that, if it had not been for M. Asplet, Hubert would have been a dead man.

M. Asplet, in his official capacity, intervened, and took Hubert from them. Beauvais threw away his knife; they left the spy alone. Two or three went into the corners, dropped their faces into their hands and wept.

Meanwhile I had gone home.

It was close on midnight, as I was going to bed, that I heard a carriage stop at the door. The bell rang, and the moment afterwards Charles came into my room and told me that Beauvais had come.

I went downstairs. All the refugees had united to pronounce sentence on Hubert. They kept him in custody, and they had sent Beauvais to seek for me. I hesitated. To judge this man in this nightly sitting, this *Vehmgericht* of the refugees, all that appeared strange and repugnant to my habits. Beauvais insisted.

"Come," said he to me; "if you do not, I cannot answer for Hubert." Then he continued, "I cannot answer for myself. If it had not been for Asplet, I should have stabbed him."

I followed Beauvais, taking with me my two sons. As we proceeded we were joined by Cahigne, Ribeyrolles, Frond, Lefèvre the cripple, Cauvat, and many other refugees who lived at Havre-des-pas.

Midnight was striking when we reached our destination.

The room in which they were going to try Hubert is called the Refugee's Club, and is one of those large, square rooms which one finds in almost all English houses. These rooms, not much appreciated by French people, overlook the two façades of the mansion, back and front.

This one, situated on the first floor of Beauvais's house, No. 20, Don Street, has two windows looking into an inner court, and three upon the street opposite the large red front of the building destined for the public halls, which is here called Hôtel de Ville. Some of the inhabitants of the town, aroused by the rumours in circulation, were chattering in low tones beneath the windows. Refugees were arriving from all directions.

When I entered, they had nearly all assembled. They were distributed in the two compartments of the room, and spoke to each other in grave tones. Hubert had come to see me in Brus-

sels and in Jersey, but I had no recollection of him. When I entered I asked Heurtebise where Hubert was.

"Behind you," said Heurtebise.

I turned round and saw, seated at a table with his back to the wall, near the street, beneath the centre window, a pipe in front of him, his hat on his head, a man about fifty years old, ruddy, marked with smallpox, with very white hair and black moustaches. His eyes were steady and calm. From time to time he raised his hat and wiped his forehead with a large blue handkerchief.

His brown paletot was buttoned to the chin. Now that one knew what he was, one discovered the mien of a serjeant-de-ville.

People passed and repassed before him and round him speaking of him.

"There is the coward," said one.

"Look at the bandit," said another. He heard these remarks exchanged, and seemed as indifferent to them as if they had been spoken of some one else.

Although the room was crowded by the new arrivals, there was a space left near him. He was alone at the table and on that bench. Four or five refugees stood upright by the window guarding him. One of them was Boni, who teaches us to ride on horseback.

The proscription was nearly complete, although the convocation had been arranged hastily in the middle of the night when the greater number of the refugees were in bed and asleep.

Nevertheless, one remarked some absentees. Pierre Leroux, having assisted at the first collision of Hubert and the refugees, had gone away and had not returned; and of all the numerous family which they call here the Leroux tribe, Charles was the only member present. There was also absent the greater number of those whom we call *les exaltés*, and among them the author of the manifesto entitled "Du Comité Révolutionaire," Seigneuret.

They sent for the commission which had started the proscription. It arrived. Mathé, who had just got out of bed, seemed still half-asleep.

Among the refugees present an old man, grown aged in conspiracy, was conversant with these sorts of summary processes among refugees in the catacombs,—a kind of free-justice meetings, where mystery does not exclude solemnity, and where he more than once had pronounced terrible sentences, which all sanctioned and some carried out. This old man was Cahaigne. Old in face, young in heart, flat nose buried in a grey beard, and white hair, a republican with the face of a Cossack, a democrat with the manners of a gentleman, a poet, a man of the world, a man of action, a fighter at barricades, a veteran in conspiracy. Cahaigne is a personage.

They called on him to preside. For secretaries they gave him Jarassé, who is of the "Fraternité" Society, and Heurtebise, of the "Fraternelle" Society.

These societies do not live fraternally together.

The sitting was open. A deep silence prevailed.

The room at this moment presented a strange aspect. In the two compartments, each lighted, and very feebly, by two gas-jets, were arranged and

grouped, seated, standing up, stooping, leaning on their elbows, on benches, chairs, stools, tables, on the window-sills, some with arms folded leaning against the wall, all pale, grave, severe, almost sinister, were the seventy refugees in Jersey. They filled the two compartments of the room, leaving only in the compartment with three windows looking into the street a small space occupied by three tables,—the table by the wall where Hubert sat alone, a table close by, at which were Cahaigne, Jarassé, and Heurtebise, and opposite a very small one, on which Rattier, the reporter, had placed his note-book. Behind this table a bright fire was burning in the grate, and was from time to time attended to by a lad. On the mantelpiece above a pipe-rack, amid a crowd of bills emanating from the refugees, between the announcement of Charles Leroux, recommending his sewing establishment, and the placard of Ribot, inaugurating the hat manufactory of the *Chapeau rouge*, was exhibited, stuck up with some wafers, the placard calling for an inquiry and "prompt justice," signed, Hubert.

Here and there upon the table were glasses of brandy and pots of beer. All round the room hung on hooks were glazed caps, straw and felt hats, and an old draught-board the white squares of which were scarcely whiter than the black ones, was hanging on the wall above Hubert's head.

I was seated with Ribeyrolles and my sons in an angle near the chimney.

Some of the refugees were smoking, —some pipes, others cigars,—so there was little light and much smoke in the room. The upper part of the windows, *en guillotines* English fashion, were open to let out the smoke.

The proceedings commenced by the interrogation of Hubert. At the first words Hubert doffed his cap. Cahaigne questioned him with a somewhat theatrical gravity; but which, whatever the tone, was felt lugubrious and serious.

Hubert gave his two Christian names, Julien Damascène.

Hubert had had time to regain his presence of mind. He answered precisely and without delay. At a certain time, when they were speaking to him concerning his return by the department of the Eure, he rectified some little mistake of Cahaigne's: "Pardon me, Louviers is on the right bank and Andelys on the left." Beyond that he confessed nothing.

The interrogation finished, they passed to the reading of the official report of the commission, the witnesses, and the proofs.

This reading commenced amid profound silence, which was succeeded by a murmur which increased in volume in proportion as the black and odious facts were dragged to light. Stifled murmurs were audible. "Ah, the rascal, the scoundrel, why do not we strangle this blackguard on the spot?"

In the midst of this volley of imprecations the reader was forced to raise his voice. Rattier was reading. Mathé passed him up the sheets of paper. Beauvais was holding a candle to him; the tallow kept dropping on the table.

After the depositions of the witnesses had been read, Rattier announced that he had arrived at a decisive piece of evidence. Silence was renewed,—a feverish, restless silence. Charles whispered to me, "One may learn how to treat a spy."

Rattier read the letter from Hubert to Maupas.

So long as the letter was being read the audience contained itself, hands were clinched, some men bit their handkerchiefs.

When the last word had been read, "The signature?" cried old Fombertaux.

Rattier said, "It is signed, Hubert."

Then the uproar broke out. The silence had only been caused by the expectation mingled with a sort of hesitation to believe such a thing possible. Some had even doubted up till then and said, "It is impossible." When this letter appeared, written by Hubert, dated by Hubert, signed by Hubert, evidently real, indubitable before every one, within every one's reach, the name of Maupas written by Hubert, conviction fell into the middle of the assembly like a thunder-bolt.

Furious faces were turned towards Hubert. Many individuals leaped upon the benches; threatening hands were raised against him. There was a frenzy of rage and grief; a terrible light filled all eyes.

Nothing was heard but cries of "Scoundrel!" "Ah, the miserable Hubert!" "Ah, you brigand of the Rue de Jerusalem!"

Fombertaux, whose son is at Belle Isle, exclaimed, "Those are the scoundrels to whom we give twenty years."

"Yes," added another, "it is, thanks to such creatures as he, that the young are in prison and the old in exile."

A refugee, whose name I forget, a fine, fair-haired young man, leaped upon the table, pointed to Hubert, and cried, "Citizens, death!"

"Death! death!" shouted a chorus of voices. Hubert looked about him with a bewildered air.

The same young man continued:—

"We will keep hold of him, so that he shall not escape us."

One cried, "Throw him into the Seine."

At this there was an explosion of sardonic laughter.

"Do you think you are still on the Pont Neuf?"

Then they continued, "'Throw the spy into the sea, with a stone round his neck.

"Let us send him where all is blue," said Fombertaux.

During the turmoil, Mathé had handed me Hubert's letter, and I was examining it with Ribeyrolles. It was actually written on the second page of a family letter in a rather long, neat, legible hand, with some erasures, but altogether in Hubert's hand. At the bottom of this rough draft, after the manner of an illiterate man, he had signed his name in full.

Cahaigne proclaimed silence, but the tumult was indescribable. Every one spoke at the same time, and it seemed as if a single mind was hurling from sixty mouths the same malediction upon the miserable man.

"Citizens," cried Cahaigne, "you are judges!"

This was sufficient. All was silent, raised hands were lowered, and each man, folding his arms or resting his elbow on his knee, resumed his place with lugubrious dignity.

"Hubert," said Cahaigne, "do you recognize this letter?"

Jarassé presented the letter to Hubert, who replied, "Yes."

Cahaigne continued, "What explanation have you to give?"

Hubert was silent.

"So," pursued Cahaigne, "you confess yourself a spy?"

Hubert raised his head, looked at Cahaigne, struck his fist upon the table, and said, "That—no!"

A murmur pervaded the audience like an angry shiver. The explosion, which had only been suspended, very nearly recommenced, but as they saw that Hubert was about to continue, they kept silence.

Hubert declared, in a thick, broken voice, but which had, nevertheless, a certain firmness and, sad to say, sincerity in it, that he had never done any one any harm; that he was a Republican; that he would die ten thousand deaths before he brought to the ground by his own fault a hair from the head of a Republican. That, if arrests had been made in Paris, he was innocent of them; that they had not paid sufficient attention to the first letter to the Prefect of the Eure. That, as regards the letter to Maupas, it was a draft, a project; that he had written it, but had never sent it. That they would recognize the truth too late, and would regret their action. That, as for the pamphlet, "The Republic impossible because of Republicans," he had written that too, but had not published it.

They all cried out. "Where it is?"

He calmly replied, "I have burned it."

"Is that all you have to say?" inquired Cahaigne.

Hubert shook his head and continued:—

"He owed nothing to Mélanie Simon; those who had seen money in his possession were mistaken. The citizen Rattier was deceived; he (Hubert) had never been in the shop of the tobacconist Hurel. His passports were a very simple matter; being amnestied, he had a right to them. He had paid back the fifty francs to Rioteau of Angers; he was an honest man; he had never had a bank-note. The money he had expended he had received from the woman, about one hundred and sixty francs in all. He had met Citizen Boisson in Paris at a cheap restaurant. It was there he gave his address. If he had intended to bring the refugees to Paris, it was with a view to overturn Badinguet, not to betray his friends. If the gendarmes had allowed him to move freely about in France, it was not his fault. Definitely, there was an understanding among them to get rid of him, and all were victims of it."

He repeated two or three times, without their being able to understand to what this phrase referred, "The carpenter who made the false bottom is here to say so."

"Is that all?" said Cahaigne again.

"Yes," said he.

This word was received with a shudder. They had heard the explanations, but they had explained nothing.

"Take care!" continued Cahaigne. "You yourself have said we can judge you; we do judge you; we can condemn you."

"And execute you," cried a voice.

"Hubert," continued Cahaigne, "you risk all the dangers of punishment. Who knows what will happen to you? Take care! Disarm your judges by candid confession. Our friends are in the hands of Bonaparte, but you are in ours. Tell the facts clearly to us. Aid us to save our friends, or you are lost. Speak."

"It is you," said Hubert, raising his head,—"it is you who lose 'our friends' in Paris by speaking their names as loudly as you do in an assembly" (and he looked around him) "in which there are evidently spies. I have nothing more to say."

Then the uproar was renewed, and with such fury that it was feared some would pass from words to acts.

The cries "to death!" arose anew from a number of angry mouths.

There was in the Assembly a shoemaker of Niort, an old non-commissioned officer of artillery, called Guay, a fanatical Communist, but an excellent and honest workman, nevertheless,—a man with a long black beard, a pale face, rather sunken eyes and slow speech, of grave and resolute demeanour. He rose and said:—

"Citizens, it seems that you wish to condemn Hubert to death. That surprises me. You forgot that we are in a country which has laws that we must not violate, not attempt anything contrary to them. Nevertheless Hubert must be punished, both for the past and for the future, and impress on him an ineffaceable stigma. So, as we must do nothing unlawful, this is what I propose. We will seize Hubert and shave his hair and beard, and as hair will grow again we will cut a small piece out of his right ear. Ears do not grow again."

This proposition, enunciated in the gravest tone and in the most convinced way, was received in that lugubrious assembly with a shout of laughter which continued for some time, and which added another horror to the dread realities of the scene.

Near Guay, at the entrance to the other compartments of the room, beside Dr. Barbier, was seated a refugee named Avias. Avias, a non-commissioned officer in the army of Oudinot, had deserted before Rome, not wishing, as a Republican, to overturn a Republic. He had been caught, tried by court-martial, and condemned to death. He had succeeded in making his escape the day before the execution was to have taken place. He took refuge in Piedmont. On December 2, he crossed the frontier, and joined the Republicans of the Var in arms against the *coup d'état*. In an engagement a bullet broke his ankle. His friends carried him out of action with great difficulty, and his foot was amputated. Expelled from Piedmont he went to England, and thence to Jersey. When he arrived he came to see me. Some friends and myself assisted him, and he had finished by setting up as a dyer and scourer, and so lived.

Avias seemed to have been well acquainted with Hubert. While the extracts were being read he continued to cry, "Ah, *coquin!* ah, j—— f——!" Say that he told me Louis Blanc is a traitor! Victor Hugo is a traitor. Ledru-Rollin is a traitor!"

When Guay sat down, Avias rose and stood on his bench, then on the table.

Avias is a man thirty years old, tall, with a wide red face, projecting brows, goggle-eyes, a large mouth, and a Provençal accent. With his furious eyes, his hands discoloured by dye, his foot beating time on the table, nothing more savage than this giant with the harsh voice, and whose head nearly touched the ceiling, can be conceived.

He exclaimed, "Citizens! none of this; let us finish. Let us draw lots who is to give this traitor his *coup-de-grâce*. If no one will, then I will volunteer."

A shout of assent arose: "All! all!"

A small young man with a fair beard, who was seated in front of me said, "I will undertake it. The business of the spy will be settled to-morrow morning."

"Not so," said another, in the opposite corner. "There are four here who will charge themselves with this."

"Yes," added Fombertaux, extending his fist close to Hubert's head. "Justice upon that rascal—death!"

Not a dissenting voice was raised. Hubert, himself terrified, bent his head and seemed to say, "It is just."

I rose.

"Citizens," I said, "in a man whom you have fed, supported, and made friends with, you have found a traitor. In a man you have accepted as a brother you find a spy. This man is still wearing a coat you bought for him, and the shoes with which you provided him. You are shivering with indignation and regret. This indignation I partake, this sorrow I can understand. But take care! What mean these shouts for death? There are two beings in Hubert,—a spy and a man. The spy is infamous, the man is sacred."

Here a voice interrupted me,—the voice of a fine fellow named Cauvet, who is rich and sometimes tipsy, and who abused anything pertaining to Ledru-Rollin, to show himself a fanatic for the guillotine. A deep silence supervened. Cauvet said, in a low voice, "Ah, yes! that's it, always for soft measures."

"Yes," said I, "for moderation. Energy on one side, mildness on the other. Those are the arms which I wish to place in the hands of the Republic."

I resumed:—

"Citizens, do you know what belongs to you in Hubert? The spy, yes! the man, no! The spy is yours; the home of the traitor, the name of the traitor, his moral being, you have the right to do as you please with that; you have the right to crush it, to tear out that, to tread that under foot,—yes, you have the right to tear the name of Hubert to pieces, and to scrape up the hideous fragments in the mud.

"But do you know what you have no right to touch?—not a hair of his head."

I felt the hand of Ribeyrolles pressing mine.

"What MM. Hubert and Maupas have tried to do here is monstrous. To support a spy out of your poor-funds; to keep in the same pocket the police bank-note and the brotherly coins of the refugees; to throw our money in our eyes to blind us; to arrest the men who help us in France by the man we feed in Jersey; to pursue the proscribed in ambush; to not even leave the exile in peace; to attach the thread of an infamous plot to the holiest fibres of our heart; to betray us and rob us at the same time; to pick our pockets and sell us,—that is the snare in which we find the hands of the Imperial police.

"What have we to do? Publish the facts! Take France, Europe, the public conscience, universal probity to witness. Say to the whole world, It is infamous! Sad as the discovery may be, the occasion is fortunate. In this business the moral advantage lies with the proscribed, with the democracy, with the Republic. The situation is excellent. Do not let us spoil it!

"Do you know how we may spoil it? By misconceiving our rights, and behaving like the Venetians of the sixteenth century; instead of like Frenchmen of the nineteenth, in acting like the Council of Ten, in killing a man.

"In principle I am no more anxious about the death of a spy than of a parricide, I assure you. In fact, it is absurd!

"Touch this man, wound him, only beat him, and to-morrow the opinion that is with you will be against you. The English law will arrest you. From judges you will become the accused. M. Hubert gone, M. de Maupas gone, and what remains? You proscribed Frenchmen before a British jury.

"And instead of saying, 'Look at the baseness of that police,' they will say, 'Look at the brutality of those demagogues.'

"Citizens," I added, extending my arms towards Hubert. "I take this man under my protection, not for the man's sake, but for the Republic. I oppose any one who will do him harm now or in the future, here or elsewhere. I sum up your rights in a word: Publish, do not kill! Punishment by publicity, not by violence. A deed in open day, not by night. The skin of Hubert! Great God, what is *it* worth? What can you do with the skin of a spy? I declare no one shall touch Hubert, no one shall ill-treat him. To poniard M. Hubert would be to disgrace the poniard. To whip M. Hubert would only sully the whip."

These words, which I reproduce from memory, were listened to with profound attention and increasing adhesion at each moment. When I reseated myself the question was decided. To tell the truth, I did not think Hubert was in any danger during the sitting; but the morrow might have been fatal.

When I seated myself I distinctly heard a refugee behind me, named Fillion, who had escaped from Africa, say, "That is it. The spy is saved. We should act and not talk. That will teach us to chatter!"

These words were drowned in a general cry of "No violence! Publish the facts, appeal to public opinion, hold the police and Hubert up to execration; that is what we'll do."

Claude, Durand, Bulier, Rattier, Ribeyrolles, Cahaigne congratulated me warmly. Hubert looked at me with a mournful gaze. The sitting had been as it were suspended after my speech. The proscribed of the terrorist school looked at me angrily.

Fillion came up to me and said, "You are right. From the moment they had spoken nothing was more likely. Is it necessary that when you execute a traitor you should proclaim the fact on the house-tops? We are sixty here, fifty-six too many. Four would suffice. In Africa we had a similar case. We discovered that a man named Auguste Thomas was a detective—an old Republican too—and in every plot for the past twenty years. We had proofs of the facts at nine P. M. Next day the man had disappeared, without any one knowing what had become of him. That is the way those things should be managed."

As I was about to reply to Fillion the business was resumed. Cahaigne raised his voice and said, "Seat yourselves, citizens. You have heard Citizen Victor Hugo. What he proposes is moral punishment."

"Yes, yes. Very good," exclaimed a multitude of voices.

Cauvet, the man who had interrupted me, moved upon the table on which he was seated.

"*Parbleu!* that is beautiful, a moral punishment, and you will let him off! To-morrow he will go to France to denounce and sell all our friends. We ought to kill the cur!"

This was one great objection. Hubert at liberty was dangerous.

Beauvais interfered.

"There is no need to kill him, and you need not let him go. I have kept Hubert since April, and lodged him for almost nothing. I was willing to help a refugee, but not to feed a spy. Now M. de Maupas must pay me M. Hubert's expenses,—eighty-three francs. To-morrow morning M. Asplet shall arrest M. Hubert and drop him into prison for debt, at least, unless he produces the bank-notes which M. de Maupas gave him. I shall be glad to see them."

There was laughter at this. Beauvais had in fact settled the question.

"Yes," cried Vincent, "but he will be off to-morrow morning."

"We will guard him," said Boni.

"Search him," cried Fombertaux.

"Yes, yes, search the spy."

A number of men precipitated themselves on Hubert.

"You have neither the right to guard him nor search him. To guard him is to curtail his liberty, to search him is to assault him."

The searching moreover was senseless. It was evident that Hubert, since the investigation, had nothing compromising about him.

Hubert cried, "Let them search me; I consent to it."

This was a little astonishing.

"He consents," they cried. "He consents. Let us search him."

I stopped them, and asked Hubert, "Do you consent?"

"Yes."

"You must give your consent in writing."

"I am quite willing."

Jarassé wrote the consent, and Hubert signed it. Meantime he was being searched, for they had not the patience to wait for the signature.

His pockets were emptied and turned out. Nothing was found except a few coppers, his large handkerchief, and a piece of the "Jersey Chronicle."

"His shoes—search his shoes."

Hubert pulled off his shoes, and put them on the table.

"There was nothing in them," he said, "but the feet of a Republican."

Cahaigne then spoke. He put my proposition, and it was adopted nem. con.

While the proposition was being signed, Hubert had put on his shoes and his hat, he had taken up his pipe, and seemed as if he wanted some one to give him a light.

At this moment Cauvet approached him and said, in a low voice, "Would you like a pistol?"

Hubert made no answer.

"Would you like a pistol?" repeated Cauvet.

Hubert kept silence. Cauvet began again: "'I have a pistol at home, a good one. Will you have it?"

Hubert shrugged his shoulders and pushed the table with his elbows.

"Will you?" said Cauvet.

"Leave me alone," said Hubert.

"You don't want my pistol?"

"No."

"Then shake hands."

And Cauvet, quite drunk, held out his hand to Hubert, who did not take it.

Meanwhile I was talking with Cahaigne, who said to me, "You have done well to put them off, but I am afraid that to-morrow their anger will break out again, in two or three like Avias, and that they will kill him in some corner or other."

I had not signed the deposition. All had signed except me.

Heurtebise handed me the pen.

"I will sign it in three days," I said.

"Why?" asked several.

"Because I am afraid of blows. I will sign in three days, when I shall be sure that the threats have not been carried out, and that no ill has come to Hubert."

They shouted on all sides, "Sign, sign; we will not harm him."

"You will guarantee it?"

"We promise you."

I signed.

Half an hour after I reached home; it was six o'clock A.M. The sea-breeze whistled about the Rocher des Proscrits.

The first rays of dawn were lighting up the sky. Some little silver clouds played amid the stars.

At the same hour M. Asplet, directed by Beauvais, arrested Hubert, and put him in prison for debt.

On the morning of October 21, about six o'clock, Sieur Lament, who is French vice-consul here, came to M. Asplet's house. He came, he said, to claim a Frenchman illegally imprisoned.

"For debt," replied M. Asplet. He then produced the order of arrest signed by the deputy, Viscomte M. Horman.

"Will you pay the amount?" said M. Asplet.

The consul bowed and went away.

It seems to be Hubert's destiny to be fed at the refugees' expense. At this moment they are keeping him in his prison at an expense of sixpence a day.

Looking over my papers, I found a letter from Hubert. There is in this letter a sad phrase: "Hunger is a bad counsellor!"

So Hubert has been hungry.

The Ninety-Four Thousand Franc Fraud

July, 1847.

ON the evening of the day when the judicial committee of Peers determined to prosecute M. Teste, Minister of Public Works, chance willed it that the chancellor had to go to Neuilly with the Bureau of the Chamber to present to the king a bill which had been passed.

The chancellor and the Peers of the Bureau (among whom was Count Daru) found the king in a furious state of mind. He had been informed of the prosecution of M. Teste. Immediately he caught sight of them he advanced towards them with rapid strides.

"What! Chancellor," he said, "was not one of my former ministers enough for you? Must you have a second? You have taken Teste now. So that after I have spent seventeen years in

France in setting up authority once more, in one day, in one hour, you have allowed it to be cast down again. You destroy the whole work of my reign. You debase authority, power, the government. And you do that,—you, the chancellor of the House of Peers!" *et cetera.*

The squall was a violent one. The chancellor was very firm. He resolutely refused to give in to the king. He said that, doubtless, policy was to be considered, but that it was necessary also to listen to justice; that the Chamber of Peers also had its independence as a legislative power, and its sovereignty as a judicial power; that this independence and sovereignty must be respected, and if need be, would make themselves respected; that, moreover, in the present state of opinion, it would have been a very serious matter to refuse satisfaction to it; that it would be doing an injury to the country and to the king not to do what this opinion demanded, and what justice required; that there were times when it was more prudent to advance than to retreat; and that finally what had been done was done. "And well done," added Daru. "We shall see," said the king.

And from anger he relapsed into uneasiness.

July 8.

Half-past twelve. The Court enters. A crowd in the galleries. No one in the reserved galleries except Colonel Poizat, governor of the Palace. In the diplomatic galleries two persons only,— Lord Normanby, the English ambas-

sador, and Count de Lœvenhœlm, the Swedish minister.

The accused are brought in. Three tables, with a green baize covering, have been placed facing the Court, to each of these tables there is a chair, and at the back is a bench for the counsel. President Teste sits down at the middle table, General Cubières at the right-hand table, Parmentier at the left-hand table. All three are dressed in black.

Parmentier entered some time after the two Peers. Teste, who is commander of the Legion of Honour, has the rosette of the decoration in his button-hole; Cubières, who is a Grand Officer, the plain ribbon. Before sitting down, the general converses with his counsel, then turns over, with a very busy air, the volume of documents relating to the case. He wears his ordinary look. Teste is pale and calm. He rubs his hands like a man who is pleased. Parmentier is stout, bald, has white hair, a red face, a hooked nose, a mouth like a sabre-cut, thin lips; the appearance of a rascal. He wears a white tie, as does also President Teste. The general wears a black cravat. The three defendants do not look at each other. Parmentier casts his eyes down, and affects to be playing with the gold chain of his watch, which he displays with the ostentation of a country bumpkin against his black waistcoat. A young man with a thin black moustache, who is said to be his son, is seated at his left.

Being questioned as to his position in life, Teste rises and says, "I thought it would not be seemly to bring to this bar the honours which I have had conferred upon me." (Visible impression on the Court.) "I placed them yesterday in the hands of the king." (This makes a manifest favourable impression.)

The indictment is read. It sets forth the following facts:—

Parmentier, Director of the Mines of Gouhenans, alleges that he remitted to General Cubières ninety-four thousand francs for the purpose of obtaining from M. Teste, Minister of Public Works, a grant of a salt-mine. M. Teste emphatically denies having received this sum. Parmentier is quite ready to believe that it was intercepted and that he was thus defrauded of it either by M. Cubières or another shareholder in the mines, M. Pellapra, who, it appears, acted as a go-between from the general to M. Teste. Parmentier is accused of corruption; Cubières and Pellapra of corruption and fraud; Teste of "having received gifts and presents to perform an act of his duty not subject to payment."

Pellapra has fled. Cubières, Teste, and Parmentier appear.

While the indictment is being read Cubières hides his face and forehead in his left hand, and follows the reading of the volume which has been circulated. Teste also follows it, and annotates his copy with a steel pen. He has put on his eye-glasses. From time to time he takes snuff out of a great boxwood snuffbox, and converses with his counsel, M. Paillet. Parmentier appears very attentive.

July 10.

This is what I can make out of it after the two first days.

I have spoken to General Cubières

four or five times in my life, and to President Teste once only, and yet, in this affair, I am as much interested in their fate as though they were friends of mine of twenty years' standing. Why? I will say at once. It is because I believe them to be innocent.

I "believe" is not strong; I see them to be innocent. This view may, perhaps, be modified, for this affair changes like the waves, and alters its aspect from one moment to another; but at the present time, after much perplexity, after many transitions, after many painful intervals, in which I have more than once trembled and shuddered in my conscience, I am convinced that General Cubières is innocent of the act of fraud, that President Teste is innocent of the act of corruption.

What is this affair, then? To my mind, it resumes itself in two words,— commission and black-mail; commission deducted by Pellapra, black-mail extorted by Parmentier. A commission, tainted with fraud and swindling, was the cause of the first act alleged in the indictment; black-mail was the cause of the scandal. Hence the whole case.

I have no leaning towards guilt which is not invincibly proved to me. My inclination is to believe in innocence. As long as there remains in the probabilities of a case a possible refuge for the innocence of the accused, all my theories, I will not say incline, but precipitate themselves towards it.

SUNDAY, July 11.

An adjournment takes place over today. The second and third hearings were devoted to the examination of the accused.

At the opening of Friday's sitting were read communications which had been unexpectedly made by Messrs. Léon de Malleville and Marrast, and which appear to throw a strong light upon this trial. The defendants entered the Court pale and dejected, Parmentier, however, with more assurance than the others. M. Teste listened to the reading of the new documents, while leaning his elbow upon the table and half hiding his face in his hand; General Cubières, with his eyes cast downward; Parmentier with perceptible embarrassment.

The examination began with the general.

M. Cubières has a doll-like face, an undecided look, a hesitating manner of speaking, red cheeks; I believe him to be innocent of fraud; however, I am not deeply impressed with him. During the examination he stood up, and gently beat a tattoo upon the table with the tip of a wooden paper-knife with a look of profound ease. The procurator-general, M. Delangle, a rather commonplace lawyer, treated him once or twice with insolence; Cubières, a Waterloo man, did not venture to say a word in return to make his ears tingle. I felt for him. In the opinion of the Court he is already convicted.

The first part of the examinaton was badly conducted. There was but one expression of opinion at the refreshment-bar. The chancellor is a remarkable veteran,—out of the common,— but then, he is eighty-two years of age; at eighty-two years of age one cannot face either a woman or a crowd.

Parmentier, interrogated by the general, spoke with ease and a sort of vulgar glibness which was sometimes witty, at others shrewd, skilful throughout, never eloquent. He is a man who, to tell the truth, is a scoundrel. He is not aware of it himself. This shameless creature has a twist in his mind, and exposes his nakedness just as Venus would do. A toad who fancies he is beautiful is a repulsive spectacle. He was hissed. At first he either did not hear, or did not understand; however, he ended by understanding; then the perspiration stood in beads upon his face. Every now and then, amid the marks of disgust of the assemblage, he nervously wiped the streaming surface of his bald head, looked about him with a certain air of entreaty and bewilderment, feeling that he was lost, and trying to recover himself. Yet he continues to speak, and to expose his mental defects, while low tones of indignation drowned his utterances, and his anguish increased. At this moment I felt pity for the wretched man.

M. Teste who was examined yesterday, spoke like an innocent man; frequently he was exceedingly eloquent. He was not an advocate; he was a real man, who suffered, who tore out his very vitals and exposed them to view before his judges, saying, "See there!" He profoundly impressed me. While he spoke, a light broke in upon me that this whole affair might be explained by a fraud committed by Pellapra.

Teste is sixty-seven years of age; he has a southern accent, a large and expressive mouth, a tall forehead, giving him a look of intelligence, the eyes deep set and at times sparkling; his whole bodily activity overwhelmed and crushed, but he is energetic withal. He moved about, started, shrugged his shoulders, smiled bitterly, took snuff, turned over his papers, annotated them rapidly, held in check the procurator-general or the chancellor, shielded Cubières, who is his ruin, showed his contempt for Parmentier, who defends him, threw out notes, interruptions, replies, complaints, shouts. He was turbulent, yet ingenuous; overcome with emotion, yet dignified. He was clear, rapid, persuasive, supplicating, menacing, full of anguish without any trepidation, moderate and violent, haughty and tearful. At one point he powerfully affected me. His very soul found expression in the cries which he uttered. I was tempted to rise and say to him, "You have convinced me; I will leave my seat and take up my position on the bench at your side; will you let me be your counsel?" And then I restrained myself, thinking that if his innocence continued to be made manifest to me, I should perhaps be more useful to him as a judge among his judges.

Pellapra is the pivot on which the case turns. Teste appears sincerely grieved at his flight. If Pellapra returns, all will be clear. I ardently hope that Teste is innocent, and that, if innocent, he will be saved.

At the rising of the Court, I followed him with my eyes as he went out. He slowly and sadly crossed the benches of the Peers, looking to right and left upon these chairs, which perhaps he will never occupy again. Two ushers, who guarded him, walked one in front of him, and the other behind him.

July 12.

The aspect of the case has suddenly changed. Some fresh documents are terribly incriminating to Teste. Cubières rises, and confirms the authenticity and importance of these documents. Teste replies haughtily and energetically, but for all that his confidence diminishes. His mouth contracts. I feel uneasy about him. I begin to tremble for fear he has been deceiving us all. Parmentier listens, almost with a smile, and with his arms carelessly folded. Teste sits down again, and takes an immense number of pinches of snuff out of his great boxwood snuffbox, then wipes the perspiration off his forehead with a red silk handkerchief. The Court is profoundly agitated.

"I can imagine what he suffers by what I suffer myself," M. de Pontécoulant said to me. "What torture it is!" said General Neigre. "It is a slow guillotine stroke," said Bertin de Vaux. Apprehension is at its height among the members of the Court and the public. All are anxious not to lose one word. The Peers cry out to those who address them, "Speak up! Speak up! We cannot hear." The chancellor begs the Court to consider his great age.

The heat is insupportable.

The stock-broker Goupil gives his evidence. Teste makes a desperate struggle.

M. Charles Dupin questions the stock-broker. Teste follows him with his eyes, and applauds him with a smile. Anything more doleful than this smile could not be imagined.

On this occasion the private conference was held before the sitting in the old Chamber. The Peers buzzed like a swarm of bees. The chancellor came to the bench on which I was seated, and spoke to me of matters connected with the Académie; then of the trial, of his feeling of fatigue and grief; saying how pleasant was a meeting of the Académie after a sitting of the Court of Peers.

In his evidence M. Legrand, Undersecretary of State for Public Works, described Teste as "a person who is sitting behind me." Teste shrugged his shoulders.

After the serious evidence of the notary Roquebert, the face of Teste assumes an agonized expression.

At the production of the document for the Treasury he turned red, wiped his forehead in anguish, and turned towards his son. They exchanged a few words; then Teste began once more to turn his papers, and the son buried his head in his hands.

In one hour Teste has aged ten years; his head moves, his lower lip twitches. Yesterday he was a lion; to-day he is a booby.

Everything in this affair moves by fits and starts. Yesterday I *saw* that Teste was innocent, to-day I see that he is guilty. Yesterday I admired him, to-day I should be tempted to despise him were he not so miserable. But I no longer feel anything but pity for him.

This trial was one of the most terrible spectacles which I have ever witnessed in my life. It is a moral dismemberment.

That which our forefathers saw eighty years ago in the Place de Grève, on the day of the execution of Damiens, we have seen to-day, on the day of the execution of President Teste in the Court of Peers. We have seen a man tortured with hot irons and dismembered in the spirit. Every hour, every minute, something was torn from him: at twelve o'clock his distinction as a magistrate; at one o'clock his reputation as an upright minister; at two o'clock his conscience as an honest man; half an hour later, the respect of others; a quarter of an hour afterwards, his own self-respect. In the end, he was but a corpse. It lasted for six hours.

For my own part, as I said to the Chief President Legagneur, I doubt whether I should ever have the hardihood, even were Teste convicted and guilty, to add any punishment whatever to this unparalleled chastisement, to this frightful torment.

July 13.

As I entered the cloak-room Viscount Lemercier, who was there, said to me, "Have you heard the news?" "No." "Teste has attempted to commit suicide, and failed."

The fact is as stated. M. Teste, yesterday evening, at nine o'clock, fired two pistol-shots at himself; he fired two shots simultaneously, one with each hand. One he aimed in his mouth, and the cap missed fire; the other at his heart, and the bullet rebounded, the shot being fired from too close a distance.

The chancellor read in the private conference the official documents detailing the occurrence; they were afterwards re-read at the public sitting. The pistols were deposited upon the table of the Court. They were two very little pistols, quite new, with ivory handles.

Teste, not having succeeded in destroying himself, refuses henceforth to appear before the Court. He has written to the chancellor a letter in which he abandons his defence, "the documents produced yesterday leaving no room for contradiction." This is the language of an advocate, not of a man; a man would have said, "I am guilty."

When we entered the Court, M. Dupin the elder, who was seated behind me on the Deputies' bench, said to me, "Guess what book Teste sent for to kill time with?" "I do not know." " 'Monte-Cristo!' 'Not the first four volumes,' he said, 'I have read them.' 'Monte-Cristo' was not to be found in the library of the House of Peers. It had to be borrowed from a public reading-room, which only had it in periodical parts. Teste spends his time in reading these parts."

My neighbour, the Duke of Brancas, who is a kind and worthy veteran, says to me, "Do not oppose the condemnation. It is God's justice which will be done."

Yesterday evening, when General Cubières was informed that Teste had fired two pistol-shots at himself, he wept bitterly.

I note that to-day is a fatal day,— the 13th of July. The seat lately occupied by Teste is empty at the sitting. The clerk of the court, La Chauvinière, reads the indictment. M. Cubières listens with an air of profound sadness, then hides his face in his hand. Parmentier holds his head down the whole time. The events of yesterday—the attempted suicide of Teste and his letter to the chancellor—destroy in its very foundations the abominable lines of defence of Parmentier.

At ten minutes past one the Procurator-general Delangle rises to address the Court. He twice repeats, amid the painful impression which prevails, "Messieurs les Pairs"—then stops short, and continues "The trial is ended." The procurator-general spoke only for ten minutes.

It is a curious fact that Teste and Delangle have all their lives been brought into close association, Delangle following Teste, and in the end prosecuting him. Teste was the *bâtonnier* of the bar; Delangle held the office immediately after him. Teste was appointed president of the Court of Cassation; Delangle entered the same court as advocate-general. Teste is accused, Delangle is procurator-general.

I now understand the meaning of the movement of the father and son which I noticed yesterday at the moment of the production of the document from the Treasury; the father said to the son, "Give me the pistols." The son handed them to him, and then sank his head in his hands. It is in this way, I think, the sombre tragedy must have happened.

At the opening of the sitting the chancellor reads a letter, in which Cubières resigns his position as a Peer.

The question is put as to whether the accused are guilty.

"Is Cubières guilty of fraud?" Unanimously "No."

Upon the question of corruption:—

"Is Teste guilty?" Unanimously "Yes."

"Is Cubières guilty?" Unanimously, with the exception of three votes, "Yes."

"Is Parmentier guilty?" Unanimously "Yes."

Sentences:—

Teste is sentenced to civil degradation unanimously, with the exception of one vote.

Upon the question of the fines, I rose in my turn, and said, "I desire to punish a guilty man; I do not desire to punish a family,—that is to say, innocent persons. The restitution of the money received, to my mind, would be sufficient. No fine. My lords, the example is not in a fine; the example is in the terrible things which you have seen; the example is in the terrible act to which you have just committed yourselves. A fine deteriorates the example. It places a question of money in the place of a question of honour."

Teste was condemned to pay a fine of ninety-four thousand francs.

At half-past six a fresh letter from General Cubières is read, in which he states that he has requested that he may be placed on the retired list. The unhappy man throws something overboard at every moment.

July 15.

At half-past twelve the calling of the names takes place. The Court is profoundly and painfully agitated. The law officials claim the whole law, the whole penalty, against Cubières; the nobles are more humane.

The Court proceeds to pass sentence.

Upon the question whether Teste should be imprisoned, I said, "My lords, the guilty man has already been sufficiently punished. At the present moment he is sixty-seven years of age; in five years he will be seventy-two. I

will not add one word. No imprisonment!"

Teste is sentenced to three years' imprisonment.

Respecting Cubières and the penalty of civic degradation, when my turn came, I said, "I feel that the Court is weary, and I am suffering myself from a feeling of agitation which unsettles me; I rise notwithstanding. I have studied, as you have, my lords, with whatever intelligence and power of attention I may have, the whole of the indictment in this deplorable case. I have examined facts. I have contrasted persons. I have endeavoured to penetrate not only into the heart of the case, but into the hearts of these men you are trying at this moment. Well, this is the conclusion I have arrived at: In my opinion, General Cubières was led astray,—led astray by Pellapra, defrauded by Parmentier. Under these circumstances, there has been, I acknowledge, weakness,—a weakness censurable, inexcusable, gravely culpable even, but after all only weakness; and weakness is not baseness, and I do not wish to punish weakness with infamy. I will avow, and the Court will pardon this avowal, that during the many hours that this unfortunate affair has occupied our minds I imagined that you were going to render an altogether different decision in your all-powerful and sovereign justice. I should have wished to leave in his terrible isolation the painful and conspicuous figure of the principal defendant. This man, who, by dint of talent, has contrived—a miracle which, for my part, I should always have thought impossible—to be great in his abasement and touching in his shame; this man I should have liked to punish simply with civic degradation. And I should have wished to add nothing to this fearful penalty; in such a case that which increases diminishes. For the weak and unfortunate General Cubières, I should have wished a sentence of deprivation, for a certain period of time, of the civic and civil rights mentioned in Article 401. And finally, for the men of money, I should have wished money penalties; for the miscreants, humiliating penalties; for Parmentier, fine and imprisonment. For these men of such diversity of guilt I should have wished for a diversity of penalties, which your omnipotence would permit you to decree, and the observance of this proportion between the misdeeds and the punishments appeared to me to be in accordance with conscience, and I will add,—although that concerns me less,—in accordance with public opinion. In your wisdom you have judged otherwise. I bow to it, but I beg of you, nevertheless, to approve my remaining of the same opinion. In an assembly in which there are so many men of importance who have occupied, or who will yet occupy, the highest functions in the State and the government, I appreciate, I honour, I respect that noble feeling of outraged decency which leads you to inflict unusually heavy penalties at this juncture, and to afford not only the most just but also the most cruel satisfaction to public opinion. I, gentlemen, am not a lawyer, I am not a soldier, I am not a public functionary, I am an ordinary tax-payer; I am a member, like any one else, of the great crowd from which emanates that public opinion to which

you defer; and it is for this, it is because I am simply this, that I am perhaps qualified to say to you, Enough! Stop! Go as far as the limits of justice; do not overstep them. The example has been set. Do not destroy that isolation of the condemned man Teste, which is the grand aspect, the grand moral lesson of the trial. As long as it was a question only of this unhappy man, I spoke to you merely in the language of pity; I speak to you now in the language of equity, solemn and austere equity. I conjure you, give credit to General Cubières for his sixty years of honourable life, give credit to him for the agony he has suffered for those four years of torture which he endured at the villainous hands of Parmentier, for this public exposure upon that bench during the four days; give credit to him for that unjust accusation of fraud, which was also a torture to him; give credit to him for his generous hesitation to save himself by ruining Teste; give credit to him, finally, for his heroic conduct upon the battle-field of Waterloo, where I regret that he did not remain. I formally propose to sentence M. Cubières to the penalty provided by Article 401, together with Article 42; that is to say, to a suspension of civil and civic rights for ten years. I vote against civic degradation."

At seven o'clock there still remain eighty Peers who have not voted. The chancellor proposes an adjournment until the morrow. Objections are made: An adjournment while the voting is taking place! M. Cauchy reads precedent from the Quénisset trial. Uproar. The adjournment is carried.

July 16.

Continuation of the voting upon the question of the penalty to be inflicted upon General Cubières.

The penalty of civic degradation is carried by 130 votes to 48.

He is condemned besides to a fine of ten thousand francs.

No imprisonment.

It appears that the decision in favour of inflicting the penalty of civic degradation upon General Cubières, which has just been arrived at, has reached the prison. Just now I heard in the street the dreadful cries of Madame de Cubières and Madame de Sampays, her sister, who were with the general at the moment when the news was communicated to him.

July 17.

Sentence upon Parmentier.

Upon the question of civic degradation I said, "I should have wished, as the Court is aware, in order that a great example might be made, that President Teste should have been left in his degrading isolation, alone under the burden of civic degradation." The Court did not agree with me; it thought proper to associate with him General Cubières. I cannot do otherwise than associate with him Parmentier. I vote for civic degradation, while profoundly regretting that I am obliged, after this great social and public penalty has been inflicted upon two ex-Ministers, upon two Peers of France, to whom it is everything, to inflict it upon this wretch to whom it is nothing.

Parmentier is condemned to civic degradation and a fine of ten thousand francs. No imprisonment.

As we were about to leave, and were in the cloak-room, Anatole de Montesquiou, who constantly voted in the most lenient sense, pointed out to me, in the second compartment of the cloak-room near that in which I am putting on my things, an old Peer's robe hanging at the side of the robe of the Minister of Public Instruction. This robe is worn at the elbows, the gilt of the buttons is rubbed off, the embroidery faded; an old ribbon of the Legion of Honour is in the button-hole, more yellow than red, and half untied. Above this coat was written, according to the custom, the name of him to whom it belonged: "M. TESTE."

My opinion is that the public will consider the decree of the Court of Peers just in the case of Teste, harsh in that of Cubières, and lenient in that of Parmentier.

At half-past four the doors were thrown open to the public. An immense crowd had been waiting since the morning. In a moment the galleries were noisily filled. It was like a wave. Then profound silence when the calling of the names began. The Peers replied, generally speaking, in a barely audible and weary tone of voice.

Then the chancellor put on his shaped hat of black velvet lined with ermine, and read the decree. The procurator-general was at his post. The chancellor read the decree in a firm tone, very remarkable in an old man of eighty years of age. Whatever may have been said by certain newspapers, he did not shed "silent tears."

The judgment will be read presently by the Chief Clerk of the Court to the condemned men.

It will be just a month ago to-morrow, the 18th, that Teste was arraigned by the judicial committee of the Peers, and that he said to them, "I thank you for placing me in a position which gives me the precious privilege of defending myself."

July 21.

It is a curious fact that M. Teste, who, as Minister of Public Works, had this Luxembourg prison built, is the first minister who has been confined in it. This reminds one of the gibbet of Montfaucon, and of Enguerrand de Marigny.

M. Teste occupies in this prison an apartment separated only by a partition from the apartment of General Cubières. The partition is so thin that, as M. Teste speaks loudly, Mme. de Cubières was obliged on the first day to tap upon the wall to warn M. Teste that she heard all he said. The pistol-shot, too, made General Cubières start as though it had been fired in his own apartment.

The sitting of the 12th had been so decisive that some act of desperation was thought probable. During the very sitting the Duke Decazes had had iron bars put to the windows of the prisoners. They found these bars in the windows on coming back, but did not feel any surprise on seeing them. They also had their razors taken from them, and had to dine without knives.

Policemen were to remain day and night by their side. However, it was thought that M. Teste might be left alone with his son and the counsel who were defending him. He dined with them almost in silence,—a remarkable fact, for he was a great talker. The little he did say was concerning matters foreign to the trial. At nine o'clock the son and the barristers retired. The policeman who was to watch M. Teste received orders to go up directly. It was during the few minutes which elapsed between the departure of his son and the entrance of the policeman that M. Teste made his attempt to commit suicide.

Many persons had doubted whether this attempt was seriously intended. This was the tone of the comments in the Chamber. M. Delessert, the prefect of police, whom I questioned on this subject, told me there could be no doubt about it that M. Teste had tried to kill himself in downright good earnest, but he believes that only one pistol-shot was fired.

After his condemnation, General Cubières received many visits; the sentence of the Court missed its mark by reason of its excessive severity. The general's visitors, in going to his cell, passed before that of Parmentier, which was only closed with a door having, instead of a glass pane, a white curtain, through which he could be seen. All of them in passing by loaded Parmentier with terms of contempt, which obliged the fellow to hide in a corner where he was no longer visible.

During the trial the heat was intense. At every moment the chancellor had to summon back the Peers who went off to the refreshment-bars or the lobbies.

Lord Normanby did not miss a single sitting.

July 22.

The name of Teste has already been removed from his seat in the House of Peers. It is General Achard now who occupies his chair.

Yesterday, Tuesday, the 21st of July, as I was proceeding from the Académie to the House of Peers, towards four o'clock, I met near the exit of the Institute, in the most deserted part of the Rue Mazarin, Parmentier coming out of prison. He was going in the direction of the Quay. His son accompanied him. Parmentier, dressed in black, carried his hat in his hand behind his back; with his other arm he leaned upon his son. The son had a downcast look. Parmentier appeared completely overwhelmed. He had the appearance of exhaustion,—of a man who has just come from a long walk. His bald head seemed to bend beneath his shame. They were walking slowly.

It was stated to-day at the Chamber that Madame de Cubières gave a *soirée* two days after the condemnation. It appears that in reality she simply contented herself with not shutting her door. She has just written to the newspapers a letter, which will not do her husband much good, but in which there is nevertheless one fine passage, as follows: "He has had his peerage, his rank, everything taken from him, even to his dignity as a citizen. He retains his wounds."

The chancellor offered to let M. de Cubières leave the prison by one of the private gates of the chancellor's official residence in the Luxembourg. A hired conveyance would have awaited M. de Cubières, and he would have got in without being seen by any one in the street. M. de Cubières refused. An open carriage, drawn by two horses, came and took up its position at the gate-way of the Rue de Vaugerard, in the midst of the crowd. M. de Cubières got into it, accompanied by his wife and Madame de Sampays, and this is how he came out of prison. Since then he has had, every evening, more than a hundred visitors. There are always some forty carriages at his door.

Capital Punishment

I avow openly, that "The Last Days of a Condemned" is only a pleading, direct or indirect, for *the abolition of punishment by death.* My design herein (and what I would wish posterity to see in my work, if its attention should ever be given to so slight a production) is, not to make out the special defence of any particular criminal, such defence being transitory as it is easy. I would plead generally and permanently for *all* accused persons, present and future; it is the great point of Human Right stated and pleaded before society at large,—that highest judicial court; it is the sombre and fatal question which breathes obscurely in the depths of each capital offence, under the triple envelopes of pathos in which legal eloquence wraps them; it is the question of life and death, I say, laid bare, denuded of the sonorous twistings of the bar, revealed in daylight, and placed where it should be seen, in its true and hideous position,—not in the law courts, but on the scaffold,—not among the judges, but with the Executioner!

This is what I have desired to effect. If futurity should award me the glory of having succeeded,—which I dare not hope,—I desire no other crown.

I proclaim and repeat it, then, in the name of all accused persons, innocent or guilty, before all courts, juries, or judges. And in order that my pleadings should be as universal as my cause, I have been careful, while writing "The Last Days of a Condemned," to omit any thing of a special, individual, contingent, relative, or modifiable nature, as also any episode, anecdote, known event, or real name,—keeping to the limit (if "limit" it may be termed!) of pleading the cause of *any* condemned prisoner whatever, executed at any time, for any offence; happy if, with no other aid than my thoughts, I have mined sufficiently into my subject to make a heart bleed, under the *æs triplex* of a magistrate! happy if I could render merciful those who consider themselves just! happy if I penetrate sufficiently deep within the Judge to reach the man.

When this book first appeared, some people thought it was worth while to dispute the authorship. Some asserted that it was taken from an English work, and others that it was borrowed from an American author. What a singular mania there is for seeking the origin of matters at a great distance,—trying to trace from the source of the Nile the streamlet which flows through our village! In this work there is no English, American, or Chinese assistance. I formed the idea of "The Last Days of a Condemned" where you all might form it,—where perhaps you may all have formed it (for who is there that has not reflected and had reveries of "the last day of a condemned"?—there, on the public walk, the place of execution!

It was there, while passing casually during an execution, that this forcible idea occurred to me; and, since then, after those funereal Thursdays of the Court of Cassation, which send forth through Paris the intelligence of an approaching execution, the hoarse voices of the assembling spectators, as they hurried past my windows, filled my mind with the prolonged misery of the person about to suffer, which I pictured to myself, from hour to hour, according to what I conceived was its actual progress. It was a torture which commenced from daybreak, and lasted, like that of the miserable being who was tortured at the same moment, until *four o'clock*. Then only, whence once the *ponens caput expiravit* was announced by the heavy toll of the clock, I breathed again freely, and regained comparative peace of mind.

One day at length—I think it was after the execution of Ulbach—I commenced writing this work; and since then I have felt relieved. When one of those public crimes called *legal executions* is committed, my conscience now acquits me of participation therein. This, however, is not sufficient; it is well to be freed from self-accusation, but it would be still better to endeavour to save human life. I do not know any aim more elevated, more holy, than that of seeking the abolition of capital punishment; with sincere devotion I join the wishes and efforts of those philanthropic men of all nations who have laboured, of late years, to throw down the patibulary tree,—the only tree which revolution fails to uproot! It is with pleasure that I take my turn to give my feeble stroke, after the all-powerful blow which, seventy years ago, Beccaria gave to the ancient gibbet, which had been standing during so many centuries of Christianity.

I have just said that the scaffold is the only edifice which revolutions do not demolish. It is rare indeed that revolutions are temperate in spilling blood; and although they are sent to prune, to lop, to reform society, the punishment of death is a branch which they have never removed! I own, however, if any revolution ever appeared to me capable and worthy of abolishing capital punishment, it was the Revolution of July, 1830. It seemed, indeed, as if it belonged to the merciful popular rising of modern times to erase the barbarous enactments of Louis the Eleventh, of Richelieu, and of Robespierre, and to inscribe at the head of the code, "the inviolability of human life!" 1830 was worthy of breaking the axe of 1793.

At one time we really hoped for it. In August, 1830, there seemed so much generosity afloat, such a spirit of gentleness and civilization in the multitude, that we almost fancied the punishment of death was abolished, by a tacit and unanimous consent, with the rest or the evils which had oppressed us. For some weeks confiding and credulous, we had faith in the inviolability of life, for the future, as in the inviolability of liberty.

In effect, two months had scarcely passed, when an attempt was made to resolve into a legal reality the sublime Utopia of Cæsar Bonesana. Unfortunately, this attempt was awkward, imperfect, almost hypocritical, and made in a different spirit from the general interest.

It was in the month of October, 1830, as may be remembered, that the question of capital punishment was brought before the Chamber of Deputies, and discussed with much talent, energy, and apparent feeling. During two days there was a continued succession of impressive eloquence on this momentous subject; and what was the subject?—to abolish the punishment of death? Yes and No! Here is the truth.

Four "gentlemen,"—four persons well known in society,—had attempted in the higher range of politics one of those daring strokes which Bacon calls *crimes,* and which Machiavel calls *enterprises.* Well! crime or enterprise,—the law, brutal for all, would punish it by death; and the four unfortunates were prisoners, legal captives guarded by three hundred tricoloured cockades at Vincennes. What was now to be done? You understand the impossibility of sending to the place of execution, in a common cart, ignobly bound with coarse ropes, seated back to back with that functionary who must not be named,— four men of our own rank,—four "gentlemen!"

If there were even a mahogany Guillotine!

Well, to settle the matter, they need only *abolish the punishment of death;* and thereupon the Chamber set to work!

Only yesterday they had treated this abolition as Utopian,—as a theory, a dream, poetic folly. This was not the first time that an endeavour had been made to draw their attention to the cart, the coarse ropes, and the fatal machine. How strange it is that these hideous details acquired such sudden force in their minds!

Alas! it was not on account of the general good that they sought to abolish capital punishment, but for their own sakes,—as Deputies, who might become Ministers. And thus an alloy of egotism alters and destroys the fairest social combinations. It is the dark vein of statuary marble, which, crossing everywhere, comes forth at each moment unexpectedly under the chisel!

It is surely unnecessary for me to declare that I was not among those who desired the death of the Ministers. When once they were imprisoned, the indignant anger I had felt at their attempt changed with me, as with every one else, into profound pity. I reflected on the prejudices of education of some among them; on the ill-developed head of their chief (fanatic and obstinate relapse of the conspiracies of 1804), whitened before its time, in the damp cells of state prisons; on the fatal necessity of their common position; on the impossibility of their placing a drag on that rapid slope down which monarchy rushed blindly on the 8th of August, 1829; on the influence of personal intercourse with Royalty over them, which I had hitherto under-rated; and finally I reflected, above all, on the dignity which one among them spread, like a purple mantle, over their misfortunes! I was among those who sincerely wished their lives saved, and would have readily lent my aid to that effect.

If a scaffold had been raised for them in Paris, I feel quite certain (and if it be an illusion, I would preserve it) that there would have been an insurrection to pull it down; and I should have been one of the rioters.

Here I must add that, in each social crisis, of all scaffolds, the political one is the most abominable, the most fatal, the most mischievous, the most necessary to extirpate.

In revolutionary times, beware of the first execution. It excites the sanguinary passions of the mob.

I therefore agreed thoroughly with those who wished to spare the four Ministers, both as a matter of feeling and of political reasoning. But I should have liked better that the Chamber had chosen another occasion for proposing the abolition of capital punishment. If they had suggested this desirable change not with reference to those four Ministers, fallen from a Palace to a Prison, but in the instance of the first highwayman,—in the case of one of those wretches to whom you neither give word nor look, and from whom you shrink as they pass; miserable beings, who, during their ragged infancy, ran barefoot in the mud of the crossings; shivering in winter near the quays, or seeking to warm themselves outside the ventilator from the kitchens of the hotels where you dine; scratching out, here and there, a crust of bread from the heaps of filth, and wiping it before eating; scraping in the gutter all day, with a rusty nail, in the hopes of finding a farthing; having no other amusement than the gratuitous sight of the King's fête, and the public executions,—that other gratuitous sight,—poor devils! whom hunger forces on theft, and theft to all the rest; children disinherited by their stepmother, the world; who are adopted by the House of Correction in their twelfth year,—by the Galleys at eighteen,—and by the Guillotine at forty! unfortunate beings whom, by means of a school and a workshop, you might have rendered good, moral, useful; and with whom you now know not what to do,—flinging them away like a useless burthen, sometimes into the red ant-heaps of Toulon, sometimes into the silent cemetery of Clamart; cutting off life after taking away liberty.

If it had been in the instance of one of these outcasts that you had proposed to abolish the punishment of death, oh, then your councils would have indeed been noble, great, holy, majestic! It has ever belonged to those who are truly great and truly powerful, to protect the lowly and weak. How grand would be a Council of Bramins advocating the cause of the Paria! And with us the cause of the Paria is the cause of the people. In abolishing the penalty of death for sake of the people, and without waiting until you were personally interested in the question, you would have done more than a political work, —you would have conferred a social benefit.

Instead of this, you have not yet even completed a political act, while seeking to abolish it not for the abolition's sake, but to save four unfortunate Ministers detected in political delinquency. What has happened? As you were not sincere, the people were distrustful; when they suspected the cause of your change, they became angry at the question altogether, and, strange to say, they declared in favour of that condign punishment, the weight of which presses entirely on themselves.

Immediately after the famous discussion in the Chamber, orders were given to respite, indefinitely, all executions. This was apparently a great step gained; the opponents of punishment by death were rendered happy; but the illusion was of short duration. The lives of the Ministers were spared, and the fortress of Ham was selected as a medium, between death and liberty. These different arrangements once completed, all fear was banished from the minds of the ruling statesmen; and along with fear humanity was also banished. There was no farther question of abolishing capital punishment; and, when they no longer wished to prove to the contrary, Utopia became again Utopia!

There were yet in the prisons some unfortunate condemned wretches, who, having been allowed during five or six months to walk about the prison-yards and breathe the fresh air, felt tranquil for the future, sure of life, mistaking their reprieve for pardon.

There had indeed been a reprieve for six months for these hapless captives, whose sufferings were thus gratuitously aggravated, by making them cling again to life: then, without reason, without necessity, without well knowing why, the respites were all revoked, and all these human beings were launched into eternity.

Let me add, that never were executions accompanied by more atrocious circumstances than since that revocation of the reprieve of July. Never have the "anecdotes" been more revolting, or more effectual to prove the execration of capital punishment. I will cite here two or there examples of the horrors which have attended recent executions.

I must shock the nerves of the wives of king's counsel. *A wife is sometimes a conscience!*

In the South, towards the close of last September, the following circumstances occurred: I think it was at Pamiers. The officers went to a man in prison, whom they found quietly playing at cards, and gave him notice that he was to die in two hours. The wretched creature was horror-struck; for during the six months he had been forgotten, he had no longer thought of death; he was confessed, bound, his hair cut off, he was placed in the fatal cart, and taken to the place of execution. The Executioner took him from the Priest; laid him down and bound him on the Guillotine, and then let loose the axe. The heavy triangle of iron slowly detached itself, falling by jerks down the slides, until, horrible to relate, it wounded the man, without killing him! The poor creature uttered a frightful cry. The disconcerted Executioner hauled up the axe, and let it slide down again. A second time, the neck of the malefactor was wounded, without being severed. Again he shrieked, the crowd joining him. The Executioner raised the axe a third time, but no better effect attended the third stroke. Let me abridge these fearful details. Five times the axe was raised and let fall, and after the fifth stroke, the condemned was still shrieking for mercy. The indignant populace commenced throwing missiles at the Executioner, who hid himself beneath the Guillotine, and crept away behind the gendarmes' horses: but I have not yet finished. The hapless culprit, seeing he was left alone on the scaffold, raised himself on the plank, and there standing, frightful, streaming with blood, he demanded with feeble cries that some one would unbind him! The populace, full of pity, were on the point of forcing the gendarmes to help the hapless wretch, who had five times undergone his sentence. At this moment the servant of the Executioner, a youth under twenty, mounted on the scaffold, told the sufferer to turn round, that he might unbind him: then taking advantage of the posture of the dying man, who had yielded himself without any mistrust, sprang on him, and slowly cut through the neck with a knife! All this happened; all this was seen.

According to law, a judge was obliged to be present at this execution; by a sign he could have stopped all. Why was he leaning back in his carriage then, this man, while they massacred another man? What was he doing, this punisher of assassins, while they thus assassinated, in open day, his fellow-creature? And the Judge was not tried for this; nor the Executioner was not tried for it; and no tribunal inquired into this monstrous violation of all law on one of God's creatures.

In the seventeenth century, that epoch of barbarity in the criminal code, under Richelieu, under Chistophe Fouquet, Monsieur de Chalais was put to death at Nantes by an awkward soldier, who, instead of a sword-stroke, gave him thirty-four strokes of a cooper's adze. But at last it was considered execrable by the parliament of Paris, there was an inquest and a trial; and, although Richelieu and Fouquet did not suffer, the soldier was punished,—an injustice doubtless, but in which there was some show of justice.

In the modern instance, nothing was done. The fact took place after July, in times of civilization and march of intellect, a year after the celebrated lamentation of the Chamber on the penalty of death. The circumstance attracted no attention; the Paris papers published it as an anecdote, and no one cared about it. It was only known that the Guillotine had been put out of order by a dismissed servant of the Executioner, who, to revenge himself, had taken this method of action.

Another instance. At Dijon, only three months ago, they brought to the scaffold a woman (a woman!). This time again the axe of the Guillotine failed of its effect, and the head was not quite detached. Then the Executioner's servants pulled the feet of the woman; and, amidst the yells of the populace, thus finished the law!

At Paris, we have come back to the time of secret executions; since July they no longer dare to decapitate in the town, for they are afraid. Here is what they do. They took lately from the Bicêtre prison a man, under sentence of death, named Desandrieux, I think; they put him into a sort of panier on two wheels, closed on every side, bolted and padlocked; then with a gendarme in front, and another at the back, without noise or crowd, they proceeded to the deserted barrier of St. James. It was eight in the morning when they arrived, with but little light. There was a newly erected Guillotine, and for spectators, some dozens of little boys, grouped on the heaps of stones around the unexpected machine. Quickly they withdrew the man from the basket; and without giving him time to breathe, they furtively, secretly, shamefully deprived him of life! And that is called a public and solemn act of high justice! Infamous derision! How then do the lawgivers understand the word civilization? To what point have we attained? Justice reduced to stratagems and frauds! The law reduced to expedient! Monstrous! A man condemned to death, it would seem, was greatly to be feared, since they put an end to him in this traitorous fashion!

Let us be just, however; the execution was not quite secret. In the morning people hawked and sold, as usual, the sentence of death through the streets. It appears there are people who live by such sales. The crime of a hapless fellow-creature, its punishment, his torture, his agony, forms their stock in trade—a paper that they sell for a penny. Can one conceive anything more hideous than this coin, *verdisgrised* in blood?

Here are enough facts; here are too many. Is not all this horrible? What can be alleged in favour of punishment by death?

I put this question seriously. I ask it that it may be answered; I ask it of Legislators, and not of literary gossips. I know there are people who take "the excellence of punishment by death" for a text of paradoxes, like any other theme; there are others who only advocate capital punishment because they hate so-and-so who attack it. It is for them almost a literary question, a question of persons, and proper names; these are the envious, who do not find more fault with good lawyers than with good artists. The Joseph Grippas are no more wanting to the

Filangieri than the Torregiani to the Michael Angelos, and the Scuderies to the Corneilles.

It is not to these that I address myself, but to men of law, properly so called,—to logicians, to reasoners; to those who love the penalty of death for its beauty, its goodness, its grace!

Let them give their reasons.

Those who judge and condemn say that "punishment by death is necessary, —first, because it is requisite to remove from the social community a member which has already injured it, and might injure it again."

If this be all, perpetual imprisonment would suffice. What is the use of inflicting death? You argue that a prisoner may escape from jail,—keep watch more strictly! If you do not believe in the solidity of iron bars, how do you venture to have menageries? Let there be no executioner where the jailer can be sufficient.

They continue, "But society must avenge itself, society must punish." Neither one nor the other; *vengeance* is an individual act, and *punishment* belongs to God. Society is between the two; punishment is above its power, retaliation beneath it. Society should not punish, to avenge itself; it should correct, to ameliorate others!

Their third and last reason remains, the theory of example. "We must make examples. By the sight of the fate inflicted on criminals, we must shock those who might otherwise be tempted to imitate them!"

Well, in the first place, I deny the power of the example. I deny that the sight of executions produces the desired effect. Far from edifying the common people, it demoralizes and ruins their feeling, injuring every virtue; proofs of this abound and would encumber my argument if I chose to cite them. I will allude to only one fact, amongst a thousand, because it is of recent occurrence. It happened only ten days back from the present moment when I am writing; namely, on the 5th of March, the last day of the Carnival. At St. Pol, immediately after the execution of an incendiary named Louis Camus, *a group of Masqueraders came and danced round the still reeking scaffold!*

Make, then, your fine examples! Shrove Tuesday will turn them into jest.

If, notwithstanding all experience, you still hold to the theory of example, then give us back the Sixteenth Century; be in reality formidable. Restore to us a variety of suffering; restore us Farinacci; restore us the sworn torturer; restore us the gibbet, the wheel, the block, the rack, the thumb-screw, the live-burial vault, the burning cauldron; restore us in the streets of Paris, as the most open shop among the rest, the hideous stall of the Executioner, constantly full of human flesh; give us back Montfaucon, its cave of bones, its beams, its crooks, its chains, its rows of skeletons; give us back, in its permanence and power, that gigantic outhouse of the Paris Executioner! This indeed would be wholesale example; this would be a system of execution in some proportion,—which, while it is horrible, is also terrible!

But do you seriously suppose you are making an example, when you take the life of a poor wretch, in the most deserted part of the exterior Boule-

vards, at eight o'clock in the morning? Do not you see then, that your public executions are done in private? That fear is with the execution, and not among the multitude? One is sometimes tempted to believe, that the advocates for capital punishment have not thoroughly considered in what it consists. But place in the scales, against any crime whatever, this exorbitant right, which society arrogates to itself, of taking away that which it did not bestow: that most irreparable of evils!

The alternatives are these: First, the man you destroy is without family, relations, or friends, in the world. In this case, he has received neither education nor instruction; no care has been bestowed either on his mind or heart; then, by what right would you kill this miserable orphan? You punish him because his infancy trailed on the ground, without stem, or support; you make him pay the penalty of the isolated position in which you left him! you make a crime of his misfortune! No one taught him to know what he was doing; this man lived in ignorance: the fault was in his destiny, not himself. You destroy one who is innocent.

Or, Secondly,—the man has a family; and then do you think the fatal stroke wounds him alone?—that his father, his mother, or his children will not suffer by it? In killing him, you vitally injure all his family: and thus again you punish the innocent.

Blind and ill-directed penalty; which, on whatever side it turns, strikes the innocent!

Imprison for life this culprit who has a family: in his cell he can still work for those who belong to him. But how can he help them from the depth of the tomb? And can you reflect without shuddering, on what will become of those young children, from whom you take away their father, their support? Do you not feel that they must fall into a career of vice?

In the Colonies, when a slave is condemned to public execution, there are a thousand francs of indemnity paid to the proprietor of the man! What, you compensate a master, and you do not indemnify a family! In this country, do you not take the man from those who possess him? Is he not, by a much more sacred tie than master and slave, the property of his father, the wealth of his wife, the fortune of his children?

I have already proved your law guilty of assassination; I have now convicted it of robbery!

And then another consideration. Do you consider the soul of this man? Do you know in what state it is, that you dismiss it so hastily?

This may be called "sentimental reasoning," by some disdainful logicians, who draw their arguments only from their minds. I often prefer the reasonings of the heart; and certainly the two should always go together. Reason is on our side, feeling is on our side, and experience is on our side. In those States where punishment by death is abolished, the mass of capital crime has yearly a progressive decrease. Let this fact have its weight.

I do not advocate, however, a sudden and complete abolition of the penalty of death, such as was so heedlessly attempted in the Chamber of Deputies. On the contrary, I desire every precaution, every experiment, every suggestion of prudence: besides, in addition to this gradual change, I would have the whole penal code examined, and reformed; and time is a great ingredient requisite to make such a work complete. But independently of a partial abolition of death in cases of forgery, incendiarism, minor thefts, et cætera, I would wish that, from the present time, in all the greater offences, the Judge should be obliged to propose the following question to the Jury: "Has the accused acted from Passion, or Interest?" And in case the Jury decide "the accused acted from Passion," then there should be no sentence of death.

Let not the opposite party deceive themselves; this question of the penalty of death gains ground every day. Before long, the world will unanimously solve it on the side of mercy. During the past century, punishments have become gradually milder: the rack has disappeared, the wheel has disappeared; and now the Guillotine is shaken. This mistaken punishment will leave France; and may it go to some barbarous people,—not to Turkey, which is becoming civilized, not to the savages, for they will not have it; but let it descend some steps of the ladder of civilization, and take refuge in Spain, or Russia!

In the early ages, the social edifice rested on three columns, Superstition, Tyranny, Cruelty. A long time ago a voice exclaimed, "Superstition has departed!" Lately another voice has cried, "Tyranny has departed!" It is now full time that a third voice shall be raised to say, "The Executioner has departed!"

Thus the barbarous usages of the olden times fall one by one; thus Providence completes modern regeneration.

To those who regret Superstition, we say, "GOD remains for us!" To those who regret Tyranny, we say, "OUR COUNTRY remains!" But to those who could regret the Executioner we can say nothing.

Let it not be supposed that social order will depart with the scaffold; the social building will not fall from wanting this hideous keystone. Civilization is nothing but a series of transformations. For what then do I ask your aid? The civilization of penal laws.

The gentle laws of CHRIST will penetrate at last into the Code, and shine through its enactments. We shall look on crime as a disease, and its physicians shall displace the judges, its hospitals displace the Galleys. Liberty and health shall be alike. We shall pour balm and oil where we formerly applied iron and fire; evil will be treated in charity, instead of in anger. This change will be simple and sublime.

THE CROSS SHALL DISPLACE THE GIBBET.

The Minds and the Masses

THE PEOPLE

FOR the last eighty years memorable things have been done. A wonderful heap of demolished materials covers the pavement.

What is done is but little by the side of what remains to be done.

To destroy is the task: to build is the work. Progress demolishes with the left hand; it is with the right hand that it builds.

The left hand of Progress is called Force; the right hand is called Mind.

There is at this hour a great deal of useful destruction accomplished; all the old cumbersome civilization is, thanks to our fathers, cleared away. It is well, it is finished, it is thrown down, it is on the ground. Now, up with you all, intellects! to work, to labour, to fatigue, to duty; it is necessary to construct.

Here three questions: To construct what? To construct where? To construct how?

We reply: To construct the people. To construct the people according to the laws of progress. To construct the people according to the laws of light.

SOCIALISM

To work for the people,—that is the great and urgent necessity.

The human mind—an important thing to say at this minute—has a greater need of the ideal even than of the real.

It is by the real that we exist; it is by the ideal that we live. Now, do you wish to realize the difference? Animals exist, man lives.

To live, is to understand. To live, is to smile at the present, to look toward posterity over the wall. To live, is to have in one's self a balance, and to weigh in it the good and the evil. To live, is to have justice, truth, reason, devotion, probity, sincerity, commonsense, right, and duty nailed to the heart. To live, is to know what one is worth, what one can do and should do. Life is conscience. Cato would not rise before Ptolemy. Cato lived.

Literature is the secretion of civilization, poetry of the ideal. That is why literature is one of the wants of societies. That is why poetry is a hunger of the soul. That is why poets are the first instructors of the people. That is why Shakespeare must be translated in France. That is why Molière must be translated in England. That is why comments must be made on them. That is why there must be a vast public literary domain. That is why all poets, all philosophers, all thinkers, all the producers of the greatness of the mind must be translated, commented on, published, printed, reprinted, stereotyped, distributed, explained, recited, spread abroad, given to all, given cheaply, given at cost price, given for nothing.

Poetry evolves heroism. M. Royer-Collard, that original and ironical friend of routine, was, taken all in all, a wise and noble spirit. Some one we know heard him say one day, "Spartacus is a poet."

That wonderful and consoling Ezekiel —the tragic revealer of progress—has all kinds of singular passages full of a profound meaning: "The voice said to me: Fill the palm of thy hand with red-hot coals, and spread them on the city." And elsewhere: "The spirit having gone into them, everywhere the spirit went, they went." And again:

"A hand was stretched towards me. It held a roll which was a book. The voice said to me: Eat this roll. I opened the lips and I ate the book. And it was sweet in my mouth as honey." To eat the book is a strange and striking image,—the whole formula of perfectibility, which above is knowledge, and below, teaching.

We have just said, "Literature is the secretion of civilization." Do you doubt it? Open the first statistics you come across.

Here is one which we find under our hand: Bagne de Toulon, 1862. Three thousand and ten prisoners. Of these three thousand and ten convicts, forty know a little more than to read and write, two hundred and eighty-seven know how to read and write, nine hundred and four read badly and write badly, seventeen hundred and seventy-nine know neither how to read nor write. In this wretched crowd all the merely mechanical trades are represented by numbers decreasing according as they rise toward the enlightened pursuits, and you arrive at this final result: goldsmiths and jewellers, four; ecclesiastics, three; lawyers, two; comedians, one; artist musicians, one; men of letters, not one.

The transformation of the crowd into the people,—profound labour! It is to this labour that the men called socialists have devoted themselves during the last forty years. The author of this book, however insignificant he may be, is one of the oldest in this labour; "Le Dernier Jour d'un Condamné" dates from 1828, and "Claude Gueux" from 1834. He claims his place among these philosophers because it is a place of persecution. A certain hatred of socialism, very blind, but very general, has been at work for fifteen or sixteen years, and is still at work most bitterly among the influential classes. (Classes, then, are still in existence?) Let it not be forgotten, socialism, true socialism, has for its end the elevation of the masses to the civic dignity, and therefore its principal care is for moral and intellectual cultivation. The first hunger is ignorance; socialism wishes then, above all, to instruct. That does not hinder socialism from being calumniated, and socialists from being denounced. To most of the infuriated, trembling cowards who have their say at the present moment, these reformers are public enemies. They are guilty of everything that has gone wrong. "O Romans!" said Tertullian, "we are just, kind, thinking, lettered, honest men. We meet to pray, and we love you because you are our brethren. We are gentle and peaceable like little children, and we wish for concord among men. Nevertheless, O Romans! if the Tiber overflows, or if the Nile does not, you cry, 'to the lions with the Christians!'"

LIBERTY

THE democratic idea, the new bridge of civilization, undergoes at this moment the formidable trial of overweight. Every other idea would certainly give way under the load that it is made to bear. Democracy proves its solidity by the absurdities that are heaped on, without shaking it. It must resist everything that people choose to place on it. At this moment they try to make it carry despotism.

The people have no need of liberty,—such was the pass-word of a certain in-

nocent and duped school, the head of which has been dead some years. That poor honest dreamer believed in good faith that men can keep progress with them when they turn out liberty. We have heard him put forth, probably without meaning it, this aphorism: Liberty is good for the rich. These kinds of maxims have the disadvantage of not being prejudicial to the establishment of empires.

No, no, no! Nothing out of liberty.

Servitude is the blind soul. Can you figure to yourself a man blind voluntarily? This terrible thing exists. There are willing slaves. A smile in irons! Can anything be more hideous? He who is not free is not a man; he who is not free has no sight, no knowledge, no discernment, no growth, no comprehension, no will, no faith, no love; he has no wife, he has no children: he has a female and young ones; he lives not,—*ab luce principium*. Liberty is the apple of the eye. Liberty is the visual organ of progress.

Because liberty has inconveniences, and even perils, to wish to create civilization without it is just the same as to try cultivation without the sun; the sun is also a censurable heavenly body. One day, in the too beautiful summer of 1829, a critic, now forgotten,—and wrongly, for he was not without some talent,—M. P., suffering from the heat, sharpened his pen, saying, "I am going to excoriate the sun."

Certain social theories, very distinct from socialism such as we understand and want it, have gone astray. Let us discard all that resembles the convent, the barrack, the cell and the straight-line system. Paraguay, minus the

Jesuits, is Paraguay just the same. To give a new fashion to evil is not a useful task. To recommence the old slavery is idiotic. Let the nations of Europe beware of a despotism made anew from materials they have to some extent themselves supplied. Such a thing, cemented with a special philosophy, might well last. We have just mentioned the theorists, some of whom otherwise right and sincere, who, by dint of fearing the dispersion of activities and energies, and of what they call "anarchy," have arrived at an almost Chinese acceptation of absolute social concentration. They turn their resignation into a doctrine. Provided man eats and drinks, all is right. The happiness of the beast is the solution. But this is a happiness which some other men would call by a different name.

We dream for nations something else besides a felicity solely made up of obedience. The bastinado procures that sort of felicity for the Turkish fellah, the knout for the Russian serf, and the cat-o'-nine-tails for the English soldier. These socialists by the side of socialism come from Joseph de Maistre, and from Ancillon, without suspecting it perhaps; for the ingenuousness of these theorists rallied to the *fait accompli* has —or fancies it has—democratic intentions, and speaks energetically of the "principles of '89." Let these involuntary philosophers of a possible despotism think a moment. To teach the masses a doctrine against liberty; to cram intellects with appetites and fatalism, a certain situation being given; to saturate it with materialism; and to run the risk of the construction which might proceed from it,—that would be

to understand progress in the fashion of the worthy man who applauded a new gibbet, and who exclaimed, "This is all right! We have had till now but the old wooden gallows. To-day the age advances; and here we are with a good stone gibbet, which will do for our children and grandchildren!"

LIGHT

To enjoy a full stomach, a satisfied intestine, a satiated belly, is doubtless something, for it is the enjoyment of the brute. However, one may place one's ambition higher.

Certainly, a good salary is a fine thing. To tread on this firm ground, high wages, is pleasant. The wise man likes to want nothing. To insure his own position is the characteristic of an intelligent man. An official chair, with ten thousand sesterces a year, is a graceful and convenient seat. Great emoluments give a fresh complexion and good health.. One lives to an old age in pleasant, well-paid sinecures. The high financial world, rich in plentiful profits, is a place agreeable to live in. To be well at Court settles a family well and brings a fortune. As for myself, I prefer to all these solid comforts the old leaky vessel in which Bishop Quodvultdeus embarks with a smile.

There is something beyond gorging one's self. The goal of man is not the goal of the animal.

A moral enhancement is necessary. The life of nations, like the life of individuals, has its minutes of depression; these minutes pass, certainly, but no trace of them ought to remain. Man, at this hour, tends to fall into the stomach. Man must be replaced in the heart; man must be replaced in the brain. The brain,—behold the sovereign that must be restored! The social question requires to-day, more than ever, to be examined on the side of human dignity.

To show man the human end, to ameliorate intelligence first, the animal afterward, to disdain the flesh as long as the thought is despised, and to give the example on their own flesh,—such is the actual, immediate urgent duty of writers.

It is what men of genius have done at all times.

You ask in what poets can be useful? In imbuing civilization with light,—only that.

LITERATURE

Up to this day there has been a literature of *literati*. In France, particularly, as we have said, literature had a disposition to form a caste. To be a poet was something like being a mandarin. Words did not all belong by right to the language. The dictionary granted or did not grant the registration. The dictionary had a will of its own. Imagine the botanist declaring to a vegetable that it does not exist, and Nature timidly offering an insect to entomology, which refuses it as incorrect. Imagine astronomy cavilling at the stars. We recollect having heard an Academician, now dead, say in full academy that French had been spoken in France only in the seventeenth century, and then for only twelve years,—we do not remember which twelve. Let us give up,

for it is time, this order of ideas; democracy requires it. The actual enlarging of thoughts needs something else. Let us leave the college, the conclave, the cell, the weak taste, weak art, the small chapel. Poetry is not a coterie. There is at this hour an effort made to galvanize dead things. Let us strive against this tendency. Let us insist on the truths which are urgent. The *chefs-d'œuvre* recommended by the manual of bachelorship, compliments in verse and in prose, tragedies soaring over the head of some king, inspiration in full official dress, the brilliant nonentities fixing laws on poetry, the *Arts poétiques* which forget La Fontaine, and for which Molière is doubtful, the Planats castrating the Corneilles, prudish tongues, the thoughts enclosed between four walls, and limited by Quintilian, Longinus, Boileau, and La Harpe,—all that, although official and public teaching is filled and saturated with it, all that belongs to the past. Some particular epoch, which is called the grand century, and for a certainty the fine century, is nothing else in reality but a literary monologue. Is it possible to realize such a strange thing,—a literature which is an aside? It seems as if one read on the frontal of art "No admittance." As for ourselves, we understand poetry only with the door wide open. The hour has struck for hoisting the "All for All." What is needed by civilization, henceforth a grown-up woman, is a popular literature.

1830 has opened a debate, literary on the surface, at the bottom social and human. The moment is come to close the debate. We close it by asking a literature having in view this purpose: "The People."

The author of these pages wrote, thirty-one years ago, in the preface to "Lucrèce Borgia," a few words often repeated since: "Le poëte a charge d'âmes." He would add here, if it were worth saying, that, allowing for possible error, the words, uttered by his conscience, have been his rule throughout life.

MACCHIAVELLI

MACCHIAVELLI had a strange idea of the people. To heap the measure, to overflow the cup, to exaggerate horror in the case of the prince, to increase the crushing in order to stir up the oppressed to revolt, to cause idolatry to change into a curse, to push the masses to extremities,—such seems to be his policy. His "yes" signifies "no." He loads the despot with despotism in order to make him burst. The tyrant becomes in his hands a hideous projectile, which will break to pieces. Macchiavelli conspires. For whom? Against whom? Guess. His apotheosis of kings is just the thing to make regicides. On the head of his prince he places a diadem of crimes, a tiara of vices, a halo of baseness; and he invites you to adore his monster, with the air of a man expecting an avenger. He glorifies evil with a squint toward the darkness,— the darkness wherein is Harmodius. Macchiavelli, the getter-up of princely outrages, the valet of the Medici and of the Borgias, had in his youth been put to the rack for having admired Brutus and Cassius. He had perhaps plotted with the Soderini the deliverance of Florence. Does he recollect it? Does he continue? His advice is followed, like the lightning, by a low rumbling in the cloud,—alarming reverberation. What did he mean to say? On whom has he a design? Is the advice for or against him to whom he gives it? One day, at Florence, in the garden of Cosmo Ruccelaï, there being present the Duke of Mantua and John de Medici, who afterward commanded the Black Bands of Tuscany, Varchi, the enemy of Macchiavelli, heard him say to the two princes: "Let the people read no book,—not even mine." It is curious to compare with this remark the advice given by Voltaire to the Duke de Choiseul,—at the same time advice to the minister, and insinuation for the king: "Let the boobies read our nonsense. There is no danger in reading, my lord. What can a great king like the King of France fear? The people are but rabble, and the books are but trash." Let them read nothing, let them read everything: these two pieces of contrary advice coincide more than one would think. Voltaire, with hidden claws, is purring at the feet of the king, Voltaire and Macchiavelli are two formidable indirect revolutionists, dissimilar in everything, and yet identical in reality by their profound hatred, disguised in flattery, of the master. The one is malignant, the other is sinister. The princes of the sixteenth century had as theoriest on their infamies, and as enigmatical courtier, Macchiavelli, an enthusiast dark at heart. The flattery of a sphinx,—terrible thing! Better yet be flattered, like Louis XV., by a cat.

Conclusion: Make the people read

Macchiavelli, and make them read Voltaire.

Macchiavelli will inspire them with horror of, and Voltaire with contempt for, crowned guilt.

But the hearts should turn, above all, toward the grand pure poets, whether they be sweet like Virgil or bitter like Juvenal.

PROGRESS

THE progress of man by the education of minds,—there is no safety but in that. Teach! learn! All the revolutions of the future are enclosed and imbedded in this phrase: Gratuitous and obligatory instruction.

It is by the unfolding of works of the highest order that this vast intellectual teaching should be crowned. At the top the men of genius.

Wherever there is a gathering of men, there ought to be in a special place, a public expositor of the great thinkers.

By a great thinker we mean a beneficent thinker.

The perpetual presence of the beautiful in their works maintains poets at the summit of teaching.

No one can foresee the quantity of light which will be brought forth by letting the people be in communication with men of genius. This combination of the hearts of the people with the heart of the poet will be the Voltaic pile of civilization.

Will the people understand this magnificent teaching? Certainly. We know of nothing too lofty for the people. The people are a great soul. Have you ever gone on a fête-day to a theatre open gratuitously to all? What do you think of that auditory? Do you know of any other more spontaneous and intelligent? Do you know, even in the forest, of a vibration more profound? The court of Versailles admires like a well-drilled regiment; the people throw themselves passionately into the beautiful. They pack together, crowd, amalgamate, combine, and knead themselves in the theatre,—a living paste that the poet is about to mould. The powerful thumb of Molière will presently make its mark on it; the nail of Corneille will scratch this ill-shaped heap. Whence does that heap come? Whence does it proceed? From the Courtille, from the Porcherons, from the Cunette; it is shoeless, it is bare-armed, it is ragged. Silence! This is the human block.

The house is crowded, the vast multitude looks, listens, loves; all consciences, deeply moved, throw off their inner fire; all eyes glisten; the huge beast with a thousand heads is there,—the Mob of Burke, the *Plebs* of Titus Livius, the *Fex urbis* of Cicero. It caresses the beautiful; smiling at it with the grace of a woman. It is literary in the most refined sense of the word; nothing equals the delicacy of this monster. The tumultous crowd trembles, blushes, palpitates. Its modesty is surprising; the crowd is a virgin. No prudery however; this brute is not brutal. Not a sympathy escapes it; it has in itself the whole keyboard, from passion to irony, from sarcasm to sobbing. Its compassion is more than compassion; it is real mercy. God is felt in it. All at once the sublime passes, and the sombre electricity of the abyss heaves up suddenly all this pile of hearts and entrails;

enthusiasm effects a transfiguration. And now, is the enemy at the gates, is the country in danger? Appeal to that populace, and it would enact the sublime drama of Thermopylæ. Who has called forth such a metamorphosis? Poetry.

The multitude (and in this lies their grandeur) are profoundly open to the ideal. When they come in contact with lofty art they are pleased, they shudder. Not a detail escapes them. The crowd is one liquid and living expanse capable of vibration. A mass is a sensitive-plant. Contact with the beautiful agitates ecstatically the surface of multitudes,—sure sign that the depth is sounded. A rustling of leaves, a mysterious breath, passes, the crowd trembles under the sacred insufflation of the abyss.

And even where the man of the people is not in a crowd, he is yet a good hearer of great things. His ingenuousness is honest, his curiosity healthy. Ignorance is a longing. His near connection with Nature renders him subject to the holy emotion of the true. He has, toward poetry, secret natural desires which he does not suspect himself. All the teachings are due to the people. The more divine the light, the more it is made for this simple soul. We would have in the villages a pulpit from which Homer should be explained to the peasants.

THE IDEAL

Too much matter is the evil of our day. Hence a certain dulness.

It is necessary to restore some ideal in the human mind. Whence shall you take your ideal? Where is it? The poets, the philosophers, the thinkers are the urns. The ideal is in Æschylus, in Isaiah, in Juvenal, in Alighieri, in Shakespeare. Throw Æschylus, throw Isaiah, throw Juvenal, throw Dante, throw Shakespeare into the deep soul of the human race.

Pour Job, Solomon, Pindar, Ezekiel, Sophocles, Euripides, Herodotus, Theocritus, Plautus, Lucretius, Virgil, Terence, Horace, Catullus, Tacitus, Saint Paul, Saint Augustine, Tertullian, Petrarch, Pascal, Milton, Descartes, Corneille, La Fontaine, Montesquieu, Diderot, Rousseau, Beaumarchais, Sedaine, André Chénier, Kant, Byron, Schiller,—pour all these souls into man. And with them pour all the wits from Æsop up to Molière, all the intellects from Plato up to Newton, all the encyclopædists from Aristotle up to Voltaire.

By that means, while curing the illness for the moment, you will establish forever the health of the human mind.

You will cure the middle class and found the people.

As we have said just now, after the destruction which has delivered the world, you will construct the edifice which shall make it prosper.

What an aim,—to make the people! Principles combined with science; every possible quantity of the absolute introduced by degrees into the fact; Utopia treated successively by every mode of realization,—by political economy, by philosophy, by physics, by chemistry, by dynamics, by logic, by art; union replacing little by little antagonism, and unity replacing union; for religion God, for priest the father, for prayer virtue, for field the whole earth, for language the verb, for law the right, for motive-power duty, for hygiene labour, for economy universal peace, for canvas the very life, for the goal progress, for authority liberty, for people the man,—such is the simplification.

And at the summit the ideal.

The ideal!—inflexible type of perpetual progress.

To whom belong men of genius if not to thee, people? They do belong to thee; they are thy sons and thy fathers. Thou givest birth to them, and they teach thee. They open in thy chaos vistas of light. Children, they have drunk thy sap. They have leaped in the universal matrix, humanity. Each of thy phases, people, is an avatar. The deep essence of life, it is in thee that it must be looked for. Thou art the great bosom. Geniuses are begotten from thee, mysterious crowd.

Let them therefore return to thee.

People, the author, God, dedicates them to thee.

FRATERNIZATION

THE nineteenth century springs from itself only; it does not receive its impulse from any ancestor; it is the offspring of an idea. Doubtless, Isaiah, Homer, Aristotle, Dante, Shakespeare, have been or could be great starting-points for important philosophical or poetical formations; but the nineteenth century has an august mother,—the French Revolution. It has that powerful blood in its veins. It honours men of genius. When denied it salutes them, when ignored it proclaims them, when persecuted it avenges them, when insulted it crowns them, when dethroned it replaces them upon their pedestal; it venerates them, but it does not proceed from them. The nineteenth century has for family itself, and itself alone. It is the characteristic of its revolutionary nature to dispense with ancestors.

Itself a genius, it fraternizes with men of genius. As for its source, it is where theirs is,—beyond man. The mysterious gestations of progress succeed each other according to a providential law. The nineteenth century is born of civilization. It has a continent to bring into the world. France has borne this century; and this century bears Europe.

The Greek stock bore civilization, narrow and circumscribed at first by the mulberry leaf, confined to the Morea; then civilization, gaining step by step, grew broader, and formed the Roman stock. It is to-day the French stock,—that is to say, all Europe,—with young shoots in America, Africa, and Asia.

The greatest of these young shoots is a democracy,—the United States, the sprouting of which was aided by France in the last century. France, sublime essayist in progress, has founded a republic in America before making one in Europe. *Et vidit quod esset bonum.* After having lent to Washington an auxiliary, Lafayette, France, returning home, gave to Voltaire, dismayed within his tomb, that formidable successor, Danton. In presence of the monstrous past, hurling every thunder, exhaling every miasma, breathing every darkness, protruding every talon, horrible and terrible, progress, constrained to use the same weapons, has had suddenly a hundred arms, a hundred heads, a hundred tongues of fire, a hundred roarings. The good has transformed itself into a hydra. It is this that is termed the Revolution. Nothing can be more august.

The Revolution ended one century and began another.

An intellectual awakening prepares the way for an overthrow of facts,—and this is the eighteenth century. After which the political revolution, once accomplished, seeks expression, and the literary and social revolution completes it: this is the nineteenth century. With ill-will, but not unjustly, has it been said that romanticism and socialism are identical: hatred, in its desire to injure, very often establishes, and, so far as is in its power, consolidates.

A parenthesis. This word, *romanticism,* has, like all war-cries, the advantage of readily summing up a group of ideas. It is brief,—which pleases in the contest; but it has, to our idea, through its militant signification, the objection of appearing to limit the movement that it represents to a warlike action. Now, this movement is a matter of intellect, a matter of civilization, a matter of soul; and this is why the writer of these lines has never used the words *romanticism* or *romantic.* They will not be found in any of the pages of criticism that he has had occasion to write. If to-day he derogates from his usual prudence in polemics, it is for the sake of greater rapidity and with all reservation. The same observation may be made on the subject of the word *socialism,* which admits of so many different interpretations.

The triple movement—literary, philosophical, and social—of the nineteenth century, which is one single movement, is nothing but the current of the revolution in ideas. This current, after having swept away facts, is perpetuated in minds with all its immensity.

This term, *"literary '93,"* so often quoted in 1830 against contemporaneous literature, was not so much an insult as it was intended to be. It was certainly as unjust to employ it as characterizing the whole literary movement as it is iniquitous to employ it to describe all the political revolutions; there is in these two phenomena something besides '93. But this term, *"literary '93,"* was relatively exact, insomuch as it indicated, confusedly but truthfully, the origin of the literary movement which belongs to our epoch, while endeavouring to dishonour that movement. Here again the clairvoyance of hatred was blind. Its daubings of mud upon the face of truth are gilding, light, and glory.

The Revolution, turning climacteric of humanity, is made up of several years. Each of these years expresses a period, represents an aspect, or realizes a phase of the phenomenon. Tragic '93 is one of those colossal years. Good news must sometimes have a mouth of bronze. Such a mouth is '93.

Listen to the immense proclamation proceeding from it. Give attention, remain speechless, and be impressed. God himself said the first time *Fiat lux,* the second time he has caused it to be said.

By whom?

By '93.

Therefore, we men of the nineteenth century hold in honour that reproach, "You are '93."

But do not stop there. We are '89 as well as '93. The Revolution, the whole Revolution,—such is the source of the literature of the nineteenth century.

On these grounds put it on its trial, this literature, or seek its triumph; hate it or love it. According to the amount of the future that you have in you, outrage it or salute it; little do animosities and fury affect it. It is the logical deduction from the great chaotic and genesiacal fact that our fathers have witnessed, and which has given a new starting-point to the world. He who is against the fact is against that literature; he who is for that fact is on its side. What the fact is worth the literature is worth. The reactionary writers are not mistaken; whenever there is revolution, patent or latent, the Catholic and royalist scent is unfailing. Those men of letters of the past award to contemporaneous literature an honourable amount of diatribe; their aversion is convulsive. One of their journalists, who is, I believe a bishop, pronounces this word *poet* with the same accent as the word *Septembrist;* another, less of a bishop, but quite as angry, writes, "I feel in all this literature Marat and Robespierre." This last writer is rather mistaken; there is in "this literature" Danton rather than Marat.

But the fact is true: democracy is in this literature.

The Revolution has forged the clarion; the nineteenth century sounds it.

Ah, this affirmation suits us, and, in truth, we do not recoil before it; we avow our glory,—we are revolutionists. The thinkers of the present time,—poets, writers, historians, orators, philosophers, —all are derived from the French Revolution. They come from it, and it alone. It was '89 that demolished the Bastille; it was '93 that took the crown from the Louvre. From '89 sprung Deliverance, and from '93 Victory. From '89 and '93 the men of the nineteenth century proceed: these are their father and their mother. Do not seek for them another affiliation, another inspiration, another insufflation, another origin. They are the democrats of the idea, successors to the democrats of action. They are the emancipators. Liberty bent over their cradles,—they all have sucked her vast breast; they all have her milk in their entrails, her marrow in their bones, her sap in their will, her spirit of revolt in their reason, her flame in their intellect.

Even those among them (there are some) who were born aristocrats, who came to the world banished in some degree among families of the past, who have fatally received one of those primary educations whose stupid effort is to contradict progress, and who have commenced the words that they had to say to our century with an indescribable royalist stuttering,—these, from that period, from their infancy (they will not contradict me), felt the sublime monster within them. They had the inner ebullition of the immense fact. They had in the depth of their conscience a whispering of mysterious ideas; the inward shock of false certainties troubled their mind; they felt their sombre surface of monarchism, catholicism, and aristocracy tremble, shudder, and by degrees split up. One day, suddenly and powerfully, the swelling of truth within them prevailed, the hatching was completed, the eruption took place; the light flamed in them, causing them to burst open,—not falling on them, but (more beautiful mystery!) gushing out of these amazed men, enlightening them, while it burned within them. They were craters unknown to themselves.

This phenomenon has been interpreted to their reproach as a treason. They passed over, in fact, from right divine to human right. They turned their back on false history, on false tradition, on false dogmas, on false philosophy, on false daylight, on false truth. The free spirit which soars up,—bird called by Aurora,—offends intellects saturated with ignorance and the fœtus preserved in spirits of wine. He who sees offends the blind; he who hears makes the deaf indignant; he who walks offers an abominable insult to cripples. In the eyes of dwarfs, abortions, Aztecs, myrmidons, and pygmies, forever subject to rickets, growth is apostasy.

The writers and poets of the nineteenth century have the admirable good fortune of proceeding from a genesis, of arriving after an end of the world, of accompanying a reappearance of light, of being the organs of a new beginning. This imposes on them duties unknown to their predecessors—the duties of intentional reformers and direct civilizers. They continue nothing; they remake everything. For new times, new duties. The function of thinkers in our days is complex; to think is no longer sufficient,—they must love; to think and love is no longer sufficient,—they must act; to think, to love, and to act, no longer suffices,—they must suffer. Lay down the pen, and go where you hear the grapeshot. Here is a barricade; be one on it. Here is exile; accept it. Here is the scaffold; be it so. Let John Brown be in Montesquieu, if needful. The Lucretius required by this century in labour should contain Cato. Æschylus, who wrote the "Orestias," had for a brother Cynegyrus, who fastened with his teeth on the ships of the enemies: that was sufficient for Greece at the time of Salamis, but it no longer suffices for France after the Revolution. That Æschylus and Cynegyrus are brothers is not enough; they must be the same man. Such are the actual requirements of progress. Those who devote themselves to great and pressing things can never be too great. To set ideas in motion, to heap up evidence, to pile up principles, that is the redoubtable movement. To heap Pelion on Ossa is the labour of infants beside that work of giants, the placing of right upon truth. To scale that afterward, and to dethrone usurpations in the midst of thunders,— such is the work.

The future presses. To-morrow cannot wait. Humanity has not a minute to lose. Quick! quick! let us hasten; the wretched ones have their feet on red-hot iron. They hunger, they thirst, they suffer. Ah, terrible emaciation of the poor human body! Parasitism laughs, the ivy grows green and thrives, the mistletoe is flourishing, the tapeworm is happy. What a frightful object the prosperity of the tapeworm! To destroy that which devours,—in that is safety. Your life has within itself death, which is in good health. There is too much misery, too much desolation, too much immodesty, too much nakedness, too many brothels, too many prisons, too many rags, too many crimes, too much weakness, too much darkness, not enough schools, too many little innocents growing up for evil! The trucklebeds of poor girls are suddenly covered with silk and lace,—and in that is worse misery; by the side of misfortune there is vice, the one urging the other. Such a society requires prompt succour. Let us seek for the best. Go all of you in this search. Where are the promised lands? Civilization would go forward; let us try theories, systems, ameliorations, inventions, progress, until the shoe for that foot shall be found. The attempt costs nothing, or costs but little,—to attempt is not to adopt,— but before all, above all, let us be lavish of light. All sanitary purification begins in opening windows wide. Let us open wide all intellects. Let us supply souls with air.

Quick, quick, O thinkers! Let the human race breathe; give hope, give the ideal, do good. Let one step succeed another, horizon expand into horizon, conquest follow conquest. Because you have given what you promised do not think you have performed all that is required of you. To possess is to promise; the dawn of to-day imposes on the sun obligations for to-morrow.

Let nothing be lost. Let not one strength be isolated. Every one to work! there is vast urgency for it. No more idle art. Poetry the worker of civilization, what more admirable? The dreamer should be a pioneer; the strophe should mean something. The beautiful should be at the service of honesty. I am the valet of my conscience; it rings for me: I come. "Go!" I go. What do you require of me, O truth, sole majesty of this world? Let each one feel in haste to do well. A book is sometimes a source of hoped-for succour. An idea is a balm, a word may be a dressing for wounds; poetry is a physician. Let no one tarry. Suffering is losing its strength while you are idling. Let men leave this dreamy laziness. Leave the kief to the Turks. Let men labour for the safety of all, and let them rush into it and be out of breath.

Do not be sparing of your strides. Nothing useless; no inertia. What do you call dread nature? Everything lives. The duty of all is to live; to walk, to run, to fly, to soar, is the universal law. What do you wait for? Who stops you? Ah, there are times one might wish to hear the stones murmur at the slowness of man!

Sometimes one goes into the woods. To whom does it not happen at times to be overwhelmed?—one sees so many sad things. The stage is a long one to go over, the consequences are long in coming, a generation is behindhand, the work of the age languishes. What! so many sufferings yet? One might think he has gone backward. There is everywhere increase of superstition, of cowardice, of deafness, of blindness, of imbecility. Penal laws weigh upon brutishness. This wretched problem has been set,—to augment comfort by putting off right; to sacrifice the superior side of man to the inferior side; to yield up principle to appetite. Cæsar takes charge for the belly, I make over to him the brains,—it is the old sale of a birth-right for the dish of porridge. A little more, and this fatal anomaly would cause a wrong road to be taken toward civilization. The fattening pig would no longer be the king, but the people. Alas! this ugly expedient does not even succeed. No diminution whatever of the malady. In the last ten years—for the last twenty years—the low water-mark of prostitution, of mendicity, of crime, has been stationary, below which evil has not fallen one degree. Of true education, of gratuitous education, there is none. The infant nevertheless requires to know that he is man, and the father that he is citizen. Where are the promises? Where is the hope? Oh, poor wretched humanity! one is tempted to shout for help in the forest; one is tempted to claim support, assistance, and a strong arm from that grand mournful Nature. Can this mysterious *ensemble* of forces be indifferent to progress? We supplicate, appeal, raise our hands toward the shadow. We listen, wondering if the rustlings will become voices. The duty of the springs and streams should be to babble forth the word "Forward!" One could wish to hear nightingales sing new Marseillaises.

Notwithstanding all this, these times of halting are nothing beyond what is normal. Discouragement would be puerile. There are halts, repose, breathing spaces in the march of peoples, as there are winters in the progress of the seasons. The gigantic step, '89, is all the same a fact. To despair would be absurd, but to stimulate is necessary.

To stimulate, to press, to chide, to awaken, to suggest, to inspire,—it is this function, fulfilled everywhere by writers, which impresses on the literature of this century so high a character of power and originality. To remain faithful to all the laws of art, while combining them with the law of progress,—such is the problem, victoriously solved by so many noble and proud minds.

Thence this word *deliverance,* which appears above everything in the light, as if it were written on the very forehead of the ideal.

The Revolution is France sublimed. There was a day when France was in the furnace,—the furnace causes wings to grow on certain warlike martyrs,—and from amid the flames this giant came forth archangel. At this day by all the world, France is called Revolution; and henceforth this word *revolution* will be the name of civilization, until it can be replaced by the word *harmony.* I repeat it: do not seek elsewhere the starting-point and the birth-place of the literature of the nineteenth century. Yes, as many as there be of us, great and small, powerful and unknown, illustrious and obscure, in all our works good or bad, whatever they may be,—poems, dramas, romances, history, philosophy,—at the tribune of assemblies as before the crowds of the theatre, as in the meditation of solitudes; yes, everywhere; yes, always; yes, to combat violence and imposture; yes, to rehabilitate those who are stoned and run down; yes, to sum up logically and to march straight onward; yes, to console, to succour, to relieve, to encourage, to teach; yes, to dress wounds in hope of curing them; yes, to transform charity into fraternity, alms into assistance, sluggishness into work, idleness into utility, centralization into a family, iniquity into justice, the *bourgeois* into the citizen, the populace into the people, the rabble into the nation, nations into humanity, war into love, prejudice into free examination, frontiers into solderings, limits into openings, ruts into rails, vestry-rooms into temples, the instinct of evil into the desire of good, life into right, kings into men; yes, to deprive religions of hell and societies of the galley; yes, to be brothers to the wretched, the serf, the fellah, the *prolétaire,* the disinherited, the banished, the betrayed, the conquered, the sold, the enchained, the sacrificed, the prostitute, the convict, the ignorant, the savage, the slave, the negro, the condemned, and the damned, —yes, we are thy sons, Revolution!

Yes, men of genius; yes, poets, philosophers, historians; yes, giants of that great art of previous ages which is all the light of the past,—O men eternal, the minds of this day salute you, but do not follow you; in respect to you they hold to this law,—to admire everything, to imitate nothing. Their function is no longer yours. They have business with the virility of the human race. The hour which makes mankind of age has struck. We assist, under the full light of the ideal, at that majestic junction of the beautiful with the useful. No actual or possible genius can surpass you, ye men of genius of old; to equal you is all the ambition allowed: but, to equal you, one must conform to the necessities of our time, as you supplied the necessities of yours. Writers who are sons of the Revolution have a holy task.

O Homer, their epic poem must weep; O Herodotus, their history must protest; O Juvenal, their satire must dethrone; O Shakespeare, their "thou shalt be king," must be said to the people; O Æschylus, their Prometheus must strike Jupiter with thunderbolts; O Job, their dunghill must be fruitful; O Dante, their hell must be extinguished; O Isaiah, thy Babylon crumbles, theirs must blaze forth with light! They do what you have done; they contemplate creation directly, they observe humanity directly; they do not accept as a guiding light any refracted ray,— not even yours. Like you, they have for their sole starting-point, outside them, universal being: in them, their soul. They have for the source of their work the one source whence flows Nature and whence flows art, the infinite. As the writer of these lines said forty years ago: "The poets and the writers of the nineteenth century have neither masters nor models." No; in all that vast and sublime art of all peoples, in all those grand creations of all epochs, —no, not even thee, Æschylus, not even thee, Dante, not even thee, Shakespeare, —no, they have neither models nor masters. And why have they neither masters nor models? It is because they have one model, Man, and because they have one master, God.

The Face of Cain

HERE is the advent of the new constellation.

It is certain that at the present hour that which has been till now the light of the human race grows pale, and that the old flame is about to disappear from the world.

The men of brutal force have, since human tradition existed, shone alone in the empyrean of history; theirs was the only supremacy. Under the various names of kings, emperors, captains, chiefs, princes,—summed up in the word heroes,—this group of an apocalypse was resplendent. They were all dripping with victories. Terror transformed itself into acclamation to salute them. They dragged after them an indescribable tumultuous flame. They appeared to man in a disorder of horrible light. They did not light up the heavens,— they set them on fire. They looked as if they meant to take possession of the Infinite. Rumbling crashes were heard in their glory. A red glare mingled with it. Was it purple? Was it blood? Was is shame? Their light made one think of the face of Cain. They hated one another. Flashing shocks passed from one to the other; at times these enormous planets came into collision, striking out lightnings. Their look was furious. Their radiance stretched out into swords. All that hung terrible above us.

That tragic glare fills the past. To-day it is in full process of waning.

There is decline in war, decline in despotism, decline in theocracy, decline in slavery, decline in the scaffold. The blade becomes shorter, the tiara is fading away, the crown is simplified; war is raging, the plume bends lower, usurpation is circumscribed, the chain is lightened, the rack is out of countenance. The antique violence of the few against all, called right divine, is coming to an end. Legitimacy, the grace of God, the monarchy of Pharamond, nations branded on the shoulder with the *fleur-de-lis*, the possession of peoples by the right of birth, the long series of ancestors giving right over the living,— these things are yet striving in some places; at Naples, in Prussia, etc.; but they are struggling rather than striving. —it is death that strains for life. A stammering which to-morrow will be utterance, and the day after to-morrow a full declaration, proceeds from the bruised lips of the serf, of the vassal, of the *prolétaire*, of the pariah. The gag breaks up between the teeth of the human race. The human race has had enough of the sorrowful path, and the patient refuses to go farther.

From this very time certain forms of despotism are no longer possible. The Pharaoh is a mummy, the sultan a phantom, the Cæsar a counterfeit. This stylite of the Trajan columns is anchylosed on its pedestal; it has on its head the excrement of free eagles; it is nihility rather than glory; the bands of the sepulchre fasten this crown of laurels.

The period of the men of brutal force is gone. They have been glorious, certainly, but with a glory that melts away. That species of great men is soluble in progress. Civilization rapidly oxidizes these bronzes. At the point of maturity to which the French Revolution has already brought the universal conscience, the hero is no longer a hero without a good reason; the captain is discussed, the conqueror is inadmissible. In our days Louis XIV. invading the Palatinate would look like a robber. From the last century these realities began to dawn. Frederick II., in the presence of Voltaire, felt and owned himself somewhat of a brigand. To be a great man of matter, to be pompously violent, to govern by the sword-knot and the cockade, to forge right upon force, to hammer out justice and truth by blows of accomplished facts, to make brutalities of genius,—is to be grand, if you like; but it is a coarse manner of being grand, —glories announced with drums which are met with a shrug of the shoulders. Sonorous heroes have deafened human reason until to-day; that pompous noise begins now to weary it. It shuts its eyes and ears before those authorized slaughters that they call battles. The sublime murderers of men have had their time; it is in a certain relative forgetfulness that henceforth they will be illustrious and august; humanity, become greater, requires to dispense with them. The food for guns thinks; it reflects, and is actually losing its admiration for being shot down by a cannon-ball.

A few figures by the way may not be useless.

All tragedy is part of our subject. The tragedy of poets is not the only one; there is the tragedy of politicians and statesmen. Would you like to know how much that tragedy costs?

Heroes have an enemy; that enemy is called finance. For a long time the amount of money paid for that kind of glory was ignored. In order to disguise the total, there were convenient little fireplaces like that in which Louis XIV. burned the accounts of Versailles. That day the smoke of one thousand millions of francs passed out the chimney of the royal stove.

The nation did not even take notice. At the present day nations have one great virtue,—they are miserly. They know that prodigality is the mother of abasement. They reckon up; they learn bookkeeping by double entry. Warlike glory henceforth has its debit and credit account: that renders it impossible.

The greatest warrior of modern times is not Napoleon, it is Pitt. Napoleon carried on warfare; Pitt created it. It is Pitt who willed all the wars of the Revolution and of the empire; they proceeded from him. Take away Pitt and put Fox in his place, there would then be no reason for that exorbitant battle of twenty-three years, there would be no longer any coalition. Pitt was the soul of the coalition, and he dead, his soul remained amidst the universal war. What Pitt cost England and the world, here it is. We add this bas-relief to his pedestal.

In the first place, the expenditure in men. From 1791 to 1814 France alone, striving against Europe, coalesced by England,—France constrained and compelled, expended in butcheries for military glory (and also, let us add, for the defence of territory) five millions of men; that is to say, six hundred men per day. Europe, including the total of France, has expended sixteen millions, six hundred thousand men; that is to say, two thousand deaths per day during twenty-three years.

Secondly, the expenditure of money. We have, unfortunately, no authentic total, save the total of England. From 1791 to 1814 England, in order to make France succumb to Europe, became indebted to the extent of eighty-one millions, two hundred and sixty-five thousand, eight hundred and forty-two pounds sterling. Divide this total by the total of men killed, at the rate of two thousand per day for twenty-three years, and you arrive at this result,—that each corpse stretched on the field of battle has cost England alone fifty pounds sterling.

Add the total of Europe,—total unknown, but enormous.

With these seventeen millions of dead men, they might have peopled Australia with Europeans. With the eighty millions expended by England in cannonshots, they might have changed the face of the earth, begun the work of civilization exerywhere, and suppressed throughout the entire world ignorance and misery.

England pays eighty millions for the two statues of Pitt and Wellington.

It is a fine thing to have heroes, but it is an expensive luxury. Poets cost less.

SPLENDOUR IN THE DISTANCE

THE discharge of the warrior is signed: it is splendour in the distance. The great Nimrod, the great Cyrus, the great Sennacherib, the great Sesostris, the great Alexander, the great Pyrrhus, the great Hannibal, the great Cæsar, the great Timour, the great Louis, the great Frederic, and more great ones,—all are going away.

It would be a mistake to think that we reject these men purely and simply. In our eyes five or six of those that we have named are legitimately illustrious; they have even mingled something good in their ravages; their definitive total embarrasses the absolute equity of the thinker, and they weigh nearly even weights in the balance of the injurious and the useful.

Others have been only injurious. They are numerous, innumerable even; for the masters of the world are a crowd.

The thinker is the weigher. Clemency suits him. Let us therefore say, Those others who have done only evil have one attenuating circumstance,—imbecility.

They have another excuse yet,—the mental condition of the human race itself at the moment they appeared; the medium surrounding facts, modifiable, but encumbering.

It is not men that are tyrants, but things. The real tyrants are called frontier, track, routine; blindness under the form of fanaticism, deafness and dumbness under the form of diversity of languages; quarrel under the form of diversity of weights, measures, and moneys; hatred resulting from quarrel, war resulting from hatred. All these tyrants may be called by one name,—separation. Division, whence proceeds irresponsible government,—this is despotism in the abstract.

Even the tyrants of flesh are mere things. Caligula is much more a fact than a man; he is a result more than an existence. The Roman proscriber, dictator, or Cæsar, refuses the vanquished fire and water,—that is to say, puts his life out. One day of Gela represents twenty thousand proscribed, one day of Tiberius thirty thousand, one day of Sylla seventy thousand. One evening Vitellius, being ill, sees a house lighted up, where people were rejoicing. "Do they think me dead?" says Vitellius. It is Junius Blesus who sups with Tuscus Cæcina, the emperor sends to these drinkers a cup of poison, that they may realize by this sinister end of too joyous a night that Vitellius is living. (Reddendam pro intempestiva licentia mœstam et funebrem noctem qua sentiat vivere Vitellium et imperare.) Otho and this same Vitellius forward assassins to each other. Under the Cæsars, it is a marvel to die in one's bed; Pison, to whom this happened, is noted for that strange incident. The garden of Valerius Asiaticus pleases the emperor; the face of Statilius displeases the empress,—state crimes: Valerius is strangled because he has a garden, and Statilius because he has a face. Basil II., Emperor of the East, makes fifteen thousand Bulgarians prisoners; they are divided into bands of a hundred, and their eyes are put out, with the exception of one, who is charged to conduct his ninety-nine blind comrades. He afterward sends into Bulgaria the whole of this army without eyes. History thus describes Basil II.: "He was too fond of glory." Paul of Russia gave out this axiom: "There is no man powerful save him to whom the emperor speaks; and his power endures as long as the word that he hears." Philip V. of Spain, so ferociously calm at the *auto-da-fés*, is frightened at the idea of changing his shirt, and remains six months in bed without washing and without trimming his nails, for fear of being poisoned, by means of scissors, or by the water in the basin, or by his shirt, or by his shoes. Ivan, grandfather of Paul, had a woman put to the torture before making her lie in his bed; had a newly married bride hanged, and placed the husband as sentinel by her side, to prevent the rope from being cut; had a father killed by his son; invented the process of sawing men in two with a cord; burns Bariatinski himself by slow fire, and while the patient howls, brings the embers together with the end of his stick. Peter, in point of excellence, aspires to that of the executioner; he exercises himself in cutting off heads. At first he cuts off but five per day,— little enough; but, with application, he succeeds in cutting off twenty-five. It is a talent for a czar to tear away a woman's breast with one blow of the knout.

What are all those monsters? Symptoms,—running sores, pus which oozes from a sickly body. They are scarcely more responsible than the sum of a column is responsible for the figures in that column. Basil, Ivan, Philip, Paul, etc., are the products of vast surrounding stupidity. The clergy of the Greek Church, for example, having this maxim, "Who can make us judges of those who are our masters?" what more natural than that a czar,—Ivan himself,—should cause an archbishop to be sewn in a bear's skin and devoured by dogs? The czar is amused,—it is quite right. Under Nero, the man whose brother was killed goes to the temple to return thanks to the gods; under Ivan, a Boyard empaled employs his agony, which lasts for twenty-four hours, in repeating, "O God! protect the czar." The Princess Sanguzko is in tears; she presents, upon her knees, a supplication to Nicholas: she implores grace for her husband, conjuring the master to spare Sanguzko (a Pole guilty of loving Poland) the frightful journey to Siberia. Nicholas listens in silence, takes the supplication, and writes beneath it, "On foot." Then Nicholas goes into the streets, and the crowd throw themselves on his boot to kiss it. What have you to say? Nicholas is a madman, the crowd is a brute. From "khan" comes "knez;" from "knez" comes "tzar;" from "tzar" the "czar,"—a series of phenomena rather than an affiliation of men. That after this Ivan you should have this Peter, after this Peter this Nicholas, after this Nicholas this Alexander, what more logical? You all rather contribute to this result. The tortured accept the torture. "The czar, half putrid, half frozen," as Madame de Staël says,—you made him yourselves. To be a people, to be a force, and to look upon these things, is to find them good. To be present, is to give one's consent. He who assists at the crime, assists the crime. Unresisting presence is an encouraging submission.

Let us add that a preliminary corruption began the complicity even before the crime was committed. A certain putrid fermentation of pre-existing baseness engenders the oppressor.

The wolf is the fact of the forest; it is the savage fruit of solitude without defence. Combine and group together silence, obscurity, easy victory, monstrous infatuation, prey offered from all parts, murder in security, the connivance of those who are around, weakness, want of weapons, abandonment, isolation,—from the point of intersection of these things breaks forth the ferocious beast. A dark forest, whence cries cannot be heard, produces the tiger. A tiger is a blindness hungered and armed. Is it a being? Scarcely. The claw of the animal knows no more than does the thorn of a plant. The fatal fact engenders the unconscious organism. In so far as personality is concerned, and apart from killing for a living, the tiger does not exist. Mouravieff is mistaken if he thinks that he is a being.

Wicked men spring from bad things. Therefore let us correct the things.

And here we return to our starting-point: An attenuating circumstance for despotism is—idiocy. That attenuating circumstance we have just pleaded.

Idiotic despots, a multitude, are the mob of the purple; but above them, beyond them, by the immeasurable distance which separates that which radiates from that which stagnates,—there are the despots of genius; there are the captains, the conquerors, the mighty men of war, the civilizers of force, the ploughmen of the sword.

These we have just named. The truly great among them are called Cyrus, Sesostris, Alexander, Hannibal, Cæsar, Charlemagne, Napoleon; and, with the qualifications we have laid down, we admire them.

But we admire them on the condition of their disappearance. Make room for better ones! Make room for greater ones!

Those greater, those better ones, are they new? No. Their series is as ancient as the other; more ancient, perhaps, for the idea has preceded the act, and the thinker is anterior to the warrior. But their place was taken, taken violently. This usurpation is about to cease; their hour comes at last; their predominance gleams forth. Civilization, returned to the true light, recognizes them as its only founders; their series becomes clothed in light, and eclipses the rest; like the past, the future belongs to them; and henceforth it is they whom God will perpetuate.

HISTORY

THAT history has to be re-made is evident. Up to the present time, it has been nearly always written from the miserable point of view of accomplished fact; it is time to write it from the point of view of principle,—and that, under penalty of nullity.

Royal gestures, warlike uproars, princely coronations; marriages, baptisms, and funerals, executions and fêtes; the finery of one crushing all; the triumph of being born king, the prowess of sword and axe; great empires, heavy taxes; the tricks played by chance upon chance; the universe having for a law the adventures of any being, provided he be crowned; the destiny of a century changed by a blow from of a century changed by a blow from the lance of a fool through the skull of

an imbecile; the majestic *fistula in ano* of Louis XIV.; the grave words of the dying Emperor Mathias to his doctor, trying for the last time to feel his pulse beneath his coverlet and making a mistake,—"Erras, amice hoc est membrum nostrum imperiale sacrocæsareum;" the dance, with castanets of Cardinal Richelieu, disguised as a shepherd before the Queen of France, in the private villa of the Rue de Gaillon; Hildebrand completed by Cisneros; the little dogs of Henri III.; the various Potemkins of Catherine II.,—Orloff here, Godoy there, etc.; a great tragedy with a petty intrigue,—such was history up to our days, alternating between the throne and the altar, lending one ear to Dangeau and another to Dom Calmet, sanctimonious and not stern, not comprehending the true transitions from one age to the other, incapable of distinguishing the climacteric crises of civilization, making the human race mount upward by ladders of silly dates, well versed in puerilities while ignorant of right, of justice, and of truth, and modelled far more upon Le Ragois than upon Tacitus.

So true is this, that in our days Tacitus has been the object of strong attack.

Tacitus on the other hand,—we do not weary of insisting upon it,—is, like Juvenal, like Suetonius and Lampridius, the object of a special and merited hatred. The day when in the colleges professors of rhetoric shall put Juvenal above Virgil, and Tacitus above Bossuet, will be the eve of the day in which the human race shall have been delivered; when all forms of oppression shall have disappeared,—from the slave-owner up to the pharisee, from the cottage where the slave weeps to the chapel where the eunuch sings. Cardinal Duperron, who received for Henri IV. blows from the Pope's stick, had the goodness to say, "I despise Tacitus."

Up to the epoch in which we live, history has been a courtier. The double identification of the king with the nation and of the king with God, is the work of courtier history. The grace of God begets the right divine. Louis XIV. says, "I am the State!" Madame du Barry, plagiarist of Louis XIV., calls Louis XV. "France;" and the pompously haughty saying of the great Asiatic king of Versailles ends with "France, your coffin taints the camp!"

Bossuet writes without hesitation, though palliating facts here and there, the frightful legend of those old thrones of antiquity covered with crimes, and, applying to the surface of things his vague theocratic declamation, satisfies himself by this formula: "God holds in his hand the hearts of kings." That is not the case, for two reasons,—God has no hand, and kings have no heart.

We are only speaking, of course, of the kings of Assyria.

History, that old history of which we have spoken, is a kind of person for princes. It shuts its eyes when a highness says, "History, do not look this way." It has, imperturbably, with the face of a harlot, denied the horrible skull-breaking casque with an inner spike, destined by the Archduke of Austria for the Swiss magistrate Gundoldingen. At the present time this machine is hung on a nail in the Hôtel de Ville of Lucerne; anybody can go and see it: yet history repeats its de-

nial. Moréri calls St. Bartholomew's day " a disturbance." Chaudon, another biographer, thus characterizes the author of the saying to Louis XV., cited above: "A lady of the court, Madame du Barry." History accepts for an attack of apoplexy the mattress under which John II. of England stifled the Duke of Gloucester at Calais. Why is the head of the Infant Don Carlos separated from the trunk in his bier at the Escurial? Philip II., the father, answers: "It is because the Infant having died a natural death, the coffin prepared for him was not found long enough, and they were obliged to cut off the head." History blindly believes in the coffin being too short. What! the father to have his son beheaded! Oh, fie! Only demagogues would say such things.

The ingenuousness with which history glorifies the fact, whatever it may be, and however impious it may be, shines nowhere better than in Cantemir and Karamsin,—the one a Turkish historian, the other a Russian historian. The Ottoman fact and the Muscovite fact evidence, when confronted and compared with each other, the Tartar identity. Moscow is not less sinisterly Asiatic than Stamboul. Ivan is in the one as Mustapha is in the other. The gradation is imperceptible between that Christianity and that Mahometanism. The Pope is brother of the Ulema, the Boyard of the Pacha, the knout of the bowstring, and the moujik of the mute. There is to men passing through the streets little difference between Selim who pierces them with arrows, and Basil who lets bears loose on them. Cantemir, a man of the South, an ancient Moldavian hospodar, long a Turkish subject, feels, although he has passed over to the Russians, that he does not displease the Czar Peter by deifying despotism, and he prostrates his metaphors before the sultans: this crouching upon the belly is Oriental, and somewhat Western also. The sultans are divine; their scimitar is sacred, their dagger is sublime, their exterminations are magnanimous, their parricides are good. They call themselves merciful, as the furies are called Eumenides. The blood that they spill smokes in Cantemir with an odour of incense, and the vast slaughtering which is their reign blooms into glory. They massacre the people in the public interest. When some padischah (I know not which)—Tiger IV. of Tiger VI.—causes to be strangled one after the other his nineteen little brothers running frightened round the chamber, the Turkish native historian declares that "it was executing wisely the law of the empire." The Russian historian, Karamsin, is not less tender to the Tzar than was Cantemir to the Sultan; nevertheless, let us say it, in comparison with Cantemir's the fervency of Karamsin is lukewarmness. Thus Peter, killing his son Alexis, is glorified by Karamsin, but in the same tone in which we excuse a fault. It is not the acceptation pure and simple of Cantemir, who is more upon his knees. The Russian historian only admires, while the Turkish historian adores. No fire in Karamsin, no nerve,—a dull enthusiasm, greyish apotheoses, good-will stuck into an icicle, caresses benumbed with cold. It is poor flattery. Evidently the climate has something to do with it. Karamsin is a chilled Cantemir.

Thus is the greater part of history made up to the present day; it goes from Bossuet to Karamsin, passing by the Abbé Pluche. That history has for its principle obedience. To what is obedience due? To success. Heroes are well treated, but kings are preferred. To reign is to succeed every morning. A king has to-morrow: he is solvent. A hero may be unsuccessful,—such things happen,—in which case he is but a usurper. Before this history, genius itself, even should it be the highest expression of force served by intelligence, is compelled to continual success. If it fails, ridicule; if it falls, insult. After Marengo, you are Europe's hero, the man of Providence, anointed by the Lord; after Austerlitz, Napoleon the Great; after Waterloo, the ogre from Corsica. The Pope anointed an ogre.

Nevertheless, impartial Loriquet, in consideration of services rendered, makes you a marquis. The man of our day who has best executed that surprising gamut from Hero of Europe to Ogre of Corsica, is Fontanes, chosen during so many years, to cultivate, develop, and direct the moral sense of youth.

Legitimacy, right divine, negation of universal suffrage, the throne a fief, the nation an entailed estate, all proceed from that history. The executioner is also part of it; Joseph de Maistre adds him, divinely, to the king. In England such history is called "loyal" history. The English aristocracy, to whom similar excellent ideas sometimes occur, have imagined a method of giving to a political opinion the name of virtue,— *Instrumentum regni.* In England, to be a royalist, is to be loyal. A democrat is disloyal; he is a variety of the dishonest man. This man believes in the people,—shame! He would have universal suffrage,—he is a chartist! are you sure of his probity? Here is a republican passing,—take care of your pockets! That is clever. All the world is more witty than Voltaire: the English aristocracy has more wit than Macchiavelli.

The king pays, the people do not pay,—this is about all the secret of that kind of history. It has also its own tariff of indulgences. Honour and profit are divided,—honour to the master, profit to the historian. Procopius is perfect, and, what is more, Illustrious by special decree (which does not prevent him from being a traitor); Bossuet is bishop, Fleury is prelate prior of Argenteuil, Karamsin is senator, Cantemir is prince. But the finest thing is to be paid successively by For and by Against, and, like Fontanes, to be made senator through idolatry of, and peer of France through spitting upon, the same idol.

What is going on at the Louvre? What is going on at the Vatican, in the Seraglio, Buen Retiro, at Windsor, at Schoenbrünn, at Potsdam, at the Kremlin, at Oranienbaum? Further questions are needless; for there is nothing interesting for the human race beyond those ten or twelve houses, of which history is the door-keeper.

Nothing can be insignificant that relates to war, the warrior, the prince, the throne, the court. He who is not endowed with grave puerility cannot be an historian. A question of etiquette, a hunt, a gala, a grand levee, a procession, the triumph of Maximilian, the number of carriages the ladies have fol-

lowing the king to the camp before Mons, the necessity of having vices congenial with the faults of his majesty, the clocks of Charles V., the locks of Louis XVI.; how the broth refused by Louis XV. at his coronation, showed him to be a good king; how the Prince of Wales sits in the Chamber of the House of Lords, not in the capacity of Prince of Wales, but as Duke of Cornwall; how the drunken Augustus has appointed Prince Lubormirsky, who is starost of Kasimirow, under-cupbearer to the crown; how Charles of Spain gave the command of the army to Pimentel because the Pimentels have the title of Benavente since 1308; how Frederic of Brandenburg granted a fief of forty thousand crowns to a huntsman who enabled him to kill a fine stag; how Louis Antoine, grand-master of the Teutonic Order and Prince Palatine, died at Liége from displeasure at not being able to make the inhabitants choose him bishop; how the Princess Borghèse, dowager of Mirandole and of the Papal House, married the Prince of Cellamare, son of the Duke of Giovenazzo; how my Lord Seaton, who is a Montgomery, followed James II. into France; how the Emperor ordered the Duke of Mantua, who is vassal of the empire, to drive from his court the Marquis Amorati; how there are always two Cardinal Barberins living, and so on,—all that is the important business. A turned-up nose becomes an historical fact. Two small fields contiguous to the old Mark and to the duchy of Zell, having almost embroiled England and Prussia, are memorable. In fact, the cleverness of the governing and the apathy of the governed have arranged and mixed things in such a manner that all those forms of princely nothingness have their place in human destiny; and peace and war, the movement of armies and fleets, the recoil of the progress of civilization, depend on the cup of tea of Queen Anne or the fly-flap of the Dey of Algiers.

History walks behind those fooleries, registering them.

Knowing so many things, it is quite natural that it should be ignorant of others. If you are so curious as to ask the name of the English merchant who in 1612 first entered China by the north; of the worker in glass who in 1663 first established in France a manufactory of crystal; of the citizen who carried out in the States General at Tours, under Charles VIII.: the sound principle of elective magistracy (a principle which has since been adroitly obliterated); of the pilot who in 1405 discovered the Canary Islands; of the Byzantine lutemaker who in the eighth century invented the organ and gave to music its grandest voice; of the Campanian mason who invented the clock by establishing at Rome on the temple of Quirinus the first sundial; of the Roman lighterman who invented the paving of towns by the construction of the Appian Way in the year 312 B. C.; of the Egyptian carpenter who devised the dove-tail, one of the keys of architecture, which may be found under the obelisk of Loxor; of the Chaldean keeper of flocks who founded astronomy by his observation of the signs of the zodiac, the starting-point taken by Anaximenes; of the Corinthian calker who, nine years before the first Olympiad, calculated the power of the triple lever, devised the trireme, and created a tow-boat anterior by two thousand six hundred years to the steamboat; of the Macedonian ploughman who discovered the first gold mine in Mount Pangæus,—history does not know what to say to you: those fellows are unknown to history. Who is that,—a ploughman, a calker, a shepherd, a carpenter, a lighterman, a mason, a lutemaker, a sailor and a merchant? History does not lower itself to such rabble.

There is at Nüremberg, near the Egydienplatz, in a chamber on the second floor of a house which faces the church of St. Giles, on an iron tripod, a little ball of wood twenty inches in diameter, covered with darkish vellum, marked with lines which were once red, yellow, and green. It is a globe on which is sketched out an outline of the divisions of the earth in the fifteenth century. On this globe is vaguely indicated, in the twenty-fourth degree of latitude, under the sign of the Crab, a kind of island named Antilia, which one day attracted the attention of two men. The one who had constructed the globe and drawn Antilia showed this island to the other, placed his finger upon it, and said, "It is there." The man who looked on was Christopher Columbus; the man who said, "It is there," was called Martin Behaim. Antilia is America. History speaks of Fernando Cortez, who ravaged America, but not of Martin Behaim, who divined it.

Let a man have "cut to pieces" other men; let him have "put them to the sword;" let him have made them "bite the dust,"—horrible expressions, which have become hideously familiar,—and if you search history for the name of that man, whoever he may be, you will find it. But search for the name of the man who invented the compass, and you will not find it.

In 1747, in the eighteenth century, under the gaze even of philosophers, the battles of Raucoux and Lawfield, the siege of Sas-de-Gand and the taking of Bergop-Zoom, eclipse and efface that sublime discovery which to-day is in course of modifying the world,—electricity. Voltaire himself, about that year, celebrated passionately some exploit of Trajan.

A certain public stupidity is the result of that history which is superimposed upon education almost everywhere. If you doubt it, see, among others, the publications of Périsse Brothers, intended by the editors, says a parenthesis, for primary schools.

A prince who gives himself an animal's name makes us laugh. We rail at the Emperor of China, who makes people call him "His Majesty the Dragon," and we placidly say "Monseigneur le Dauphin."

History is the record of domesticity. The historian is no more than the master of ceremonies of centuries. In the model court of Louis the Great there are four historians, as there are four chamber violinists. Lulli leads the one, Boileau the others.

In this old method of history,—the only authorized method up to 1789, and classic in every acceptation of the word, —the best narrators, even the honest ones (there are few of them), even those who think themselves free, place themselves mechanically in drill, stitch tradition to tradition, submit to accepted custom, receive the pass-word from the

ante-chamber, accept, pell-mell with the crowd, the stupid divinity of coarse personages in the foreground,—kings, "potentates," "pontiffs," soldiers,—and, all the time thinking themselves historians, end by donning the livery of historiographers, and are lackeys without knowing it.

This kind of history is taught, is compulsory, is commended and recommended; all young intellects are more or less saturated with it, its mark remains upon them, their thought suffers through it and releases itself only with difficulty, —we make schoolboys learn it by heart, and I who speak, when a child, was its victim.

In such history there is everything except history. Shows of princes, of "monarchs," and of captains, indeed; but of the people, of laws, of manners, very little; and of letters, of arts, of sciences, of philosophy, of the universal movement of thought,—in one word, of man,—nothing. Civilization dates by dynasties and not by progress; some king or other is one of the stages along the historical road; the true stages, the stages of great men, are nowhere indicated. It explains how Francis II. succeeds to Henri II., Charles IX. to Francis II., and Henri III. to Charles IX.; but it does not tell us how Watt succeeds to Papin, and Fulton to Watt; behind the heavy scenery of the hereditary rights of kings a glimpse of the mysterious sovereignty of men of genius is scarcely obtained. The lamp which smokes on the opaque façades of royal accessions hides the starry light which the creators of civilization throw over the ages. Not one of this series of historians points out the divine relation, of human affairs,—the applied logic of Providence; not one makes us see how progress engenders progress. That Philip IV. comes after Philip III., and Charles II. after Philip IV., it would indeed be shameful not to know; but that Descartes continues Bacon, and that Kant continues Descartes; that Las Casas continues Columbus, that Washington continues Las Casas, and that John Brown continues and rectifies Washington; that John Huss continues Pelagius, that Luther continues John Huss, and that Voltaire continues Luther,—it is almost a scandal to be aware of this!

CHANGE

IT is time that all this should be altered. It is time that the men of action should take their place behind, and the men of ideas come to the front. The summit is the head. Where thought is there is power. It is time that men of genius should precede heroes. It is time to render to Cæsar what is Cæsar's, and to the book what is the book's: such or such a poem, such a drama, such a novel, does more work than all the Courts of Europe together. It is time that history should proportion itself to the reality, that it should allow to each influence its true measure, and that it should cease to place the masks of kings on epochs made in the image of poets and philosophers. To whom belongs the eighteenth century,—to Louis XV. or to Voltaire? Confront Versailles with Ferney, and see from which of these two points civilization flows.

A century is a formula; an epoch is a thought expressed,—after which, civilization passes to another. Civilization has phrases: these phrases are the centuries. It does not repeat here, what it says there; but its mysterious phrases are bound together by a chain,—logic (*logos*) is within,—and their series constitutes progress. All these phrases, expressive of a single idea,—the divine idea,—write slowly the word Fraternity.

All light is at some point condensed into flame; in the same way every epoch is condensed into a man. The man having expired, the epoch is closed,—God turns the page. Dante dead, is the full-stop put at the end of the thirteenth century: John Huss can come. Shakespeare dead, is the full-stop put at the end of the sixteenth century; after this poet, who contains and sums up every philosophy, the philosophers Pascal, Descartes, Molière, Le Sage, Montesquieu, Rousseau, Diderot, Beaumarchais can come. Voltaire dead, is the full-stop put at the end of the eighteenth century: the French Revolution, liquidation of the first social form of Christianity, can come.

These different periods, which we name epochs, have all their dominant points. What is that dominant point? Is it a head that wears a crown, or is it a head that bears a thought? Is it an aristocracy, or is it an idea? Answer yourself. Do you see where the power is? Weigh Francis I. in the scales with Gargantua: put all chivalry in the scale against "Don Quixote."

Therefore, every one to his right place. Right about face! and let us now regard the centuries in their true light. In the first rank, minds; in the second, in the third, in the twentieth, soldiers and princes. To the warrior the darkness, to the thinker the pedestal. Take away Alexander, and put in his place Aristotle. Strange thing, that up to this day humanity should have read the Iliad in such a manner as to annihilate Homer under Achilles!

I repeat it, it is time that all this should be changed. Moreover, the first impulse is given. Already, noble minds are at work; future history begins to appear, some specimens of the new and magnificent though partial treatments of the subject being already in existence; a general recasting is imminent,—*ad usum populi.* Compulsory education demands true history; and true history will be given: it is begun.

Effigies must be stamped afresh. That which was the reverse will become the face, and that which was the face will become the reverse. Urban VIII. will be the reverse of Galileo.

The true profile of the human race will re-appear on the different proofs of civilization that the successive ages will offer.

The historical effigy will no longer be the man-king; it will be the man-people.

Doubtless,—and we shall not be reproached for not insisting on it,—real and veracious history, in indicating the sources of civilization wherever they may be, will not lose sight of the appreciable utility of the sceptre-bearers and sword-bearers at given periods and in special states of humanity. Certain wrestling matches necessitate some resemblance between the two combatants; barbarity must sometimes be pitted against savageness. There are cases of progress by violence. Cæsar is good in Cimmeria, and Alexander in Asia; but

for Alexander and Cæsar the second rank suffices.

Veracious history, real history, definitive history henceforth charged with the education of the royal infant,—namely, the people,—will reject all fiction, will fail in complaisance, will logically classify phenomena, will unravel profound causes, will study philosophically and scientifically the successive commotions of humanity, and will take less account of the great strokes of the sword than of the grand strokes of the idea. The deeds of light will pass first; Pythagoras will be a much greater event than Sesostris. We have just said it,—heroes, men of the twilight, are relatively luminous in the darkness; but what is a conqueror beside a sage? What is the invasion of kingdoms compared with the opening up of intellects? The winners of minds efface the gainers of provinces. He through whom we think, he is the true conqueror. In future history, the slave Æsop and the slave Plautus will have precedence over kings; and there are vagabonds who will weigh more than certain victors, and comedians who will weigh more than certain emperors.

Without doubt, to illustrate what we are saying by means of facts, it is useful that a powerful man should have marked the halting-place between the ruin of the Latin world and the growth of the Gothic world; it is also useful that another powerful man, coming after the first, like cunning on the footsteps of daring, should have sketched out under the form of a catholic monarchy the future universal group of nations, and the beneficial encroachments of Europe upon Africa, Asia, and America. But it is more useful yet to have written the "Divina Commedia" and "Hamlet." No bad action is mixed up with these great works; nor is here to be charged to the account of the civilizer a debt of nations ruined. The improvement of the human mind being given as the result to be obtained, Dante is of greater importance than Charlemagne, and Shakespeare of greater importance than Charles the Fifth.

In history, as it will be written on the pattern of absolute truth, that intelligence of no account, that unconscious and trivial being,—the *Non pluribus impar*, the Sultan-sun of Marly,—will appear as nothing more than the almost mechanical preparer of the shelter needed by the thinker disguised as a buffoon, and of the environment of ideas and men required for the philosophy of Alceste. Thus Louis XIV. makes Molière's bed.

These exchanges of parts will put people in their true light; the historical optic, renewed, will re-adjust the *ensemble* of civilization, at present a chaos; for perspective, that justice of geometry, will size the past,—making such a plan to advance, placing another in the background. Every one will assume his real stature; the head-dresses of tiaras and of crowns will only make dwarfs more ridiculous; stupid genuflexions will vanish. From these alterations will proceed right.

That great judge We ourselves,—We all,—having henceforth for measure the clear idea of what is absolute and what is relative, deductions and restitutions will of themselves take place. The innate moral sense within man will know its power; it will no longer be obliged to ask itself questions like this,—Why,

at the same minute, do people revere in Louis XV. and all the rest of royalty the act for which they burn Deschauffours on the Place de Grève? The quality of kingship will no longer be a false moral weight. Facts fairly placed will place conscience fairly. A good light will come, sweet to the human race, serene, equitable, with no interposition of clouds henceforth between truth and the brain of man, but a definitive ascent of the good, the just, and the beautiful toward the zenith of civilization.

Nothing can escape the law which simplifies. By the mere force of things, the material side of facts and of men disintegrates and disappears. There is no shadowy solidity; whatever may be the mass, whatever may be the block, every combination of ashes (and matter is nothing else) returns to ashes. The idea of the atom of dust is in the word "granite,"—inevitable pulverizations. All those granites of oligarchy, aristocracy, and theocracy, are doomed to be scattered to the four winds. The idea alone is indestructible. Nothing lasts save the mind.

In this indefinite increase of light which is called civilization, the processes of reduction and levelling are accomplished. The imperious morning light penetrates everywhere,—enters as master, and makes itself obeyed. The light is at work; under the great eye of posterity, before the blaze of the nineteenth century, simplifications take place, excrescences fall away, glories drop like leaves, reputations are riven to pieces. Do you wish for an example,—take Moses. There is in Moses three glories, —the captain, the legislator, the poet.

Of these three men contained in Moses, where is the captain to-day? In the shadow, with brigands and murderers. Where is the legislator? Amidst the waste of dead religions. Where is the poet? By the side of Æschylus.

Daylight has an irresistible corroding power on the things of night. Hence appears a new historic sky above our heads, a new philosophy of causes and results, a new aspect of facts.

Certain minds, however, whose honest and stern anxiety please us, object: "You have said that men of genius form a dynasty; now, we will not have that dynasty any more than another." This is to misapprehend, and to fear the word where the thing is reassuring. The same law which wills that the human race should have no owners, wills that it should have guides. To be enlightened is quite different from being enslaved. Kings possess; men of genius conduct,—there is the difference. Between "I am a Man" and "I am the State" there is all the distance from fraternity to tyranny. The forward-march must have a guide-post. To revolt against the pilot can scarcely improve the ship's course; we do not see what would have been gained by throwing Christopher Columbus into the sea. The direction "this way" has never humiliated the man who seeks the road. I accept in the night the guiding authority of torches. Moreover, a dynasty of little encumbrance is that of men of genius, having for a kingdom the exile of Dante, for a palace the dungeon of Cervantes, for a civil list the wallet of Isaiah, for a throne the dunghill of Job, and for a sceptre the staff of Homer.

Let us resume.

GUIDANCE

HUMANITY, no longer owned but guided,—such is the new aspect of facts.

This new aspect of facts history henceforth is compelled to reproduce. To change the past, that is strange; yet it is what history is about to do. By falsehood? No, by speaking the truth. History has been a picture; she is about to become a mirror. This new reflection of the past will modify the future.

The former king of Westphalia, who was a witty man, was looking one day at an inkstand on the table of some one we know. The writer, with whom Jerome Bonaparte was at that moment, had brought home from an excursion among the Alps, made some years before in company with Charles Nodier, a piece of steatitic serpentine carved and hollowed in the form of an inkstand, and purchased of the chamois-hunters of the Mer de Glace. It was this that Jerome Bonaparte was looking at. "What it this?" he asked. "It is my inkstand," said the writer; and he added, "it is steatite. Admire how Nature with a little dirt and oxide has made this charming green stone." Jerome Bonaparte replied, "I admire much more the men who out of this stone made an inkstand."

That was not badly said for a brother of Napoleon, and due credit should be given for it; for the inkstand is to destroy the sword. The decrease of warriors,—men of brutal force and of prey; the undefined and superb growth of men of thought and peace; the re-appearance on the scene of the true colossals,—in this is one of the greatest facts of our great epoch. There is no spectacle more pathetic and sublime,—humanity delivered from on high, the powerful ones put to flight by the thinkers, the prophet overwhelming the hero, force routed by ideas, the sky cleaned, a majestic expulsion.

Look! raise your eyes! the supreme epic is accomplished. The legions of light drive backward the hordes of flame.

The masters are departing; the liberators are arriving! Those who hunt down nations, who drag armies behind them,—Nimrod, Sennacherib, Cyrus, Rameses, Xerxes, Cambyses, Attila, Genghis Khan, Tamerlane, Alexander, Cæsar, Bonaparte,—all these immense wild men are disappearing. They die away slowly,—behold them touch the horizon; they are mysteriously attracted by the darkness; they claim kindred with the shade,—thence their fatal descent. Their resemblance to other phenomena of the night restores them to that terrible unity of blind immensity, a submersion of all light; forgetfulness, shadow of the shadow, awaits them.

But though they are thrown down, they remain formidable. Let us not insult what has been great. Hooting would be unbecoming before the burying of heroes; the thinker should remain grave in presence of this donning of shrouds. The old glory abdicates, the strong lie down: mercy for those vanquished conquerors! peace to those warlike spirits now extinguished! The darkness of the grave interposes between their glare and ourselves. It is not without a kind of religious terror that one sees planets become spectres.

While in the engulfing process the flaming pleiad of the men of brutal force descends deeper and deeper into the abyss with the sinister pallor of approaching disappearance, at the other extremity of space, where the last cloud is about to fade away, in the deep heaven of the future, henceforth to be azure, rises in radiancy the sacred group of true stars,—Orpheus, Hermes, Job, Homer, Æschylus, Isaiah, Ezekiel, Hippocrates, Phidias, Socrates, Sophocles, Plato, Aristotle, Archimedes, Euclid, Pythagoras, Lucretius, Plautus, Juvenal, Tacitus, Saint Paul, John of Patmos, Tertullian, Pelagius, Dante, Gutenberg, Joan of Arc, Christopher Columbus, Luther, Michael Angelo, Corpernicus, Galileo, Rabelais, Calderon, Cervantes, Shakespeare, Rembrandt, Kepler, Milton, Molière, Newton, Descartes, Kant, Piranesi, Beccaria, Diderot, Voltaire, Beethoven, Fulton, Montgolfier, Washington. And this marvellous constellation, at each instant more luminous, dazzling as a glory of celestial diamonds, shines in the clear horizon, and ascending mingles with the vast dawn of Jesus Christ.

The Souls

PRODUCTION

THE production of souls is the secret of the unfathomable depth. The innate, what a shadow! What is that concentration of the unknown which takes place in the darkness, and whence abruptly bursts forth that light, a genius? What is the law of these events, O Love? The human heart does its work on earth, and that moves the great deep. What is that incomprehensible meeting of material sublimation and moral sublimation in the atom, indivisible if looked at from life, incorruptible if looked at from death? The atom, what a marvel! No dimension, no extent, nor height, nor width, nor thickness, independent of every possible measure, and yet, everything in this nothing! For algebra, the geometrical point. For philosophy, a soul. As a geometrical point, the basis of science; as a soul, the basis of faith. Such is the atom. Two urns, the sexes, imbibe life from the infinite; and the spilling of one into the other produces the being. This is the normal condition of all, animal as well as man. But the man more than man, whence comes he?

The Supreme Intelligence, which here below is the great man, what is the power which invokes it, incorporates it, and reduces it to a human state? What part do the flesh and the blood take in this prodigy? Why do certain terrestrial sparks seek certain celestial molecules? Where do they plunge, those sparks? Where do they go? How do they manage? What is this gift of man

to set fire to the unknown? This mine, the infinite, this extraction, a genius, what more wonderful! Whence does that spring up? Why, at a given moment, this one and not that one? Here, as everywhere, the incalculable law of affinities appears and escapes. One gets a glimpse, but sees not. O forger of the unfathomable, where art thou?

Qualities the most diverse, the most complex, the most opposed in appearance, enter into the composition of souls. The contraries do not exclude each other,—far from that; they complete each other. More than one prophet contains a scholiast; more than one magian is a philologist. Inspiration knows its own trade. Every poet is a critic: witness that excellent piece of criticism on the theatre that Shakespeare puts in the mouth of Hamlet. A visionary mind may be at the same time precise,—like Dante, who writes a book on rhetoric, and a grammer. A precise mind may be at the same time visionary,—like Newton, who comments on the Apocalypse; like Leibnitz, who demonstrates, *nova inventa logica,* the Holy Trinity. Dante knows the distinction between the three sorts of words, *parola piana, parola sdrucciola, parola tronca;* he knows that the *piana* gives a trochee, the *sdrucciola* a dactyl and the *tronca* an iambus. Newton is perfectly sure that the Pope is the Antichrist. Dante combines and calculates; Newton dreams.

No law is to be grasped in that obscurity. No system is possible. The currents of adhesions and of cohesions cross each other pell-mell. At times one imagines that he detects the phenomenon of the transmission of the idea, and fancies that he distinctly sees a hand taking the light from him who is departing, to give it to him who arrives. 1642, for example, is a strange year. Galileo dies, Newton is born, in that year. Good. It is a thread; try and tie it, it breaks at once. Here is a disappearance: on the 23rd of April, 1616, on the same day, almost at the same minute, Shakespeare and Cervantes die. Why are these two flames extinguished at the same moment? No apparent logic. A whirlwind in the night.

Enigmas constantly. Why does Commodus proceed from Marcus Aurelius?

These problems beset in the desert Jerome, that man of the caves, that Isaiah of the New Testament. He interrupted his deep thoughts on eternity, and his attention to the trumpet of the archangel, in order to meditate on the soul of some Pagan in whom he felt interested. He calculated the age of Persius, connecting that research with some obscure chance of possible salvation for the poet, dear to the cenobite on account of his strictness; and nothing is so surprising as to see this wild thinker, half naked on his straw, like Job, dispute on this question, so frivolous in appearance, of the birth of a man, with Rufinus and Theophilus of Alexandria,—Rufinus observing to him that he is mistaken in his calculations, and that Persius having been born in December under the consulship of Fabius Persicus and Vitellius, and having died in November, under the consulship of Publius Marius and Asinius Gallus,

these periods do not correspond rigorously with the year II. of the two hundred and third Olympiad, and the year II. of the two hundred and tenth, the dates fixed by Jerome. The mystery thus attracts deep thinkers.

These calculations, almost wild, of Jerome, or other similar ones, are made by more than one dreamer. Never to find a stop, to pass from one spiral to another like Archimedes, and from one zone to another like Alighieri, to fall, while fluttering about in the circular well, is the eternal lot of the dreamer. He strikes against the hard wall on which the pale ray glides. Sometimes certainty comes to him as an obstacle, and sometimes clearness as a fear. He keeps on his way. He is the bird under the vault. It is terrible. No matter, the dreamer goes on.

To dream is to think here and there, —*passim*. What means the birth of Euripides during that battle of Salamis where Sophocles, a youth, prays, and where Æschylus, in his manhood fights? What means the birth of Alexander in the night which saw the burning of the temple of Ephesus? What tie between that temple and that man? Is it the conquering and radiant spirit of Europe which, destroyed under the form of the *chef-d'œuvre*, revives under the form of the hero? For do not forget that Ctesiphon is the Greek architect of the temple of Ephesus. We have mentioned just now the simultaneous disappearance of Shakespeare and Cervantes. Here is another case not less surprising. The day when Diogenes died at Corinth, Alexander died at Babylon. These two cynics, the one of the tub, the other of the sword, depart together; and

Diogenes, longing to enjoy the immense unknown radiance, will again say to Alexander: "Stand out of my sunlight!"

What is the meaning of certain harmonies in the myths represented by divine men? What is this analogy between Hercules and Jesus which struck the Fathers of the Church, which made Sorel indignant, but edified Duperron, and which makes Alcides a kind of material mirror of Christ? Is there not a community of souls, and, unknown to them, a communication between the Greek legislator and the Hebrew legislator, creating at the same moment, without knowing each other, and without their suspecting the existence of each other, the first the Areopagus, the second the Sanhedrim? Strange resemblance between the jubilee of Moses and the jubilee of Lycurgus! What are these double paternities,—paternity of the body, paternity of the soul, like that of David for Solomon? Giddy heights, steeps, precipices.

He who looks too long into this sacred horror feels immensity racking his brain. What does the sounding-line give you when thrown into that mystery? What do you see? Conjectures quiver, doctrines shake, hypotheses float; all the human philosophy vacillates before the mournful blast rising from that chasm.

The expanse of the possible is, so to speak under your eyes. The dream that you have in yourself, you discover it beyond yourself. All is indistinct. Confused white shadows are moving. Are they souls? One catches, in the depths below, a glimpse of vague archangels passing along; will they be men at some future day? Holding your head between your hands, you strive to see and to know. You are at the window looking into the unknown. On all sides the deep layers of effects and causes, heaped one behind the other, wrap you with mist. The man who meditates not lives in blindness; the man who meditates lives in darkness. The choice between darkness and darkness, that is all we have. In that darkness, which is up to the present time nearly all our science, experience gropes, observation lies in wait, supposition moves about. If you gaze at it very often, you become *vates*. Vast religious meditation takes possession of you.

Every man has in him his Patmos. He is free to go or not to go on that frightful promontory of thought from which darkness is seen. If he goes not, he remains in the common life, with the common conscience, with the common virtue, with the common faith, or with the common doubt; and it is well. For the inward peace it is evidently the best. If he ascends to that peak, he is caught. The profound waves of the marvellous have appeared to him. No one sees with impunity that ocean. Henceforth he will be the thinker enlarged, magnified, but floating,—that is to say, the dreamer. He will partake of the poet and of the prophet. A certain quantity of him now belongs to darkness. The boundless enters into his life, into his conscience, into his virtue, into his philosophy. He becomes extraordinary in the eyes of other men, for his measure is different from theirs. He has duties which they have not. He lives in a sort of vague prayer, attaching himself, strangely enough, to an indefinite certainty which he calls God. He distinguishes in that twilight enough of the anterior life and enough of the ulterior life to seize these two ends of the dark thread, and with them to tie up his soul again. Who has drunk will drink; who has dreamed will dream. He will not give up that alluring abyss, that sounding of the fathomless, that indifference for the world and for life, that entrance into the forbidden, that effort to handle the impalpable and to see the invisible; he returns to them, he leans and bends over them; he takes one step forward, and two,—and thus it is that one penetrates into the impenetrable; and thus it is that one plunges into the boundless chasms of infinite meditation.

He who walks down them is a Kant; he who falls down them is a Swedenborg.

To keep one's own free will in that dilatation, is to be great. But, however great one may be, the problems cannot be solved. One may ply the fathomless with questions. Nothing more. As for the answers, they are there, but mingled with shadows. The huge lineaments of truth seem at times to appear for one moment, then go back, and are lost in the absolute. Of all those questions, that among them all which besets the intellect, that among them all which rends the heart, is the question of the soul.

Does the soul exist? Question the first. The persistency of the self is the thirst of man. Without the persistent self, all creation is for him but an immense *cui bono?* Listen to the astounding affirmation which bursts forth from all consciences. The whole sum of God that there is on the earth, within all men, condemns itself in a single cry,—

to affirm the soul. And then, question the second: Are there great souls?

It seems impossible to doubt it. Why not great minds in humanity as well as great trees in the forest, as well as great peaks in the horizon? The great souls are seen as well as the great mountains. Then, they exist. But here the interrogation presses further; interrogation is anxiety: Whence come they? What are they? Who are they? Are these atoms more divine than others? This atom, for instance, which shall be endowed with irradiation here below, this one which shall be Thales, this one Æschylus, this one Plato, this one Ezekiel, this one Macchabœus, this one Apollonius of Tyana, this one Tertullian, this one Epictetus, this one Marcus Aurelius, this one Nestorius, this one Pelagius, this one Gama, this one Copernicus, this one John Huss, this one Descartes, this one Vincent de Paul, this one Piranesi, this one Washington, this one Beethoven, this one Garibaldi, this one John Brown,—all these atoms, souls having a sublime function among men, have they seen other worlds, and do they bring on earth the essence of those worlds? The master souls, the leading intellects, who sends them? Who determines their appearance? Who is judge of the actual want of humanity? Who chooses the souls? Who musters the atoms? Who ordains the departures? Who premeditates the arrivals? Does the atom conjunction, the atom universal, the atom binder of worlds, exist? Is not that the great soul?

To complete one universe by the other; to pour upon the too little of the one the too much of the other; to increase here liberty, there science, there the ideal; to communicate to the inferiors patterns of superior beauty; to exchange the effluvia; to bring the central fire to the planet; to harmonize the various worlds of the same system; to urge forward those which are behind; to mix the creations,—does not that mysterious function exist?

Is it not fulfilled, unknown to them, by certain elects, who momentarily and during their earthly transit, partly ignore themselves? Is not the function of such or such atom, divine motive power called soul, to give movement to a solar man among earthly men? Since the floral atom exists, why should not the stellary atom exist? That solar man will be, in turn, the savant, the seer, the calculator, the thaumaturge, the navigator, the architect, the magian, the legislator, the philosopher, the prophet, the hero, the poet. The life of humanity will move onward through them. The volutation of civilization will be their task; that team of minds will drag the huge chariot. One being unyoked, the others will start again. Each completion of a century will be one stage on the journey. Never any solution of continuity. That which one mind will begin, another mind will finish, soldering phenomenon to phenomenon, sometimes without suspecting that welding process. To each revolution in the fact will correspond an adequate revolution in the ideas, and reciprocally. The horizon will not be allowed to extend to the right without stretching as much to the left. Men the most diverse, the most opposite, sometimes will adhere by unexpected parts; and in these adherences will burst forth the imperious logic of progress. Orpheus, Buddha, Confucius,

Zoroaster, Pythagoras, Moses, Manou, Mahomet, with many more, will be the links of the same chain. A Gutenberg discovering the method for the sowing of civilization and the means for the ubiquity of thought, will be followed by a Christopher Columbus discovering a new field. A Christopher Columbus discovering a world will be followed by a Luther discovering a liberty. After Luther, innovator in the dogma, will come Shakespeare, innovator in art. One genius completes the other.

But not in the same region. The astronomer follows the philosopher; the legislator is the executor of the poet's wishes; the fighting liberator lends his assistance to the thinking liberator; the poet corroborates the statesman. Newton is the appendix to Bacon; Danton originates from Diderot; Milton confirms Cromwell; Byron supports Botzaris; Æschylus, before him, has assisted Miltiades. The work is mysterious even for the very men who perform it. Some are conscious of it, others not. At great distances, at intervals of centuries, the correlations manifest themselves, wonderful. The modification in human manners, begun by the religious revealer, will be completed by the philosophical reasoner, so that Voltaire follows up Jesus. Their work agrees and coincides. If this concordance rested with them, both would resist, perhaps,—the one, the divine man, indignant in his martyrdom, the other, the human man, humiliated in his irony; but that is so. Some one who is very high orders it in that way.

Yes, let us meditate on these vast obscurities. The characteristic of revery is to gaze at darkness so intently that it brings light out of it.

Humanity developing itself from the interior to the exterior is, properly speaking, civilization. Human intelligence becomes radiance, and step by step, wins, conquers and humanizes matter. Sublime domestication! This labour has phases; and each of these phases, marking an age in progress, is opened or closed by one of those beings called geniuses. These missionary spirits, these legates of God, do they not carry in them a sort of partial solution of this question, so abstruse, of free will? The apostolate, being an act of will, is related on one side to liberty, and on the other, being a mission, is related by predestination to fatality. The voluntary necessary. Such is the Messiah; such is Genius.

Now let us return—for all questions which append to mystery form the circle, and one cannot get out of it,— let us return to our starting-point, and to our first question: What is a genius? Is it not perchance a cosmic soul, a soul imbued with a ray from the unknown? In what depths are such souls prepared? How long do they wait? What medium do they traverse? What is the germination which precedes the hatching? What is the mystery of the ante-birth? Where was this atom? It seems as if it was the point of intersection of all the forces. How come all the powers to converge and tie themselves into an indivisible unity in this sovereign intelligence? Who has bred this eagle? The incubation of the fathomless on genius, what an enigma! These lofty souls, momentarily belonging to earth, have they not seen something else? Is it

for that reason that they arrive here with so many intuitions? Some of them seem full of the dream of a previous world. Is it thence that comes to them the sacred wildness that they sometimes have? Is it that which inspires them with wonderful words? Is it that which gives them strange agitations? Is it thence that they derive the hallucination which makes them, so to speak, see and touch imaginary things and beings? Moses had his fiery thicket; Socrates his familiar demon; Mahomet his dove; Luther his goblin playing with his pen, and to whom he would say, "Be still, there!" Pascal his gaping chasm that he hid with a screen.

Many of those majestic souls are evidently conscious of a mission. They act at times as if they knew. They seem to have a confused certainty. They have it. They have it for the mysterious *ensemble*. They have it also for the detail. John Huss dying predicts Luther. He exclaims, "You burn the goose [Huss], but the swan will come." Who sends these souls? Who creates them? What is the law of their formation anterior and superior to life? Who provides them with force, patience, fecundation, will, passion? From what urn of goodness have they drawn sternness? In what region of the lightnings have they culled love? Each of these great newly arrived souls renews philosophy of art or science or poetry, remakes these worlds after its own image. They are as though impregnated with creation. At times a truth emanates from these souls which lights up the questions on which it falls. Some of these souls are like a star from which light would drip. From what wonderful source, then, do they proceed, that they are all different? Not one originates from the other, and yet they have this in common that they all bring the infinite. Incommensurable and insoluble questions. That does not stop the good pedants and the clever men from bridling up, and saying, while pointing with the finger at the sidereal group of geniuses on the heights of civilization: "You will have no more men such as those. They cannot be matched. There are no more of them. We declare to you that the earth has exhausted its contingent of master spirits. Now for decadence and general closing. We must make up our minds to it. We shall have no more men of genius."— Ah, you have seen the bottom of the unfathomable, you!

BOUNDLESSNESS

No, Thou art not worn out. Thou hast not before thee the bourn, the limit, the term, the frontier. Thou hast nothing to bound thee, as winter bounds summer, as lassitude the birds, as the precipice the torrent, as the cliff the ocean, as the tomb man. Thou art boundless. The "Thou shalt not go farther," is spoken by thee, and it is not said of thee. No, thou windest not a skein which diminishes, and the thread of which breaks; no, thou stoppest not short; no, thy quantity decreaseth not; no, thy thickness becometh not thinner; no, thy faculty miscarrieth not; no, it is not true that they begin to perceive in thy all-powerfulness that transparence which announces the end, and to get a glimpse behind thee of another thing besides thee. Another thing! And what

then? The obstacle. The obstacle to whom? The obstacle to creation, the obstacle to the everlasting, the obstacle to the necessary! What a dream!

When thou hearest men say, "This is as far as God advances,—do not ask more of him; he starts from here, and stops there. In Homer, in Aristotle, in Newton he has given you all that he had; leave him at rest now,—he is empty. God does not begin again; he could do that once, he cannot do it twice; he has spent himself altogether in this man,—enough of God does not remain to make a similar man;" when thou hearest them say such things, if thou wast a man like them, thou wouldst smile in thy terrible depth; but thou art not in a terrible depth, and being goodness, thou hast no smile. The smile is but a passing wrinkle, unknown to the absolute.

Thou struck by a powerful chill; thou to leave off; thou to break down; thou to say "Halt!" Never. Thou shouldst be compelled to take breath after having created a man! No; whoever that man may be, thou art God. If this weak swarm of living beings, in presence of the unknown, must feel wonder and fear at something, it is not at the possibility of seeing the germ-seed dry up and the power of procreation become sterile; it is, O God, at the eternal unleashing of miracles. The hurricane of miracles blows perpetually. Day and night the phenomena surge around us on all sides, and, not less marvellous, without disturbing the majestic tranquillity of the Being. This tumult is harmony.

The huge concentric waves of universal life are boundless. The starry sky that we study is but a partial apparition. We steal from the network of the Being but some links. The complication of the phenomenon, of which a glimpse can be caught, beyond our senses, only by contemplation and ecstasy, makes the mind giddy. The thinker who reaches so far, is, for other men, only a visionary. The necessary entanglement of the perceptible and of the imperceptible strikes the philosopher with stupor. This plenitude is required by thy all-powerfulness, which does not admit any blanks. The permeation of universes into universes makes part of thy infinitude. Here we extend the word universe to an order of facts that no astronomer can reach. In the Cosmos that the vision spies, and which escapes our organs of flesh, the spheres enter into the spheres without deforming each other, the density of creations being different; so that, according to every appearance, with our world is amalgamated, in some inexplicable way, another world invisible to us, as we are invisible to it.

And thou, centre and place of all things, as though thou, the Being, couldst be exhausted! that the absolute serenities could, at certain moments, fear the want of means on the part of the Infinite! that there would come an hour when thou couldst no longer supply humanity with the lights which it requires! that mechanically unwearied, thou couldst be worn out in the intellectual and moral order! that it would be proper to say, "God is extinguished on this side!" No! no! no! O Father!

Phidias created does not stop you from making Michael Angelo. Michael Angelo completed, there still remains to thee the material for Rembrandt. A Dante does not tire thee. Thou art no more exhausted by a Homer than by a star. The auroras by the side of auroras, the indefinite renewing of meteors, the worlds above the worlds, the wonderful passage of these incandescent stars called comets, the geniuses and again the geniuses, Orpheus, then Moses, then Isaiah, then Æschylus, then Lucretius, then Tacitus, then Juvenal, then Cervantes and Rabelais, then Shakespeare, then Molière, then Voltaire, those who have been and those who will be,—that does not weary thee. Swarm of constellations! there is room in thy immensity.

Mirabeau

I

In 1781, there was a serious debate in the bosom of a family in France between a father and an uncle. The subject in dispute was a good-for-nothing whom this family did not know what to do with. He had already passed the first hot stage of youth and yet was still wholly plunged in all the frantic excesses of that passionate time. Overwhelmed by debts, ruined by follies, and separated from his wife, he had carried off the wife of another, had been condemned to death for the act, had been decapitated in effigy, had fled from France and now was back again having, according to his own account, seen the error of his ways; and purged of his contumacy, he was now asking to be restored to his family and to regain possession of his wife. The father desired such an arrangement, for he wanted to have grandchildren to perpetuate his name; and he hoped besides, to be more lucky as a grandfather than he had been as a father.

But the prodigal son was thirty-three years old, and he had to be made over again from top to bottom. A difficult task that! After he took his place again in society, to whose hands should he be confided? Who would undertake to straighten the backbone of such a character? Hence the controversy between his two relatives. The father wished to give him to the uncle, the uncle wished to leave him to the father.

"Take him," said the father.

"I won't have him," said the uncle.

"Now, in the first place," returned the father, "lay this to heart. This man is nothing,—nothing at all. He is a mixture of good taste and charlatanism, has the air of knowing everything, has action, turbulence, daring, is the life and soul of a company, and has some dignity too. In authority he is neither harsh nor hateful. Well, with all this he takes no note of the day or the morrow, the impulse of the moment is his guide; a parrot sort of fellow he, an abortive man, taking thought neither of the pos-

sible nor of the impossible, careless of comfort or discomfort, of pleasure or pain, of action or repose, and giving up at once as soon as things become too tough for him. Yet I think he might be made an excellent tool of, if one laid hold of him by the sleeve of his vanity. You would not let him slip. I do not spare him my ratiocinations in the morning. He grasps my well-founded code of ethics and my perennially enduring lessons, because they revolve on an ever-real pivot; namely, that our nature can rarely be changed, but that reason serves to protect the weak side, and by knowing the weak side we prevent people from running foul thereon."

"Oh, there you are again," replied the uncle, "with your posteromania, hard at work tutoring a game-cock of thirty-three! A nice task it is to undertake the rounding of a character that is only a hedgehog, all points and all too little body!"

The father insisted: "Have pity on your nephew Whirlwind (l'Ouragan). He confesses all his follies,—indeed, he is the greatest hand at confessing in the universe; but no one could have more wit and aptitude. He is a very thunderbolt of labour and activity. At bottom, he is no more thirty-three than I am sixty-six; and it is not stranger to see a man of my years able, though grown grey from mishaps, to weary the legs and the minds of the young folk by hunting and studying eight hours a day, than to see a great bloated barrel, pitted with small-pox, and looking like an old man, call me "papa" and not know how to conduct himself. He has an immense need of being governed. He feels it very well. Oh, you must take charge of him. He knows you have always been my pilot and compass, and you must be the same to him. He is vain of nothing so much as of his uncle. I give him to you as a rare fellow to be trained for the future. You have all the saturnine qualities to balance his mercurial ones. But when you hold him, don't let him slip. Though he did miracles, hold him still and pluck him by the sleeve; the poor devil has need of it. If you be a father to him, you will be well pleased with him; if only an uncle, he is lost. Love this young man."

"No," said the uncle. "I know that fellows of a certain stamp can be all smirks and smiles betimes; and he himself when he lived near me was as timid as a daughter-in-law if I only wrinkled my forehead. But I won't have him. I'm not young enough to collar the impossible, and it is not my taste, either."

"O brother!" replied the suppliant old man, "If this hackled creature is ever to be patched up again, you alone are the one to do it. Since he has to be set to rights, I could not think of giving him a better master than you. Take him, be kind and firm, and you'll be his saviour; he will be the best piece of work you ever turned out. Let him know that in that long body of yours and under your cold, stiff demeanour dwells the best man that ever was,—a man formed of the odds and ends left after the angels were made! Sound his heart, raise his head. *Tu es omnis spes et fortuna nostri nominis!*"

"No," returned the uncle, "nor is it because he has committed so great a crime under the circumstances. Quite too much has been made of that busi-

ness. A young and pretty woman gets in the way of a young man of twenty-six. Where is the young man who would not pick up a thing like that if he found it in his path? But he is a turbulent spirit, a haughty, pretentious, insubordinate fellow, a malicious and vicious character! He does his very best to please you. It is right. I know he is seductive and that he is the rising sun. All the more reason for me not to expose myself to be his dupe. Youth always gets the upper hand when it is dealing with the old."

"You did not always think so," sadly answered the father; "there was a time when you wrote to me; 'As for me, this child unlocks my heart.'"

"Yes," said the uncle, and your answer was: 'Be cautious, be on your guard against the gilding of his beak.'"

"What would you have me do, then?" cried the father, driven to his last stand. "You are too equitable not to feel that one does not cut off a son as one would an arm. If that was possible I would have been one-armed long ago. After all, many a race has sprung from a fellow ten thousand times weaker and madder than he. Now, brother, as far as we are concerned, he is as he is. I leave myself out of the question. If I had not you, I would be but a poor broken-down old man. And as long as we are with him still, we must help him."

But the uncle, that peremptory man, cut short all prayers at last by these plain words:—

"I won't have him! It is madness to want to have anything to do with that man. Send him, as his good wife says, to the insurgents, and let him get his head broken. Your posteromaniac fury has possession of you now; but just think how lucky Cyrus and Marcus Aurelius would have been if neither of them had a Cambyses or a Commodus!"

Does it not seem to you, while reading this, as if you were present at one of the fine scenes of high domestic comedy in which the gravity of Molière almost reaches the grandeur of Corneille? Is there anything in Molière more striking for beauty and distinction of style, more profoundly human and true than these two imposing old men whom the seventeenth century seems to have left behind it in the eighteenth as two exemplars of the grand manner? Do you not see them meet, full of important business, stiff and rigid in their demeanour, resting on their long canes, recalling by their costume Louis the XIV. more than Louis XV., and Louis XIII. more than Louis XIV.?

Is not the language they speak the very language of Molière and Saint-Simon? That father and that uncle are the two eternal types of comedy; they are the two austere mouths by which she scolds, instructs, and moralizes, amid so many other mouths which only make us laugh; it is the Marquis and the Commander, Géronte and Ariste, wisdom and goodness, the admirable duo to which Molière always returns.

THE UNCLE.

Where would you run?

THE FATHER.

Alas! what do I know?

THE UNCLE.

Methinks 't were well that we advise each other
As to what should be done in this event.

The scene is complete; it lacks nothing, not even the *rascal of a nephew*.

But the most striking circumstance of all in the present case is that the scene we have just described is a real thing, that this dialogue of the father and the uncle took place, as we have recorded it, by letters,—letters which the public may read at this very hour; that, all unknown to these two old men, the subject of their grave discussion was one of the greatest men of our history; that the *marquis* and the *commander* are here a real marquis and a real commander. The one was named Victor de Riquetti, Marquis de Mirabeau; the other, Jean Antoine de Mirabeau, Bailli of the Order of Malta; the *rascal of a nephew* was Honoré Gabriel de Riquetti whom his family in 1781 called Whirlwind, and whom the world to-day calls Mirabeau.

So, what Mirabeau was for his family in 1781 was an *abortive man*, a *hackled creature*, a fellow *with whom nothing could be done*, a head good *to get broken* by the insurgents, and a scourge besides.

Ten years after, on the 1st of April, 1791, an immense crowd thronged the approaches of a house in the Chaussée d'Antin. This crowd was gloomy, silent, panic-stricken, and profoundly sad. In that house a man was in his last agony. All this crowd inundated the street, the court, the staircase, and the antechamber. Several had remained there for three days. Men spoke low, they seemed afraid to breathe, they questioned anxiously those who came and went. The feeling of this crowd for this man was that of a mother for her child The doctors no longer hoped. From time to time bulletins, wrested from their bearers by a thousand hands, were scattered among the multitude, and the sobs of women were heard. A young man, raging with grief, offered in a loud voice to open an artery so that his rich and pure blood might be infused into the veins of the dying. All, even the least intelligent, seemed weighted to the earth under the thought that it was not merely a man, it was a people, that was about to die.

The citizens addressed but one question to each other. This man expired.

Some minutes after the physician who stood at the head of his bed had said, "He is dead!" the president of the National Assembly rose in his seat and said, "He is dead!" such the fatal cry that in a few moments filled all Paris. One of the principal orators of the Assembly, M. Barrère de Vienzac, rose weeping, and said in a voice broken by sobs: "I ask that the Assembly record on the minutes of this calamitous day the testimony of the sorrow it feels at the loss of this great man, and that there be given, in the name of the country, an invitation to all the members of the Assembly to be present at his funeral."

A priest, a member of the Right, cried, "Yesterday, in the midst of his sufferings, he caused the Bishop of Autun to be summoned to his presence, and handing him a work he had just finished on inheritances, asked him as a last mark of friendship to read it to the Assembly. It is a sacred duty. The Bishop of Autun must exercise here the functions of testamentary executor of the great man we all lament."

Trouchet, the president, proposed that a deputation attend the funeral. The Assembly replied, "We shall all go!"

The Sections of Paris demanded that he should be entombed "in the Plain of the Federation, under the Altar of the County."

The Directory of the Department proposed to give him for his tomb the "new church of Saint Genevieve," and to decree that "this edifice be henceforward destined to receive the ashes of great men."

On this subject, M. Pastoret, the procurator-general syndic of the commune, said, "The tears that the loss of a great man cause us to shed ought not to be barren tears. Several ancient peoples provided separate monuments for their priests and heroes. The species of adoration they rendered to piety and courage, let us to-day render to the love of the happiness and the liberty of men. Let the temple of liberty become the temple of the country! Let the tomb of a great man become the altar of liberty!"

The Assembly applauded.

Barnave exclaimed, "He has, indeed, merited the honours which ought to be decreed by the nation to the great men who have served her well."

Robespierre, that is to say, Envy, rose also, and said, "It is not at the moment when we hear from all parts the regrets excited by the loss of this illustrious man, who in the most critical times displayed so much courage against despotism, that we could oppose the marks of honour which ought to be decreed him. I support the proposal with all my energies, or rather with all my sensibilities."

On that day there was neither Left nor Right in the Natinoal Assembly. All with one voice passed the following decree:—

"The new edifice of Saint Gene-vieve shall be destined to receive the ashes of great men. There shall be engraved above its front these words,—

TO GREAT MEN

THE COUNTRY GRATEFUL

"The Legislative Body alone shall decide to what men this honour shall be decreed.

"Honoré Riquetti Mirabeau is judged worthy of receiving this honour."

The man who had just died was Honoré de Mirabeau. The *great man* of 1791 was the *abortive man* of 1781.

On the next day the procession of the people at his funeral extended for more than a league. His father was not there; he had died, as was proper in the case of an old gentleman of his kind, on the 13th of July, 1789, the eve of the fall of the Bastille.

It is not without an object that we have brought together these two dates, 1781 and 1791, their memories and their history,—Mirabeau before and Mira-beau after, Mirabeau judged by his family and Mirabeau judged by the people. There is an inexhaustible source of meditation in this contrast. How was it that in ten years the demon of a family became the god of a nation? A profound question this.

II

WE must not believe, however, that at the moment this man issued from the family to make his appearance before the people, he was immediately and by acclamation hailed as a *god*. Things of themselves never march in this fashion. Where genius rises, Envy rears her head. On the contrary, until the very hour of his death, never was man so constantly and so thoroughly gainsaid in every sense as Mirabeau.

When he arrived at the States General as Deputy of Aix, he excited the jealousy of nobody. Obscure and disreputable, he was little sought after by those of good report; ugly and awkward, he inspired the graceful and well-proportioned lords with pity. His nobility vanished under the black habit, his physiognomy under the small-pox. Who, then, could dream of being jealous of this species of adventurer, this released convict, deformed in body and feature, ruined besides, whom the rabble of Aix had sent as deputy to the States General in a moment of frenzy, thoughtlessly, no doubt, and without knowing why? This man, in truth, did not count. Beside him the most commonplace person was handsome, rich, and worthy of consideration. He did not offend any vanity, he did not elbow any pretention. He was a mere cipher which the ambitious, however jealous of one another they might be, scarcely reckoned in their calculations. Little by little, however, as the twilight of all ancient things was approaching, a sufficient shadow was created around the monarchy for the sombre splendour, peculiar to the great men or revolutions, to become visible to the eye. Mirabeau was beginning to radiate.

Then Envy came to this radiance as every bird of night does to the light. To date from that moment, Envy seized on Mirabeau and never let go her hold. And above all, a thing happened which seems strange and yet is not strange. What she refused to his last breath, what she denied him incessantly to his face, was precisely that which crowns him in the eye of posterity,—his oratorical genius. This is the method that Envy always pursues besides; it is at the finest front of a building that she hurls her stones. And, then, it must be admitted that Envy had an inexhaustible supply of good reasons for her work. *Probitas,* the orator should be a man without reproach,—M. de Mirabeau deserves reproach in every direction; *præstantia,* the orator ought to be handsome,—M. de Mirabeau is ugly; *vox amœna,* the orator should have a pleasing organ,—M. de Mirabeau's voice is harsh, dry, shrill, thundering always and never speaking; *subrisus audientium,* the orator ought to be welcome to his hearers,—M. de Mirabeau is hated by the Assembly, etc.; and a crowd of people very well content with themselves, came to this conclusion: *M. de Mirabeau is not an orator.*

Now, far from proving this, all these reasonings prove only one thing; that is, that the Mirabeaus are not foreseen by the Ciceros.

Certainly, he was not an orator after the fashion understood by those people; he was an orator according to his own nature, his organization, his soul, his life. He was an orator because he was hated, just as Cicero was an orator because he was loved. He was an orator because he was ugly, just as Hortensius was an orator because he was well-favoured. He was an orator because he had suffered, because he had failed, because he had been while still young and at that period of life when the heart expands to every influence, repulsed, mocked, humiliated, despised, defamed, banished, robbed, exiled, imprisoned, and condemned; because, like the people of 1789 whose perfect symbol he was, he had been kept in leading-strings long after the age of reason; because a father's hand had been as heavy for him as royalty had been for the people, because, like the people, he had been badly reared; because, like the people, a bad education caused a vice to grow on the root of every virtue. He was an orator, because the wide issues opened by 1789 enabled him at last to pour out into society all the ebullitions that had been so long repressed in his family; because from the very fact that he was abrupt, unequal, violent, vicious, cynical, sublime, diffuse, incoherent, full of instincts still more than of thoughts, with his feet soiled and his head radiant, he was in everything like the ardent years in which he shone, and in which every day passed away, marked on the brow with one of his words. In fine, to those fatuous men who understood their time so poorly as to ask him, at the same time raising a thousand objections often ingenious enough, if he seriously believed he was an orator, he might have simply answered "Inquire of the monarchy that is ending, inquire of the revolution that is beginning!"

It is hard to believe to-day that it is a certain fact many people of 1790, and among those people a number of fair-spoken friends, advised Mirabeau, "to abandon the tribune in his own interest; he would never be entirely successful in it," or at least, "to appear there less often." We have the words under our eyes. It is hard to believe that, during those memorable sessions, when he stirred the Assembly like water in a vase, when the resounding ideas of the moment were dashed together under the impulse of his mighty hand, when he beat out and amalgamated with his powerful eloquence his own personal passion and the passion of all, after he had spoken and while he was speaking and before he spoke, the applause was always mingled with hooting, laughter, and hisses. Miserable petty details which his glory has discounted to-day! The journals and pamphlets of the time are but insults, outrages, and indignities directed against the genius of this man. He is reproached with every offence at every turn. But the reproach that is never for a moment silent, that appears to spring from some kind of mania is "his rough and harsh voice" and the "thundering tones in which he always speaks." What answer can be given to this? His voice is rough, because apparently the time for smooth voices has passed. His tones are thundering, because great issues are thundering beside him, and it is the property of great men to rise to the height of great events.

And then, and this too is a policy that has always been used against men of genius; he was attacked not only by supporters of the monarchy, but by those of his own party—for one is nowhere better hated than in his own party —who were ever agreed, by a sort of tacit convention, on opposing him incessantly and on giving the preference to some other orator, adroitly selected by envy among those who held the same opinions as Mirabeau and Barnave. And it will be always so. It often happens that, in a given period, the same idea is represented in different degrees at the same time by a man of genius and a man of talent. This position offers a happy chance to the man of talent. He is sure of present and undisputed success; this success, it is true, proves nothing and quickly fades. Jealousy and hate at once cross the path of the strongest. Mediocrity would be very much troubled by the presence of the man of talent, if the man of genius were not there; but the man of genius is there, and so she supports the man of talent, and makes use of him against the master of both. She deludes herself with the chimerical hope of overthrowing the one, and in that case (which, however, cannot be realized) she reckons on making a good bargain with the second. Meanwhile she supports the latter, and elevates him as high as she can. Mediocrity is in favour of him who annoys her the least and resembles her the most. In this circumstance, all that is hostile to the man of genius is friendly to the man of talent. The comparison which should crush the latter exalts him. Out of all the stones that pickaxe and spade and calumny and diatribe and insult can tear away from the base of the great man, a pedestal is erected for the second-rate man. What is made to fall from the one serves for the construction of the other. It was in that way that, towards 1790, Barnave was built up with the materials taken from as much of the ruin of Mirabeau as was available.

Rivarol said, "M. Mirabeau is more of a writer, M. Barnave is more of an orator."—Pelletier said, "Barnave yes, Mirabeau no."—"The memorable session of the 13th," wrote Chamfort, "has proved more than ever the pre-eminence, already demonstrated long before, of Barnave to Mirabeau as an orator."— "Mirabeau is dead," murmured M. Target, grasping the hand of Barnave; "his discourse on the formula of promulgation has killed him."—"Barnave, you have buried Mirabeau," added Duport, supported by the smile of Lameth, who was to Duport as Duport was to Barnave, — a diminutive. — "M. Barnave gives pleasure," said M. Goupil, "and M. Mirabeau gives pain."—"The Count de Mirabeau has flashes," said M. Camus, "but he will never make a discourse; he will never even know what a discourse is. Talk to me of Barnave!" —"It is useless for M. de Mirabeau to sweat and weary himself," cackled Robespierre, "he will never reach Barnave, who does not seem to have so much pretension, but is far superior." Such poor little samples of injustice stung Mirabeau and caused him suffering in the midst of his power and his triumphs. Pin-pricks of the kind do make a giant wince.

And if hatred, when it determined to get some one to oppose him, no matter whom, had not found a man of talent suitable for the purpose, she would have taken a man of mediocrity. The equality of the stuff out of which she makes her flag never embarrasses her. Mairet has been preferred to Corneille, Pradon to Racine, and not a hundred years ago Voltaire exclaimed:—

"And dare they then
Prefer the barbarous Crebillon to me!"

In 1808, Geoffroy, the best known critic in Europe, placed "M. Lafon very much about M. Talma." Marvellous instinct of cliques! In 1798, Moreau was thought superior to Bonaparte; in 1815, Wellington ranked higher than Napoleon. We repeat, because in our opinion the thing is singular, that Mirabeau stooped to be irritated by these petty miseries. The parallel with Barnave offended him. If he could have looked into the future he would have smiled; but it is the special defect of political orators, who are above all men of the present, to keep their eyes too much fixed on contemporaries and not enough on posterity. These two men, Barnave and Mirabeau, presented besides a perfect contrast. When either rose in the Assembly, Barnave was always received with a smile, and Mirabeau with a storm. Barnave possessed as his property the ovation of the moment, the triumph of the quarter of an hour, the glory of the report in the "Gazette," the applause of all, even of the Right. To Mirabeau were allotted the struggle and the turmoil. Barnave was a rather handsome young man, and a very fine speaker. Mirabeau, as Rivarol ingeniously observed, was a *monstrous babbler*. Barnave was one of those men who take each morning the measure of their hearers; who handle the pulse of their audience; who never venture outside the possibility of being applauded; who always humbly kiss the feet of success; who ascend the tribune, sometimes with the idea of to-day, oftenest with that of yesterday, never— from dread of the risk,—with that of to-morrow; who have an even, smooth, easy fluency of speech on which they jog along, making little noise, and pass round with their other baggage, the commonplace ideas of their times; who, fearing that their thoughts might not be sufficiently impregnated with the atmosphere of everybody, unceasingly adjust and arrange their opinions in front of the street as they would a thermometer at the window. Mirabeau, on the contrary, was the man of the new idea, of the sudden illumination, of the risky proposition; fiery, hare-brained, imprudent, always saying something unexpected everywhere, jostling, wounding, overturning, obeying only himself, seeking success undoubtedly, but after many other things, and preferring the applause of the passions of his heart to that of the people in the tribune; noisy, agitated, rapid, profound, seldom transparent, never fordable, and rolling along confusedly in his foamy current all the ideas of his era,—ideas that often suffered a rude shock when coming into collision with his own.

The fame of Mirabeau is to-day so great and so universally recognized, that there is considerable difficulty in forming an idea of the fashion in which he was treated by his colleagues and contemporaries. We have M. de Guillermy exclaiming during one of the great tribune's harangues: "M. Mirabeau is a scoundrel, an assassin!" MM. d'Ambly

and de Lautrec vociferating, "This Mirabeau is a great scoundrel!" And then M. de Foucault shook his fist at him, and M. de Virien said, "Monsieur Mirabeau, you insult me!" When hatred did not speak, contempt did. "This shabby Mirabeau!" said M. de Castellanet of the Right. "That extravagant fellow!" said M. Lapoule of the Left. And when he had spoken, Robespierre mumbled between his teeth: "His words have no value."

Sometimes his eloquence showed traces of the effect exercised on him by the hostility of so large a part of his audience, and—in the midst of his magnificent discourse on the Regency, for example—his scornful lips gave vent to such words as these, words at once simple and resigned, melancholy and proud, which every man placed in similar circumstances would do well to meditate on:—

"While I was giving my ideas on the Regency, I have heard some of my hearers say, with the charming sense of incapability of error to which I have been long accustomed: 'That is absurd! that is extravagant! that is unworthy of being brought before us!' But a little serious reflection would not be out of place either."

He spoke these words on the 25th of March, 1791, seven days before his death.

Outside the Assembly, the press tore him to pieces with a strange fury. A hailstorm of pamphlets beat on this man. The extreme parties put him on the same pillory. His name was pronounced in the same tone in the barrack of the Royal Guards and in the club of the Cordeliers. M. de Champceneta said, "That man has the small-pox in his soul." M. de Lambesc proposed to have him seized and *taken to the galleys* by twenty horsemen. Marat shouted, "Citizens, raise eight hundred gibbets, hang all these traitors on them, and at their head the infamous Riquetti the elder!" And Mirabeau refused to consent to his prosecution by the National Assembly. He contented himself with saying, "It seems a great deal of extravagant nonsense is published. The man who wrote that must have been drunk."

Thus, up to April the 1st, 1791, Mirabeau is a scoundrel, an extravagant fellow, a rascal, an assassin, a madman, an orator of the second rank, a mediocre man, a man dead, a man buried, a monstrous babbler, hooted, hissed, scouted more than applauded; Larmbesc would send him to the galleys, Marat to the gibbet. On the 2nd of April he dies. On the 3d the Pantheon was invented for his behoof.

III

THE people, however, which has a peculiar sense and a visual ray always singularly straight, which is not hateful because it is strong, which is not envious because it is great, the people, which knows men, although itself a child,—the people was for Mirabeau. There are no finer spectacles for the thinker than those close embraces of genius and the multitude.

The influence of Mirabeau was gainsaid, and it was immense. It was always he, after all, that had the upperhand; but he won his victories over the Assembly only through the people, and he governed the curule chairs through the tribunes. The precise words which Mirabeau uttered were re-uttered by the crowd accompanied by applause; and under the dictation of this applause the Legislature, often against its will, wrote. Libels, pamphlets, calumnies, insults, interruptions, menaces, hoots, roars of laughter, hisses, were all but pebbles flung into the current of his words, which at times served to make him foam. That was all.

When this sovereign orator, smitten by some sudden thought, mounted the tribune; when this man found himself face to face with his people; when he was standing there and walking on the envious Assembly, as the Man-God on the waters, without sinking; when his sardonic and luminous glance, reaching from the elevation of his tribune the men and ideas of his time, seemed to measure the littleness of the men on the scale of the greatness of the ideas, then was he no longer caluminated, nor hooted, nor insulted. All their deeds, all their words, all the slanders heaped up against him, were vain; the first breath from his mouth as he opened it to speak, scattered them to the winds. On the tribune he was transfigured, and detraction vanished in his presence.

Mirabeau, in 1789, was, then, loved and hated at the same time,—as a genius, hated by the wits; as a man, beloved by the people. His was an illustrious and desirable existence, for he swayed at will all hearts then opening to the future, converted by magic words and by some mysterious kind of alchemy the vague instincts of the multitude into thoughts and systems, into well-planned methods and rational schemes of amelioration and reform, fed the spirit of his time with all the ideas which his great intelligence crumbled into fragments and flung among the crowd, beat and threshed on the table of the tribune, like the wheat on the threshing-floor, the men and things of his century, without rest, and with all his might and main, separating the straw the Republic was to consume from the wheat the Revolution was to fructify, causing sleepless nights to Louis XVI. and to Robespierre at the same time,—to Louis XVI., whose throne he destroyed; to Robespierre, whose guillotine he would have attacked, saying every morning as he awoke, "What ruin shall my words bring about to-day?" a pope in this sense, that he guided souls; a god in this sense, that he guided events.

He died in time. His was a sovereign and sublime head, '91 crowned it. '93 would have cut it off.

IV.

As we follow Mirabeau step by step, from the humble baptismal font of Bignon to the Pantheon, we see that like all men of his stamp and stature he was predestined.

Such a child could not fail to be a great man.

At the moment when he came into the world, the enormous size of his head placed the life of his mother in peril. When the old French monarchy, his other mother, brought forth his fame, she too nearly died of it.

At the age of five, Poisson, his tutor, told him to write on whatever came into his head. The "little one," as we are told by his father, wrote literally as follows:—

"Monsieur *Me*, I beg that you will pay attention to your writing and not make blots on your copy. Pay attention to what you are doing; obey your father, your tutor, and your mother; never contradict; no double-dealing on the point of honour above all. Attack no one, except you are attacked yourself. *Defend your country.* Do not be unkind to the servants. Do not be familiar with them. Hide the faults of your neighbour, because you may want them to do the same for you."

When he was eleven, the Duke de Nivernois wrote of him to the Bailli de Mirabeau, in a letter dater from St. Maur, on the 11th of September, 1760:—

"The other day he won a prize at a running-match. It was a hat. He turned round to a youth who had a cap, and giving him his own, which was a very good one, said: 'Here, I haven't two heads!' This stripling appeared to me then worthy to be the emperor of the world. There was something or other godlike about him. I mused on it, I wept, and the lesson did me good."

At twelve, his father said of him: "There is a noble heart under the jacket of that bantling. He has a strange instinct of pride, but of a generous character. This little bit of a man is a bully in a flurry, and would swallow the whole world before he is twelve years old."

At fifteen, he had an air of such daring and haughtiness that the Prince de Conti asked: "What would you do if I slapped your face?" He answered. "That question might have been embarrassing before the invention of pistols for two."

At twenty-one (1770), he began writing a history of Corsica, when some one else was being born there. Singular instinct of great men!

At the same time his father, who held a very tight rein over him, uttered this strange prognostic: "He is a bottle that has been corked and corded for twenty-one years. If he is ever uncorked suddenly, and without great care, there will be a fine evaporation."

At twenty-two, he was presented at court. Madame Elizabeth, then a child of six, asked him *if he had been inoculated.* And all the court laughed. No, he had not been inoculated. He bore within him the germ of a contagion that later on was to spread through a whole people.

He presented himself at court with extreme assurance, with a head as high as the king's, a strange object to all, a hateful one to many. "He is as insinuating as I was shy," said the father, who had never desired to "dance attendance on Versailles," not he; "he was a wild bird that nested between four turrets."—"He turns the great round and round as if they were a bundle of fagots. He has 'that terrible gift of familiarity' as Gregory the Great used to say." And then the proud old gentleman adds, "Well, as the Mirabeaus, who have never been built like

other people, have been endured for the last five hundred years, I suppose they will be endured still."

At twenty-four, the father, as a philosophic agriculturist, wishes to take his son away with him, "and make him rural." He cannot succeed in this. "It is a very hard thing to handle the mouth of that fiery animal!" exclaims the old man.

The uncle, the Bailli, coolly examines the young man, and says, "If he is not worse than Nero, he will be better than Marcus Aurelius."

"After all, we must let this green fruit ripen," replies the marquis.

The father and the uncle corresponded with each other constantly on the future of the young man who had already advanced so far on the road of a bad life. "Your nephew Whirlwind," said the father. "Your son, Monsieur le Comte de la Bourrasque," (squall) replied the uncle.

The Bailli, an old sailor, adds, "The thirty-two winds of the compass are in his head."

At thirty, *the fruit was ripe.* Already strange things are glistening in the deep eyes of Mirabeau. It is seen that he is full of thoughts. "That brain is an overloaded furnace," says the prudent Bailli. At another time, the Bailli, in his alarm, makes this observation: "When anything passes into his head, he pushes it forward, and looks nowhere."

The father, on his side, is astonished at "his tearing of ideas piecemeal and only seeing by flashes." He exclaims, "Rummage in his head, and you find a library all topsy-turvy, a talent for dazzling by superficialities; he has swallowed all formulas and can't substantiate!" He adds, no longer comprehending this creature of his own making: "In childhood he was nothing but a monster of the male species, morally and physically." To-day, he is a man "all reflex and reverberation," a madman "drawn on the right by his heart and on the left by his head, which is always four yards away from him." And then the old man adds, with a melancholy and resigned smile: "I am trying to empty out into this man my brains, my soul, and my heart." At last, like the uncle, he has also his presentiments, his terrors, his anxieties, and his doubts. The father feels all that is stirring in the head of the son, "as the root feels the quivering of the leaves."

Such was Mirabeau at thirty. He was the son of a father who has thus described himself: "And I too, madame, stiff and dull-witted as you see me now, preached when I was three years old; at six, I was a prodigy; at twelve, an object of hope; at twenty, a fire-brand; at thirty, a theoretical statesman; at forty, I am merely a good-natured old fellow."

At forty, Mirabeau is a great man.

At forty, he is the man of the Revolution.

At forty, there breaks out around him in France one of those formidable anarchies of ideas in which societies that have had their day are melted down. Mirabeau was its master.

It was he who, silent till then, cried out to M. de Brézé, on the 23d of June, 1789: "Go tell your master . . . " Your master! It was to declare the King of France a foreigner. A whole frontier was traced between the throne and the people. It was the Revolution giving utterance to its cry. Nobody before Mirabeau would have dared this. Only great men pronounce the decisive words of the epochs.

Later on, Louis XVI. shall be insulted more gravely in appearance, shall be beaten to the earth, mocked in his chains, hooted on the scaffold. The Republic, with arms akimbo, will coif herself in her red bonnet, and speak coarse words to him, and call him Louis Capet; but nothing can ever be spoken to Louis XVI. so terrible and effective as that fatal sentence of Mirabeau. Louis Capet!—it is royalty smote on the face; *your master!*—it is royalty stricken to the heart.

And so, to date from these words, Mirabeau is the man of the country, the man of the great social convulsion, the man the end of that century had need of. To be popular and yet not plebeian is a rare thing in such times. His private life is then absorbed in his public life. Honoré de Riquetti, that abandoned man, is henceforth illustrious, worthy of attention and worthy of consideration. The love of the people is his armour against the sarcasms of his enemies. His person is the cynosure of every eye. The passers-by stop as he crosses the street; and, for two years that are left him, the little children of the people write his name unrebuked on all the corners of the walls of Paris, —that name which Saint-Simon eighty years before wrote Mirebaut, with the scorn natural to a peer and duke, and without suspecting that Mirebaut would become Mirabeau.

There are very striking parallels in the lives of certain men. Cromwell while still obscure, despairing of his future in England, wishes to embark for Jamaica; the orders of Charles I. prevent him. The father of Mirabeau, not seeing any possible existence for his son in France, wishes to send the young man to the Dutch Colonies. An order from the king forbids it. Now, take away Cromwell from the English Revolution, take away Mirabeau from the French Revolution, and you perhaps take away from the two revolutions two scaffolds. Who knows if Jamaica would not have saved Charles I., and Batavia Louis XVI.?

But no, the King of England will keep Cromwell; the King of France will keep Mirabeau. When a king is condemned to death, Providence bandages his eyes.

Strange that what is greatest in the history of a society should depend on what is least in the life of a man!

The first part of the life of Mirabeau is filled up with Sophie, the second with the Revolution.

A domestic storm, then a political storm, such was the destiny of Mirabeau. When we give a closer examination of this destiny, we gain an idea of whatever was fatal and necessary in it. The deviations of his heart are explained by the shock of his life.

For just consider the matter. Never have causes been more closely joined to effects than here. Chance gave him a father who taught him to despise his mother; a mother who taught him to hate his father; a tutor, Poisson, who did not like children, and who used him harshly because he was small and ugly; a valet, Grévin, who was the base spy of his enemies; a colonel, the Marquis de Lambert, who was as pitiless for the youth as Poisson had been for the child; a step-mother (not married though), Madame de Pailly, who hated him because he was not her own; a wife, Mademoiselle de Marignane, who repulsed him; a caste, the *noblesse*, which repudiated him; judges, the parliament of Besançon, who condemned him to death; a king, Louis XV., who bastilled him.

Thus, father, mother, wife, his tutor, his colonel, the magistracy, the *noblesse*, the king, that is to say, all that surrounds and skirts the existence of a man in the legitimate and natural order, was for him a cross, an obstacle, a stumbling-block, an occasion of wounds and bruises, a stone hard to his naked feet, a thicket of thorns tearing him on his way. Family and society were both his step-mothers. He met in life only two things that treated him well and loved him, two irregular things in revolt against order,—a mistress and a revolution.

Do not be astonished then, if for the mistress he broke all domestic ties, if for the revolution he broke all social bonds.

Do not be astonished to solve the question in the terms we have laid down at the beginning, if this demon of a family becomes the idol of a mistress in rebellion against her husband, and the god of a nation divorced from its king.

V

THE grief caused by the death of Mirabeau was a grief general, universal, and national. It was felt that something of the public thought had vanished with that soul. But a striking fact, and one necessary to speak of, because it would be artless to attribute it to the hasty and unreflecting admiration of his contemporaries, is that the court wore mourning for him as well as the people.

An insurmountable feeling of shame hinders us from sounding here certain mysteries, certain shameful qualities of the great man, which besides, in our opinion are lost in the colossal proportions of the *ensemble;* but it appears proved that in the latter part of his days the court had, as it affirmed, something to hope from him. It is patent that at this period he fired up angrily more than once at the excess of revolutionary enthusiasm; that he manifested at times the desire to cry halt and bring back somewhat of the past; that he who had such powerful lungs did not follow without breathlessness the march of new ideas becoming ever more and more accelerated, and that on some occasions he essayed to spoke the wheels of the Revolution, though he himself had forged them.

Fatal wheels, which crush so many venerable things on their passage!

There are still to-day many persons who think that if Mirabeau had lived longer he would have finally subdued the movement he had unchained. In their sense, the French Revolution might have been arrested by a single man; and that man was Mirabeau. According to this opinion, founded on some words of Mirabeau on his death-bed, which he surely never uttered, the death of Mirabeau was the ruin of the monarchy; if Mirabeau had lived, Louis XVI. would not have died; and the 2d of April,

1791, has brought to life the 21st of January, 1793.

According to us, those who believed so at the time, Mirabeau himself among the number, were mistaken, and so are those who believe so to-day. A pure optical illusion in Mirabeau as in others, proving that a great man has not always a plain idea of the kind of power that is in him.

The French Revolution was not a simple fact. There was more in it than Mirabeau.

The going out from it of Mirabeau would not suffice to empty it.

There was in the French Revolution something of the past and something of the future. Mirabeau was but the present.

To indicate here only two culminating points the French Revolution was complicated with Richelieu in the past and with Bonaparte in the future.

There is this peculiarity about revolutions, that they cannot be killed when they are still pregnant.

Moreover, even supposing the question more trivial than it really is, it is to be observed that, in political matters especially, what a man has done can rarely be undone except by another man.

The Mirabeau of '91 was impotent against the Mirabeau of '89. His work was stronger than he.

And then, men like Mirabeau are not the lock with which the gates of revolutions can be closed. They are but the hinge on which it turns, to close, it is true, as well as to open. To shut that fatal door, on whose panels are ever beating all the restless ideas, all the restless interests, and all the restless passions of society, a sword in guise of a bolt must be thrust into the iron-work.

VI

WE have attempted to characterize what Mirabeau was in the family and what he has been in the nation. It now remains for us to examine what he will be among posterity.

Notwithstanding certain reproaches of which he has deservingly been made the target, we believe that Mirabeau will continue great.

In presence of posterity every man and everything is absolved by greatness.

To-day, when almost all the things he has sown have given us their fruits which we have tasted, the greater part good and healthful, some bitter; to-day, when the successes and failures of his life have nothing incongruous in our eyes, so much do the years that pass place men in their true perspective; to-day, when there is for his genius neither adoration nor execration, and this man, so furiously tossed about from post to pillar while he lived, has taken the calm and serene attitude that death gives to great historic figures; to-day, when his memory, so long dragged in the mud and kissed on the altar, has been withdrawn from the Pantheon of Voltaire and the sewer of Marat, we may coldly say, "Mirabeau is great." The odour of the Pantheon and not the odour of the sewer clings to him. Impartial history in wiping his locks, sullied in the gutter, has not taken from him his aureole. The mud has been washed from that visage, and it still continues to shine.

After rendering an account of the immense political consequences produced by the sum total of his faculties, we may consider Mirabeau under a twofold aspect, as a writer and as an orator. Here we take the liberty of differing with Rivarol,—we believe Mirabeau was greater as an orator than as a writer.

The Marquis de Mirabeau, his father, had two kinds of style,—two pens, as it were, in his inkstand. When he wrote a book, a good book for the public, for effect, for the court, for the Bastille, for the grand staircase of the Palace of Justice, the worthy patrician draped himself, stiffened his limbs, swelled out his proportions, veiled his thoughts, already obscure enough of themselves, with all the pomps of expression; and it is impossible to fancy under what a style, at once flat and bombastic, heavy and languid, with interminable phrases dragging at its tail, loaded with neologies to such an extent as to banish all cohesion from the tissue,—under what a style, we repeat, altogether colourless and incorrect, the natural and indisputable originality of this strange writer is travestied; writer, half gentleman and half philosopher, preferring Quesnay to Socrates and Lefranc de Pompignan to Pindar; disdaining Montesquieu as behind the times, and submitting to be scolded by his curé; an amphibious dweller among the reveries of the eighteenth century and the prejudices of the sixteenth. But when this man, this same man, wished to write a letter, when he forgot the public and addressed himself only to *the long, stiff, and rigid demeanour* of his venerable brother, the Bailli, or his daughter, *little Saillanette*. "the most emollient woman that ever was," or to the pretty, smiling face of Madame de Rochefort, then that spirit, inflated with pretension, relaxed; no more effort, no more fatigue, no more apopletic distention in the expression; his thoughts, as they are scattered over the family letter become vivid, original, highly coloured, curious, amusing, profound, gracious,— in fine, natural; the echo of that grand aristocratic style of the time of Louis XIV., which Saint-Simon spoke with all the qualities of the man and Madame de Sévigné with all the qualities of the woman. An idea may be formed of it from the fragments we have quoted. After a book of the Marquis de Mirabeau, a letter of his is a revelation. We can hardly believe our eyes. Bouffon would not comprehend such contrasts in the same writer. You have two styles and only one man.

In this respect the son bore some likeness to the father. It might be said, though with certain limitations and modifications, that there is the same difference between his written style and his spoken style. Let us only remark this, that the father was at his ease in a letter, the son in a discourse. To be himself, to be natural, to be in his proper environment, the one needed a family, the other a nation.

The Mirabeau that writes is something less than Mirabeau. Whether he demonstrates to the young American Republic the folly of its "Order of Cincinnatus," and the inconsistency of an order of chivalry among ploughmen; or with his "Sur la liberté de l'Escaut" plagues Joseph II., the philosophic emperor, the Titus of Voltaire, the bust of a Roman Cæsar after the Pompadour style; or rummages in both bottoms of the cabinet at Berlin and draws therefrom that *Histoire secrète* which the court of France ordered to be judicially consigned to the flames on the steps of the Palace of Justice (a noteworthy blunder; for from those books burned by the hand of the executioner there always escaped some little flakes and sparks, which scattered at the will of the wind and alighted on the worm-eaten roof of the great European society, on the carpentry of monarchies, on all minds full of inflammable ideas, on all heads made of tow at that period); or casually inveighs against that cart-load of charlatans which made so much noise on the pavement of the eighteenth century,—Necker, Beaumarchais, Lavater, Calonne, and Cagliostro; in fine, whatever be the book he writes, his thought is always adequate to the subject, but his style is not always adequate to the thought. His ideas are ever grand and lofty; but to get out of his brain they have to stoop and shrink as if under a door too low. Except in his eloquent letters to Madame de Monnier, in which he is his real self, speaking rather than writing, and which are harangues of love quite as much as his discourse to the Constituant are harangues of revolution,—except these, we repeat, the style he discovers in his inkstand is in general commonplace in form, badly connected, pithless, nerveless at the end of his phrases, dry besides, coloured in dull fashion by means of trite epithets, poor in images, or offering here and there only ecccentric mosaics of incoherent metaphors. We feel while reading that the ideas of this man are not, like those of the great prose-writers to the manner born, made up of that peculiar substance which, soft and subtle, lends itself to all the chisellings of expression which finds its way boiling and liquid into all the nooks of the mould into which the writer pours it, and then hardens; lava first, granite after. We feel while reading that many things have remained in his head which it were as well had not stayed there, that this genius has not been so fashioned as to express itself completely in a book, and that a pen is not the best possible conductor for all the fluids compressed in that brain filled with thunders.

The Mirabeau who speaks is the real Mirabeau. The Mirabeau who speaks is the water running, the wave foaming, the fire sparkling, the bird in its flight, something that makes its own peculiar noise, a nature fulfilling its own law. A spectacle of eternal sublimity and harmony!

On the tribune all his contemporaries are unanimous on this point, Mirabeau was something magnificent. There he was himself, wholly himself, a self all-powerful. There, no more table, no more paper, no more inkstand bristling with pens, no more solitary cabinet, no more silence and meditation; but a marble which can be smote, a ladder which can be mounted, a tribune that is a species of cage for this wild beast, on which he can come and go, walk, stop, breathe, gasp, cross his arms, clinch his fists, paint his words by a gesture, and illumine his idea by a glance; a heap of men he can gaze on eye to eye; a great tumult,—magnificent accompaniment for a great voice; a crowd that hates the orator (the Assembly) enveloped in a crowd that loves him (the people); around him all these intelligencies, all these passions, all these mediocrites, all these ambitions, all these diverse natures which he knows, and from which he can draw whatever sound he wills as from an immense harpsichord; above him the vault of the hall of the Constituent Assembly, towards which his eyes are often raised as if to seek there his thoughts, for monarchies are overthrown by the ideas that fall from such a vault on such a head.

Oh, how much that man is at ease there, on his own ground! How sure and firm his footing! How great is that genius in a discourse which becomes so small in books! How happily the tribune has changed the conditions of exterior production for that thought! After Mirabeau the writer, Mirabeau the orator,—what a transfiguration!

In him everything was potent. His abrupt and sudden gestures were full of empire. In the tribune he had a colossal movement of the shoulders, like the elephant that carries an armed tower in battle. He too was carrying his thought. His voice, even at the time he but thundered a word from his bench, had a formidable and revolutionary tone which was recognized in the Assembly as like the roar of the lion in the menagerie. His locks, when he shook his head, were not unlike a mane. The movement of his eyebrows agitated all around him, like that of Jupiter, *cuncta superalio moventis.* His hands sometimes seemed to knead the marble of the tribune. His whole countenance, his whole attitude, his whole person, was swollen with a plethoric arrogance that had its grandeur. His head had a grandiose and thunderous ugliness whose effect was at moments electric and terrible. In the early stages, when nothing was visibly decided for or against royalty; when the contest seemed still nearly equal between the monarchy, still strong, and the theories, which were still weak; when none of the ideas which were, later on, to hold the future had yet arrived at their perfect growth; when the Revolution, badly guarded and badly armed, could apparently be easily taken by assault, it sometimes happened that the Right, believing it had thrown down some wall of the fortress, rushed on in *en masse* with cries of victory; then the monstrous head of Mirabeau appeared at the breach and petrified the assailants. The genius of the Revolution had forged an ægis with all the amalgamated doctrines of Voltaire, Helvetius, Diderot, Bayle, Montesquieu, Hobbes, Locke, and Rousseau, and had fixed the head of Mirabeau in the middle.

He was not only great on the tribune, he was great in his seat; in him the interrupter was equal to the orator. He often put as much in a word as in a discourse. "Lafayette has an army," he said to M. de Suleau, "but I have my head." He interrupted Robespierre with this profound remark: "That man will go far, he believes every word he says."

He dealt thus with the court when an occasion arose: "The court is starving the people. Treason! The people will sell it to the Constitution for bread!" All the instinct of the great revolutionist is in that word.

"The Abbé Sieyès!" he said, "a metaphysician travelling on a map." A keen thrust at the man of theory ever ready to bestride seas and mountains.

His simplicity at times was admirable. One day, or rather one evening, in his discourse of the 3d of May, at the moment when he was struggling, like an athlete with a cestus on each hand, with his left arm aimed at the Abbé Maury and his right at Robespierre, M. de Cazalès, with all the assurance of mediocrity, interrupted him in this fashion: "You are a babbler, and that is all." Mirabeau turned towards the Abbé Gontes, who was in the chair: "Monsieur le President," he said with childlike grandeur, "please stop M. de Cazalès, who is calling me a babbler."

The National Assembly wanted to begin an address to the king with these words: "The Assembly brings to the feet of your Majesty an offering," etc. "Majesty has no feet," said Mirabeau coldly.

A little farther on the Assembly wished to say that "it is intoxicated with the glory of its king." "Really?" objected Mirabeau; "people who make laws and who are intoxicated!"

Sometimes with a phrase that might have been translated from Tacitus, he characterized the history and nature of an entire sovereign house. He cried out to the ministers, for example: "Speak not to me of your Duke of Savoy, a bad neighbour to all liberty!"

Sometimes he laughed,—a formidable thing the laugh of Mirabeau.

He ridiculed the Bastille. "There have been," he said, "fifty-four *lettres de cachets* in my family, and I have had seventeen for my share. So you see I was treated as an elder brother of Normandy." He ridiculed himself. He was

WORKS OF VICTOR HUGO

accused by M. de Valfond of having gone through the ranks of the Regiment of Flanders on the 6th of October, with a naked sabre in his hand, and of speaking to the soldiers. Some one proved that the matter concerned M. de Gamaches, and not Mirabeau; and Mirabeau added, "So everything having been weighed, everything having been examined, the deposition of M. de Valfond contains nothing very unpleasant for any one except M. de Gamaches, who finds himself legally and vehemently suspected of being very ugly, since he resembles me."

Sometimes he smiled. When the question of the Regency was on debate before the Assembly, the Left thought of the Duke of Orleans, and the Right of the Prince of Condé, then an *émigré* in Germany. Mirabeau moved that no prince can be regent, except he took the oath to the Constitution. M. de Montlosier objected that a prince might have reasons for not having taken the oath; for instance, he might have made a journey beyond the sea. Mirabeau answered, "The discourse of the last speaker will be printed. I demand leave to correct an error in it. For 'beyond the sea,' read, 'beyond the Rhine.'" And this pleasantry decided the question. Thus did the great orator sometimes play with what he killed. To believe the naturalist, there is something of the cat in the lion.

On another occasion, when the *procureurs* of the Assembly had muddled a text of law with their bad editing, Mirabeau rose: "I ask leave to make a few timid reflections on the propriety of the National Assembly speaking French, and even writing in French the laws it proposes."

At moments, in the midst of his most violent popular harangues, he suddenly recalled who he was, and there would be some flashes of the patrician from him. It was at that time an oratorical custom to interject into every discourse some imprecation or other on the massacres of Saint Bartholomew. Mirabeau uttered his imprecation like everybody else; but he said, in passing: "The Admiral de Coligny, who, by way of parenthesis, was my cousin." The parenthesis was worthy of the man whose father wrote: "There has been only one misalliance in my family, the Medicis."—"My cousin, the Admiral de Coligny," would have been pointless at the court of Louis XIV.; it was sublime at the court of the people of 1791. At another time he spoke of his "worthy cousin the Keeper of the Seals," but it was in a different tone.

On the 22d September, 1789, the king made an offer of his gold and silver plate for the needs of the State. The Right fell into ecstasies of admiration and wept. "As for myself," cried Mirabeau, "I do not easily become tearful over the faïence of the great."

His disdain was fine, his laugh was fine, but his anger was sublime.

When an effort to irritate him succeeded, when one of those keen blades that make the orator and the bull bound from the earth, was plunged into his side, if this, for example, occurred in the middle of a discourse, he at once abandoned everything, left his ideas still incomplete, troubled himself little that the edifice of reasoning he had been building up crumbled behind him for want of the final crowning stone; he gave up the question on the spot, and rushed with lowered head on the incident. Then, woe to the interrupter! woe to the toreador who has flung the banderilla! Mirabeau was on him at once, seized him by the waist, raised him in the air, and trampled him under his feet. He drew back from him, returned, bruised and mangled him. He took hold of the entire man in the words he uttered, whoever he was, great or small, wicked or worthless, mud or dust, and caught him up with his life, his character, his ambition, his vices, his follies; he omitted nothing, he spared nothing, he missed nothing; he knocked him against the four corners of the tribune in his desperation; he made his hearers tremble, he made them laugh. Every word told, every phrase was an arrow; he had fury in his heart; he was terrible and superb. His was the anger of the lion. A great and potent orator, but never so fine as then! Then was the time to see in what fashion he chased away all clouds from the discussion! Then was the time to see how his stormy breath made every head in the assembly bristle with terror! Strange fact! he never reasoned better than when he was in a rage. The most violent irritation, far from disuniting the chain of his eloquence in the shocks which it caused him, set free a sort of superior logic within his mind, and he found arguments in fury as others do metaphors. Whether the sharp-pointed teeth of his sarcasm left their mark on the pale forehead of Robespierre, who, two years later, was to treat heads as Phocion treated discourses; or whether he chewed in his rage the wearisome

dilemmas of the Abbé Maury and spat them back at the Right, twisted, torn, dislocated, half devoured, and all covered with the foam of his wrath; or plunged the claws of his syllogism into the soft and flabby phrase of the advocate Target, he was great and magnificent, and had a sort of formidable majesty that the most frantic bounds never disordered. Our fathers have told us that they who had not seen Mirabeau in anger had not seen Mirabeau. In anger his genius was at its best and displayed all its splendours. Anger suited this man, as the tempest does the ocean. And, without intending, in what we have just written for the purpose of shadowing forth the supernatural eloquence of Mirabeau, we have painted him by a confusion of images even. Mireabeau was, in fact, not merely the bull, or the lion, or the tiger, or the athlete, or the archer, or the eagle, or the peacock, or the tempest, or the ocean; he was, by an indefinite series of surprising metamorphoses, all this at once; he was Proteus.

For whoever has seen or heard him, his discourses are to-day a dead letter. The colour, the breath, the life, the soul, the flash, the relief, have all disappeared. Everything in these fine harangues lies to-day flat on the earth. Where is the inspiration that whirled all these ideas around like leaves in a hurricane? The word is there, but where is the gesture? The cry is there, but where is the accent? The language is there, but where is the look? The discourse is there, but where is the drama of that discourse? For it is necessary to say that in every orator there are two things,—the actor and the man.

Talma is entirely dead. Mirabeau is half dead.

In the Constituent Assembly there was one thing that frightened those who regarded it attentively,—it was the Convention. To all who have studied this epoch, it was evident that from 1789 the Convention was in the Constituent Assembly. It was there in the state of germ, in the state of fœtus, in the state of outline. To the multitude it was still somethin.g indistinct; for him who could see, it was already something terrible. A nothing doubtless; a shade blacker than the general colour; a note sometimes thundering in the orchestra; a surly refrain in a chorus of hopes and illusions; a detail in which there was a certain want of concord with the *ensemble;* a sombre group in an obscure corner; some mouths giving a certain accent to certain words; thirty voices (only thirty voices), which later were to branch out, according to an appealing law of multiplication, into Girondins, the Plain and the Mountains,—'93 in a word; the dark spot in the azure sky of '89. Everything was already in this dark spot: the 21st of January, the 31st of May, the 9th Thermidor,—a bloody trilogy; Buzot, who was to devour Louis XVI., Robespierre, who was to devour Buzot, Vadier, who was to devour Robespierre,—a sinister trinity. Among these men the most vulgar and the most ignorant, Hébrard and Putraink, for example, smiled strangely during the discussions, and seemed to have some thought on the future which they did not tell. In our opinion, the historian ought to have microscopes for the purpose of examining the formation of one assembly in the womb of another. It is a species of gestation which is often reproduced in history, and which, as far as we can see, has not been sufficiently observed. In the present case this mysterious excrescence on the surface of the legislative body was no insignificant detail, containing as it did the scaffold already prepared for the King of France; a vulture's egg born by an eagle. From that time several sound minds in the Constituent Assembly were frightened at the presence of these few impenetrable men who seemed to be holding themselves in reserve for another epoch. They felt that there were many whirlwinds in these breasts from which scarcely a breeze escaped. They asked themselves whether or not these tempests would be let loose some day, and what then should become of all the things essential to civilization which '89 had not uprooted. Rabaut Saint-Etienne, who believed the Revolution terminated, and said so quite aloud, gave anxious attention to Robespierre, who did not believe it begun, and said so quite low. The present demolishers of the monarchy trembled before the future demolishers of society. The latter, like all men who hold the future and who know it, were supercilious, morose, arrogant, and the lowest among them disdainfully elbowed the leaders of the Assembly. The most worthless and the most obscure hurled insolent interruptions at the most thoughtful orators, as their humour and fancy led them; and as every one knew that there were events ready at hand for these men to deal with in the near future, none dare reply to them. It was in such moments, when the Assembly that one day was to be, terrified the Assembly that was,—it was then that the exceptional power of Mirabeau shone in all its splendour. With the feeling of his omnipotence, and with no suspicion that he was doing a great thing, he cried to the sinister group, which was preventing a speaker from being heard: "Silence among the thirty voices!" and the Convention held its peace.

That cave of Æolus remained still and was curbed as long as Mirabeau held his foot on the cover.

When Mirabeau was dead, all the ulterior anarchic projects broke loose.

As we said before, we believe Mirabeau died seasonably. After unchaining many tempests in the State, it is evident that for a time he crushed under his weight all the divergent forces for which the completion of the ruin he had begun was reserved. But the very pressure on them condensed them, and sooner or later the revolutionary explosion must, in our opinion, have found an issue, and would have hurled Mirabeau far in the distance, giant though he was.

Let us conclude.

If we had to sum up Mirabeau in one word, we would say: Mirabeau is not a man, is not a people, but an event,—an event which speaks.

An immense event,—the fall of the monarchical government in France!

With Mirabeau, neither the monarchy nor the republic were possible. The monarchy excluded him by its hierarchy, the republic by its level. Mirabeau is a man that passes through an epoch in a state of preparation. In order that the wings of Mirabeau should unfold at their ease, it was necessary for the social atmosphere to be in that condition in which there is nothing fixed, nothing rooted in the soil which can resist, in which every obstacle to the free course of theories is easily stemmed, in which the principles that are one day to make the solid basis of future society are yet in suspension, without too much form of consistency, waiting, in their intermediate state, where they float confusedly in eddies, till the moment comes for falling and crystallizing. Every institution firmly established has corners against which the genius of Mirabeau would have broken its wings. Mirabeau had a profound sense of things; he also had a profound understanding of men. After his arrival at the States General, he studied with close attention and silence the various groups, so picturesque at the time of the different parties, outside the Assembly as well as within. He detected the incapacity of Mounier, Malouet, and De Rabaut Saint-Etienne, who all were pondering a settlement on English constitutional lines. He estimated with calmness the passion of Chapelier, the succinctness of Pétion, the literary magniloquence of Volney, the Abbé Maury, who sought a place; D'Eprémenil and Adrian Duport, parliamentarians in ill-humour and not tribunes; Roland, that zero, whose wife was the numeral; Gregoire, who was in a condition of political somnambulism. He looked into the depths of the soul of Sieyès, hard though it was to fathom. He intoxicated Camille Desmoulins with his ideas, whose head was not strong enough to bear them. He fascinated Danton, who resembled him in being less great and more ugly. He did not attempt to win the Guillermys, the Lautrecs, or the Cazalès, for these had characters irresolvable in revolutions. He felt that everything was going on so fast that there was no time to lose. Besides being full of courage and never afraid of the man of the day, which is rare, nor of the man of the morrow, which is rarer still, he was during all his life bold with those who were powerful; he attacked in succession and during their periods of authority, Maupeon and Terray, Calonne and Necker. He approached the Duke of Orleans, touched him, and left him at once. He looked Robespierre in the face and askance at Marat.

He had been locked up successively in the Ile de Rhé, in the Castle of If, in the fort of Joux, and the keep of Vincennes. He had revenge for all in the taking of the Bastille.

In his captivities he read Tacitus; he devoured him; he lived on him; and when he ascended the tribune in 1789, he had his mouth still full of this marrow of lions. The first words he uttered showed it.

He had no understanding of the aims of Robespierre and Marat. He looked on the one as a lawyer without cases, and on the other as a doctor without patients, and he supposed their disappointments had driven them insane,—an opinion which had its true side also. He turned his back completely on the things that were advancing with such rapid strides behind him. Like all great radical regenerators, his eyes were much more firmly fixed on social questions than on political questions. His work was not the Republic, it was the Revolution.

That he was the truly great, the essential man of those times, is proved by the fact that he has remained greater to-day than any of the men who became great after him in the same order of ideas.

His father, who no more understood him, although he had begotten him, than the Constituant understood the Convention, said of him: "That man is neither the end nor the beginning of a man." He was right. "That man" was the end of one society and the beginning of another.

Mirabeau was not of less importance to the general work of the eighteenth century than Voltaire had been. These two men had like missions,— to destroy what was old and to prepare what was new. The labours of the one were continued, and occupied him during his whole life, and that before the eyes of Europe. The other appeared upon the scene but a few instants. To do their common work, Voltaire was granted years and Mirabeau days; yet Mirabeau has not done less than Voltaire. Each attacked the life of the social body after his fashion. Voltaire decomposed; Mirabeau crushed. The method of Voltaire is in some sort chemical, that of Mirabeau is entirely physical. After Voltaire, a society is in a state of dissolution; after Mirabeau, it is dust. Voltaire is an acid, Mirabeau a club.

VII

IF now, in order to complete the sketch we have endeavoured to give of Mirabeau and his epoch, we give a glance to our situation, it is easy to see, on viewing the point the social movement begun in '89 has reached to-day, that we shall no longer have men like Mirabeau; nor can any one tell us what proportions the great statesmen reserved for us by the future, may take.

The Mirabeaus are no longer necessary; besides, they are no longer possible.

Providence does not create such men when they are useless. It does not fling such seed to the wind.

And in fact, what service could a Mirabeau render now? A Mirabeau is a thunderbolt; what is there to strike with the thunder? Where are there objects in the political regions so highly placed that they attract the thunder? We are no longer in 1789, when inequalities in the social order were so enormous.

To-day the soil is pretty nearly level; everything is smooth, open and even. A tempest like Mirabeau passing over us would not find a single summit on which to lay hold.

But we must not say that, because we shall no longer need a Mirabeau, therefore, we no longer need great men. Quite the reverse. There is surely much work to be done yet. Everything has been unmade, nothing has been made anew.

In times like those in which we live, the party of the future is divided into two classes,—the men of revolution and the men of progress. It is the men of revolution who tear up the old political ground, dig the furrow and scatter the seed; but their day is short. To the men of progress belong the slow and laborious culture of principles, the study of the seasons favourable to the grafting of such and such an idea, the watering of the young plant, the manuring of the

soil, the harvest for all. They are bent and patient, under sun or rain, in the public field, removing the stones from that land covered with ruins, grubbing up the stumps of the past, which still keep their hold here and there, uprooting the dead stocks of the old *régimes,* hoeing out abuses, those weeds that grow so quick in all the swamps of the law. To do this they require a good eye, a good foot, and a good hand. Worthy and conscious toilers, often very badly paid!

Now, in our opinion, the men of the revolution have accomplished their task at this very time. They have recently had their Three Days of July. Let them, then, permit the men of progress to accomplish theirs. After the furrow, the ear of corn.

Mirabeau was the great man of revolution. We want now the great man of progress.

We will have him. France has too important an initiative in the civilization of the globe, to ever experience the need of special men for her special work. France is the majestic mother of all the ideas that are to-day doing their mission among all the nations. We may say that France, for two centuries, has been feeding the nations with the milk of her breasts. The blood of the great nation is generous and rich and her womb fruitful; her supply of genius is inexhaustible; she draws out of her bosom all the great intellects she needs; she has always men who rise to the height of her issues; and when the occasion calls, she lacks neither Mirabeaus to begin her revolutions nor Bonapartes to end them.

Providence is sure not to refuse the great social man she feels the want of; the political man she requires no longer.

While hoping for his advent, we must admit that the men who are making history to-day, are, with very few exceptions, small; undoubtedly the great bodies of the State lack general ideas and broad sympathies, and it is sad that they should do so; undoubtedly it is melancholy to see the time that should be employed in rearing structures employed in mere plastering; undoubtedly it is strange men should forget that the true sovereignty is that of the intellect, that, above all, the masses should be enlightened, and that when the people shall be intelligent, then only shall it be sovereign; undoubtedly it is shameful that the magnificent premises of '89 should have brought in their train certain corollaries, just as the head of the mermaid brings in its train the tail of the fish, and that bricklayers should have laid so many laws of plaster over walls of granite; undoubtedly it is deplorable that the French Revolution should have so many unskilful accoucheurs; undoubtedly all this is to be lamented.

But nothing has yet been done that cannot be repaired. No essential principle has been stifled in the revolutionary childbirth; no abortion has taken place; all the ideas important to future civilization have been born with a capacity for living, and are each endowed with strength, beauty, and health. Assuredly, when 1814 arrived, all these ideas, the daughters of the Revolution, were still very young and very small, and, indeed, quite in the cradle; and the restoration was, we must admit, but a lean and sorry nurse for them. But we must admit also that she killed none of them. The group of principles is complete.

All criticism is possible at the present hour; still, the wise man ought to view his whole epoch with a benevolent eye. He ought to hope, to trust, to wait. He ought to have consideration for the men of theory, on account of the slowness with which they urge their ideas; for the men of practice, on account of their narrow and useful love of the things that are, without which successive experiments would disorganize society; for the passions, with their fruitful and generous disgressions; for self-interest, because its calculations, in the absence of creeds, bind the classes together; for governments, on account of their tentative gropings in the dark towards the general good; for the opposing parties, because the goad they have ever in their hands forces the oxen to trace the furrow; for the moderate parties, because of the mildness they bring to transitions; for the extreme parties, because of the activity they give to the circulation of ideas, which are the life-blood of civilization; for the friends of the past, because of the care they take of such roots as still live; for the zealots of the future, because of their love of those fine flowers which will one day be fine fruits; for middle-aged men, because of their moderation; for young men, because of their patience; for some, on account of what they are doing; for others, on account of what they wish to do; for all, on account of the difficulty of everything.

Nor shall we deny either all that is stormy and troubled in the age in which we live. Most of the men who are do-

ing something in the State do not know what they are doing. They are working in the night, and do not see. To-morrow, when it is day, they will be, perhaps, surprised at their work. Charmed or frightened, who knows? There is no longer anything settled in political science. All compasses are lost; society is dragging its anchors; during the last twenty years that great mast which is called *dynasty*, and which is always the first stricken by the lightning, has been changed three times.

The final law of anything is not yet revealed. The government, such as it is, is not the affirmation of anything; the press, otherwise so great and useful, is only the perpetual negation of everything. No clear formula of civilization and progress has so far been drawn up.

The French Revolution opened for all social theories an immense book, a sort of grand testament. There Mirabeau wrote his word, Robespierre his, Napoleon his. Louis XVIII. made an erasure, Charles IX. tore out a page. The Chamber of the 2d of August pasted it

in again, almost; but this is all. The book is there, the pen is there. Who will dare write?

The men of the present seem of little account, no doubt; yet every one who thinks ought to fix on the present effervescence an attentive look.

Certainly, our confidence is firm and our hope assured.

Who among us does not feel, amid the tumult and the tempest, amid the conflicts of all the systems and all the ambitions that raise so much smoke and dust, that under yonder veil still hiding from our eyes the social and providential statue hardly yet hewn, behind that cloud of theories, passions, and chimeras, crossing, jostling, and devouring one another in the fog lit up only by their flashes, beyond that sound of the human word which speaks all tongues at the same time through all mouths, under that violent whirlwind of things, men, and ideas called the nineteenth century, who does not feel that something great is being accomplished?

God remains calm and does his work

Voltaire

FRANÇOIS MARIE AROUET, so celebrated under the name of Voltaire, was born at Chatenay on the 20th of February, 1694. His family belonged to the magistracy. He was educated by the Jesuits at the college of Louis le Grand, and one of his teachers, Father Lejay, we are told, predicted that he would be the corypheus of deism in France.

Hardly had Arouet left college, where his faculties had sprung to life with all the strength and ingenuousness of youth, when he encountered an inflexible father on the one hand, and a suave corrupter on the other. The latter was his godfather, the Abbé de Châteauneuf. The father condemned all literary studies without knowing why. and consequently with insurmountable obstinacy. The godfather, on the contrary, encouraged the essays of Arouet, and showed a great liking for verses, especially such as breathed a decided savour of licentiousness or impiety. The one would imprison the poet in a lawyer's office; the other led, or rather misled, the young man into all the salons. M. Arouet forbade all reading to his son. Ninon de Lenclos bequeathed a library to the pupil of her friend Châteauneuf. Thus at its birth the genius of Voltaire was unfortunately subjected to two opposite and equally fatal forces, one tending to stifle that sacred fire which cannot be extinguished; the other feeding it thoughtlessly at the expense of all that is noble and worthy in the intellectual order as well as in the social order. These are the two contrary impulses, stamped at the same time on the first flight of this powerful imagination, which vitiated its direction forever. At least we may attribute to them the first aberrations of the talent of Voltaire, vexed in this fashion at once by the bridle and the spur.

We need not be astonished then, if at the very beginning of his career, certain verses, poor and pointless enough, were attributed to him and lodged him in the Bastille,—a somewhat rigorous punishment for bad rhymes. It was during this enforced leisure that Voltaire, at the age of twenty-two, sketched the outline of his tiresome poem the "Ligue," afterwards the "Henriade," and finished his noteworthy drama "Oedipe." After some months in the Bastille, he was freed and pensioned at the same time by the Regent Orleans, whom he thanked for taking care of his board,

but begged that he might be allowed henceforth to take care of his lodging himself.

"Oedipe" was played with success in 1718. Lamotte, the oracle of the period, deigned to consecrate the triumph by a few sacramental words, and the fame of Voltaire began its course. To-day, Lamotte is immortal only perhaps because he is named in the writings of Voltaire.

The tragedy of "Artémise" succeeded the "Oedipe." It fell flat. Voltaire went on a trip to Brussels to see J. B. Rousseau, to whom, oddly enough, the epithet great has been attached. The two poets were full of respect for each other before meeting. They separated enemies. It has been said that they were mutually jealous, which could hardly be a sign of superiority in either.

"Artémise," recast and played in 1724 under the name of "Marianne," had considerable success, though its new form was by no means an improvement on the old. France had not so far had an epic poem; but the "Ligue" or the "Henriade" appeared at this time. Voltaire substituted Mornay for Sully in his work, because he had grounds of complaint against the descendant of the great minister. The vengeance seems hardly worthy of a philosopher; there is, however, some excuse for Voltaire, who had been insulted in a cowardly fashion in front of the Hôtel de Sully by a certain Chevalier de Rohan, and finding no redress in the law, he adopted the only retaliation in his power.

Justly indignant at the refusal of the courts to deal with his contemptible antagonist, Voltaire, who was now a celebrity, withdrew into England where he devoted himself to the study of some of the sophists of that nation. Still all his leisure was not wasted; he composed two new tragedies, "Brutus" and "César," many scenes of which Corneille might have acknowledged.

After returning to France, he gave in succession the "Eryphile," which was a failure, and "Zaïre," a masterpiece planned and finished in eighteen days. It is defective only in local colouring and from the absence of a certain severity of style. The success of "Zaïre," was prodigious, and it was well deserved. The tragedy of "Adélaïde du Guesclin" (afterwards the "Duc de Foix") succeeded "Zaïre," but was far from attaining the same success. Some publications of a less important character, the "Temple du Goût," "Lettres sur les anglais," etc., troubled the life of Voltaire for several years.

However, his name was already spreading over Europe. Retiring to Cirey, where he lived in the household of the Marquise du Châtelet, a lady, in the words of Voltaire, fit for all sciences except the science of life, he tried to dull his fine imagination by studying algebra and geometry, wrote "Alzire," "Mahomet," the sprightly "Histoire de Charles XII.," collected materials for the "Siècle de Louis XIV.," prepared the "Essai sur les mœurs des nations," and sent madrigals to Frederick, Crown Prince of Prussia. "Mérope," also composed at Cirey, set the seal on the dramatic reputation of Voltaire. He thought he might now present himself for admission to the French Academy and fill the chair of Cardinal de Fleury. He was not received. So far he had nothing but genius to back him. But

some time after, he set himself the task of flattering Madame de Pompadour, and this with such obstinate and complacent servility that he obtained, at the same time, the academic chair, the post of gentleman of the bedchamber, and the office of historiographer of France. His favour was not of long duration. Voltaire found a refuge now at Lunéville with Stanislas, the good King of Poland and Duke of Lorraine; now with Madame du Maine, at Sceaux, w h e r e he wrote the "Sémiramis, Oreste," and "Rome Sauvée;" and again at Berlin with Frederick, become King of Prussia. He passed several years in the last retreat with the title of chamberlain, the Prussian cross of merit and a pension. He was admitted to the royal suppers along with Maupertuis, D'Argens, and Lamettrie, atheist of the king,—of that king, who, like Voltaire himself, lived without court, without council, and without worship. It was not the sublime friendship of Aristotle and Alexander, of Terence and Scipio. A few years of friction sufficed to wear out all that the soul of the despot philosopher and the soul of the sophist poet had in common. Voltaire wished to escape from Berlin. Frederick hunted him.

Dismissed by Prussia, rejected by France, Voltaire spent two years in Germany, where, to oblige the Duchess of Saxe-Gotha, he compiled and published the "Annales de l'Empire;" then he planted himself at the gates of Geneva with his niece, Madame Denis.

The "Orphelin de la Chine," a tragedy in which nearly every characteristic of his talent is conspicuous, was the first fruit of this retreat, in which he would have lived in peace, if greedy booksellers had not published his odious "Pucelle." It was also at this period and in his different residences of Les Délices, Tournay, and Ferney, that he wrote the poem on the "Earthquake of Lisbon," the tragedy of "Tancrède," some tales, and a number of his minor productions. It was then he defended, with a generosity in which there was too great an admixture of ostentation, Calas, Sirven, La Barre, Montballi, and Lalli, those lamentable victims of judicial mistakes. It was then he quarrelled with Jean Jacques, gained the friendship of Catherine of Russia, for whom he wrote the history of her ancestor Peter the Great, and became reconciled to Frederick. It is from the same time that his co-operation in the "Encyclopédie" dates,—a work in which men who tried to show their strength have only shown their weakness, a monstrous monument of which the "Montieur" of our Revolution is the frightful sequel.

When borne down by the weight of years, Voltaire wished to see Paris once more. He returned to that Babylon which was in sympathy with his genius. Hailed by universal acclamations the unhappy old man was enabled to see before his death how much his work had advanced, was enabled to be delighted or terrified by his glory. His vital power no longer sufficed to support the emotions of the journey, and Paris witnessed his death on the 30th of May, 1778. The freethinkers claimed that he carried with him his infidelity to the tomb. We shall not follow him there.

We have related the private life of Voltaire: we must now try to paint his public and private existence.

To name Voltaire is to characterize the whole eighteenth century; it is to fix at one stroke the historical and literary physiognomy of this epoch, which was, after all, only a period of transition, for society as well as for poetry. The eighteenth century will always appear in history as a century stifled between the age that precedes and the age that follows it. Voltaire is its principal and in some sort its typical representative, and, however prodigious the man may be, his proportions seem paltry enough between the great image of Louis XIV. and the gigantic figure of Napoleon.

There are two beings in Voltaire. His life had two influences. His writings had two results. It is on this twofold action, controlling literature on the one side, manifested in events on the other, we wish to dwell for a moment. We shall study separately each of these two influences of the genius of Voltaire. We must not forget, however, that their double power was intimately co-ordinated, and that the effects of this power, rather intermingled than interlinked, have always had something simultaneous and common. If, in this note, we examine them separately, it is solely because it would be beyond our strength to embrace at a single glance a unity that eludes our grasp. In this we imitate the artifice of those oriental artists, who, finding that they are incapable of representing an entire face, succeed in giving a tolerable idea of the human countenance by painting two profiles and enclosing them in a frame.

In literature Voltaire has left one of those monuments whose appearance is astonishing from its size rather than imposing from its grandeur. There is nothing august in the edifice he has constructed. It is not the palace of kings, nor is it the shelter of the poor. It is a bazaar, vast and elegant, irregular and convenient; making a display of countless wealth amid surrounding filth; supplying all interests, all vanities, and all passions with what exactly suits them; dazzling and fetid; an exchange of prostitutions and pleasures; peopled by vagabonds, merchants, and idlers, but seldom the resort of the priest or of the needy. Here, you see brilliant galleries thronged incessantly by astonished crowds; there, secret caverns which no one cares to boast of having entered. Under these sumptuous arcades you will find a thousand masterpieces of taste and art, everything resplendent with gold and diamonds; but do not look for the statue of bronze with its antique and severe lines. You will find ornaments for your salons and boudoirs; do not look for such decorations as beseem the sanctuary. And woe to the weakling whose soul is his entire fortune, if he expose it to the seductions of this magnificent den,—this monstrous temple in which there are testimonies for all that which is not truth, adoration for all that which is not God!

Certainly though we may wish to speak of a monument of this kind with admiration, we cannot be required to speak of it with respect.

We would pity a city in which the bazaar was crowded, and the church deserted; we would pity a literature that abandoned Corneille and Bossuet to run in the traces of Voltaire.

Far from us the thought, nevertheless, of denying the genius of this extraordinary man. It is because of our conviction that this genius was perhaps one of the finest ever bestowed on a writer that we deplore with the greater bitterness its frivolous and destructive employment. We regret, for his own sake as for the sake of literature, that he turned against Heaven the intellectual power he had received from Heaven. We bewail the glorious genius that did not comprehend its sublime mission. We sorrow over the ingrate who has profaned the chastity of his Muse and the sanctity of his country, over the deserter who did not remember that the tripod of the poet has its place close by the altar. And, it is a profound and inevitable truth, his very crime contained its chastisement. His glory is much less great than it might have been, because he aimed at every species of glory, even at that of Erostates. He has cleared all fields, he cannot be said to have cultivated any. And because he had the guilty ambition of sowing in them nutritive germs and venomous germs with equal impartiality, to his eternal shame, it is the poisons that have borne most fruit. The "Henriade," as a literary composition, is very inferior to the "Pucelle,"—which does not at all mean that this vicious work is among the best, even of its shameful class. His satires, sometimes branded with an infernal impress, are very much superior to his most innocent comedies. His lighter verses, often instinct with shameless cynicism, are preferred to his lyric poems, in which religious and weighty verses are occasionally found. His tales, in fine, so cheerless in their incredulity and scepticism, are far above his histories, where the same defect is felt a little less perceptibly, but where the perpetual absence of dignity is out of harmony with the very nature of this class of literature. As to his tragedies, in which he really shows himself a great poet, often finding the true touches of character and words fresh from the heart, it cannot be denied that, in spite of some admirable scenes, he is still very far from Racine, and still farther from Corneille. And our opinion on this point will be the less suspected, as a deep study of the dramatic work of Voltaire has convinced us of his signal superiority on the theatre. We are inclined to believe that if Voltaire, instead of scattering the colossal forces of his thought over twenty different points, had combined them in one single direction, tragedy, he might have surpassed Racine and, perhaps, equalled Corneille. But he expended his genius in witty sallies. He was, therefore, marvellously sprightly and sparkling, and the seal of his genius is impressed rather on the vast entirety of his works than on any one of them in particular. Ever absorbed by his age, he was too neglectful of posterity, that austere image which should tower above all the meditations of the poet. Engaged in a capricious and frivolous struggle with his capricious and frivolous contemporaries, he wished at once to please and flout them. His Muse, who would have been so beautiful if she had been content to rely on her beauty, often borrowed her charms from the colours of the paint-box and the grimaces of coquetry, and we are constantly tempted to address her in these words of the jealous lover:—

"Why give yourself such trouble? Art for you was not invented, you require it not."

Voltaire appeared to ignore the fact that there is much grace in strength, and that whatever is sublimest in the works of the human intellect is also, perhaps, that which is most simple. Imagination can reveal its heavenly origin without having recourse to foreign artifices. She has but to walk to show that she is a goddess. *Et vera incessu patuit dea.*

If it were possible to summarize the manifold idea which the literary existence of Voltaire presents, we could only class it among those prodigies which the Latins call *monstra.* Voltaire, in truth, is a phenomenon,—a phenomenon perhaps unique which could only arise in France and in the eighteenth century. There is this difference between his literature and that of the great century preceding him, that Corneille, Molière, and Pascal belonged more to society, Voltaire to civilization. We feel, when reading him, that he is the writer of an enervated and feeble age. He has a certain pleasantness but no grace, a certain brilliancy but no real charm, a certain lustre but no majesty. He can flatter but he cannot console. He fascinates but does not persuade. Except in tragedy, which was his native element, he lacks tenderness and sincerity. We feel that everything is the result of an organization, and not the effect of an inspiration; and, though it is an atheist physician who tells you that all Voltaire was in his sinews and in his nerves, you acknowledge with a shudder that he is right. Moreover, like another ambitious personage of later days, who aspired to political supremacy, it is in vain that Voltaire has aimed at literary supremacy. Absolute monarchy is not suitable to man. If Voltaire had understood what is true greatness, he would have placed his glory in unity rather than in universality. Strength is not revealed by a perpetual changing of place, by indefinite metamorphoses, but rather by a majestic immobility. Force is Jupiter not Proteus.

Here begins the second part of our task: it will be shorter, because, thanks to the French Revolution, the political results of Voltaire's philosophy are unfortunately frightfully notorious. It would, however, be supremely unjust to attribute that fatal revolution to the writings of the "patriarch of Ferney" alone. We must above all see in it the effect of a social decomposition commenced long before. Voltaire and the age in which he lived may reciprocally accuse and excuse each other. Too strong to obey his time, Voltaire was also too weak to control it. From this equality of influence there resulted a perpetual reaction between himself and his century, a mutual exchange of impieties and follies, a continual flux and reflux of innovations, which in their oscillations always carried away some old pillar of the social edifice. Let us only consider the political features of the eighteenth century, the scandals of the Regency, the turpitudes of Louis XV.; violence in the ministry, violence in the parliaments, force nowhere; moral corruption descending by degrees from the head to the heart, from the great to the people; the prelates of the court and the abbés of the boudoir; the ancient monarchy, the ancient society staggering on their common foundation, and no longer opposing to the attacks of the innovators anything except the magic of that glorious name Bourbon; let us fancy Voltaire flung into this society in dissolution like a serpent into a swamp, and we shall no longer be astonished at seeing the contagious action of his thought hasten the end of that political order which Montaigne and Rabelais in vain assailed in its youth and vigour. It was not he who rendered the disease mortal, but it was he who developed its germ, and increased the malignity of the outburst. All the venom of Voltaire was needed in order to set this dung-heap in effervescence; and, therefore, a great many of the monstrous occurrences of the Revolution may be justly attributed to this unhappy man. As to the Revolution itself, it was natural that it should be unprecedented. Providence wished to place it between the most formidable of the sophists and the most formidable of the despots. At its dawn, Voltaire appeared in a funereal saturnalia; at its decline, Bonaparte arose amid a massacre.

Sir Walter Scott

SURELY there is something strange and marvellous in the talent of this man, who disposes of his reader as the wind disposes of a leaf; who leads him at his will into all places and into all times; unveils for him with ease the most secret recesses of the heart, as well as the most mysterious phenomena of nature, as well as the obscurest pages of history; whose imagination caresses and dominates all other imaginations, clothes with the same astonishing truth the beggar with his rags and the king with his robes, assumes all manners, adopts all garbs, speaks all languages; leaves to the physiognomy of the ages all that is immutable and eternal in their lineaments, traced there by the wisdom of God, and all that is variable and fleeting, planted there by the follies of men; does not force, like certain ignorant romances, the personages of the past to colour themselves with our brushes and smear themselves with our varnish; but compels, by his magic power, the contemporary reader to imbue himself, at least for some hours, with the spirit of the old times, to-day so much scorned, like a wise and adroit adviser inviting ungrateful children to return to their father. The skilful magician desires above all, however, to be correct. He does not refuse his pen to any truth, not even to that which springs from the portraiture of error,—that daughter of men who might be believed immortal if her changing and capricious humour left us at all in doubt as to her claims to eternity. Few historians are as faithful as this roman-cer. We feel that he wishes his portraits to be pictures and his pictures portraits. He paints for us our forefathers with all their passions, their vices, and their crimes, but in such sort that the instability of superstition and the impiety of fanaticism but serve to show forth more vividly the perpetuity of religion and the sanctity of beliefs. We delight in finding again our ancestors with their prejudice, often so noble and salutary, as well as with their splendid plumes and stout breastplates.

Walter Scott has been able to draw from the springs of nature and truth an unknown species. It is new to us, because he makes himself as ancient as he wills. He unites to the minute exactness of the chronicles the majestic grandeur of history and the all-compelling interest of romance. His potent and curious genius divines the past; his true pencil traces a faithful portrait after a confused shadow, and forces us to recognize even what we have not seen; his flexible and solid mind takes the peculiar impress of every age and of every country, like soft wax, and preserves this impress for posterity like imperishable bronze.

Few writers have so well fulfilled as Walter Scott the duties of the romancer in relation to his art and to his age; for it would be an almost culpable error in the man of letters to believe himself above the general interest and above national needs, to exempt his mind from all action over the minds of his contemporaries, and to isolate his life from the great life of the social body. What voice is likely to rise in the tempest if not that of the lyre which can calm it? And who will brave the hatreds of anarchism and the disdain of despotism, if not he to whom ancient wisdom assigned the task of reconciling nations and kings, and to whom modern wisdom has given that of dividing them?

It is not, then, to mawkish gallantries, to paltry intrigues, or coarse adventures that Walter Scott devotes his talent. Warned by the instinct of his glory, he has felt that something else was needed by a generation that has just written with its blood and with its tears the most extraordinary page of all human histories. The times which immediately preceded and immediately followed our convulsive Revolution were such periods of weakness as persons in a fever experience before and after their paroxysms. Then books the most stupidly atrocious, the most vapidly impious, the most monstrously obscene, were greedily devoured by a diseased society, whose depraved tastes and blunted faculties rejected all palatable and healthy nourishment. It is this which explains those scandalous triumphs awarded at the time by the plebeians of the drawing-room and the patricians of the coffee-house to certain insipid or obscene writers whom we disdain to name, who are to-day reduced to the necessity of begging the applause of lackeys and the smiles of prostitutes. Now, popularity is no longer distributed by the populace; it springs from the only source that can impress on it a character of immortality as well as of universality,—from the suffrage of that minority of discriminating minds, of exalted souls and sober heads, that represent morally all civi-

lized peoples. It is this which Scott has obtained, borrowing as he does from the annals of nations compositions made for all nations, and from the records of ages works written for all ages. No romancer ever hid so much teaching under so much witchery, so much truth under so much fiction. There is a visible alliance between the form he has made his own and all the literary forms of the past and of the future, and the epic romances of Scott may be considered as a transition from the literature of the present to the grand romances, the grand epics in verse or in prose which our poetic era promises and will give us.

What should be the intention of the romancer? It should be to express through the medium of an interesting fable a useful truth. And when once this fundamental idea is chosen, this explanatory action is invented, should not the author seek for its development a method of execution which gives to his romance the semblance of life, which gives to the imitation the likeness of its model? And is not life a singular drama in which the good and the bad, the beautiful and the ugly, the high and the low are intermingled,—a law whose power only expires beyond creation? Should, then, the writer limit himself, like some Flemish painters, to the composition of pictures altogether dark, or like the Chinese, to that of pictures entirely luminous, since Nature everywhere shows the struggle between light and darkness? Now romancers, before Walter Scott, adopted two distinctly antagonistic methods of composition; both vicious precisely because they are antagonistic. The one class gave to their work the form of a narrative arbitrarily divided into chapters, without very well knowing why, or for the purpose of relaxing the tension of the reader, as the title *descanso* (rest), placed at the head of his chapters by an old Spanish author, innocently confesses. The others unfold their fable in a series of letters, supposed to be written by the different actors in the romance. In the narrative, the characters disappear, the author is ever in front; in the letters, the author passes out of sight so that the characters alone may come into view. The narrative romancer cannot give place to natural dialogue, to real action; he must substitute for these a certain monotonous movement of style, which is as it were a mould in which the most diverse events take the same form, and under which the most elevated creations, the most profound inventions, are lost, just as the inequalities of a field are levelled under the roller. In the romance by letters, the same monotony springs from another cause. The several characters arrive each in their turn with their several epistles after the manner of those strolling actors, who, as they can only appear after one another, appear in succession with a big placard above their heads which informs the public of their various rôles. Again, the romance by letters may be compared to those laborious conversations of deaf-mutes who write in turn what they have to say to each other, so that to express their anger or their joy they must have constantly a pen in the hand and a note-book in the pocket. Now I ask, where is the appropriateness of a tender reproach which you must carry to the post-office? And is not the stor-

my explosion of passion a little hampered between the obligatory preamble and the polite formula which are the vanguard and the rearguard of every letter written by the well-born? Do you believe that the procession of the compliments and the baggage of the civilities accelerate the progress of the interest and hasten on the march of the action? Ought we not, then, to suppose some radical and insurmountable defect in a kind of composition which has sometimes succeeded in chilling even the eloquence of Rousseau?

Now let us assume that for the narrative romance, in which everything would seem to be thought of except the interest, in which the absurd custom is adopted of ushering in every chapter by a summary, often very detailed,— the story of a story as it were; let us assume that for the epistolary romance, whose very form forbids all vehemence and all rapidity, some creative mind should substitute the dramatic romance, in which the dramatic action is unfolded in true and varied tableaux, just as the events of real life are unfolded; which should know of no other vision than that of the different scenes to be developed; which, in fine, would be a long drama, where descriptions take the place of decorations and costumes, where the characters are delineated by themselves, and represent, by their various and multiplied movements, all the forms of the individual idea of the work. You will find in this new species the advantages of the two old species united without their drawbacks. Having at your disposal the picturesque and, in some sort, magical activities of the drama, you can leave behind the scene those thousand tedious and transitory details which the mere narrator, obliged to follow his actors step by step, as if they were children in leading strings, must expound at length, if he does not wish to be obscure; and you can turn to account those intense and sudden strokes more fruitful for meditation than entire pages flashing from the movements of a scene, but excluded by the rapidity of a tale.

After the picturesque but prosaic romance of Walter Scott, another kind of romance will have still to be created, in our opinion of a finer and more finished kind. It will be the romance which is at once dramatic and epic, picturesque but poetic, real but ideal, true but grand, Walter Scott and Homer in combination.

Like every creator, Walter Scott has up to the present hour been assailed by infuriate critics. He who drains a swamp must resign himself to the croaking of the frogs around him.

For our part, we fulfil a conscientious duty in placing Sir Walter Scott very high among romancers, and "Quentin Durward" in particular, very high among romances. It would be hard to find a book better interwoven, and one in which the moral effect is better linked with the dramatic effect.

The author has wished, in our view, to demonstrate how much more certain loyalty, though found among the obscure, the young and the poor, is likely to obtain its purpose than perfidy, though aided by all the resources of power, riches, and experience. The first of these rôles is embodied by a young Scotchman, Quentin Durward, an orphan, wrecked on all kinds of shoals,

exposed to the best laid snares, without other compass to guide him than the love of one whom to love is madness; but it often happens that when love resembles insanity it is really a virtue. The second is intrusted to Louis XI., a king more adroit than the most adroit courtiers, an old fox armed with the lion's claws, powerful and crafty, served in the shadow as well as in the light, covered by his guards as by a buckler, and accompanied by his executioners as by a sword. These two personages, so different in all respects, act and react on each other so as to express the fundamental idea with singularly striking truth. It is by his faithful obedience to the King that the loyal Quentin serves without knowing it, his own interests, while the projects of Louis XI., of which Quentin was to be at once the instrument and the victim, all turn out to the confusion of the cunning old man and the advantage of his simple-minded agent.

A superficial examination would at first sight lead to the belief that the primary intention of the poet is shown in the historic contrast, painted with such talent, of the King of France, Louis of Valois, with Charles the Bold, Duke of Burgundy. This fine episode is perhaps after all a defect in the composition of the work, as it rivals in interest the subject of the romance. But this fault, if it be a fault, in no way diminishes the imposing and comical aspects of the situation in which these two princes are set in opposition; the one, a subtle and ambitious despot, despising the other, a harsh and warlike tyrant, who would scorn him if he dared. They both hate each other. But Louis braves the hatred of Charles, because it is rude and savage; Charles dreads the hatred of Louis, because it is caressing. The Duke of Burgundy, in the midst of his camp and his states, is disturbed by the presence of the King of France, who is defenceless, as the bloodhound is in the neighbourhood of the cat.

The cruelty of the duke springs from his passions, that of the king from his character. The Burgundian is loyal, because he is violent; he never dreams of hiding his bad deeds; he feels no remorse; for he has forgotten his crimes as speedily as his angers. Louis is superstitious, perhaps because he is a hypocrite; mere religion does not suffice the man who is tormented by his conscience and who will not repent; but it is vain for him to believe in useless expiations; the memory of the evil he has done ever lives within him close to the thought of the evil he is about to do, because we always remember what we have long meditated on, and crime, when it has been a desire and a hope, becomes also a memory. The two princes are very devout; but Charles swears by his sword before swearing by God, and Louis tries to gain the good-will of the saints by gifts of money or offices at court,—mingles diplomacy with his prayers, and intrigues even with Heaven. In case of war, Louis is measuring its danger, while Charles is already resting after victory. The policy of the one is in the might of his arm, but the eye of the other reaches farther than the arm of the duke. In fine, Walter Scott proves, by engaging the two rivals in action, that prudence is stronger than daring, and

that he who appears to dread nothing is really afraid of him who seems to fear everything.

With what art the illustrious writer paints for us the King of France when, by a refinement of trickery, he presents himself to his fair cousin of Burgundy, and asks his hospitality at the very moment the haughty vassal was about to make war on him! And what can be more dramatic than the news of a revolt fomented in the states of the duke by the agents of the king falling like a thunderbolt between the two rulers at the very moment when the same table united them! Thus fraud is foiled by fraud, and the prudent Louis is delivered into the hands of an enemy justly irritated. History tells us something about this; but at this point I prefer to believe in romance rather than in history, because I count moral truth more desirable than historic truth. A still more remarkable scene perhaps is that where the two princes, whom the safest counsel has failed to bring together, are reconciled by an act of cruelty imagined by the one and executed by the other. For the first time they burst into a laugh of mutual cordiality and enjoyment. And this laugh, excited by the torture of a poor wretch, effaces for a moment their discord. This terrible idea makes the reader thrill with admiration.

We have heard the picture of the debauch criticized as hideous and revolting. It is in our opinion one of the finest chapters of the book. As Walter Scott had undertaken the task of painting that famous cut-throat, surnamed the Boar of Ardennes, his description would have been a failure if it did not excite horror. We must always enter frankly into a dramatic idea, and in everything search out the end to be attained. In this, emotion and interest have their source. It belongs only to timid spirits to capitulate with a strong conception and recoil before the path they themselves have traced.

We shall justify on the same principle two other passages which do not seem to us less worthy of meditation and praise. The first is the execution of Hayraddin,—a singular personage whom the author might perhaps have made more of. The second is the chapter in which Louis XI., arrested by the Duke of Burgundy, arranges with Tristan l'Hermite in his prison the punishment of the astrologer who has deceived him. It is a singularly fine idea to show us this cruel king finding his dungeon even wide enough for his vengeance, seeking for agents to deal justice on those who were lately his servants, and testing all the authority left him by an execution.

We might multiply these observations and try to show in what direction the new drama of Sir Walter Scott seems to us defective, particularly in the denouncement; but the romancer could doubtless supply much better reasons for his justification than we could for attacking him, and against such a formidable champion our weak arms would scarcely be at an advantage. We shall confine ourselves to saying that the witticism put in the mouth of the Duke of Burgundy's fool on the arrival of King Louis XI. at Peronne, really belongs to the fool of Francis I., who uttered it at the time of the passage of Charles V. through France in 1535. As the immortality of this poor Triboulet depends entirely on this quip, it is but fair to let him have it. We think also that the ingenious expedient imagined by Galeotti for the escape of Louis XI. had been tried a thousand years before by the philosopher who wished to put Dionysius of Syracuse to death. We do not attach to these remarks more importance than they deserve; a romancer is not a chronicler. We are astonished only that the king should, in the council of Burgundy, address certain knights of the Holy Ghost, as this Order was not founded for a century later, by Henri III. We believe that even the Order of Saint Michael, with which the noble author decorates the brave Lord Crawford, was not instituted by Louis XI. until after his captivity. Sir Walter Scott must permit us these little chronological quibbles. By winning a slight triumph of a somewhat pedantic kind over so illustrious an *antiquary*, we are not able to refrain from feeling some of that harmless delight which transported his Quentin Durward, when he unhorsed the Duke of Orleans and held Dunois in check, and we are tempted to ask his pardon for our victory in the words of Charles V. to the Pope: *Sanctissime Pater, indulge victori.*